# THE KNIGHTS OF FUZZ™

## the new garage & psychedelic music explosion

## Timothy Gassen

## 2014 BOOK CREDITS

published in the United States of America

GARAGE NATION
a division of PCMP LLC
PO Box 121
Tucson, Arizona
85702 USA

www.purple-cactus.tv
knights@purple-cactus.tv

ISBN: 978-0-9797337-3-4

**Front Cover art:** Darren Merinuk. **Thanks to** Ed Bertschy for previous graphic assistance.

**Special Thanks to the Guest Authors:** P.J. Crittenden, Dennis Dalcin, Eric Geevers, Colin Mason, Bart Mendoza, Dave O'Halloran, Spiros Pelikis, Glynis Ward. **Thanks also to** Dave O'Halloran for editorial assistance.

**Special thanks to the Fan Submission Authors:** Michael Bennet, James Bond, Blair Buscareno, Axel Gieseking, William Grapes, Fernando Jiminez, John Kennedy, Dave Pauwels, Wiebren Rijkeboer, Pierpaolo Rizzo, L.T. Selmer, Mike Spenser, Erin Truscott.


## 1995 BOOK CREDITS

**Design and layout for the 1995 edition:** Matthew Bardram
**Editorial assistance for the 1995 edition:** Sarah Garrecht

**Special thanks for providing special materials, information or written assistance for the 1995 edition:**
David Andriese (Holland), Jim Maher (USA), Cosimo Pecere (Italy), Darren Ross (France), Ingo Schittko (Germany), and Glynis Ward (Canada).

**The author also extends his appreciation for materials and further support:** Greg Shaw & Bomp! Records, Mike Stefanik & Collectables Records, Lee Joseph & Dionysus Records, Gregg Kostelich & Get Hip Records, Steven Lorber & Metro Music, J.D. Martignon & Midnight Records, Lutz Rauber & Soundflat Mailorder, Aram Heller & Stanton Park Records.

**The author would also like to thank the following for valuable assistance in the completion of this book:**
Vernon Joynson, Hugh MacLean, Iain MacLean & all at Borderline, plus Ivan Andreini, Matt Becher, Takis Boufounos, Piergiorgio Cavazza, Vic Conrad, Debra Dickey, Nelle Garrecht, Apostolos Kanakaris, Shane Kenyon, Hans Kesteloo & Music Maniac Records, Julian Levsby, Joe Longone, Steve Magee, Michael Metzger and The Tucson Weekly, Milly Muleskinner, James Peirce, Orin Portnoy, Roland Reschke, Jean Marc Rimette, Paul Roosenstein, Rocky Serkowney, Dino Sorbello, John Stebbins, Markus Steenbock, Karl Taylor, Marcus Tybalt, Jr., Allan Waite, Richard Ward, Alan Wright, Andreas Wunderlin, and all of the other bands, photographers, artists and record labels that answered my hundreds of questions – **and many thanks to any others who I've inadvertently missed on this list.**

*dedicated to*
*the memory of*

**Greg Shaw** 1949-2004
and **Ray Manzarek** 1939-2013

# FIND THE FUZZ

# FOREWORD

"The Sound" – that wail of guitar fuzz and pulsating lysergia – refuses to die. Wave after wave of lame mainstream music marketing bangs away at the faithful, but against all odds the garage and psychedelic flame persists. The garage spirit has survived the addled 1970s, the bland 1980s, the bored 1990s, the narcissistic Internet 2000s. It has taken a deep breath and bravely fights on.

I saw signs of the neo-garage culture waxing and waning while finishing my "Echoes In Time" book in 1991, and then again in 1995 while wrapping up the paper version of "The Knights of Fuzz" – then again in 2001 and 2006 when "The Knights of Fuzz" lived as a CD-ROM and video DVD. But each time a blast of new bands and enthusiasm swept me up, kept me up, and wouldn't let go.

So we are well into a new century and you'll still find kids in Beatle boots and bowl haircuts, Vox guitars in tow with a beat-up Farfisa organ in the back of the van. They've got a gig. They want to play loud. They have "The Sound."

And we still need to listen.

*Timothy Gassen*
*August 2014*

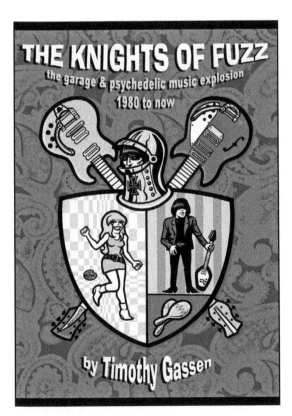

*The 1991 paper book (top right) and the 2006 video and electronic text DVD edition (above).*

## ABOUT THIS NEW EDITION

While many consider this book a "bible" for the neo-garage scene, it is **not** an encyclopedia. You must remember that this book is not meant to be a documentation of each and every garage-psych band or release since 1980. *(Please read the introductions to the original 1995 book and the 2014 updates!)*

This 2014 edition of "The Knights of Fuzz" presents a complete re-print of the 1980-1995 book, almost unchanged, as a time capsule. We then add new sections: my own extensive 1995-2014 updates, my own garage-related feature articles, a new photo section, and reproductions from my own vintage garage fanzine.

I also invited some of the most enthusiastic garage authorities from around the globe to contribute their own views and updates, adding a variety of voices to our documentation. Fans and band members sent to us much more information, and that has been edited and included as well.

*We write here about the bands that both inspire us and which also have releases available for us to discuss.* Even with my continued dedication, and the dedication of my guest authors, it is impossible to find, own, hear, include (and like) everything. We repeatedly invited bands and labels (both personally and through extensive public advertising) to submit to us their sounds and information. *Keep sending us your sounds!*

I've undertaken all of this effort, *over four decades*, because I love this music. I have approached this daunting task with an honest and open heart, and I invite you to accept this sincere work with the same goodwill.

*Timothy Gassen*
*August 2014*

the Knights of Fuzz

The Garage and Psychedelic Music Explosion, 1980-1995

By Timothy Gassen

# THE KNIGHTS OF FUZZ:
## The Garage and Psychedelic Music Explosion, 1980-1995

### By TIMOTHY GASSEN

# CONTENTS

# WELCOME TO THE ZOO

## *Two Introductions*

*"There's so much hope involved in people choosing to find answers, to find a direction that attempts to solve problems. I think that's the most encouraging thing about the vision that some of these '60s revivalists are locked into: the energy of hope."*

— Sean Bonniwell
(of the legendary 1960s band The Music Machine)
*Creem Magazine*, 1986

## Introduction For The First Edition:

Every generation since the birth of rock has had its musical punks — the rockabilly roughnecks and the bowl-cut fuzz demons, the safety pin New Wavers and the mohawk moshers. Whenever (and wherever) there is an establishment, there is also youth ready to stand up in opposition.

The 1980s were no different, and in many ways that decade illustrated just how far rock music and culture had come — and how little further it could go.

The buzz phrase of the decade was "retro," as it seemed that every trend in music and popular culture was simply a regurgitation of a formula that worked before.

So it is of little surprise that one faction of the 1980s punk movement would embrace the "golden age" of musical rebellion: the 1960s garage and psychedelic era. It offered the individuality, style and humanity absent in the contemporary culture, and was also inherently defiant.

Some observers saw this fascination with the mid-1960s as mere nostalgia; a wistful longing for a time passed. While some practitioners of the garage sub-culture were immersed in that emotion, most were using the model of the '60s punk with opposite intentions.

Nostalgia is generally considered to be rooted in psychological depression; it's an uneasiness with the present, or at least an unwillingness to deal with the problems of the present. Most builders of the 1980s garage and psychedelic "scene," however, were dissatisfied with the general blandness of the decade — and were determined to take *action*. This faction of punk-youth refused to accept the 1970s-styled notion of helplessness and nihilism, and instead resurrected a model of successful counter-culture.

This book celebrates those individualistic souls who made sure to twist a thorn once again in the side of a blasé pop-culture world. Many of the groups presented here would probably not admit to any intentional or conscious antagonism of the mainstream — but every loud scream, every fuzzed-out guitar and blaring Farfisa organ tone sent a clear message: like the generations before, the 1980s and '90s would have their cavemen, and they would not be forgotten.

This author participated in many of the events surrounding the 1980s and '90s garage and psychedelic "scene," and has fond first-hand memories of many interesting bands and musicians. I've interjected my thoughts and recollections into this chronicle to help bring this story alive; to share my personal vision of a vibrant time.

I stress that this book is a product of my personal observation. After more than 15 years of professional writing, I do not subscribe to the journalistic fantasy of "objectivity." Journalistic "objectivity" is an accepted academic convention that simply cannot and does not exist in *actual life*. Instead, I humbly offer a personal account, based on fact and observation, and motivated by my love of the music.

The excitement of these sounds has echoed through time, like a long-lost radio signal, from one generation to the next. I can hear the joyous ringing in my ears, even now.

*Timothy Gassen*
*Tucson, May 1991*

## Introduction For The Second Edition:

The garage and psychedelic music scene has witnessed yet another resurgence since I wrote the first introduction to this book four years ago. The fire and passion of the music is obviously passing onto another generation.

This second edition, retitled *The Knights Of Fuzz*, will attempt to address this latest wave of garage mayhem, while also correcting and adding to the first edition's contents.

I send my sincere gratitude to all who have written and called me over the past few years to help with this update. I have been literally inundated with letters, cassettes, records, CDs and photos. I've listed some thanks to specific individuals elsewhere — and my apologies in advance to anyone who I've inadvertently missed for this list.

It was stimulating to correspond with so many rabid fans of this music, and many who wrote were also relieved to see that someone else shared their passion. Many corrections and additions in this edition are the direct result of these fans' help.

I also dedicated several years of research to make this new book as accurate as possible. I traveled throughout Europe in 1992 — performing with my band The Overcoat — hunting down clues to many mysteries that eluded me for the first edition. I also wrote hundreds upon hundreds of letters to record labels, bands and fans around the world in search of additional information.

Most importantly, I continued to be amazed at the enduring high quality of the garage and psychedelic output from all corners of the globe. At some point I realized that there is more "new" garage and psych music "out there" than I'll ever know — *more than any one of us will ever experience.*

But the echoes will sing — for as long as we listen.

*Timothy Gassen*
*Tucson, August 1995*

1

# IT WAS THIRTY YEARS AGO TODAY?

## A History Of Garage & Psychedelic Music In The 1980s and 1990s

*"The liberation of rock and roll from Top Forty dictums, fashion's brief love affair with paisley and day-glo, the use of drugs as hippie sacraments — was called psychedelia. In its brief lifetime, 1965 through '68, it drastically altered the face as well as future of rock culture. And now it's back for a second try."* (1)

**— David Fricke, *Rolling Stone Magazine*, 1985**

The 1970s punk explosion changed everything.

It forced youth to analyze rock music. It made them aware of what had happened since the R&B and "race" music scene gave birth to rock'n'roll in the early 1950s; it helped them to understand that rock music had an actual history.

Writer Nicholas Schaffner addressed this point, saying *"The very idea of 'rock history' may seem something of a contradiction. One of the music's greatest attributes has always been its up-to-the-minute immediacy. Yet rock has also been around longer than half the countries in the U.N. have — long enough to have accumulated a great deal of history."* (2)

Most punkers didn't reflect on this history in order to glorify that past — just the opposite. Their realization enabled them to reject that rock heritage and attempt to start their own legacy.

Not all punks looked on their forefathers with disgust, however. One other by-product of this introspection was the seemingly sudden ability for youth to appreciate the forgotten *trends* of rock's past. They realized that rock didn't have to be a disposable form thrown away with each passing generation.

Earlier rock culture left tangible remnants: records, video, magazines, photos and clothes. It could be recaptured and repeated and kept alive through the attention of new generations.

Punk displays contemporary dissatisfaction with the mainstream, but youth also can show that displeasure by embracing any of the countless sub-genres of past rock culture. "Revivalism" became hot press in the late '70s, as factions of punk-youth embraced the highly identifiable trends of the past — from rockabilly to heavy metal, to every one-hit category in-between.

The most surprisingly durable musical phoenix, however, was the colorful genesis of the 1980s and '90s garage and psychedelic

*BOBBY BEATON OF THE GRUESOMES DELIVERS THE GARAGE SACRAMENT, CIRCA 1987*

scene. Lasting almost *three times* the original inspiration of 1964-1968, the decade-and-a-half "revival" is one of the most intriguing underground music and culture anomalies in recent pop memory.

It's no mistake that the movement of '77 punkers led to the growing interest in the garage punks of '66. Both shared the do-it-yourself attitude, the crude musical abilities and the unstoppable urge to be heard and to disturb.

Early on in the '77 punk movement bands could be seen paying homage to the "original" fuzz punks of the prior decade. Details like the use of vintage musical equipment or period stage costumes displayed the growing affection for yesterday's forgotten rebels; such details would be increasingly studied by the new garage bands, and dutifully duplicated.

As the 1980s dawned, there would be enough kids educated about the intricacies of the 1960s garage and psych movement to display it as a new world movement — though it began with little more than a trickle.

**Greg Shaw** of Bomp Records formed the subsidiary Voxx Records in 1979 specifically to document the oncoming rush of new garage youth. It took him two years, however, to gather enough tracks for 1981's ground-breaking *Battle Of The Garages* compilation album.

While a few enterprising bands had already released their own discs, this was the record that gave birth to what would become the widespread 1980s garage scene. It was the loudspeaker to kids that something was *happening,* and the message was received and passed on well past the remainder of the decade. (The early '80s UK compilation *A Splash Of Colour* could be considered the European counterpart to the initial *Battle Of The Garages,* though its influence was less far-reaching.)

Voxx organized an east coast U.S. tour for some of the bands represented on the LP, and **Shaw** commented on the changing times in the tour's press release, stating, *"In these surrealistic times, the return of psychedelic music was inevitable, and where else should it return from than the wigged-out garages of suburban America — where it all started? Quietly but steadily, over the past year or two there has been an underground resurgence of the garage band mentality that once inspired The Electric Prunes, Chocolate Watchband, et al. The Time (sic.) has now come for it to explode in our collective consciousness."* (3)

The 1981 summer tour dates led from Minneapolis to New York, and helped to display that the new scene was alive and kicking. The "sound" was popping up again all over the world, but once again America's pop culture was in the lead.

The language of these new garage maniacs was simple and clear: they emulated their long-forgotten 1960s heroes by dredging up and regurgitating the most obscure original garage records possible, adding vintage clothing to their stage act — and perhaps more importantly — somehow tracking down the best vintage musical equipment.

**PLASTICLAND GAVE BIRTH TO THE NEW AMERICAN PSYCHEDELIC SCENE**

Jeff Tamarkin, in his introduction to the excellent *Goldmine Magazine Garage Sale* compilation cassette of 1985, noted, *"The (1980s) garage bands can't play just any old instruments. The only way to get an authentic, savage '60s sound, is with authentic '60s gear, and the best stuff was made by such companies as Rickenbacker, Vox and Farfisa, equipment that these new bands find and use. And of course, the vocalist must know how to put the right snarl in his voice; it should be a sound so grungy and wicked that mice jump on chairs when they hear it."* (4)

This highly identifiable style was one important reason the "scene" spread throughout the world. The look and sound was instantly recognizable, yet unusual enough to be perceived as being "underground" and "punk" in nature. There was a street sensibility about the resurgence that avoided the bitter taste of corporate commerciality — garage and psychedelic music was spontaneous fun!

The mainstream press reacted curiously to the rebirth of interest in the '60s garage/psych phenomenon. Many simply mistook it for the also ever-present nostalgia by Woodstock baby-boomers, not realizing that the new musical genre was manned by kids who were *born* in the 1960s, not those *in* their 60s!

Some realized that the garage upheaval was at its core anti-commercial; it didn't help sell the current trends, so it could not (or should not) be considered significant. (*"How many units did it sell?!"*)

To this day, most mainstream media deny or are unaware that this movement ever existed. Joe Longone aptly counters in his *The Great Rock 'N' Roll Survey* of the 1980s, *"Even though you haven't read much about it, heard it on the radio, or seen it on sale in your local record chain outlet, it doesn't mean it didn't exist."* (5)

(As you will see in the later chapters of this book, the 1980s/1990s garage movement left behind a substantial body of sounds. The constant output is impressive for *any* musical genre, especially one repeatedly labeled by the mainstream as being insignificant.)

Some media figures sat on the fence, and watched to see if this new scene was to become the "next big thing." Greg Turner wrote in the March, 1986 *Creem Magazine* the somewhat smug appraisal, *"The repertoire is a ceaseless diet of reverb and tuned-out tremelo, Vox guitars and Beatle boots. In this regard, the vision is strict retrograde and more imitative of a well-worn prototype than anything original or at least stamped in a contemporary context. Hard to figure out what it all adds up to; passing fad or mounting ground-swell? Fashion show or swap meet?"* (6)

Some young people discounted the burgeoning garage and psychedelic movement because it was an indirect insult to their own generation. The garage kids were rejecting the corporate, bland, "modern music culture," and the less-adventurous youth saw this as a threat to their "underground" status. Many kids who thought they were truly the occupants of the hip "alternative" scene became defensive because they didn't *understand* the

Beatle boots, flowery shirts and fuzz guitars.

Many kids were also insulted by the contention that their "contemporary" scene lacked the perceived importance of their parents' teenage years. They found themselves inexplicably "out-hipped" by the history of their parents, and now kids of their own generation rubbed their noses in it by re-creating an "out-dated" and purposely primitive scene!

Playwright David Gale put it this way, *"The '60s get a pretty bad press these days. The '80s find the '60s hopelessly into its feelings, hopelessly vulnerable, hopelessly open, hopelessly unanalytical. This is to some extent the symptom of an '80s malaise. The '80s is embarrassed by the '60s."* (7)

The 1980s was a decade of restriction, the increasing acceptance of technological machinations and encouraged humanistic denial. The mainstream's rejection of the new garage scene was inevitable, as they saw youth looking backward to history for answers (instead of forward to technology), and embracing a philosophy of humanism rather than the preferred empty programming of commerce and property.

A vital difference between this new youth movement and its 1960s model, however, was its (lack of) connection to a larger societal influence. The mop-topped teens of '64-'66 grew up to take control of college campuses in '67-'69, changing the structure of grass-roots politics. That was a generation with a myriad of items on its agenda, and for the first time, a youth movement influenced society as a whole. The 1980's generation was more cautious in its exuberance, and for the most part without political convictions.

Despite the U.S. war machine's rampages through El Salvador, Nicaragua, Grenada, Libya, Panama and Iraq — to name a few — there was no united front of concern like the stand taken against the war in Viet Nam and southeast Asia. (George Harrison noted in the mid '80s that the world's musical and political consciousness seemed to have slipped back to about a 1962 pre-activist level.)

Most bands and followers of the "'60s sound" avoided heavy political or personal social commitment, many feeling hopelessness in the Reagan, Bush (and Thatcher) years of ever effecting any positive change. Perhaps they didn't equate their rejection of current trends with a return to humanism; perhaps they couldn't commit themselves openly to ideals so constantly rejected by the masses of their own generation.

Others simply wished to avoid the perceived fate of the dreaded 1960s political-hippie: burning-out into a life of tie-dye, bell bottoms and **Grateful Dead** concerts. It should be made obvious that the model for the '60s re-explosion ends somewhere around 1967, with the height of stylized teen garage mania recognized as occurring sometime in a mythical and idyllic 1966. The image of the barefoot hippie, stoned at Woodstock (either the original event or the lame corporate 1990s sequel) was definitely not revered by the 1980s garage-nik!

Interestingly, though, drugs such as pot, acid, mushrooms (and alcohol) remained popular recreational devices of this new generation — though devoid of their symbolic use as defiance against the "establishment."

A 1985 documentary titled *The Greenhouse Effect* focused on the new garage bands' lack of political intent. The crude but amazing 30-minute Super-8 film was produced by Ken and Dave Greenhouse for a high school film project. It discussed the revival bands' fashion and sound, then compared it to the era of 1960s activism.

Along with rare and surprisingly good-sounding concert footage of **The Fuzztones, Blacklight Chameleons, Vipers** and the all-female **Maneaters** are interviews portraying a feeling of general political hopelessness and apathy — intercut with a then-contemporary speech by (original 1960s) activist Abbey Hoffman pleading for this latest generation to get off their butts and take some action.

It became obvious that the 1980s garage and psychedelic rebirth would strictly be one of artistic creativity, unfortunately not blossoming into another unique and widespread *overt* societal youth statement.

Still, the bland American mass-media superficially and briefly lunged at the new scene. While most mainstream media ignored the trend, scattered articles and news reports did pop up in *Newsweek*, *Psychology Today* (!), *People* and even the formerly counter-culture *Rolling Stone*. The July 4, 1985 *Rolling Stone* ran a three-page spread on the movement, mostly of color fashion photos, but with some side text. While the piece shows interest mainly in the veneer of the scene, one stab at the mainstream managed to get through: *"Disc jockey Rodney Bingenheimer, patron saint of Los Angeles' Paisley Underground, claims his audience is 'sick of this synthesizer stuff they're hearing on the radio.'"* (8)

The battle lines were clearly drawn, and **Greg Shaw** elaborated on this in a 1986 issue of his *Voxx Teen Beat* newsletter, saying, *"Also working in our favor is the growing backlash against vapid '80s pop music. As more young people itch to start their own bands and take rock back to the streets, they discover our scene already staked out on those very streets, and their eagerly-welcomed energy can only push the scene to new frontiers of creativity and give it the cultural relevance it needs to break free of cult status."* (9)

**Shaw** was one visionary who had been around for the initial psychedelic movement, and could see the shortcomings of a new movement based solely on style. He also commented in 1986, *"One thing I'm really aware of from this scene is (its lack of) cultural relevance. It has nothing to do with what's going on today. The issues that are being discussed in these songs are issues of 1966. Girlfriends and high school and that stuff.*

*"I like the sounds, but what made punk important in the '70s was that it was talking about now and handing out answers for now and that's why it touched so many people. It gave them a way to express*

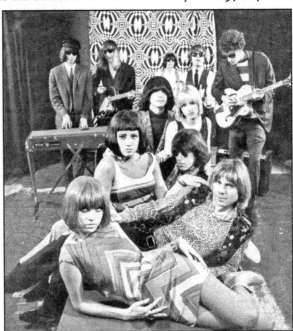

**THIS INFAMOUS PHOTO FROM PEOPLE MAGAZINE — TAKEN INSIDE L.A.'s "CAVERN CLUB," CIRCA 1985 — INCLUDES MEMBERS OF THE TELL-TALE HEARTS, YARD TRAUMA, UNTOLD FABLES, VOXX's GREG SHAW (second from bottom), PLUS THREE OF THE CLUB'S "CHICKS"**

*how they felt about things happening in their lives. I think what's going to happen in the late '80s is what happened in the late '70s, similar to punk but only on the opposite side of the spectrum: instead of negative energy and pessimism there'll be a creative energy force."* (10)

**Shaw** was in a perfect position of observance, because he had seen many musical movements wax and wane. His involvement with the "underground" began as a San Francisco-area teenager in the 1960s, putting out one of the earliest rock fanzines ever — then as a record collector and editor of the seminal *Who Put The Bomp* late 1970s punk and power-pop magazine. He was an early champion of **The Ramones**, and claims to be the first American to ever see the **Sex Pistols** in concert — while on a visit to England. **Shaw** can also be credited with helping to bring the **Flamin' Groovies** back into the spotlight, as he managed them to their late '70s Sire Records LPs.

Since then he's released over 200 LPs on his Bomp, Voxx and associated labels, as well as numerous compilations of 1960s garage and psych on the *Pebbles* and *Highs In The Mid Sixties* series, among others. The importance of those two series in spreading the garage disease cannot be underestimated. Along with other series like Crypt Records' *Back From The Grave*, they inspired countless bands to form and continue the garage legacy — and gave them endless material for their concert playlists.

Another important project **Shaw** undertook was the Cavern Club. It served as the U.S. West Coast's focal point for the new scene in the mid-'80s, and saw performances by almost every important regional and touring band (all of which were documented by **Shaw** with live audio recordings).

The club also focused the debate of "form vs. content" — garage *fashion* versus *message*. This split was evident amongst the avid club-goers, as many simply wanted to dress in hipster outfits and

**7**

be seen, while others saw the underground community as a breeding ground to examine more meaningful goals.

Many Cavern Club regulars defended the fashion-consciousness of the scene by contending that its lack of intellectual content was actually its greatest asset. They saw the genre as a way to escape back to a time where teen wholesomeness was not infected by the problems of the "real world," when music culture was foremost and simply a style. Such attitudes were seen by others as morosely nostalgic.

The *L.A. Weekly* ran an expose on The Cavern Club in 1985, saying, *"This is a club dedicated to a sound, a raw, primal three-chord sound, bashed out on Vox guitars and cheesy Farfisa organs, a sound filled with fuzztones and snarly, snotty vocals mixed into pop harmonies lifted directly from Liverpool. They call it the 'garage band scene,' and the Cavern is its home."*

The question of empty-headed fashion was also quickly addressed. *"Greg Shaw and his Bomp/Voxx aide Paul Grant may insist that this is a music scene, not a clothes trip, but a lot of the kids see it differently. 'Fashion goes hand in hand with the music,' says Frank Mamlin, 22. 'I mean, this is Hollywood! That's what we came here for!'"*

Long time underground fixture Rich Coffee sensed more substance in the movement, noting, *"I think it's real music and it's real culture. I think what is most important is to get people to believe in music again. When I first got out here in '79, most of my friends were in their teens and they were frustrated. I kept telling them, 'It's not bad to be a teen. You have power, you can change things.' I think that's the spirit of the '60s, and that's the spirit of this scene."* (11)

In a *Los Angeles Times* article from January 1986, Coffee also commented that *"(The fashion) is not the main thing going on here. It's the music that is so important, and nobody is paying attention to that."*(12)

Frank Beeson made this assessment of the Cavern Club in *Bam Magazine*,

PHOTO BY CLAIRE BAKSA

**INSIDE MIDNIGHT RECORDS, CIRCA 1985, INCLUDING MEMBERS OF THE CHESTERFIELD KINGS, A-BONES, OUTTA PLACE, TRYFLES AND J.D. MARTIGNON (third from left).**

saying, *"The Cavern Club may be a humble refuge, but the off-Hollywood Boulevard retreat is important to many young people and bands trying to launch a new scene in motion. In operation every weekend since April 1985, it's a gathering of Neanderthal hairstyles, turtlenecks, paisley and Carnaby Street fashions."*

Dan West, of the band **Threw The Looking Glass**, summed up the garage mentality in the same article, saying *"Polish is important for Top-40 radio, but as far as what rock and roll stood for, it isn't truthful. And the Cavern Club is truth!"* (13)

Los Angeles had been an important focus for the "revival" since its inception at the turn of the 1980s. Teenager Michael Quercio formed the **Salvation Army** (later renamed **The Three O'Clock**), and reportedly coined the term "Paisley Underground" to describe a fertile circle of groups including the early **Dream Syndicate** and **Bangs**, later to be **The Bangles**. Quercio's much-repeated phrase would haunt him well after he tired of the '60s sound, but it accurately describes L.A.'s rediscovery of ('60s) pop mixed with ('60s) punk. (Though not included in the trendier bands' scene, **The Unclaimed** should also not be forgotten as one of the earliest and most influential of these new L.A. garage bands.)

The east coast also had an early lead on the trend — substantial bands such as **The Chesterfield Kings**, **Lyres** and **Fleshtones** all began their decade-long trek well before the turn of the '80s.

**J.D. Martignon's** New York Midnight Records label and store became an important counter-point to the California scene as well. **Martignon** released early efforts by **The Fuzztones**, **Plasticland**, **The Outta Place**, **Plan 9** and a slew of others — continuing its mission into the 1990s. (The Midnight retail store and mail-order became a mecca for rare new garage/psych discs, and it has continued in its role as a candy store of goodies for this writer on numerous occasions.)

**Martignon** points out that his widely circulated mail-order catalog, *The Midnight Tymes*, *"had articles, a news section, and loads of hype on the* garage/psych scene. It helped to propagate the music and the distribution of it worldwide."

Midnight published one of the first books detailing the contents of 1960s compilation albums, which **Martignon** notes *"was very influential on bands and collectors."* **Martignon** also says rightfully, *"Midnight became the inspiration for many of the (garage/psych) labels, mail-order companies and distributors both in the U.S. and overseas — whether they will admit to it or not!"*

(New York also boasted a new poster and art gallery specifically perched to capture the revival of interest in '60s pop culture. The Psychedelic Solution Gallery specialized in vintage posters — but more importantly it housed many shows of new contemporary psychedelic art in its 1986-1995 lifetime. An all-star farewell Group Exhibition featuring the likes of Robert Crumb, Peter Max, Victor Moscoso, H.R. Giger and Rick Griffin ended its New York psychedelic art reign in December 1994 — though the storefront would survive as a psychedelic poster retail outfit.)

**ITALY'S SICK ROSE PROVED THAT THE GARAGE DISEASE HAD SPREAD WORLDWIDE**

By the early 1980s almost every city in America would sport a new garage band, and their (indirect) influence would start to appear through the chart success of other, more commercial groups. (See Chapter Seven for a discussion of the commercial effects of the garage underground.)

The most important groups were planted firmly in the underground, however, and the English "alternative scene" has always been a diverse breeding ground for many sub-cultures and genres. The psychedelic fire spread quickly from Los Angeles to New York and across the Atlantic in the late '70s; an echo bouncing back from the punk signal the British had sent a few years before.

Englishman Vernon Joynson authored in 1988 an illuminating guide to original 1960s psych/punk titled *After The Acid Trip*. He also included a few observations on the appearance of the early 1980s English psychedelia, stating,

*"The spring of 1981 also saw a number of psychedelic venues open up around London. There was The Groovy Cellar (started by Clive Solomon, then manager of **The Mood Six**), The Clinic and Le Kilt in Soho's Wardour Street, which had a psychedelic evening every Tuesday. The fashion focus of this psychedelic revival lay in two stalls in Kensington Market, The Regal and Sweet Charity. Here the paisley shirts, caftans, chiffon blouses and kinky boots which became commonplace at clubs like The Clinic and Le Kilt could be purchased — at a price!"* (14)

Joynson also noted that the resurgence of **Doors**-mania in the 1980s focused much media attention on the psychedelic sound and look. (**The Doors** sold more records in the 1980s than they did in the 1960s, and remain a media sensation to this day.)

Looking back at the early days of the new movement, Richard Allen of the definingly psychedelic *Freakbeat Magazine* also recounted some historical events from the U.K., showing that it was indeed an active counterpart to the American explosion.

*"Alice In Wonderland was, for a while, the focus of the '80s psychedelic scene in the U.K.,"* Allen wrote. *"Running every Monday night at Gossips on Meard Street, the club was a bohemian haven, filled with all kinds of strange individuals. The Sun (newspaper) cited it as the seediest club in London which of course was a compliment, coming from them, and soon the word spread and membership began to rise...*

*"Christian Paris organized the famous Magical Mystery Trips events which were staged outside of London, the locations of which were kept secret until the last moment. The first Mystery Trip was to Chislehurst caves in '84, while the second was also in '84 and billed as a trip to fairyland. It was in fact a trip to a disused warehouse in Battersea!*

*"In 1985 punters were taken on a third Mystery Trip and were transported to a defunct Butlins in Clacton-On-Sea by a specially hired train (the*

scenes at Liverpool Street Station as over 1000 freaks invaded the platform were amazing) and when they arrived they found 12 hours of all-night psychedelic entertainment awaiting them, including most of the current psychedelic bands, psychedelic light-shows, psychedelic discos, space out rooms, body painting and more.

"The 4th and last Mystery Trip was to an old Victorian pier at Lowestoft in East Anglia in 1986. The journey began by coach from Hyde Park Corner and as 2000 strange people boarded over 40 coaches, tourists stood and stared. The pier venue was an acid head's paradise, a maze of rooms and stairways, and all of which had been decorated and bedecked with colour and light. As the sun came up and shone its rays upon the exhausted individuals who left the pier they knew that they had been a part of something special." (15)

Soon the word had spread throughout Europe. Spain, Italy, Sweden, France, Germany, England, Holland and Greece all became garage and psychedelic strongholds, with a slew of bands and vinyl pouring out to the rest of the world. Europe would be such a strong market for garage and psychedelic bands that many of the U.S. groups mounted major tours there, while still struggling at home to find suitable gigs!

*A 1987 N.Y. CITY "MIND'S EYE" SHOW FLYER, BY STEVE MAGEE*

Each country had its own divergently colorful community of musicians and fans, but with stories and "scene" histories similar to the ones from the U.S. and England. It seemed that the genre was globally universal, though admittedly less response was documented from Asia. (We should note, however, that the Japanese did revive **The Monkees'** career in the 1980s, and so indirectly the interest in '60s pop.)

Local radio shows were vital in spreading the sound internationally, as *Electric Fit* (Italy), *Fuzz Box* (Spain), *The Fuzz That Wuzz* (Canada), *Garage Grooves with Amazing Larry*

(Canada), and *Acid Rain* (U.S.), among many others, all helped to create a sense of community through the airwaves.

Many European national radio shows also gave exposure to the genre, helping to boost its perception as a viable "sound." Some influential radio hosts chimed in, most notably John Peel on the BBC and Rodney Bingenheimer on KROQ in Los Angeles. Both exposed many of the up-and-coming groups to a widespread audience for the first time.

Fanzines, home video and television also played communication roles, as we will discuss in later chapters.

The first contact most people had with the "garage band sound," however, was "live," in person. Enterprising garage-niks occupied a slew of clubs dedicated to the sound, often with temporary but elaborate light shows and acid-tinged decor. New York had Irving Plaza, The Dive, and occasionally the Peppermint Lounge, while the roving "Mind's Eye" series of shows throughout the mid to late '80s was reportedly the most interesting "happening" in Gotham City. The "Mind's Eye" series returned in 1995, as the cycle of interest in the psych underground swelled once again.

Los Angeles had the aforementioned Cavern, Raji's, Music Machine, The Shamrock and sometimes Club Lingerie. The Anti-Club took up much of the garage slack after The Cavern's demise, and in the 1990s The Blue Saloon also hosted some fine garage shows.

Even middle America had a 1980s fuzz haven as Jon McKinney of **The Royal Nonesuch** operated The Primitive A-Go-Go in the most unlikely of places — the farmlands of Springfield, Missouri!

England's early scene boasted Merlin's Cave, The Garage and 100 Club, among many others. Most of these clubs had at least one night a week dedicated to the "garage scene," while countless others came and went during the decade, some lasting for no longer than one dazzling night.

As the 1980s wore on another interesting trend developed: the movement unfolded into several definite "waves" — a turnover of groups occurring about every two years throughout the decade. Instead of dying out after each spurt, though, the interest in the garage scene revived itself constantly, bringing with it countless new bands and recordings.

There were very few bands that made it through the entire decade of the 1980s with their '60s style intact, but many survived long enough to deposit their interpretation in the wake for the next wave of garagers.

Perhaps the most important relics of the 1960s youthquake were the countless examples of fuzzadelia left on rare 45s. This enabled a new generation to look and listen; a guidepost to the "lost sound." While it is difficult to appraise the long term influence of the 1980s and '90s garage underground just yet, its successful realization cannot be denied. It left abundant physical proof — an impressive body of vinyl, cassettes and now CDs.

The number of bands able to record and release recordings increased dramatically with the punk movement of the late '70s, and many more 45s and full-length LPs appeared in the '80s than was financially possible twenty years earlier. This time-capsule of sounds insures that the style, sound and youthful spirit of the garage band will be passed onto yet another generation.

The dawn of the 1990s seemingly marked the end of the latest surge of "1960s revival," as most elements of that scene had been driven far underground once again. Pockets of fans and bands remained, however, proudly carrying the garage banner, waiting for the explosion once again.

Yet another widespread outburst of punkadelia was inevitable, and by 1992 a slew of new European garage and psych bands signaled the remarkable and continual rebirth of the genre. The fire would not be extinguished easily.

Its output will soon be documented and distributed on digital audio tape, or computer chips, or some technology not yet realized. The technological form is unimportant; it's the wigged-out content that matters, and the need for humanistic exuberance should not diminish with the years.

**Greg Shaw** summed it up in the March 1994 edition of his *Psychobabble* newsletter, saying, *"When the '60s ended, I was left with an undying vision of how vibrant youth culture can be, and the importance of music in it. It's why we're so often accused of 'retro' tendencies*

*by those unable to distinguish our view of the '60s (as a cultural benchmark worth aiming for) from a simplistic desire to 'bring back' the past. That's the last thing we'd want — we just wish today's music scene could be as much fun, or offer some hope of making the world a better place...and we're still waiting."* (16)

Despite (or perhaps because of) the resistance from the mainstream, the garage and psychedelic sound, spirit and defiance will be back.

Again and again.

## Sources:

1) *Rolling Stone Magazine,* July 4, 1985, Pgs. 39-41; "The Look Of Love: Some styles have passed the acid test of time. Psychedelia is one of them." By David Fricke

2) *The British Invasion,* McGraw-Hill Books, 1982, Pg. 1, By Nicholas Schaffner

3) *Voxx Records Battle Of The Bands Summer Tour* press kit, 1981

4) *Goldmine Magazine,* March 1, 1985; "Garage Sale!" By Jeff Tamarkin

5) *The Great Rock 'N Roll Survey — 1980s.* 1990, Pg. 2. By Joe Longone

6) *Creem Magazine,* March 1986, Pgs. 43, 56; "Cavern Club Psych-out: The 60's Are Alive And Well (Sort Of)." By Gregg Turner

7) *Classic Album Covers of the 60s,* Gallery Books, 1989, Pg. 97. By Storm Thorgerson

8) *Rolling Stone Magazine,* July 4, 1985, Pgs. 39-41; "The Look Of Love: Some styles have passed the acid test of time. Psychedelia is one of them." By David Fricke

9) *Voxx Teen Beat,* Issue #4, April/May 1986, Pg. 2. By Greg Shaw

10) *Creem Magazine,* March 1986, Pgs. 43, 56; "Cavern Club Psych-out: The 60's Are Alive And Well (Sort Of)." By Gregg Turner

11) *Los Angeles Weekly,* Vol. 7, No. 35, July 26-August 1, 1985, Pgs. 33-35; "It's A Happening: Garage Bands Turn On At The Cavern Club." By Craig Lee and Lisa Teasley

12) *Los Angeles Times,* January 1986, Pg. 2; "Days Of Flower Power Return At Cavern Club." By Jeff Spurrier

13) *BAM Magazine,* June 6, 1986, Pg. 10; "Time Traveling At The Cavern Club — I've Been Psychedelicized!" By Frank Beeson

14) *After The Acid Trip: The Flashback, The Ultimate Psychedelic Music Guide.* Borderline Productions, 1988, Pg. 121. By Vernon Joynson

15) *Freakbeat Magazine,* Issue #7, 1990, Pg. 6. By Richard Allen

16) *Psychobabble Newsletter,* #6, March 1994, pg. 1. By Greg Shaw

# ECHOES IN TIME

## A Guide To The Essential Bands: 1980-1995

*"Today it's happening again. Wherever there are a few kids who are sick of the nausea they're hearing on the radio, who don't feel comfortable with the clothes that the commercials on MTV try to sell them, and who want to learn how to really play an instrument, there's bound to be a garage band sprouting up."*

— Jeff Tamarkin, *Goldmine Magazine*, 1985

What follows is a band-by-band analysis of what I believe to be the most interesting garage and psychedelic discs of the 1980s and first half of the 1990s — though some of the entries stray a little before 1980. I do not claim that this is a listing of *every* disc or tape related to the genre; these are simply entries on groups or releases that I am aware of, and believe to be of notable significance.

The format of the First Edition of this book has been altered somewhat. I previously split bands into two chapters: "The Knights Of Fuzz" and "The Serfs Of Fuzz." The second chapter contained for the most part bands that I possessed only the slightest information, or bands only partially associated with the garage & psych genres.

Despite the definition of these categories, some readers thought the "class distinction" created by the two chapters was also a reflection of the relative *quality* of the groups. To eliminate that confusion, I've removed the two-tier structure and have included all relevant bands in this one chapter now titled "Echoes In Time."

I must also emphasize that the *amount* written about any band is not intended to signify its relevant importance. One First Edition reader literally counted the lines of type for various entries, then argued that certain bands deserved more space than others! I've included as many bands and as much relevant information as humanly possible — *the amount written about each should not be considered important.*

Likewise, I'm less concerned with opinions of which bands were more "popular" in a social scene, and more concerned with who produced (in my judgment) the best music — these two points don't always coincide.

For the most part these recordings are on independent labels, with small press runs and little distribution. These facts make it infinitely difficult to collect or research the entire history or discography of any one artist — I have even found it difficult at times to obtain copies of all the records which *I* have produced!

This means I might not even possess (or be aware of) the entire recorded output of what I consider to be the most important bands in the genre, and there could undoubtedly be some "holes" in the chronological listings of releases.

With this in mind I've also purposely deleted from discographies some releases that I don't feel are relevant to the subject of this analysis. Several notable bands included in this listing at some point drifted off into other musical genres, so those irrelevant releases are not included here. Usually these are the later recordings of a

band which started in the garage or psych style, and then switched to heavy metal or generic pop for commercial reasons.

Such lack of artistic integrity shall not be rewarded in these pages — this book is a safe haven for the garage and psychedelic music true-believer, *without apology*.

I sent seemingly countless letters worldwide requesting information to help make this updated analysis as complete as possible. A few bands and labels declined my invitation to submit materials — many others were of incalculable help in providing important music and photos.

The reader is encouraged to contact me once again with additional corrections and updates. Any additional vinyl, CDs, photos or video (NTSC standard VHS) would also be of great assistance for the Third Edition of this tome. To paraphrase a Zen saying, the more one discovers, the more it is obvious there is more to discover.

## The listings follow this format:

1) The name of the band in all-capitals, with the hometown and country (if known) listed below it in parenthesis.

2) The title of each known relevant release will then follow, plus the number of songs (if known) and format (i.e. vinyl 45, 7" EP, 12" EP, LP, CD, etc.), and then the year of initial issue. I've also included in this update the titles of 45 B-sides, when known, since many of these songs appear only on singles and this information will be of help to collectors. "b/w" is the abbreviation for "backed with," referring to the B-side of a 45.

3) The record company will then be listed below the records' titles, followed by the country where the pressing originated. To save space the name of the record company will be listed only once — after the last title released by that company.

4) An analysis or band history will follow. This can be quite detailed for the bands with much available output and information, and only a line or two for the most obscure. Again, the amount written about any band does not necessarily reflect on its importance to the genre.

5) Notes on any official video releases of significance will also be listed. With the proliferation of home video equipment in the 1980s and '90s, many of these bands also have privately

14

shot concert footage. For the most part, these home-videos are *not* listed here.

6) For a few bands the *only* information I have is their name, usually found in a catalog or magazine associated with other garage and psychedelic bands. They are listed in the hope that the reader can supply additional information.

As the 1980s led into the 1990s, more and more bands saw their product re-released or simultaneously released on digital Compact Disc (CD). I've listed the vinyl version of releases when they exist, and CD releases when I believe no vinyl to exist — and both LP & CDs are listed especially if there are variances in the track listings.

The garage and psychedelic explosion of the 1980s relied almost exclusively on the last hurrahs of vinyl, and that format remains commercially viable in the 1990s outside North America. Some of the CD versions of albums do include rare or previously unreleased tracks, though, so their importance to collectors cannot be simply ignored.

Also, some cassettes are included in the listings, though it should be noted that cassette-only releases consist mainly of small private batches with minimal commercial distribution — these were usually demonstration tapes used to secure gigs or attract record labels.

And lastly, the complete appearances by bands on compilation albums, EPs, shared "split" 45s and flexis are listed separately in the "All Together Now" chapter.

**One last important note: Please read the introduction to this chapter carefully before forming a critical assessment about the items that follow. Many concerns of the reader can be dealt with in this introduction — *if it is read.***

## A 1 MINING COMPANY
*(Melbourne, Australia)*

An occasional group from the late 1980s made up of members of the **Bo-Weevils, Puritans** and **Breadmakers**. They reportedly would jam on '60s punk songs and tunes from the first **Bo-Weevils** record. An LP was reportedly in the works as of this writing.

## THE AARDVARKS
*(London, U.K.)*

*Arthur C. Clarke* 4 song 7" EP, 1990
"You're My Loving Way" b/w "Hold On" 45, 1991
    Screaming Apple Records, Germany

This mod-tinged garage band delivers one classic-sounding tune in the title track for this EP. The remainder is enjoyable R&B-flavored garage,

**THE AARDVARKS, *1991***

but the very British sounding "Arthur C. Clarke" is undeniably the highlight.

Their follow-up A-side is a very catchy mod-beat toe-tapper, with punchy period production and a great fuzz guitar lead. "Hold On" is a bit too 1968-soul influenced for me, and the funky B-3 sounding organ doesn't help either.

Some fine vocals and a couple solid songs still make **The Aardvarks** worth a listen. I believe they have several other discs available, including a circa 1994 album that contains the second 7" tracks.

## A-BONES
*(New York City, NY USA)*

**The A-Bones** specialize in crude circa 1958-1963 pre-**Beatles** styled garage and "frat rock" sounds. They've released a slew of recordings, have toured throughout Europe several times, run their own excellent Norton record label, and even publish the essential *Kicks* magazine — which not surprisingly features their fascination for sleazy bump and grind music, 1950s juvenile delinquent movies and novels, and trashy early punk rock.

Some readers insisted they belong in this book — so here they are — but I believe their sound to be only marginally associated with the '66-fueled garage punk phenomenon. They are a fine rockin' combo deserving of their respected reputation — I simply believe most of their sounds to be a reflection of an era a few years before the main focus of this book.

Readers have recommended the following recordings of **The A-Bones**: *Tempo Tantrum* 10" on Exile Records; *Life Of Riley* LP and *I Was A Teenage Mummy* Soundtrack LP, both on Norton; "I'm Snowed" 7"; and the "Take Up The Slack Daddy-O" 7" backed with the **Girl Trouble** cut "Sister Mary Motorcycle."

## THE ACETONES
*(Holland)*

*Only Everything* 7 song cassette, 1992
*Get Ace-Toneized* 16 song cassette, 1992
*Live Lysergia* 10 song cassette, 1993
   private pressing, Holland
*Teen Trash #6* 18 song LP & CD, 1993
   Music Maniac Records, Germany
*Self-Titled* 4 song 7" EP, 1995
   Tombstone Records, USA

I've heard these Dutch garage-heads referred to as the "European Fuzztones" because of their tendency to select '60s covers that would fit

*THE ACETONES, 1993*

perfectly (or already have fit) onto **The Fuzztones'** decade-long set list. There was even talk of **The Acetones** backing Rudi Protrudi as a new version of **The Fuzztones** in 1994 and '95 — no word if this actually happened. They would certainly fit the bill, with loud perfectly Voxed guitar and wheezing (Acetone brand, of course) organ.

Most of the songs from their self-released cassettes also show up in their cover-dominated debut LP. '66 standards "Riot On Sunset Strip," "99th Floor" and "Green Slime" all get a crude work out, but with only a surprisingly few original tunes in the mix.

Regardless of the over-reliance on cover songs, this is a solid, gutsy garage outfit — and they promised a more balanced output of original material for future releases.

That promise was quickly realized with their blistering Tombstone 7" EP. The originals "Can't Get You Out Of My Mind," "Still In Love With You" and "Another Time, Another Place" all blast with a wonderfully crude vitality.

The vinyl was mastered by **Dead Moon's** Fred Cole on his vintage mono tube cutting machine, and it's a signal that **The Acetones** are creating their own aural identity.

## ACID RAIN
*(Pisa, Italy)*

Ex-**Steeple Jack** members reportedly playing in an "acid psych" mode. They privately pressed the "No Bathing Allowed/Acid Rain/Moose Made Of Dawn" 7" in 1991.

## ACT
*(Taranto, Italy)*

A reportedly psych act with the "Third Eye" b/w "Come On" split 7" on Urlo Records, 1991, and the *Dreams Aren't Useful* 12" EP on Cannibal Records in 1986.

## ADULT NET
*(U.K.)*

*Take Me* 4 song CD, 1989
    Fontana Records, U.K.

This commercial pop entry is here only because of the rather appealing, vibrant and reverent cover version of **The Strawberry Alarm Clock**'s "Incense & Peppermints." Forget about the rest.

## THE ADVENTURES OF PAISLEY
*(U.K.)*

There is nothing known about this group with a wonderful name — except that it existed circa 1992.

## AFTERHOURS
*(Milan, Italy)*

A reportedly psych pop band with the "My Big Boy" b/w "To Win Or To Destroy" 7" on Toast Records, 1987; "Shadowplay" split 7" on Vox Pop Records; *All The Good Children Go To Hell* 12" EP on Toast Records, 1989; *During Christine's Sleep* LP on Vox Pop Records, 1990; and the *Cocaine Head* 12" EP, 1992, also on Vox Pop.

## AGENTES SECRETES
*(Spain)*

I know nothing about this combo except the English translation for their name: The Secret Agents.

## ALICE IN SEXLAND
*(Padova, Italy)*

A band described as progressive psych that released a self-titled LP on the Italian Casal Gasardo Records in 1991.

## ALLISON RUN
*(Brindisi, Italy)*

"The Perfect Ecstatic Balance" split 7", 1989
    Stampa Alternativa Records, Italy
*All Those Cats In The Kitchen* 12" EP, 1987
    Mantra Records, Italy
*Sado, Goodman & Faith* 3 song 12" EP, 1988
    Vox Pop Records, Italy
*God Was Completely Deaf* LP, 1989
    Mantra Records, Italy

This seems to be a very interesting psych pop band — though I've only heard a taste from the Italian *80s Colours Volume 2* compilation LP and their 1988 three song EP. These few songs definitely merited a closer look, but I haven't been able to track anything else down.

## AMERIGOVERARDI MORGAN VUP's
*(Brindisi, Italy)*

Ex-**Allison Run** with a 1993 split 12" (ironically with **Allison Run**) and an LP on Cyclope Records.

## ANT BEE
*(Cornelius, NC USA)*

Billy James is the lovable nut-bar genius behind this amalgamation of musicians and musical styles. Loosely associated with the classic **Mothers Of Invention** sound of 1966-68, James actually wrangled the involvement of several of the ex-**Mothers** for a number of recording sessions in the late '80s and early '90s.

The resulting tapes sound remarkably like outtakes from vintage **Zappa** sessions, complete with absurd dialogue, intricate playing and bizarre compositions. Voxx issued one very odd LP around 1990, and several more CDs have since appeared.

This is difficult, complex and rewarding music — definitely belonging in the psychedelic genre — and definitely unlike anything you'll ever hear elsewhere these days.

## THE APACHES
*(Brisbane, Australia)*

"I'm Leaving Town" b/w "I Want Her" 45, 1992
    Sundown Records, Australia

These Australian natives formed in late 1988 with active '60s scene supporter and bassist James Peirce. They claim their influences as mid-'60s white R&B (**Downliners Sect**) and garage (**The**

Sonics), and their rare debut 45 displays that mixture aptly. Raw, primitive, bursting with energy, **The Apaches'** delivery is authentic and stirring.

More records were in the offing as of 1995 — but catch this rare platter if it ever appears before you.

### ARHOOLIES
*(Switzerland)*

They reportedly have two LPs/CDs and a few singles, with good exposure in their homeland. I've heard only one track, the melodic and jangley "Friend," which features professionally adept playing and some fine vocals. It's reminiscent of a cross between **The Backdoor Men** and **The Watermelon Men** — a high compliment from me.

### THE AQUAVELVETS
*(Springfield, IL USA)*

*Thrill To The Velvet Throb* 4 song 7" EP, 1992
   Velvatone Records, USA

The **Aquavelvets'** Matthew Dietrich told me that they *"are having moderate success in spreading the garage gospel across the prairie states, though most people still don't get it until they hear it, and even then they don't quite know what they've heard."*

Their EP is a do-it-yourself effort, right down to the color-copied sleeves. They mix a couple originals, "Thirteen" and "Vodka & Prozac" with the proven standards "Voices Green & Purple" and "7 & 7 Is" in a simple down-home garage fashion.

It's a nice slice of true-believing garagadelia — if you can manage somehow to find a copy. Several other 7"s have also reportedly appeared.

### ARMS OF SOMEONE NEW
*(Chicago, IL USA)*

The *Burying the Carnival* LP from 1984 and the *Susan Sleepwalking* LP from 1985 are both on Office Records. I seem to remember one of these albums having a quiet moody edge, not unlike early **Opal.**

### ARCTIC CIRCLES
*(Australia)*

The *Time* five song 12" EP features some trippy garage-psych-pop, with some excellent organ and a general swirly, moody atmosphere. The title track is especially cool, with a soaring echo fuzz guitar break and creative drumming.

This reminds me slightly of **The Stems** with more of a psychedelic element added — professionally presented but still trippy enough to remain music made by actual people. "Wasp" is another fuzzy trip number, with creepy lyrics, hypnotic vocals, and some great atmospheric studio production.

All in all this is a winner from sometime in the '80s.

### ATTILA & THE HUNS
*(Los Angeles, CA USA)*

*Under The Bodhi Tree* 13 song LP, 1991
   Music Maniac Records, Germany

This is really the "long-lost" **Unclaimed** LP, released several years after its completion under this assumed name of **Attila & The Huns.** Band founder Shelly Ganz, disenchanted with his former band-mates, is the one who changed the band name for this release — he even prints co-producer and bassist Lee Joseph's name backwards on the sleeve as one last attempted insult.

The LP itself is a worthy successor to the previous **Unclaimed** output, with better production and some tricky arrangements showing Ganz's musical growth. "Betty Cooper" is an especially pleasant folk-pop number, and the band's sound clicks on the cover of the "Village Of The Giants" movie theme.

This isn't a spectacular outing — and the cover art is abysmal — but it serves as a successful close to the **Unclaimed** story under another name.

18

## THE AUBURNAIRES
*(Cincinnati, OH USA)*

Around since 1981, this trio has managed to release five LPs on France's New Rose Records. They feature some ex-**Customs,** though I've been lead to believe that they feature much less of a garage-oriented sound and a more mainstream pop-rock style — and are therefore not important in the scope of this book.

## GLI AVVOLTOI
*(Bologna, Italy)*

*Untitled* 3 song 7" EP, 1986
Toast Records, Italy
*Il Nostre E Solo Un Mondo Beat* LP, 1988
*Quando Verra Il Giorno* LP, 1990
Contempo Records, Italy
"Sono Un Vomo" b/w "Per La Mia Felicita" 45, 1992
Discovery Records, Italy
*Ora Sia Perche!* 11 song LP, 1994
Destination X Records, Italy

This is a simple garage outfit, singing in their native tongue. Especially strange (besides the debut EP's weird cover photo) is hearing **The Kinks'** "Well Respected Man" sung in Italian. The EP's sleeve and record production is also cryptically European, and presents an odd interface with the usual American garage output.

I saw their two LPs while in their native Bologna, but later could only find the collection of "live and unreleased" tracks called *Ora Sia Perche*. Like the debut EP it centers upon well-worn garage covers, sung in Italian. The **Sonics, Kinks** and **Stones** songs are enjoyable, but the covers of T**he Who'**s "See Me Feel Me" and **Spencer Davis'** "I'm A Man" are misguided at best.

Also, the band has the strange habit of listing Italian writing credits for the cover songs, presumably because the original English lyrics were translated into Italian. Very odd, indeed.

Their band name means "The Vultures" in English.

## THE BABY FLIES
*(USA)*

"Pictures And Parties" b/w
"I Only Burn In The Morning" 45, 1983
Slow Wind Records, Holland
*Rain* LP, 1987
"Turn Around" b/w "Speedway" 45, 1987
(given away with first pressing of the *Rain* LP)
*A Colourful View* LP, 1989
Resonance Records, Holland

Ingo Schittko described **The Baby Flies** to me as *"A very underrated U.S. folk-psychedelic-pop band. Their stuff is highly recommended, only the second LP is a little bit lame. The LPs must also be released in the USA, but I cannot say on which label."*

I have never heard a word about the **Baby Flies** — which is strange since I have detailed histories about bands from halfway around the world.

## THE BACHELOR PAD
*(Glasgow, U.K.)*

This Scottish power-pop band survived from 1986 into the '90s, releasing a spattering of flexis, 45s, EPs and an LP. I've only heard an advance cassette of their 1991 *Lovely Jenny Brown* EP, and it bursts with pop energy and some well-crafted energy. There's a certain **Ramones**-meets-pop edge to this stuff that could fit in with less adventurous commercial tastes, though that is certainly not a knock on this professional sounding band.

## THE BACKDOOR MEN
*(Sweden)*

"Out Of My Mind" b/w "Magic Girl" 45, 1985
   Tracks On Wax Records, Sweden
"Going Her Own Way" b/w "Dance Of The Savages" 45, 1986
   Fab Records, Germany

Though they only contributed these two 45s (and a couple live tracks to a *Lost Trails Magazine* 7") to the movement, **The Backdoor Men** were one of the most inspirational outfits of the decade. They joined **The Nomads** in cementing Sweden's reputation for the burgeoning "new" garage sound of the 1980s — with **The Backdoor Men** specializing more in garage-pop than all-out fuzz.

Crystal-clear production and proficient playing make both of these 45s essential; "Magic Girl," from the first 45, is especially engaging, with it's vintage grinding **Stones**-pop treatment.

Plenty o' Farfisa drenches these discs along with occasionally biting guitars and Robert Jelinek's snotty and emotional vocals. Some 12-string jangle even manages to creep into the tearful "Going Her Own Way," while cave-stomping fun dominates the appropriately entitled instrumental "Dance Of The Savages."

I also dig the perfect **Brian Jones** bowl haircut that guitarist Hans Ingemansson sports on the sleeve of the second 45 — these cats had the style to match their musical prowess.

Jelinek and Ingemansson would later form the initially interesting (and ultimately banal and commercial) **Creeps**, but more about that later.

## THE BACKWARDS
*(Recco, Italy)*

*Real Life Permanent Dream* cassette, 1989
   private pressing, Italy
*First Exploding (& Inevitably Plastic)* 15 song LP, 1990
   Crazy Mannequin Records, Italy
*Or So It Seems* 15 song cassette, 1991
   Delerium Records, U.K.
*Jumble Sale* 16 song cassette, 1989
   Unhinged Magazine, U.K.
*The Ocean Inside* LP, 1994
   Magic Gnome Records, U.K.
   (subsidiary of Delerium Records)

Pierpaula Rizzo literally *is* **The Backwards**.

He began in 1988 with some friends in a band called **Chapter 24**, but by the following March had released the **Backwards** demo cassette as basically a solo project. Claudio Sorge of the influential *Lost Trails Magazine* said at the time that they were "the best psychedelic band in Italy."

The 1990 debut LP proves those words accurate. It is a swirling blender of psychedelic pop influences, ranging from **Syd Barrett** to flower-power **Beatles** and even 1960s U.S. fuzz bands. The record sleeve calls it "A stereo box of different colours, in the age of grey monoliths," and that about sums up this rare, basically unknown gem of an album.

While **The Backwards** consisted of Rizzo and studio musicians, they did play one live show after the LP's release — opening for **Bevis Frond.** The 1991 lineup would also play more shows, and record more studio tracks, including the *Or So It Seems* cassette.

Another limited edition vinyl offering was set for a late 1994 release in the U.K. The *Ocean Inside* LP takes the best from the cassette-only releases and adds some new tracks — all as a worthy follow-up to the stunning debut. Rizzo stretches his influences on this LP, with noisier and poppier efforts sitting along side the beautifully produced psych numbers.

It is amazing to me that a European or U.S. label hasn't collected a "best-of" CD from Rizzo and **The Backwards**. This music is simply too good to be left unheard, and is some of my favorite of any described in this book.

## BAG ONE
*(Arona, Italy)*

Reportedly a psych-rock-ska-beat band, with the *A Youth Explosion* private cassette in 1987.

## BALLROOM STOMPERS
(Germany)

An LP of unknown quality, *Go Ahead*, is on Fab Records. I've heard a "live" tape of the band, and they appear to be heavily influenced by R&B and European beat. They even managed to participate in a 1990 Russian talent show, playing in Moscow on national TV and placing fourth in the competition!

Early demos with the track "Oh No" certainly show a Star Club-era **Beatles**-type sound, with over-amped R&B and some fine guitar work taking center stage.

I've also heard a rough mix of unreleased studio tracks that were in much more of a folk-rock pop vein. "All Of A Sudden" is a sweet, smooth, beautifully constructed jangle treat — it would be a giant injustice if such quality material remained unfinished or unreleased!

"Dead Empty Street," "She's Alright," "You Do Everything" and the wistful "Hello Sunday Morning" all deserve to be heard as well. I can only hope that these tracks are actually on their LP, which has eluded me.


## BAM BALAMS
(Australia)

Several discs are available; I remember one 45 which had a tinge of **Long Ryders**-styled country-garage. This isn't spectacular, but worth a listen if "twang-garage" is your cup of tea.


## BANANA MEN
(London, England)

These were the **Sting Rays** in disguise, as I'll discuss later. They released an early 1980s 7" cryptically titled *Banana Men Play Songs Made Popular By The Cramps!*


## BANANA TRASH
(France)

I was reminded not to forget this wonderfully named band, though no other information could be found. How could I forget such a name!?!


## THE BANDITS
(U.K.)

Made up of former members of the U.K.'s **Primemovers**, circa early 1990s.


## THE BANGLES
(Los Angeles, CA USA)

*Self-Titled* 5 song 12" EP, 1982
Faulty Records/IRS, USA

It is of course a commonly known story that the eventually lame top-40 all-girl group **The Bangles** started out as simply **The Bangs** — their debut 12" EP with that moniker is a very collectable item. It was soon after re-released by IRS Records under the band's famous name — **The Bangles** — and the rest is pop chart history.

Despite the later million-selling hits, the five song debut is arguably the band's brightest moment, at least as far as the '60s pop style is concerned. "How Is The Air Up There" is a soaring, joyous romp, and the remainder of the disc is as fresh, energetic and enjoyable.

Their switch to the faceless, corporate Columbia Records led to a quick decline for the girls. There were a few bright moments on their debut LP — "Going Down To Liverpool" is engaging — but the pallor of blandness swept over most of the material, and that's why none of these records are listed above.

"Live" TV appearances from this period show the band attempting to come across as more of a "rock" act, coupled with vocalist Susanna Hoffs' cutesy big-eyed girl routine. They were obviously floundering.

Subsequent LPs became more watered down than "lite" beer, and the corporate money boys finally had their wish — this once very capable pop-rock band hit bottom as they aped **The Go-Gos** at their worst with the appalling "Walk Like An Egyptian." It was a mega-seller of course, hitting the top of the world charts. It was also an embarrassment to anyone who didn't get a royalty check.

This clichéd story had its obvious end — the band broke up, Hoffs attempted a silly solo "career," talk surfaced of an eventual reunion, blah, blah, blah...

But I can't forget the beauty of that debut 12". If only money hadn't gotten in the way — **The Bangles** would probably be making great garage pop right now.

## I BARBIERI
*(Siena, Italy)*

"W Il Lunedi/Conq Quella Voce/Pernoi" 7" EP, 1988
    private pressing, 1988
*Se Vuoi Me* 12 EP,
    Toast Records, 1991

A direct translation of their name is "The Barbers." Their first 45 is reportedly a '60s fuzz punk killer. Their second release is said to be a little more mainstream in style on a few cuts, but other tracks hail back to their snottier days.

The tracks "Un Tipoperte Te" and "L'ora Dello Verita" are finely produced beat pop, with atmosphere startlingly close to their '60s inspiration. The band sings in their native Italian.

## BARDS
*(Brandford, ON Canada)*

A '60s-styled folk-rock band which never recorded, but played in 1990. **The Bards** featured Bam-Bam on drums (formerly from **The Captives**), Andre from **The Captives** and **The Chessmen**, plus Gaven Dianda and Gregg Golambos. The band ended when two members reportedly left because of emotional problems and when another went to jail!?! The third member went on to form the **Swingin' Gurus** with Dan Beer, the former lead vocalist of **The Chessmen**.

## THE BARONS
*(San Diego, CA USA)*

This short-lived band featured Ex-**Tell Tale Hearts** (including Mike Stax); tapes for an unreleased 12" EP, circa 1988 exist. This is yet another unknown offshoot of the fertile San Diego scene. I'd love to hear these tapes.

## THE BARRACUDAS
*(U.K.)*

"I Want My Woody Back" b/w "Subway Surfin'" 45, 1979
    Cells Records, U.K.
"Summer Fun" b/w "Chevy Baby" 45, 1980
"His Last Summer" b/w "Barracuda Waver" 45, 1980
"(I Wish It Could Be) 1965 Again" b/w "Rendezvous" 45, 1980
"I Can't Pretend" b/w "The KGB (Made A Man Out Of Me)" 45, 1980
    EMI Records, U.K.
4 song promo 7" EP, 1982
*Drop Out With...* 14 song LP, 1982
    Voxx Records, USA / EMI, U.K.
"Inside Mind" b/w "Hour Of Degradation" 45, 1982
*Mean Time* LP, 1983

*Endeavor To Persevere* LP, 1983
"The Way We've Changed" b/w "Laughing At You" 45, 1983
Untitled 3 song 12" EP, 1984
"Stolen Heart" b/w "See Her Eyes Again" 45, 1984
    Closer Records, France
*House Of Kicks* 3 song 12" EP, 1983
    Flicknife Records, U.K.
*The Big Gap* LP, 1984
*Live 1983* 10 song LP
    Coyote Records, France
*Live EP* 4 song 12" EP, 1984
    Roadrunner Records, Spain
*I Wish It Could Be 1965 Again* 9 song 12" EP, 1985
    (includes eight of the band's EMI single tracks)
    CMG Records, France
*The World's A Burn* 12" EP, 1985
    The Trust Records, U.K.
*Live In Havre* LP, 1985
    66 Records (Bootleg)
"Very Last Day" b/w "There's A World Out There" 7" flexi, 1985
    Bucketfull Of Brains Magazine, U.K.
*The Garbage Dump Tapes!* 12 song LP, 1989
Untitled 3 song 12" EP, 1990
    Shakin' Street Records, U.K.

**The Barracudas** are an especially influential band because of the widespread international exposure they focused on the resurgent '60s sound.

Their early 45s were strictly California-surf in nature, but by their debut LP they had added equal doses of folk, garage and pop. *Drop Out With...* was first issued in 1980 by the U.K. conglomerate EMI with obviously commercial intentions, and their "Summer Fun" single even managed to break the U.K. top 20!

Remember, this was on the cusp of the eclectic "New Wave" movement, and major labels were scrambling to get a pulse on the record buying public's switch in taste. Someone in the corporate womb figured that **The Barracudas** had *something* that would sell big.

They were wrong, but the LP is still a fine combination of shimmering guitars, brute vocals and the sense of urgency that makes garage music memorable.

Ex-**Flamin' Groovie** Chris Wilson joined on guitar and ex-**Radio Birdman** bassist Jim Dikson was added after the first LP, but commercial success still eluded them. A large cult following emerged, especially in Europe, but they could never seem to get that push over the top into a wide spread consciousness. The band attempted to hold on for a few more years — releasing some fine records — but never lifted themselves above cult status.

Many collectors' albums have now appeared, featuring various "live" performances, demos and outtakes. These are somewhat dodgey, with only a few real gems amidst many tracks that were best left in the vaults.

The *Live 1983* LP displays an upbeat spirited performance, with some of their best studio tracks like "Violent Times" and "Codeine" shining brightly in a stage setting. The U.S. SFTRI label released a fine 45 in 1989, "Next Time Around," featuring two tracks which I believe also showed up on the outtake collection *The Garbage Dump Tapes*.

EMI in Canada also issued a CD collection in the early 1990s of the band's debut LP and early singles, which helped spur some new interest for one of the 1980s best power-pop garage bands.

Commercial success is rarely the measure of a band's worth. While I'm sure **The Barracudas** would have loved the financial rewards of some chart gold, they'll just have to be satisfied with a legacy of powerfully influential music.

### THE BASEMENT BRATS
*(Norway)*

These Norwegians have been described as the missing link between **The Monkees** and **The Ramones**. Their Screaming Apple LP certainly fits that description, but isn't '60s influenced in a direct or substantial way. Still, I've included it here because of the kindred garage spirit it evokes.

### THE BATMEN
*(France)*

I don't have a shred of information about this group except that they have two LPs and several 45s in the 1980s — but I can imagine them on stage in matching Batman costumes, complete with capes. Everybody sing now: *Da na na na na na na na na ... **Batmen!***

### STIV BATORS
*(Cleveland, OH USA / Los Angeles, CA USA)*

"It's Cold Outside" b/w "The Last Year" 45, 1979
*Disconnected* 10 song LP, 1980
   Bomp Records, USA

Some readers might think that the inclusion of the **Dead Boys** & **Lords Of The New Church** singer is a stretch for this book. But between those bands Stiv produced a fine 1979 power pop 45 for Bomp! of **The Choir**'s '60s nugget "It's Cold Outside," plus an interesting LP. He rips through **The Electric Prunes**' "Too Much To Dream" in fine fashion, while also depositing a power pop classic of his own, the wistful "Last Year."

Now that he's dead and buried, it's strange to hear him sing, *"This is the last year of my life, can't seem to do much more than I've done, gone and used up all the fun, and the alternative is none."* The LP and 45 tracks were reissued by Bomp in 1994 in several collectors' packages, including a 10" with complete history.

Yeah, most of **Stiv Bators'** efforts are outside the range of this book — but his few '60s-ish power pop moments rate with the best of the late 1970s sparks that brought the onslaught of more obvious garage-niks.

### THE BEACHMASTERS
*(Boston, MA USA)*

This is probably the best East Coast surf band from the 1980s. It's also probably one of the *only* surf bands on the U.S. East Coast in the 1980s! I recall a demo of spirited '60s-styled surf with a bit of sandy garage grit mixed in. These demos probably became their subsequent *Kleen Kut* LP.

### A BEATBOY
*(Belgium)*

This was a mod-beat band — one that served as a link between the early 1980s Belgian mod scene and the 1990s Belgian garage scene, since it featured garage/mod promoter J.P. Van, who produced a series of fine 1980s Belgian garage compilation records.

## BEATHOOVERS
*(Germany)*

At least two 7" releases exist: A four track EP on Chord Records and a 1986 four song EP on Hoover Beat Records, both in Germany. They do contribute a fine organ and fuzz guitar-driven version of "I Ain't No Miracle Worker," and the original "Fail Again" has that certain garage pop charm which makes so much of this music endearing. This one song reminds me a bit of Australia's wistful **Dust Collection**.

## THE BEATITUDES
*(Germany)*

Many records exist with an early **Beau Brummels** folk influence; members later formed the similarly sounding **Black Carnations**. Some of their LPs include *A History Of Nothing* (1986), *Gold Upstream* (1989), *Harvest In June* (1990), and the split LP *A Tale Of Two Cities* (1990). A pre-**Beatitudes** 45 by **The Memories** from 1976 included the track "Run Run Run."

## BEATNIK FLIES
*(Maryland USA)*

The *From Parts Unknown* LP is out in the U.S. and Europe, although I wasn't too impressed because it wasn't quite pop, wasn't quite garage, wasn't quite "New Wave" — it simply didn't deliver on any level.

## THE BEATPACK
*(London, U.K.)*

Untitled 4 song 7" EP, 1989
"Not Tonight" b/w "Frustrated 3rd Party" 45, 1990
*Could You Walk On Water?* 13 song LP, 1991
    Screaming Apple Records, Germany

Rising from the ashes of **Thee Wylde Things, Tyme Eliment** and **Mularoony Daddies,** this English combo specialized in rave-up Euro-beat music, full of screaming harmonica and pure (white) blues. They started with a cassette on Acid Tapes, and a track on the *Outsiders' Tribute* LP, plus a few other compilations — see the "All Together Now" section for details.

A pair of fine seven-inchers then followed. "Don't Stay Away," from the untitled debut disc, screeches in at a tidy 1:37, but manages to squeeze in the right amounts

of harp and buzz nonetheless. Some timely fuzz and snot highlight "The Time And The Pleasure" on the flip, all in classic beat fashion.

The "Not Tonight" 45 also shows off their respect and reverence for the R&B-punk form, in the fine tradition of the **Q65** and **Downliners Sect.**

1991's *Could You Walk On Water?* LP takes its title indirectly from **The Rolling Stones** — it seems this was the original title for **The Stones'** *Aftermath* LP, but Decca wouldn't let them use it at the time. **The Beatpack** uses it gladly in tribute to the Stones in their prime.

The LP also shows off **The Beatpack** at their finest. Solid musicianship, upbeat arrangements and a clear recording make it a solid slab of beat mentality.

## THE BEAVERS
*(Groningen, Holland)*

"Nancy, You're A Square" b/w "Don't Leave Me" 45, 1993
    Kogar Records, Holland

Crude '60s & '70s punk melds with some gritty production on what I believe is this foursome's debut disc. I especially like the subtle references to the 1966 "classic" bad movie *Rat Pfink A Boo-Boo*, and the do-it-yourself attitude that permeates the entire package.

I remember that Groningen was a cool place for rock music (and Chinese food!?!), so I would assume that **The Beavers** have been well received there.

## THE BEES
*(Belgium)*

All I've seen of this group is a photo of the band performing in striped "bee" sweaters, reportedly knit by the organist's grandmother! They were apparently a fuzz-garage and beat band with a 1986 demo.

## BEEVILLE HIVE V
*(Edinburgh, Scotland)*

A '60s punk and R&B band with one cut on the *British Raw Cuts* LP titled "Beer, Beer, Beer." They also released two demo tapes.

## THE BEGUILED
*(Los Angeles, CA USA)*

*Gone Away* 12 song LP, 1988
    Dionysus Records, USA

Video: "Honey In Her Hips" on the *Obnoxious Rock & Roll Video Hour*, Dionysus Records, 1987.

This initially short-lived outfit combined a 1950s trash image with some '60s punk sounds into a demented roots-garage platter. The entire LP is loose and raunchy, with grit to spare. Not strictly a '60s "retro" record, but with a similar attitude — if not a total fuzz punk execution.

The band broke up shortly after the album's release. Label head Lee Joseph once told me he felt as if there was the "Dionysus Curse" — as soon as he released a record, the band in question was sure to break up almost immediately.

I believe the band reformed in the early 1990s and released an album on Crypt Records in Germany, though the results were much less garage oriented. At least "the curse" was broken.

## THE BELIEVERS
*(Melbourne, Australia)*

A five song 12" is out on Australia's Rubber Records, reportedly in a British Invasion style mixed with modern pop. I'm not sure if this is the same Australian group with the 1985 "Lemon Tree" 45 on Terrace Records or the 1987 "So Many Times" 45 on Cleopatra Records.

## THE BEN WAYNE COMBO
*(San Diego, CA USA)*

Made up of members of **The Event, Nashville Ramblers, Gravedigger V** and **Crawdaddys**, this late '80s "all-star" California group mined the forms they all knew well: white R&B beat music. I don't think that this was a long-lasting serious band, but a friendly part-time project for all involved. A live tape shows dutiful versions of "Oh Yeah," "Betty Jean" and "Bad Little Woman."

## THE BERRY PICKERS
*(Los Angeles, CA USA)*

Untitled 3 song 7" EP, 1987
    Dionysus Records, USA

Here's yet another short-lived Hollywood group which paid homage to their idols, **Muddy Waters, Howlin' Wolf, Bo Diddley,** and most obviously, **Chuck Berry.** This lo-fi EP shows off those crude influences to good measure. An appearance on the *It's Happening* cable-TV show also displayed their raw blues-garage roots.

Vocalist Jeff Alexander would later shave his **Brian Jones** bowl cut and become a spike-haired screamer in **The Groovie Ghoulies.**

## BETTY'S BLUES
*(Brindisi, Italy)*

This is reportedly a psych/pop act, and members would go onto the group **Amerigo Verardi.** They had a self-titled 12" EP on Mantra Records in 1988.

## THE BEVIS FROND
*(U.K.)*

*Miasma* 10 song LP, 1987
*Inner Marshland* 11 song LP, 1987
*Bevis Through The Looking Glass* 2 LPs, 1988
*Acid Jam* LP, 1988
*Triptych* LP, 1988
*The Auntie Winnie Album* 10 song LP, 1989
*Magic Eye* LP (with Twink), 1990
*Any Gas Faster* LP, 1990
*Earsong* 12" EP, 1991
*Magic Eye* (Bevis & Twink) 9 song LP, 1991
    Reckless Records, USA / Woronzow Records, U.K.
    plus various compilations, 7" flexis, bootlegs, etc.

Nick Saloman's earliest recorded works were in 1975, and then with **The Von Trap Family** (1980) and **Room 13** (1982). He began home recordings after a traffic accident kept him bedridden for some time, resulting in the one-man heavy guitar oriented project he dubbed **Bevis Frond.**

The un-expected interest in his self-pressed LP encouraged Saloman to bring in other musicians and perform/record as an actual band. Press and reviews of the **Bevis** vinyl-flood have been universally good, and Saloman has appeared as a guest on many other LPs. His Woronzow label also releases records of other artists in a variety of complimentary styles.

The **Bevis Frond**'s inspiration is clearly post-'66, with the aforementioned emphasis on the guitar. One can hear the influences of **Hendrix, Clapton** and other late 1960s guitar-heroes et al.

Saloman and **The Frond** have become underground cult symbols of sorts, with a wide fan base in Europe and an endless demand for his brand of fiery guitar looniness. He has toured (with a band) extensively, and these live outbursts are reportedly inspired blasts of guitar mayhem.

There are countless other LPs than the ones listed above, and many of his official releases can also be found as bootlegs.

## BIFF BANG POW
*(U.K.)*

*The Girl Who Runs The Beat Hotel* 10 song LP,
  Creation Records, U.K., 1987

Creation Records caused quite a stir in the U.K. during the early and mid-'80s by selling more pop records than the majors would have liked. One of the label's pet projects was **Biff Bang Pow**, with their clean and jangley guitar pop — laced with a heavy dose of English attitude.

Some of the material sounds rather garagey, and even the more pop tracks have a certain '60s British charm. "The Happiest Girl In The World," "If I Die" and "Five Minutes In The Life Of Greenwood Goulding" are especially tasteful nuggets.

Several other discs were released in a more straight pop mode, but *The Girl...* is the best place to start.

## RODNEY BINGENHEIMER
*(Los Angeles, CA USA)*

Yes, the infamous "mayor of the Sunset Strip" put out some vinyl, including a 45 on Bomp in 1980. "Little G.T.O." is a fitting hot-rod tribute to his favorite car, complete with backing vocals from **Blondie**'s Debbie Harry.

I remember bumping into Bingenheimer several times, including a fun night at Club Lingerie in Hollywood in 1986. He was dressed in his best '66 **Beau Brummels** outfit, complete with the same bowl haircut he had when he doubled for Davy Jones on **The Monkees** TV show. No SoCal party or scene was complete unless Rodney was there or had at least heard about it.

Bingenheimer also compiled several albums featuring his favorite L.A. bands, all of which he played on his weekly KROQ radio show.

## THE BIRDMEN OF ALKATRAZ
*(Italy)*

*Glidin' Off* 3 song 12" EP, 1988
  Electric Eye Records, Italy
*From The Birdcage* LP, 1989
  Contempo Records

**The Birdmen** deliver guitar-based psychedelic rock in the best manner. The solos are tasteful and concise, the production atmospheric, and a general sense of constraint permeates the proceedings. Sure, there's room for the band to stretch out a bit on their EP's "Young Maiden Ghost," but one never feels that the band is dragging their dreamy ideas into the dirt.

The subsequent LP continues the band's development, with meaty arrangements, trippy hooks and a continued dramatic atmosphere. The title track especially captures a San Francisco folk-psych feeling, with plenty of punch and not a hint of hippy sludge. "Sea Of Shadows" is another melodic highlight — reminiscent of the U.S. 1967 West Coast sound without surrendering its own modern identity.

Not many bands have had the nerve (or interest) in covering the wonderfully goofy "A Tribute To The Oscar Meyer Wiener Wagon," but **The Birdmen Of Alkatraz** tackle it with a straight face and hit the mark again.

Along with **The Magic Potion** and **Technicolor Dream**, this might be one of the best Italian guitar psych bands of the decade.

## BIRDY HOP
*(Brindisi, Italy)*

A psych band with the *Welcome To The Insanity Ride* 12" EP on Italy's High Rise Records in 1989.

## THE BIRDY NUM NUMS
(Germany)

A memorable band name, but I've only heard the moody slow pop ballad "Don't Know" from them. That's an appropriate song title, since I don't know how much product from them has materialized on vinyl. This one song is a thickly produced dramatic taste which merits further inspection.

## BIRMINGHAMS
(Berkeley, CA USA)

An R&B/garage group with a mod following from the late '80s until early 1990. No studio sessions were released though they reportedly recorded demos. A live tape showed a passable mod-pop act doing "Real Life," "Love Is A Beautiful Dream" and "The Soldier."

## LOS BISONTES
(Barcelona, Spain)

One of the few bands — out these thousands — that I've not managed to learn one scrap of information. So I'll say that **Los Bisontes** was really another name for a secret 1986 reunion of **The Beatles**. This information is not true, but I'm sure that someone else will repeat it.

## BLACKBOARD JUNGLE
(Brindisi, Italy)

The 1989 *Silver Drops On Jesus' Skull* 12" EP on High Rise Records is reportedly in the garage genre.

## BLACK CARNATIONS
(Germany)

Several 12"s exist, melding an early "twangy" surf and garage sound. They include the "So Frequently" b/w "Black Carnations" 45, the six song *Beat The Attitude* EP, and the *These Were...* LP — all from 1985. They featured a female vocalist that reminds me somewhat of the high-pitched singer in **Rush**(!), and this was an obstacle difficult for me to overcome in my listening! This singer went onto a group called **The Rainbirds**.

## BLACK DIAMONDS
(San Francisco, CA USA)

Formerly **The Nashville Ramblers,** this Ron Silva-led trio played across California beginning around 1990. The multi-talented Silva has been involved with garage and '60s-based pop music since **The Crawdaddys'** days, and some of his other groups include **The Hedge Hogs, The Howling Men, The Wickershams, The Hottentots, The Ben Wayne Combo, The Driving Wheels, The Desperados, Jack & The Beanstalks, The Obviously Three Blooters** — and many other one-shot projects, I'm sure.

For a talented musician with years of performing, Silva does not have much officially released product. That's shame, because Ron Silva's song writing and performing talents deserve a wide audience.

## THE BLACKLIGHT CHAMELEONS
(New York, NY USA)

*Blacklight Chameleons* 6 song 12" EP, 1986
    Voxx Records, USA
*Inner Mission* 11 song LP, 1988
    National Brain Child Records, USA

Guitarist Dino Sorbello noted in *The Psychedelicatessen*, Issue #3, 1988, "In the early days of the 'scene' here in NYC, the early '80s, we suddenly had a ton of local talent. There was the **Fuzztones, Vipers, Outta Place, Cheepskates, Mad Violets,** etc... and at the time the emphasis seemed to be on who was gonna beat the other bands to cover that week's favorite song off of one of the Pebbles ('60s compilation) albums. It was garage cover city, man, with the exception of the **Mad Violets** who played originals, I'm proud to brag.

"Everyone also became very diggative on the clothes and the bowl haircuts and **Beatle** boots and wyld op-art looks, sounds, and smells. As tyme passed, newer groups started to play originals and began to pursue more individual style and sounds, but still keeping with the spirit of the neo-'60s.

"One major element missing, however, was that essence of the 1960s; the philosophy of a united front and an alternative to the crass bullshit of the status quo; the revolution of the spirit. No, nothing deeper than the clothes, haircuts and fuzzboxes going on here."

Dino Sorbello was one of the most underrated guitarists of the decade. His elegant and restrained sense of tone and arrangement deserved wider praise, as his **Chameleons** work suggests. The debut Voxx EP is excellent, but it is the follow up LP on his own label where Sorbello displays his

**THE BLACKLIGHT CHAMELEONS, 1988**

talents to full effect. Keyboardist Bill Ebauer also deserves some notice for such compositions as the searing "Blacklight Chameleon Theme" and the catchy "Poison Arrow."

A cool "live" video exists of the band shot in Tampa, Florida, 1988, where they do an instrumental version of the "Blacklight Chameleon Theme."

Sorbello headed up **The Third Half** after the **Chameleons** split, with a cut on the second *Kaleidoscope Magazine* compilation LP. Consisting of Dino Sorbello (guitar), Abbey Levine (vocals), ex-**Optic Nerve** Ken Anderson (drums) and Freddie Katz (bass), they also recorded four tracks that remain unreleased.

Sorbello's latest endeavor as of 1995 is a band called **Laughing Sky**, described by him as **"Syd Barrett** meets **Hawkwind** at a heavy metal bar."** We'll see what comes of it.

Bill Ebauer went on to form **Katfish Row**, with one CD of rootsy pop out in 1994. His new band accurately described themselves as **"Hank Williams** meeting **The Ramones** in Memphis for a beer," with standout cuts like "Ghost Town Rodeo" and "The Wild Wind" proving the point. An intriguing mix of almost-gospel emotion and modern pop songwriting skill, **Katfish Row** is a divergent sound from **The Blacklight Chameleons**, but interesting in its own right.

**28**

## BLACK MOON DOLLS
*(Bellinzona, Italy)*

A reportedly psych-rock outfit with the privately pressed *Unmasking The Sun* LP, circa 1986-87.

## BLACK SUN ENSEMBLE
*(Tucson, AZ USA)*

*Black Sun Ensemble* 12 song LP, 1985
  Pyknotic Records, USA
*Black Sun Ensemble* 10 song LP, 1988
*Lambent Flame* 9 song LP, 1989
  Reckless Records, USA

Guitarist Jesus Acedo was the mainstay behind this mostly-studio band. He brought surreal Southwest U.S. (and Egyptian!) desert imagery to much of the band's work, which was almost entirely instrumental in nature.

Their first LP was a private pressing, and is now very rare and expensive on the collectors' market. It's housed in a crudely printed black and white jacket, held together by staples. It is also the quintessential **Black Sun** recording. Some of these tracks were later collected or re-recorded for their Reckless releases, and show a musical flair that did indeed merit wider attention.

**Black Sun**'s main problem was itself, however, as Acedo showed a personal instability which resulted in a revolving door of musicians, run-ins with the law, and a general musical unreliability.

A "live" record was eventually released, but by the time of its production the band was hardly capable of performing, as I witnessed myself.

The end of the line apparently was a "solo" album titled *Psycho Master El* under the moniker **Black Sun Legion**. It features photos of Acedo with his rubber blow-up sex doll, plus his thanks to the Kino Hospital Mental Ward, various drugs and X-rated movie actresses — and on the disc some disjointed guitar based music.

The band's early recordings shared **The Overcoat**'s first drummer, John Brett.

## BLAIR 1523
*(Cornwall, U.K.)*

*Beautiful Debris* 8 song 12" EP, 1993
  Voxx Records, USA

Greg Shaw was convinced that an English-led underground movement would break through to the U.S. by the early 1990s. He subsequently sank much effort into the promotion of **The Spacemen 3**

— a move that nearly paid off. Undaunted, he set up a U.K. subsidiary of Voxx, and started signing British psych and pop acts like **Blair 1523**.

They sound very much in the Creation Records strum-pop vein, with some moody organ thrown in. Their 12" EP was a melodic bridge between purist '60s sensibilities and '90s underground pop mentality. Several of the tracks could have easily slipped onto the upper reaches of college radio charts — but like **The Spacemen 3** apparently just missed the mark.

Three of the tracks were previously released as a four song EP on Wilde Records.

Shaw has backed off a bit on his revelation about England, but as usual he's keeping his ears open. He told me in 1994 that he doesn't make the sole decision of what records his label will be releasing, so his future experiments might be limited.

## THE BLINKIES
*(Lawrence, KS USA)*

A demo of unknown proportions exists.

## THE BLOW POPS
*(Milwaukee, WI USA)*

*Charmed I'm Sure* 11 song LP, 1992
*American Beauties* 14 song LP / 16 song CD, 1994
   Get Hip Records, USA

There's simply a feeling of "near miss" around **The Blow Pops**. Their debut LP is full of melody and jangle, but repeatedly manages to sabotage itself with quirky stops, needless over-arrangement and a disposable "heard it all before" atmosphere.

There are a few highlights, like the Mersy-ish "Happiest Man Around," complete with **Lennon**-ish chord progression and backing "ahhh" vocals. The only cover on the LP — **The Who**'s "I Can't Reach You" is also picture-perfect, even more slickly delivered than the original. "Spin Spin 45" is also a pleasant homage to the joy of old-fashioned 7" vinyl.

It's interesting that the band brought in **Plasticland**'s John Frankovic and the **27 Various**' Ed Ackerson to produce their debut — I can't imagine how this material would have floundered without their sage handling.

Power pop seemed to be making a comeback in the 1990s, so it's no surprise then that producer Jeff Murphy (of the **Shoes**, a band that should-have-been-bigger-than-**The Knack**) makes sure the

sweetness level is way up on the follow-up *American Beauties* LP.

The harmonies are predictable and immaculate, the production squeaky clean and clear, but there just ain't any punch at the end of the line. Much of this evokes the classic pop of **Badfinger** or **The Hollies**, but without much propelling energy and sweat — **The Blow Pops** merely seem cute and calculated.

"I'm Seeing Love" is a nice exception — a toe-tapping ballad that sounds like **John Lennon** sitting in with **The Zombies**.

These lads were obviously making a stab at some major label attention. The irony here is that perhaps the creative strangle-hold of a major might just have been what **The Blow Pops** needed to shake off their tentative stabs and hit the pop bulls-eye.

## BLOW-UP
*(U.K.)*

A British indie pop group who do a reportedly very credible version of "1-2-5" on their self-titled 12" EP, circa 198?.

## BLUEBERRY COFFIN
*(Italy)*

I'll nominate this band into the "Garage Band Name Hall Of Fame," though I know nothing else concrete about them.

## THE BLUEBIRDS OF HAPPINESS
*(Brisbane, Australia)*

Described as trashy '60s punk, playing B-movie type flipout rave-ups sometime in the 1980s, with no known recorded product.

## BLUE BUS
*(Barcelona, Spain)*

A 1990 five song demo shows these Spaniards to have a firm grasp on garage rock with a pop touch, without forgetting that music is to be fun. They're raw yet musically adept, as was reflected in the subsequent eight song 12" EP *All Way* on Macaco Records out of Barcelona.

## THE BLUE UP?
*(Minneapolis, MN USA)*

*Now* 5 song 12" EP, 1987
  Susstones Records, USA

This was one of the few all-female garage groups of the decade. The main criticism of most of these groups was their lack of aggressive punch, and a tendency to ape the non-threatening pop sounds of **The Go Gos** or **Bangles**.

**The Blue Up?** could also be scrutinized under these guidelines, although they attempted to kick out a little rock along with their melodic pop. Their first 45, "We Are The Garden," showed some *Revolver*-era **Beatlesque** sensibilities that were also later put to use on their 12" EP.

Though their recorded output is appealing in spots, they never really hit stride in producing their own all-girl sound. The playing is too tentative, the production too rough — **The Blue Up?** is a good try but a near miss.

A suitably colourful and low-budget video followed the EP for one of their best songs, the catchy "Everything Is."

## THE BOARDWALKERS
*(California, USA)*

"Spy Vs. Spy" b/w "Boardwalker" 45, 1995
  Dionysus Records, USA

For the life of me I can't remember from where this surf band hails — but I do like their Dionysus disc. The band's name seems so familiar to me that there must be some other releases out there.

## THE BOGEYMEN
*(France)*

"You Are On My Mind" b/w "Candy" 45, 1992
  F.F. Fascination Records, France
*Introducing The...* 12 song CD (only), 1992
  Dig! Records, France
*As Live As You Want Them* 5 song 7" EP, 1993
  Guess Who Records, France

Like fellow countrymen **The Squares**, this French trio keep the formula simple and clean: direct toe-tapping songs, an uncomplicated recording technique and a sincere performance.

A slight mod and soul influence blends with R&B/garage, with Laurent Bauer's strong voice and guitar leading the way. Their previous vinyl 45 release leaned more towards blue-eyed soul, but their debut long-player adds

equal doses of the other rock influences.

The 12 tracks run a very short 29 minutes, and the sound is a bit thin and tinny, but these complaints are offset by **The Bogeymen's** vibrant energy. **The Who**-like rocker "I'm Sure You'll Get Everything You Want" is pure teen power pop, sure to make feet shuffle and heads bob, while the soulful "I Just Need Some Loving" provides a steady hip-shaking groove in the mold of a 1966-era **Steve Winwood**, à la "Give Me Some Lovin'."

They manage to cram an organ-driven instrumental, some straight-ahead garage punkers, and a couple love songs into the playlist as well.

The result is a light, fun example of kids who play music because they love it. I believe there is a 1995 LP as well.

## THE BOMBORAS
*(Los Angeles, CA USA)*

*Little Drummer Boy* EP, 1994
  S.F.T.R.I., USA
"Forbidden Planet" b/w "Moon Probe" & "Time Bomb" 7" EP, 1995
*Savage Island* 12 song LP/CD, 1995
  Dionysus Records, USA

Also a 1995 split 7" EP with **Lord Hunt & The Missing Finks** on Screaming Apple Records, Germany.

This is yet another off-shoot of **The Finks/Witchdoctors** pot of musicians, once again mining a moody '60s instrumental sound. A cool, restrained aura soaks the recording, making it a fine addition to the resurgent mid-1990s California instrumental scene. The EP's sleeve sports Easter Island stone heads, floating in outer space — a perfect compliment to the music. The Dionysus LP *must* also be cool, though it hadn't appeared as of this book's printing.

## BOOHOOS
*(Pesaro, Italy)*

A hard-psych band with several releases on Italy's Electric Eye Records: *The Sun The Snake And The Hoo* 12" EP, 1986; *Moonshiner* LP, 1987; and the *Rocks For Real* LP, 1989.

## LES BOOKMAKERS
*(Lyon, France)*

Another French combo which is highly rated in some circles. The group reportedly sounded early on like a "French **Fleshtones**" and gained acclaim for their party-styled stage presence. Later, in the early '8os, they followed the **Fleshtones** by adding a horn section — which didn't really work for the band. Their latest CD reportedly showed a return to their wild old party style, dumping the horns.

## THE BOOTHILL FIVE
*(Pisa, Italy)*

Featuring former members of **The Storks** and **The Birdmen Of Alkatraz**, this fivesome reportedly blend British beat, '6os Texas punk, acid & folk sounds. They recorded a 15 song demo tape, but no releases are known except a cut on a Misty Lane sampler cassette, circa 1993.

## THE BOSCOS
*(Eugene, OR USA)*

An unreleased 23 song cassette from 1990 shows off the influences of this **Electric Flies** off-shoot. All of the tracks are cover tunes, ranging from **The Electric Prunes** to **The Beatles** to **Standells** — with some much more obscure acts like **The Bugs** and **The Third Booth** thrown in as well.

Each is lovingly reproduced in this home recording, with fine guitar work and sparkling harmonies throughout. Their version of **The Byrds'** "The World Turns All Around Her" might even manage to top the original, and that's high praise, indeed.

Much of the material here is more expertly performed and realized than the originals, which of course isn't a difficult proposition for the cruder '66 fuzz punk offerings, but pretty amazing considering the high quality of the more polished tunes.

This is a bunch of inspired fun, and that's what it's meant to be.

## THE BOSS MARTIANS
*(Tacoma, WA USA)*

"XKE!" b/w "I'm 'A One You Need'" 45, 1993
   Hillsdale Records, USA
self-titled 15 song LP & CD, 1995
   Dionysus Records, USA

"XKE" is a reverb drenched surf-ish instrumental, expertly delivered and faithfully recorded. "I'm 'A One You Need'" is a vocal offering, showcasing the band's R&B rave-up leanings, complete with toe-tapping rhythm and **Sir Douglas**-esque pulsing organ.

### THE BOSS MARTIANS, 1995

Tony Hilder notes on the 45's sleeve, *"Nowadays, when you mention the Pacific Northwest, people think of long hair, plaid and (dare I say it?) 'grunge.' Fortunately for you and me there exists a young musical combo from Tacoma who defy this image — these rebels are clean cut, polite, and TALENTED! Just one spin of this record will prove that The Boss Martians are Washington State's premiere surfing and vocal band!"*

There are several other discs available, including a wonderful 1995 LP on Dionysus. It bursts with more timeless spring reverb and wheezing organ, plus more vocals along with the reverent instrumentals. This style seemingly burst open into greater (underground) popularity by 1995 — and **The Boss Martians** are one of the finest of these new combos. This author will be tracking down their other releases — just like the reader should.

## THE BOTSWANAS
*(New York, NY USA)*

"Little Witch" b/w "Primitive High" 45, 1994
　　Feralette Records, USA

A former member of **The Double Naught Spys** joined up on bass, but apparently after the release of this 45. It's a pop effort with a garage hint, but both songs are a bit too polite for their own good — I just can't recommend this one.


## MICHAEL J. BOWMAN
*(New York, NY USA)*

**Bowman** is a one-man home-studio fellow, who released a 10 song cassette entitled *Charm* in 1990. Most home-tapers suffer from the inability to edit themselves, but **Bowman** manages to turn in a strong effort. The trippy "Seven Rays" especially exudes a confident and well thought out aura.


## BOYS FROM NOWHERE
*(Columbus, OH USA)*

"Jungle Boy" b/w "1966" 45, 1986
"Goin' Too Far" b/w "I Don't Bother" 45, 1987
　　Young Lion Records, USA
"No Reason To Live" b/w "1966" 45, 1989
*Hired And Fired* 7 song 12" EP, 1990
　　Rubber Records, Australia

This much-overrated band is actually vocalist Mick Divvens with a variety of backing musicians. Their first 45 is unknown to me, but it and several others are reportedly collected on the Australian 12" listed above. (I think the track "Beg" — also on the *Garage Sale* cassette — is on the debut 45.) The two 45s listed above feature interesting if unexceptional garage tunes, with Divvens' snotty vocals the centerpiece.

Divvens' initial inspiration (besides his admitted idols *The Lyres*) was classic garage punk, but he had switched allegiances to pedestrian hard rock by the time his first U.S. LP was released in 1990 — *The Bridal Album* is an excruciating dredge of metal-ish guitar wankings.

A favorite story about Divvens concerns this author talking to him on the phone circa 1985. He proceeded to say unkind and rather derogatory things concerning just about every other band besides his own, including mine — but he somehow thought he was talking to someone else, not the subject of his abuse!

I continued the conversation with bemusement, and to this day I haven't let him know of his rather hilarious mistake.


## THE BO-WEEVILS
*(Australia)*

self-titled 4 song 7" EP, 1986
"That Girl" b/w "I Want You" 45, 1986
*The Vortex Took Them* 5 song 12" EP, 1987
　　Kavern 7 Records, Australia
*Where Particular People Congregate* LP, 1989
　　Mr. Spaceman Records, Australia
*Destroyer of Worlds* 9 song LP, 1990
　　Rubber Records, Australia

Also the fine garage ballad "Now She's Gone" is included with a 1986 issue of *Foreign Object Magazine* — I'm unsure if this is a 45, flexi or cassette.

**The Bo-Weevils** are one of my favorite Australian bands of the era. Their crude, early garage 45s echo the best of the '66 U.S. garage sound, yet retain a distinctive Australian edge.

### THE BO-WEEVILS, 1987

Both early seven-inchers are impossible to find now, but are absolutely essential to anyone interested in the subject of this book. Their initial 12" continues on the garage path, with a bit more psych thrown in. The swirling organ-driven "Have You Been To Mars" is especially gratifying, complete with snotty blurted vocals and requisite screams.

Dean Mittelhauser should be given a nod of thanks here. His short-lived Kavern 7 label introduced some of the best young Australian garage talent, as witnessed by the **Bo-Weevils'** first and best three discs.

I haven't been able to find their first full-length LP, but *Destroyer Of Worlds* finds the band in a much more musically sophisticated mode. Clearly they had shaken the earlier garage inspirations, but some of the LP does fit in with the earlier **Bo-Weevils** material. One reason for the evolving sound could be the significant lineup changes the band endured, with only the rhythm section making

**32**

it from their start through to their latest LP.

Bassist Neil Rogers told me in 1992, *"The scene here for garage heads is quite incestuous and friendly. Other bands in Melbourne who we're friendly with and are '60s inspired include: **The Squad** — mod band; **The Saucermen** — a garage band (used to be known as **The Mathmoss**); **Pressed Rat and Warthog** — Cream inspired."*

The **Bo-Weevils** have survived at least to the mid 1990s. Investigate their output before they're exterminated.


## BRANIAC 5
(U.K.)

The highly regarded *World Inside* LP was finally released by Reckless Records in 1988, though it was actually recorded in 1979. Its reputation has grown to mythical proportions in some fanzine circles, though this author has not been able to find anyone who has actually heard it.


## THE BREADMAKERS
(Victoria, Australia)

*Hoodoo Nightspot* & *Twelve More Miles To Midnight*
   21 song CD, 1992
   Corduroy Records, Australia
*Two Star Motel* 4 song 7" EP, 1992
   Screaming Apple Records, Germany

The CD liner notes explain that all of their output was *"Recorded in superb mono on a 1958 one track recorder between July '90 and December '91 at Preston Studios. All songs were recorded live with NO OVERDUBS."*

This detail helps explain the direct, visceral appeal of **The Breadmakers'** mid-1960s styled white R&B. Heavily influenced by the British R&B scene of **The Downliners Sect** and **Pretty Things,** this six-piece plays it pretty purist and straight, with some tasty harmonica and piano adding spark and flavor.

The CD actually combines two separate LPs, which were originally released on vinyl, I believe. They share a gutsy immediate sound, with excellent musicianship and fine vocals. The material is of a uniformly high caliber, but I especially like the moody atmosphere of "It's Your Voodoo Working" and the groove of "Walkin' And Talkin.'"

The vinyl EP delivers more of the same smoky R&B. All of this is definitely recommended for those who prefer their '60s R&B straight — without the taste of garage.


## THE BROKEN JUG
(Germany)

*Grand Junction* 5 song 7" EP, 1985
"Promised Land" b/w "Sally" 45, 1986
*William* 13 song LP, 1987
   Glitterhouse Records, Germany

Here's another outfit which began strong, then evolved into a harder, less interesting sounding group. They originally recorded a demo as **The Blackberry Jug,** then switched some members and their name to **The Broken Jug.**

Their first EP, *Grand Junction,* is an instant classic of uninhibited garage. Recorded on a four-track machine in their rehearsal room, it bursts with energy and verve. **The Jug**'s sound mixes the mystery of **The Doors'** organ with the directness of '60s punk: simple, clear and gutty.

Their first LP, *William,* treads the same territory, yet with a tighter, more professional sound. It's very distinctive and somehow innately German, yet highly identifiable by American genre standards.

Unfortunately this marked the end of **The Broken Jug** as a garage-psych group, as they later released The *Burning Down The Neighborhood* LP, *Squeeze Rodeo Live* 7" and the "Anne" b/w "Forever And A Day" 45 (all in 1987) — all in a Stooges-inspired hard-rock vein.

This was a less than inspired end for a very promising group; the early records are among the best represented in this book.


## THE BROOD
(Portland, ME USA)

"Let's Talk About Boys" 3 song 7" EP, 1986
   Primitive Records, Canada
"I Need You There" b/w "You Got Me" 45, 1988
*In Spite Of It All* 16 song LP, 1988
"But You're Gone" b/w "You Don't Need Me" 45, 1991
   Get Hip Records, USA
"Since He's Been Gone" b/w "You've Got Me Cryin'" 45, 1990
   Stanton Park Records, USA
"I'll Come Again" b/w "Knock On My Door" 45, 1992
*Vendetta* 16 song LP/CD, 1992
   Estrus Records, USA
*Hitsville* 16 song LP/CD, 1995
   Dionysus Records, USA

Also, "I Saw What You Did" on a *Tant Qu'il Y Au Du Rock* magazine 45, "Shake and Shout" and "Surfin' Eyeball" on a *Bang!* magazine compilation, "One Winter's Night" on the *Midnight X-mas #3* compilation, "In And Out" in the *Estrus Lunch Box,* a cut on Norton Records' *Sam The Sham Tribute* LP, 1994, plus several other compilations, as described in the "All Together Now" section.

Video: on Skyclad's *Frozen Ghosts* compilation, 1991, with a live cut of "Your Body Not Your Soul."

The Brood rates as another of my all-time favorite groups, but I'll let them tell you about themselves before I interject.

"The Brood came together to capture the spirit of the '6os through music that is fun. They are not one of those pretentious bands trying to be a carbon-copy of the groups they admire so much, rather, they are more interested in achieving the feeling that was so special back then.

"The Brood capture that feeling through songs of love and heartbreak, joy and sorrow and of life

Since He's Been Gone

in all of its turmoil. And that is why they continue to last while many of their better known contemporaries have called it quits." — from their press kit, 1990

The Brood is an all-woman group, but this fact alone does not make them remarkable or notable. The fiery, inspirational '6os punk garage music they create is what sets them apart. Unlike other "girl" groups which sought to cash in on the novelty of their gender, The Brood is a world-class garage group first, and talented *female* musicians second. Each discs contain a consistent rough edge, with guts and fuzz galore — and all of their output is highly recommended.

They are the definition of pure teen garage-mania.

Richard Ward conducted an interview with Chris Horne in 1988 for *The Psychedelicatessen*:

Q: Tell us about your best live show, or even your favorite live show.

Chris: My favorite show happens to be the biggest fiasco ever. It was at a small redneck tavern in Portland (Maine) with a

bad reputation, but they wanted to have bands at their place and guaranteed us enough money to pay rent. We were psyched to play there because of a light-up dance floor, but when we got there they made us set up to the side in a tiny space where they moved a couple tables out.

Then we went to the ladies room to 'brood' over a bottle of "Janice Juice" (whiskey), and just before we got to the last drop, the barmaid came in and nearly threw us out right then!

The clientele, we should have known, was not into '6os fuzz punk at all, and the dykes were yellin' for us to play songs off the juke box. The manager kept flicking the power on and off until the bass amp finally blew a fuse. I kept breaking guitar strings and had to stop each time to change 'em cuz I didn't have a back-up guitar.

At the end of the night the owner literally threw the check at us!"

I've always wanted to see The Brood in concert, where they are reported to be even better than their records.

At least I have their vinyl.

## THE BUGS
(U.K.)

*Darkside* 12 song LP, 1988?
  Big Beat Records, U.K.

The Bugs tackle the U.S. '66 garage sound, with some added mega-fuzz trash thrown in for good measure. "Just A Bad Dream" has a '77 buzz energy along with its garage roots, while the tracks "End It All" and "Six String Goddess" thump along as more anthemic garage efforts.

They also tackle the Shadows Of Knight classic "Darkside" as their title track — and like the remainder of the LP, it is marred by a big gated snare drum reverb that seems inappropriate to the surrounding lo-fi noise. This one just misses the mark, but is still of some interest.

They also have a three song EP on Mike Spencer's Hit records titled *Leavin' Here*.

## THE BURNING RAIN
(Dallas, TX USA)

"Climb To The Sky" b/w "Crystal Colored Cloud" 45, 1988
*Teen Trash # 3* 10 song LP & CD, 1993
  Music Maniac records, Germany

also the "Piece Of Your Love" 45 on Rockadelic Records, 1988; The *Visons* and *Iwaska* LPs on Mind & Eye Records, circa 1989 & 1990.

It has been said repeatedly that Texas is a strange and twisted place, and this helps to explain why Lone Star 1960s garage punk and psych is so distinctly and identifiably odd.

**The Burning Rain** carries the torch of demented Texas psych proudly. Echoing such pioneers as **The 13th Floor Elevators** and **The Golden Dawn, The Burning Rain** combines swirly organ, reverbed fuzz guitar with spooky mesmerizing arrangements.

Their "Climb To The Sky" 45 — their debut, I believe — is a perfectly moody psych experience, replete with cryptic picture sleeve. Only 500 of these early discs were pressed.

"Pictures In The Fire," from their German LP, is perhaps an archetype of the Texas psych sound, full of imagistic lyrics, hypnotic rhythm and fiery guitar. Tracks such as "Oracle" and "Evil Eye" cement the band as the best outfit to hit the wide open spaces of Texas since **The Elevators**; a claim that I do not make lightly.

The remainder of the Music Maniac LP is of the highest standard, and begs the listener to unearth the previous discs. This might be a more daunting task than one realizes — this author only heard of the band with the release of the 1993 LP, even though the band had been performing and recording for full five years previously.

Everything is bigger in Texas, so the saying goes. The impact of garage-psych is certainly larger when one hears **The Burning Rain**, which will rightfully take its place in the pantheon of classic Texas bands.

## BUTTERFLY COLLECTORS
*(Germany)*

A four track 12" EP is out on Fab Records; it's a bit light-weight in a pop vocal style.

## THE BUZZ
*(Cincinnati, OH USA)*

Here's another great band name. Mod-ish pop is delivered, with nods to both **The Who** and **Creation**. Around from April 1985 until early 1987, these folks eventually evolved into **The Cybermen**. This is pretty slick stuff, and at least three demo tracks exist.

## THE CAKE PEOPLE
*(Milwaukee, WI USA)*

"Statues" b/w "Going Away" 45, 1994
*Cake Fold Sleeve* 4 songs, 2 x 45, 1995
  November Rain Records, USA

This is a side project of Cary Wolf of **The Petals** and John Frankovic of **Plasticland**. The two songs on the debut 45 effectively meld both bands' musical leanings: vocally oriented folk and moody pop psych. Fans of either group will appreciate the duo's collaboration.

The four song, double 45 titled *Cake Fold Sleeve* appeared in 1995 — featuring artist Lance Laurie's patented nightmarish artwork — as well as the duo's best sounds to date. Colored vinyl and a full color fold-out sleeve complete the delicious package, which rates up almost as highly as any **Plasticland** or **Petals** effort.

A solo Cary Wolf album titled *Traveling By Spore* was also in the works as of this writing.

## CALAMITES
*(France)*

**The Calamites** were evidently an all-girl group playing primarily pop oriented material. They also had provided vocal backing for **The Dogs**. The tape I heard showed the ladies singing smooth and slick melodies in their native French — nothing terribly exciting, but well done nonetheless. They split circa 1988.

## EL CAMINOS
*(Kobe, Japan)*

Music fan Allen Waite saw this Japanese foursome in their native land, noting to me that *"They use almost all Vox equipment, and they're extreme '60s purists."* He adds that the instrumental surf outfit was *"ahead of their time, since they started playing before the surf revival gained attention in Japan."*

Playing from 1990 until at least 1995, **El Caminos** did circulate a 10 song demo in 1995 in advance of a planned 45 release. They also have a song on a Japanese compilation CD. A video of the band in action shows **El Caminos** to be musically adept and obviously in love with the distinctly American form of surf music. With the sprouting U.S. interest in similar Japanese bands such as **Jackie And The Cedrics,** bands like **El Caminos** might finally get their due as well.

## CANDLESTICK
*(Germany)*

A band of very young kids, reportedly ages 15 - 18, with a two song demo to their credit, circa the late '80s. "Not Made For Misery" is a spirited beat-pop effort, with some flat but sincere singing. They fare a bit better with the toe-tapping "Be My Baby," which is full of smiling teen energy.

## THE CANNIBALS
*(U.K.)*

*Hot Stuff* 12 song LP, 1985
    Hit Records, U.K.
*Trash For Cash* 9 song LP, 1985
    Homestead Records, USA

The U.K. "trash rock" scene held the underground's attention for a while in the mid-'80s, with **The Sting Rays, Milkshakes,** and **Cannibals** at the fore. **The Cannibals** fed from the carcasses of classic U.S. '60s punk garage, chewed on it and spit it out with a distinct English flavor. Unlike most of their contemporaries, these trash mongers showed that the English could indeed slobber and spit with the best of the American garage-niks.

They have several other discs available, which I've found difficult to uncover in this country. The two discs listed above share several tracks, but show off the band to good advantage, especially in their version of the seminal "Action Woman."

Many fans rate **The Cannibals** highly. The reader shouldn't interpret the limited space given to them here as an indication of their interest. This is simply all that I know of them.

## CAPTAIN FUTURE & THE ZAP GUNS
*(Sweden)*

*Explores Inner Space* 4 song 7" EP
    Dead Beat Records, Sweden

A spirited four song EP (spirited, because it's on Dead Beat Records) and another 45 are the known output of these sweaty Swedes. Primitive punk with a slight garage bent could be a fitting description.

As the back sleeve on their first EP says, "Ungawa!"

## CAPTAIN HENRY
*(Zurich, Switzerland)*

They're reportedly made up of members of other Zurich bands, with two 45s on private labels. "Starfriend" is a melodic '60s pop song, featuring smooth vocals and an instant likability — similar in flavor to classic **Badfinger.**

## CARRIER WAVE
*(Texas USA)*

All I know of these lads is that their 1994 four song demo is a wonderful exercise in dreamy psychedelia, somewhere between Syd's **Pink Floyd** and **The Rain Parade,** with a heavy dose of mesmerizing ambiance and drone repetition mixed in. It's a very modern yet thoroughly psychedelic experience. I would certainly enjoy a further dose of **Carrier Wave.**

## THE CATTLE
*(Tucson, AZ USA)*

*Escalator Stampede* 4 song 7" EP, 1987
    Addled Records, USA
*Cattle Call* 3 song 7" EP, 1989
    Dionysus Records, USA
"Hard Times In West Pho." (split) 45, 1989
    Toxic Shock Records, USA
"It's Your Grave (Can You Dig It?)"
    b/w "Lower Sonoran Desert" 45, 1990
    SFTRI Records, USA
*Good 'N' Bitter* 3 song 7" EP, 1991
    Erl Records, USA

Video: "Cattle Call," 1989

**Al Perry** is a Southwestern U.S. original. Inspired by every obscure R&B, country, garage, rock and weirdo record known (and unknown), this guitar great winds it all up into **The Cattle.**

This trio's eclectic output meandered all over the stylistic map, but never omitted one item: **Perry's** searing, cranked guitar. (He once loaned his amp to another musician for a show, but demanded that it not be turned in volume down below "10" — the maximum!) **Perry** formed **The Cattle** out of the ashes of **The Hecklers**, as described later.

Known for their "cow punk" stylings as much as their garage flavor, **The Cattle** released a swarm of 45s (as well as the rare 1985 *Cattle Crossing* LP), each with their own bent and that unmistakable guitar madness. My favorite 45 is not surprisingly also the one I produced — the "It's Your Grave, Can You Dig It?" effort. It is the most psych-garage influenced of his output.

This author's connection to **Perry** doesn't end there — he contributed his noise to the early recordings of Tucson's **Marshmallow Overcoat**. He has also released a number of more country based solo records, and has appeared in several films, including 1995's big budget western *The Quick & The Dead*.

He is well on his way to becoming legendary here in the dusty desert.

## THE CAVEDOGS
*(Torino, Italy)*

I've only heard a couple of tracks, including the fun "Murder In The Graveyard" and its follow-up "I'm a Gravdigger." It's very crude and sloppy '66 garage, just like the best of the *Pebbles* compilation inspired bands. I just love the twisted way the vocalist slurs the word "murder." The band recorded a 13 song demo, but no vinyl releases have appeared.

There was another **Cavedogs** from the U.S. in the early 1990s, this time from Boston, with a couple LPs on Capitol Records. These coincidentally have a tinge of a '60s mod-pop edge to them, but are only of marginal interest to the subject of this book.

## THE CAVE FOUR
*(Germany)*

untitled 7" EP, 1995
  Dionysus Records, USA

**The Cave Four** is an instrumental surf act that fits right in with the upswing in that genre's interest. The recordings are perfectly crude and atmospheric — but I must admit that the thought of a Dutch surf band is a bit bizarre. Only sub-par cover art keeps this from being a complete top-notch release, however.

**37**

## THE CAVEGURLS
*(Minneapolis, MN USA)*

*Just Out Of Reach* 4 song 7" EP, 1989
  Skull Duggery Records, USA

This crude little gem involves three women and, I believe, the help of (the all-male) **Funseekers**. In a way, then, **The Cavegurls** could be compared with England's **Del Monas**. They each feature mid '60s girlish vocals, and very crude and trashy backing instrumental tracks.

Sally Sweet was once in another Minneapolis all-women combo, **The Blue Up?**, and she puts her experience to use on "Just Out Of Reach."

**Cavegurl** Rena listed scootering as a hobby, and she was reportedly killed in a 1990 scooter traffic accident.

## THE CAVEMEN
*(Texas, USA)*

A slight '60s garage tinge is noticeable on an otherwise '80s-styled punk LP, *Yeah!*, on Midnight Records, 1986.

## THEE CELLAR DWELLARS
*(Carlisle, PA USA)*

"Wonderin' Why?" b/w "Dwellin'" 45, 1987
  Get Hip Records, USA

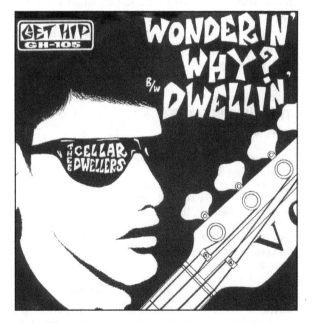

Ah, here we have another classic 1960s punk garage throwback band — and that's a supreme compliment, coming from me.

The haircuts are perfect bowls, the instruments

and fuzz boxes are just right, and there's even a chick — I mean, a young woman — on the keyboards. The sound? Pure crude one-and-a-half chord garage garbage, with swirling organ and teen zit angst. In other words — *perfect*.

I think the only other noise from these garage-niks is on a Canadian *What Wave* compilation cassette. Perhaps the lack of tracks will help seal the mysterious reputation of this combo — one classic fuzz 45 and nothing more.

This sounds like the makings of a garage band legend to me.

## CELLOPHANE FLOWERS
*(Rome, Italy)*

A garage punk band with a private demo cassette from 1992. I believe that I met a female vocalist for the group during my stay in Rome in 1992. Dressed in cool '66 mod-garage clothes, she seemed to be a perfect addition to any garage-psych combo.

## I CENTURIONI
*(Italy)*

"Misserlou" b/w "Banzai Washout" 45, 1994
    Destination X Records, Italy

I believe the English translation for the band name would be "The Centurions." While I haven't seen or heard this 45, it apparently features ex-members of fellow Italian garagers **Sciacalli**, and is in the surf-trash genre, similar to the '60s outfit **The Trashmen**.

## THE CHEEPSKATES
*(New York, NY USA)*

"Run Better Run" b/w "X-Tra Collestrial" 45, 1983
    Five & Ten Records, USA
*Run Better Run* 14 song LP, 1984
*Second And Last* 14 song LP, 1986
    Midnight Records, USA

also: *Remember* LP, *It Wings Above* LP, *Waiting For Utna* LP, "Is Love Really Fair" promo 7" — all on Music Maniac Records, Germany.

The debate over which U.S. coast "won" the battle of the 1980s garages will rage for some time. Both New York and California erupted at about the same time, both boasted a slew of good bands early on, and both coasts produced enough vinyl to state their case.

**The Cheepskates** were one of those great early New York City bands, and they deposited two fine LPs that rival the best work of the period. *Run Better Run* shows a diversity of influences, from straight Farfisa-driven garage to twangy surf to melodic pop. Simple production and Shane Faubert's gentle vocals set this effort apart from some of their noisy competitors, making this LP one of those rare garage pop records that remains truly listenable. The title track alone certifies it as a classic LP.

Like most of the other groups documented here, **The Cheepskates** did not find wide commercial acceptance for their efforts, and eventually evolved with a different sound. They did manage to leave behind one last document of their individualistic garage pop style before their initial split in 1985, the aptly titled *Second And Last* LP.

The band's diversity had expanded to an even higher degree, with a more mature sense of arrangement and a thicker production put to effective use. There are some beautiful lilting pop songs here as well, once again displaying the band's ability to create their own music, rather than simply regurgitating the past. The track "About You" is a showcase for Faubert's continuing maturation as writer and performer — his voice cannot be confused with anyone else's.

**The Cheepskates** (with Faubert) did eventually re-form as a quiet pop band with a different lineup, then released a series of records on Music Maniac. The '60s garage inspiration had evaporated by then, and the classic sounds of the group would remain on its initial two LPs.

David Herrera (and the ubiquitous Orin Portnoy) would go on to **Herrera And The Handouts**, with the *Handout From A Cheepskate* LP on Midnight in 1989. It's notable for an interesting cover of **The Optic Nerve**'s "Mayfair."

Vocalist Shane Faubert would also release a string of fine pop records on the Music Maniac label, my favorite being the gentle and haunting *San Blass*, circa 1994.

## THE CHEETA BEATS
*(New York, NY USA)*

I believe that this was a band circa 1984 which played at The Dive club. If memory serves, they played instrumental garage and surf tunes.

## CHEMISTRY SET
*(U.K.)*

Several vinyl appearances and a recommended cassette on Acid Tapes are available. The songs "Orange Juice Sun," "Minas Tirith," "The Candle Burns" and "Acacia Gardens" especially meld finely crafted melodies, tasteful guitars and tight arrangements into some of the best psych pop of the decade.

**The Tyrnaround** is the closest 1980s band I can think of for comparison — and there aren't many other bands from the period that are accomplished enough to even merit comparison. Even I have not been able to track down any vinyl from this outfit, so this short entry is caused by my lack of any additional product or information.

There are several other bands named **The Chemistry Set** in the USA, Canada, and U.K., all creating different sounds.


## CHEROKEES
*(France)*

I still haven't uncovered any information about this 1980s combo. It sounds like a standard name for an original U.S. 1960s band, doesn't it?


## THE CHERRY HOGGS
*(France)*

The "Linda" 45, 1990, features a pleasant pop ballad. The band didn't have enough money to record another song for the B-side, so they mixed an instrumental of their one song — and put it on the flip!


## CHERRY STONES
*(Perth, Australia)*

A reportedly **Byrds**-ish group which featured a member of **The Stems**. No recordings are known to exist.


## THE CHESHYRES
*(Toronto, ON Canada)*

The Cheshyres were an R&B-influenced garage band in **The Yardbirds'** tradition. They appeared on several What Wave tapes and the "Thee Cave Comes Alive" compilation LP. Drummer Ken Anderson went on to The Ultra 5, Optic Nerve and other bands.
*— Dave O'Halloran*

**39**


## THE CHESSMEN
*(Hamilton, ON Canada)*

*The Chessmen* 13 song LP, 1989
    Zapp Records, Canada

One of the most important facets of the independent rock movement was the ability for a band to record and release its own records. That ability made groups like **The Chessmen** possible. They wrote some songs, played some gigs, and unleashed an album to the public.

I love a record like this because it captures a band before self-editing sets in, before self-consciousness takes away the band's individuality. **The Chessmen** made these sounds because they enjoyed them, and I just happen to like them as well. There's a sampling of garage, Rickenbacker-fueled '60s pop, a little psych and some baroque elegance thrown in for good measure. None of this is especially groundbreaking or earth shattering, but it is honest, fun and enjoyable.

That is good enough reason for me to justify bands like **The Chessmen** putting out records. This LP is an unknown gem — and a fine example of how and why this style of music has been so inspirational over the generations.

Alan Wright reports, *"**The Chessmen** performed a great rendition of **The Count V**'s 'Peace Of Mind,' as well as 'How Does It Feel To Feel' by **The Creation** — and an extended 15 minute or so wigged-out version of their own 'Time Machine' complete with screeching feedback, phased effects and utter dementia!"*

As their LP sleeve invites, *"Drop by if you are in Hamilton."*


## THE CHESTERFIELD KINGS
*(Rochester, NY USA)*

"I Ain't No Miracle Worker" b/w "Exit 9" 45, 1979
"You Can't Catch Me" b/w "I Won't Be There" 45, 1981
"Hey Little Bird" b/w "I Can Only Give You Everything" 45, 1982
    Living Eye Records, USA
*Here Are...* 14 song LP, 1982
"I'm Going Home" b/w "A Dark Corner" 45, 1983
"She Told Me Lies" b/w "I've Gotta Way With Girls" 45, 1984
*Stop!* 12 song LP, 1985 (14 song version, 1987)
"Baby Doll" b/w "I Cannot Find Her" 45, 1987
*Don't Open Til Doomsday* 14 song LP, 1987
    (cassette has extra song)
*Night Of The Living Eyes* 14 song LP/CD/Cassette, 1989
*Drunk On Muddy Water* 13 song CD (only), 1990
*Next One In Line* 3 song 7" EP, 1991
*Let's Go Get Stoned* 14 song LP & CD, 1994
    Mirror Records, USA
*Fossils* 19 song LP, 1986(?)
    Bootleg

*Kingsized Rock 'N' Roll*, 18 song LP, 1987
  Bootleg

Compilations: *Battle of The Garages*, 1981; *Laserock 'N' Roll*, 1988, *Tribute To The Kinks*, 1989.

Video: "99th Floor," 1983; "She Told Me Lies," 1985, plus live rehearsal footage and many live concerts.

Perhaps no other garage band of the 1980s was as influential as Rochester's **Chesterfield Kings**. They were one of the very first and best of the new garage combos — and came to symbolize the entire movement by their mere existence.

The most difficult task for any artist is to start a trend in motion — once it exists, others can jump on the bandwagon with much less effort. **The Chesterfield Kings** were the ones who arguably brought back awareness to the 1960s garage-band sound, and for this alone they are owed a great debt. The fact that they went on to become one of the best garage bands themselves only cements their place in rock "history."

Their first two 45s (circa 1979 and 1981) are impossibly rare collector's items, but have been reissued (along with an unreleased third early 45) on the 1989 *Night Of The Living Eyes* LP. These early tracks show a band coming to grips with its role as the "new Chocolate Watchband," as they reverently rip through some choice obscure '60s nuggets.

Their 14 song debut LP continued their development as the world's premier fuzz outfit. The crudely recorded and performed album, made up entirely of cover versions, was the first album of its genre to appear since 1966.

Its release was a shock to the independent rock scene's system, which was still dealing with the "New Wave" movement. Many critics and fans alike wondered "What the hell is a band like this doing in the 1980s!?!" One local Rochester TV station broadcast footage of an early 1980s **Chesterfield Kings** concert in a story about the "new wave punk movement" — it had no idea what **The Kings** were doing.

The band itself would declare at the time that it didn't watch any TV shows that were made after 1966, they didn't play instruments that were made after 1966, and that their music would not sound like anything after 1966! They stood out as an enigma, one that would inspire countless other bands to form and continue the garage tradition.

Cynics have criticized the group in retrospect as being a "Sha Na Na" of the garage genre — aping nostalgia to aging hippies — but this assessment is incredibly wide of the mark. **The Kings'** appeal was with young kids,

**40**

## THE CHESTERFIELD KINGS, 1985

not their parents, and the aggressive, raw and primal sound of the band was certainly not conducive to passive nostalgia.

If anything, **The Chesterfield Kings** could be considered a different type of "roots band," in this case an American 1960s white garage combo.

This author saw them in 1983 at Washington D.C.'s 9:30 Club, where they entranced two separate sold out audiences. The young girls screamed, the band wailed, and for a brief instance — one of those moments of epiphany — I thought I was watching **The Rolling Stones** in late '64. The energy in the room was astonishing, as hundreds of kids reveled in the intensity of **The Kings**. This was not a nostalgia trip!

The band also dispelled criticisms about their lack of originality with their second LP, *Stop!* Their original compositions are the highlight of the record, especially the organ-driven teen anthem "She Told Me Lies" (sometimes jokingly performed in concert as "She Sold Me Fries"!). A generous helping of folk-rock is also present on this LP, and **The Kings** remained on the top of the garage heap.

Endless touring and European exposure brought attention to the band, but the major labels stayed away. They cut their third LP with intentions of luring a major deal, but eventually released it as an indy. *Doomsday* was feared by many to be the Kings' "sell out" attempt, but instead it might be their most musically accomplished disc.

The garage mentality is ever-present, helped with solid studio production, great guitar work, and even a song by Dee Dee King (of **The Ramones**). The band was attempting to distance itself from the "1960s revival" image, however, as the generic "rock" cover photos attest. Still, the music in the grooves is what matters, and **The Kings** had certainly not deserted their roots.

This would prove to be the apex of **The Chesterfield Kings** as a garage band. More drastic line-up changes occurred, leaving only frontman Greg Prevost and bassist Andy Babiuk from the original 1979 grouping. A new look and sound came with the new members, as the band mutated into a harder edged unit. Glam-ish fashions, tattoos and hairstyles now dominated, along with hard rock-ish songs. (A 1990 promo-only CD did show the band paying homage to their R&B heroes, however, proving that the band had, indeed, not lost sight of its roots entirely.)

More surprises were in store, though, as the band re-invented themselves again for 1994's *Let's Go Get Stoned* LP. Here they do **The Stones** better than **The Stones** ever could. It's the 1968-1972 era this time, and vocalist Greg Prevost growls and drawls with Jagger-esque precision. Equal doses of reverence, energy and barroom spirit make this a triumphant return for the boys. Former **Stone** Mick Taylor even shows up on a track; I wonder what "Britain's Chesterfield Kings" thought about all of this?

The lads from Rochester have certainly gained a place along side their original inspirations: **The Rolling Stones, Chocolate Watchband, Barbarians,** et al. **The Chesterfield Kings** awoke an entire new generation to the sounds of the masters, and in the process became masters themselves.


## THE CHEVELLES

*(Perth, Australia)*

"Be My Friend" b/w "She Don't Come Around" 45, 1991
*The Kids Ain't Hip* 5 song 12" EP, 1992
 Zero Hour Records, Australia
*In The Zero Hour* 13 song CD, 1993?
 Munster Records, Spain
"Girl For Me" 45, circa 1993
 Survival Records, Australia

The debut 45 for ex-**Stem** Richard Lane was described as "tough melodic power pop" by their record company Zero Hour. I found it to be disappointing — especially compared to **The Stems**. Conventional bombast and power chords are used instead of melody and creative arrangements — this should be labeled

an underacheivement.

The subsequent 12" EP also misses the mark, with a few power-pop moments coming tantalizingly close to something — and then slipping away into banality. The *In The Zero Hour* CD compiles the 45 and EP, along with six previously unreleased tracks. Again, these new tracks show promise, but don't complete their mission.

Lane was gone by 1992, so the band didn't have the lingering shadow of **The Stems** to carry any longer. The other members were from Perth groups **The Krytonics, The Freuds** and **The Racket.**

**The Chevelles** had many of the ingredients to make some damage as a power pop act, but they never managed to mix the right formula.


## BILLY CHILDISH
### (THE MILKSHAKES/THEE MIGHTY CEARSARS/ THEE HEADCOATS/HEADCOATEES/DEL MONAS)

There are literally hundreds of releases related to **Billy Childish**. One discography I have fills *five full pages*, and I'm certain that even it is incomplete as of this writing! In the interest of space, then, I've listed below some brief highlights of his enormous catalog.

I sometimes believe that God created **Billy Childish** to make all serious record collectors go insane.

### MILKSHAKES:
*Talking 'Bout Milkshakes* LP, 1981
*14 Rhythm & Beat Greats* LP, 1982
*The Milkshakes IV — The Men With The Golden Guitars* LP, 1983
 Milkshakes Records, U.K.
*After School Session* LP, 1983
 Upright Records, U.K.

### THEE MIGHTY CAESARS:
*Beach Bums Must Die* LP, 1985
*Thee Ceasars Of Trash* LP, 1986
 Milkshakes Records, U.K.
*Punk Rock Showcase* LP, 1987
 Hangman Records, U.K.
*Surely They Were The Sons Of God* LP, 1990
 Crypt Records, USA

### DEL MONAS:
*Dangerous Charms* LP, 1985
 Big Beat Records, U.K.

**41**

**THEE HEADCOATS:**

*Headcoats Down!* LP, 1989
    Hangman Records, U.K.
*Earls Of Suavedom* LP, 1990
    Crypt Records, USA
*Heavens To Mergatroid...* LP, 1990
    Sub Pop Records, USA
*Headcaoatitude* LP, 1991
    Shakin Street Records, U.K.

**HEADCOATEES:**

*Girlsville* LP, 1991
    Hangman Records
"Fish Pie" b/w "Cum Into My Mouth" 45, 1991
    S.F.T.R.I. Records, USA

David Andriese is a vocalist and bassist with **The Perverts,** a wonderfully crude current Dutch "rhythm & beat" band. He is also an avid **Billy Childish** collector and fan, and has written repeatedly about **Childish**'s various creative output. I asked Andriese to write the following entry on one of the garage/punk genre's most important and influential personalities.

*Billy Childish is without a doubt "thee" most productive gentleman in rock 'n' roll history. Coming out of Chatham, in the English earldom Kent, Childish started his recording career in 1979 with the punk rock group The Pop Rivits. In 1990 he had released the anniversary LP 50 Albums Great — and by this time he must have unleashed about 70 long-playing records that included his involvement.*

*In the early eighties Billy Childish recorded 13 LPs with The Milkshakes, a legendary rhythm 'n beat combo which was part of the then-current English Trash scene. They added an extra 'e' to 'the' and became Thee Milkshakes after bass player Russ Wilkins was replaced by Johnny Agnew.*

*One of the 'Shakes most marked achievements was the release of four different LPs in four different countries, all released on the very same day! Their last official album, Thee Knights of Trash, could be considered one of the finest moments of garage rock. It's loaded with fuzz and explodes with incredible energy.*

*While Thee Milkshakes lay on their deathbed, they instrumentally backed their singing girlfriends — which resulted in several LPs, singles and radio-TV appearances as The Delmonas. Because of an argument between the leading couple, Billy and Mickey Hampshire, an early 1985 split was inevitable. Years later, they would record the reunion LP Still Talking 'Bout Milkshakes.*

*Nevertheless, Billy kept on rollin' with his new three piece Thee Mighty Caesars, which he put together with*

**THEE HEADCOATS, 1990**

*Milkshakes bass-player John Agnew and drummer Bruce Brand. The latter was soon replaced by Graham Day, former singer/guitarist for The Prisoners. The sound of The Caesars was much rawer and louder than the "Medway Beat" (named after the river that runs through Chatham) of the 'Shakes. Heavily influenced by The Kinks, Downliner Sect, Bo Diddley and Link Wray, Thee Might Caesars gifted the world with 13 LPs.*

*Though they never officially split, witnessed by their Get Hip single from 1990, Childish suddenly introduced his brand new band Thee Headcoats in late 1989. Accompanied by old fellow Bruce Brand on drums and several bass players (Alan Crockford of The Prisoners, again John Agnew, Ollie Dolot — nowadays drummer for The Squares — and finally the definitive bassman Tub Johnson, a veteran of English trash-bands such as The Cannibals, The Vibes and The Purple Things).*

*In their first years Thee Headcoats released five LPs and it was then that an incredible cycle of singles and LPs from one Billy Childish project or another saw the light on his own Hangman Records or on dozens of labels from all over.*

*Besides rock and garage beat, Childish has also put out countless records containing blues, calypso and spoken word poetry; with acts like The Deltamen, Natural Born Lovers, Jack Ketch & The Crowmen, The Blackhands and Sexton Ming, or solo as The Wild Billy Childish. He has also helped shape the sound of young bands like The Mystreated (U.K.) and The Gloomies (France) as a studio producer. Childish does much more than only play music — he spends much of his time as a painter and wood-carver as well.*

*Like Thee Milkshakes, Thee Headcoats back up their girls musically — this time in the appropriately titled Thee Headcoatees. Both bands are still driving records collectors crazy with the* amount of their releases, and they occasionally tour around the world. Their shows usually last for more than three hours and one doesn't often get the opportunity to experience such a true and exciting rock 'n' roll atmosphere.

There seems to be no end in sight for the music of **Billy Childish**.

— By David Andriese, Rotterdam, Holland, November, 1994

## CHOCOLATE FACTORY
*(Germany)*

A 12" on Fab Records is R&B garage influenced, though strictly European in delivery. Their debut *We're Gonna Change The Face Of Pop Music Forever* EP is actually more interesting and garage-like — very enthusiastic, crude, but not very musical. This is not necessarily a criticism, and one has to like the optimistic attitude of their debut's title.

## THE CHOICE
*(Germany)*

*It's Time To Make...* 15 song LP, 1992
    Twang! Records, Germany

One of the most interesting elements of the worldwide garage scene is how each country has appropriated the distinctly American '66 fuzz sound — and then added its own local flavor. Spanish, Italian and French groups, for example, are all readily distinguishable and identifiable within the garage genre.

Germany's **The Choice** is no different. It pays homage at the garage altar like its American brethren, but with a distinctly Germanic aftertaste.

The best material on their lone LP, however, is contained in hyper cover versions. **The Animals'** "Cryin'" is propelled by warbly flanged vocals, while similarly rough treatment is given the classics "She Just Satisfies," "I'm Not Like Everybody Else," "It's Cold Outside" and "Glendora."

Some nice organ playing and a general upbeat feeling help raise this effort above the ordinary — though original material is the benchmark for any band, and there just isn't much here.

## THE CHUD
*(Berlin, Germany)*

"Don't Call Me Batman" b/w "Rumble At The Love-In" 45, 1986
    Twang! Records, Germany
*Silhouettes Of Sound* 10 song LP, 1986
"Cloudkisser" b/w "Gonzales" 45, 1988
*November Rain* 4 song 12" EP, 1989
*Mirage* 9 song LP, 1989
    Love's Simple Dreams Records, Germany

Named for the movie of the same name (*Cannibal Humanoid Underground Dwellars*), I first heard **The Chud** through its "Don't Call Me Batman" 45, a fun and danceable garage disc with slick pop aspirations. "Danceability" was an important part of **The Chud**'s approach, and their debut LP was as beat-worthy as it was psychedelic. The pop

*THE CHUD, 1986*

structures were augmented by the requisite Farfisa organ, fuzz guitars, and driving beat. "Cosmic One" and "Leather Room" were especially bubbly and twisted.

Their follow-up *November Rain* EP was a bit less interesting, but still carried some of the **Chud**'s identifiable German psych pop. This band was simply a colorful bit of fun, and a welcome combination of genres.

Their later efforts are reportedly more blatant "disco" dance records — and are of less interest, if this is true.

## CIRCLE OF ILL HEALTH
*(Toronto, ON Canada)*

**C.O.I.H.** was a psychedelic combo reportedly influenced by early **Echo & The Bunnymen.** They issued the *A Rhyme In Four Parts* four song 12" EP in 1990 and also appeared with two tracks on a Toronto compilation CD.

## CITIZEN SHIPS
*(Japan)*

**The Citizen Ships** were on Captain Trip Records, described by their label as, *"A great band from the Japanese underground. Their sound is reminiscent of the Velvet Underground or Television yet uniquely original."* Two cassettes are their only known output.

## CLAPHAM SOUTH ESCALATORS/ THE ESCALATORS
*(U.K.)*

Untitled 3 song 7" EP, 1981
   Upright Records, U.K.
"Munsters Theme" b/w "Monday" 45, 1983
"Something's Missing" b/w "The Edge" 45, 1983
*Moving Staircases* 13 track LP, 1983
   Big Beat Records, U.K.

This combo actually began as a studio side project of **The Meteors**. Their three song 7" was produced with extra studio time left over from the debut **Meteors** LP in 1981, and was reportedly recorded and mixed in just over an hour! **The Electric Prunes** cover, "Get Me To The World..." is a fine garage punk effort. "Leave Me Alone" is also a driving moody original, with a cool understated guitar break. The third track was titled "Cardboard Cutouts."

They shortened their name to **The Escalators** and released a few singles (including a version of *The Munsters* TV theme), plus the *Moving Staircases* LP — which I haven't heard.

## CLAY ALLISON *(see "Opal")*

## THE CLEAN
*(Germany)?*

I'm uncertain of the origin of these boys. The only song I've heard is the very bubble gum-ish "Tally Ho," which would have made **The Archies** proud with its bouncy melody and super wheezy organ. There weren't many practitioners of the late '60s bubblegum pop sound during the '80s, so this is a rather rare stab at that fun sub-genre.

## THE CLIFFHANGERS
*(Sweden)*

All I have from these cats is a dub of a 10 song demo of fun fuzz, including covers of "Wild Man," "Like No Other Man" and "Mainline," plus a **Cliffhangers** surf theme tune. Very tongue-in-cheek, with a zany party atmosphere — I'd love to hear this on vinyl.

## THE CLIQUE
*(London, England)*

Reportedly a mod band which played R&B originals and standards before heading to a more **Creation**-like sound in the early '90s. They were also slated to release a mod-psych EP for Germany's Screaming Apple Records.

## THE CLOCK EXCHANGE
*(Buffalo, NY & Cleveland, OH USA)*

Alan Wright remembers, *"They were a cool band. I saw them once in Buffalo opening for **The Cynics**, and they blew me away. They performed excellent covers of **The Blues Magoos'** 'Gotta Get Away' and **The Basement Wall's** 'Never Existed' and had a great stage presence, accented by their vintage Vox gear."*

## THE CLOCKWORK WIZARDS
*(Germany)*

Nothing known.

## CLOWN
*(Vercelli, Italy)*

All I've discovered is that this reportedly psych band had a self-titled private cassette, circa 1985-86.

## COLOUR MOVES
*(Milan, Italy)*

This was apparently a psych pop act with the *North/South/East/West* 7" on Crazy Mannequin Records, circa 198? and the *Musica Xamanti and Musica Per Esseri Proveniemtida Da Altra Spazi* 7" on Vox Pop in 1991.

## THE COMEDOWN
*(Holland)*

*N.D.E.* 5 song 7" EP, 1986
  Kelt Records, Holland
"Distorted Dreams" 45, 1988
  label?

Here's some mod-garage-art-pop, described to me by one fan as "The Dutch Kings Of Drugs And Trash!" That's a genre that takes some getting used to, I must say, though the EP's infectious "Bubblegum Eruption" is easily liked.

Spirited and definitely European in flavor, the band later released another 45 in a heavier, less stylish manner. That's too bad, because they could have just as easily turned into a very enjoyable and fanciful combo.

However, I must admit to enjoying their rather odd half-serious version of **The Doors'** "Wishful Sinful" from a compilation LP, which then turns into about a half-dozen other **Doors** songs, including "The End."

## CORNFLAKE ZOO
*(Sweden)*

"Hey Conductor" b/w "I See You" 45, 1985
  Tracks On Wax Records, Sweden
*The End Of The Beginning* 4 song 12" EP, 1986
"Just A Game" b/w "Time Hurries On" 45, 1987
  Eternal Love Records, Sweden

The wonderfully named **Cornflake Zoo** is in my estimation one of the finest Swedish psych-pop band of the 1980s. They weaved trademark harmonies, tuneful melody and tasteful musicianship into each of their few releases.

Initially named the equally playful and engaging **Knights Of Fuzz** (where have we seen that name?) this powerful foursome debuted in 1985 with an energetic cover of the '60s psych-punk classic "Hey Conductor" — it reportedly climbed as high as #8 on the Swedish independent rock charts! Interestingly, their own composition, "I See You," is relegated to the B-side. Original compositions would soon take hold, however, as their follow-up EP displays.

*The End Of The Beginning* 12" is magnificent in every detail. The production and delivery is magical, recalling the amazement of hearing mid-period **Beatles** for the first time. The ultimate highlight must be the somewhat misleadingly entitled "Hippie Hill," with its driving melody and cascading vocal lines in the finest flower-power tradition. The band told me in 1992 that they actually recorded

*CORNFLAKE ZOO, 1986*

a dozen songs for the 12", and that the remainder of the tunes remain unreleased.

An early 1987 demo shows the band stretching its influences, and includes a very modern interpretation of the **Buffalo Springfield**'s "For What It's Worth." These tracks also remain unreleased.

The band then altered their lineup slightly, adding the former **Wayward Souls'** bassist. Their next and final release, a 45 in 1987, showed a less obvious psych attachment, with more of an emphasis on "pop." It is no less engaging.

No further releases would pop up from this elegant Swedish outfit. They recorded demos up through 1991 — there is obviously a wealth of unreleased material covering the entire history of the group.

*"Due to studies abroad, the band is put on ice,"* they told me in 1992. They also expressed surprise at the attention and positive review in the first edition of this book — they apparently had not garnered the praise they deserved in their native Sweden. One other Swedish musician even wrote to me to complain about the amount of positive

**45**

coverage that I set aside for **The Zoo**. What happened to the ideal of mutual respect amongst musicians?

Regardless, a retrospective CD containing the 45s, EP and unreleased tracks would be a fitting end to **The Cornflake Zoo**'s story. I hope we won't have to wait 20 years — like some bands from the 1960s did — in order to see it.

Little known bands like **The Cornflake Zoo** make up the backbone of interest in garage and psych pop. Search out their records at all costs, because they are absolutely essential.

## LOS CORONADOS
*(France)*

A highly rated combo with two LPs and a handful of 7"s out in the late 1980s. Their debut LP is reportedly their finest — and one of the finest French garage records of the era. They're also featured on the U.S. *Battle Of The Garages LP #4*.

## THE COSMIC DROPOUTS
*(Moss, Norway)*

*Crashed Cadillac & Broken Hearts* 7" EP, 1988
*Groovy Things* 7 song 12" EP, 1989
"Let's Go To The Beach" b/w "Ain't Gonna Love You" 45, 1989
*Let's Go To The Beach* 4 song 12" EP, 1989
*Hoolabaloo!* 12 song LP, 1991
    That's Entertainment Records, Norway
"Into The Blue" & "The Witch" flexi, 1988
    Vinyl Magazine
*Groovy Things* LP, 1990
    Skyclad Records, USA
*I Was A Teenage Cosmic Fan* 4 song 7" EP, 1990
    Cukoo On A Choo-Choo Records, Norway
*Sonic Circus* 13 song CD, 1993
    Kick Records, Norway
*Dizzy* 3 song CD, 1993
    Columbia Records, Norway

This proficient Norwegian combo shows once again that the garage bug spread worldwide throughout the 1980s. **The Dropouts** take up where Sweden's **Nomads** left off, delivering revved-up '60s punk classics and their own straight-ahead, hip-shaking, garage-dance sound, along with the occasional surf-tinged track.

The warbling organ and snarling vocals are up front, along with some ultra-distorted guitar and solid rhythm backing. Excellent sound production helps push this band's appeal beyond strict garage circles, but these lads are obviously true-blue garage-niks in colorful paisley shirts and cool long hair.

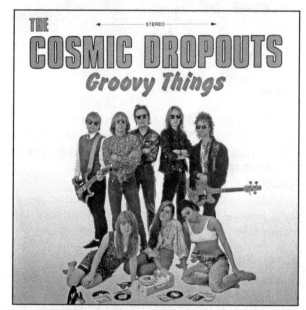

### THE COSMIC DROPOUTS, 1989

The *Groovy Things* EP is their shining (half) hour, with enough blistering tracks to make anyone sweaty and smiling. Additional songs were added to the EP for the U.S. release of the same title. Vocalist Arne Thelin then left the band in 1990 to form the also-cool **Lust-O-Rama**.

The first long-player without him, *Hoolabalool,* is a blistering affair. The garage bug was still obviously raging hard within the re-vamped band's veins, as they blurt out expertly realized anthems — somewhere between **The Fuzztones** and **Hoodoo Gurus** in style and execution. This was obviously a professional group that must have shredded audiences in concert, and made it impossible to not dance upon hearing their infectious theme song, "Do The Dropout."

Perhaps 1992 winter Olympic athletes used the *Sonic Circus* super-charged Norwegian disc as an adrenaline substitute. Equal parts spit, grit, with some sweet hooks thrown in, these dropouts remind us that long hair doesn't automatically bring on a lame haze of endless guitar solos and metal wankings.

The obvious pick-hit is the sparkling cover of Tommy Roe's "Dizzy," but that's just window-dressing for the real meal of fuzz-driven pop on a stick. **The Cosmic Dropouts** have guts galore, and they sing in English too.

Caution: continuous toe-tapping is imminent.

## COSMIC KANGAROOS
*(Germany)*

An untitled four song 7" EP of unknown proportions appeared in 1987 on Purple Turtle Records.

## COUNT BACKWARDS
*(San Francisco, CA USA)*

"Double Decker Bus" b/w "Bad Little Woman" 45, 1994
   Big City Records, U.K.

Members of **The Trashwomen** and **The Mummies** pay tribute to **The Count V** — with another of their no-fi super poor quality recordings. The playing isn't bad, but captured less than perfectly by whatever portable cassette machine they probably used at a rehearsal spot.

The most interesting part of this release, perhaps, is the B-side. Both songs are placed on the A-side, so on the flip there is nothing — except a run-out groove that runs backwards (get it?) from the hub of the record to the outer edge.

## THE CRACKED JAFFERS
*(Melbourne, Australia)*

"Drop In..." 3 song 7" EP, 1986
   Kavern 7 Records, Australia

Here we have basic, three chord teen garage music: a little bit of jangle, fuzz, and snotty vocals, mixed into a raw recording. There's also a distinctively Australian ambiance to this recording. It's a quality that I can't really describe, but each and every release on Kavern 7 has a certain individualistic flavor — and this is no exception. It's recommended highly for any '66 fuzz fan.

I've heard only one other song, the more polished and intricate "Flowers." I'm unsure of its origin.

## THE CRAMPS
*(New York, NY/Los Angeles, CA USA)*

The continuing influence of **The Cramps** on the worldwide garage movement since their late 1970s birth should not be underestimated. Rather than give a thumbnail sketch of their long and distinguished career, I'll recommend the book *The Wild Wild World Of The Cramps* by Ian Johnston, published in 1990 by Omnibus Press.

There is more than another five years

plus of history to add to that book's content, of course, but information on **The Cramps** is readily available in the mainstream press.

## THE CRAWDADDYS
*(San Diego, CA USA)*

*Crawdaddy Express* 15 song LP, 1979
*5 x 4 5* song 7" EP, 1980
"There She Goes Again" b/w "Why Don't You Smile Now" 45, 1980
*Here 'Tis* 15 song LP, 1987
   Voxx Records, USA
4 song 7" EP, 1988
   Romilar-D Records, Spain

**The Crawdaddys** were inventing their magic in the summer of '78 on the West Coast at about the same time **The Chesterfield Kings** began their journey in the East. Manic white R&B was the shared interest, with **The Crawdaddys** delving less obviously into the "garage" formula, instead opting to stay closer to the classics of **Willie Dixon, Muddy Waters, Chuck Berry** and **Bo Diddley.**

An early filmed-video of the band looks like a lost '60s clip of **The Pretty Things** or **Downliner's Sect** — two bands that **The Crawdaddys** surely appreciated.

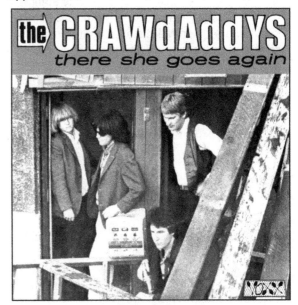

Their two 7"s and debut LP are now impossibly rare, though they were hardly sought after at the time of their release. It is only in retrospect that **The Crawdaddys** are getting the attention and credit that they deserve.

I guess late is better than never.

The band went through countless lineup changes in its six-year-plus existence, and it was eight years between releases of their LPs. (There is also a German LP entitled *Still Steamin'*, which is a re-issue of the first LP. The *Mystic Crawdaddys* LP is a re-issue of the first LP with their early single tracks as a bonus. Bomp also re-issued these tracks on CD in 1993.)

Both long-players drip with manic R&B stylings, chocked full of harmonica and some piano mixed in at just the correct moment. This is very good blues music by any standards, and it helped to turn on many young suburban (white) kids to the stuff for the first time.

San Diego would spawn many influential groups throughout the 1980s, but few received as much respect from other musicians as **The Crawdaddys**. They were after their time, before their time, and in the end they ran out of time.

I'm just glad that they found the time to record some tracks before joining the "legendary dead band" heap.

## CRAWDADDY SIMONE
*(Norway)*

"Crawdaddy Simone" b/w "Absence" 45, 1985
    Some People Are Records, Norway

Three women and guitarist Willy B. made up this Norwegian combo. Their debut 45 theme song is a meaty **Sonics**-like head-bobber, full of background "heys!" and an inspired distorted guitar lead. The B-side is a more pedestrian pop-rock effort. There was a follow-up 45, featuring a passable cover of the R&B standard "Roadrunner." Willy B. would go onto to form **The Willy B. Review** in 1986, with four singles and a 12" EP on Norwegian labels up until 1991, reportedly in a more straight R&B style.

## CRAWLING WALLS
*(Albuquerque, NM USA)*

*Inner Limits* 11 song LP, 1985
    Voxx Records, USA

I've not been able to find one person who ever saw this band perform "live," so I'm not sure if this is a studio-only group or not. Their lone LP, *Inner Limits,* is a rather odd effort, with only a few solid tracks — "Fly Tonight" and "One Last Kiss" are the stand-outs.

The foursome is obviously trying to fit into the garage-psych formula, and I think their conscious attempt is what bothers me the most. There is certainly a desert influence involved here, but the sound just doesn't come together like other "desert psych" such as the seminal **13th Floor Elevators** or **The**

**48**

**Golden Dawn.**
Their lone LP was also released in France by Lolita Records in 1985 — no word on what kind of cactus graced the album cover there.

## THE CREATURES (OF THE GOLDEN DAWN)
*(Pennsylvania USA)*

Untitled 4 song 7" EP, 1987
    Chaos Records, USA
*Live And Outta Sight* 4 song 7" EP, 1988
    Egarag Records, USA
*Creatures Of The Golden Dawn* 21 song cassette
    no label demo, 1990
*Creatures Of The Golden Dawn* 3 song 7" EP, 1991
*1000 Shadows* 15 song CD (only), 1993
    Dionysus Records, USA
*Standing At The Gates Of Time* 18 song CD, 1995
    Collectables Records, USA

These beings formed in early 1985 around frontman Mark Smith, who would survive an onslaught of different lineups. Three former members went on to form **The Original Sins** in 1987; a breakup which was less than amicable, though it seems that Smith is the one who gained musically from the split!

The band would later refer to themselves with the somewhat psychedelic moniker "The Creatures Of The Golden Dawn," though the music remained firmly in the garage idiom. Anyone notice that "Egarag" records is "Garage" spelled backwards?!?

A few vinyl tastes of these backwoods Pennsylvanians trickled out over their early years: four-song EPs in 1987 and '88, a three songer in '91 — and then finally a full-length CD-only effort. Even this "debut" long-player took two years to assemble, since indy bands make records the old fashioned way: they earn them through hard work, dedication, and minuscule recording budgets shaved from the monthly grocery budget. The years of macaroni and cheese have paid off for The Creatures Of The Golden Dawn, because *1000 Shadows* became the stellar garage effort of 1993.

Garage, not grunge, is the entity here, for those who are not reading closely. Guitars are fuzzed, not muffled and layered until they make sick vacuum cleaner noises. Drums are played by people instead of machines, and vocalists scream because they mean it, not because it's expected. Garage music is the realm of the disenfranchised, not the popular, and **The Creatures** make sure that you know they really are alone and unwanted.

Not trendy perhaps, but this six-man gang is musically talented. Vintage guitars alternately buzz and jangle when needed, drums and bass never stray from the sweat-inspiring beat, and the vocal snot quotient never falls below a perfect 100% on the sneer-o-meter. Early on in the disc, Mark Smith delivers the line "listen while I softly tell you lies" with the vulnerable frustration and anger that only a garage band true-believer can deliver.

*1000 Shadows* is a perfect case of attitude, effort, and determination combining into an emotional time capsule. This is direct, visceral, real music, aimed at ripping apart the eardrums while pounding at the chest in an effort to get our collective hearts beating. These guys may never sell a million records, but they've done something so much more significant; they've won their personal battle over indifference by creating their dream soundtrack.

**Madonna** and **Springsteen** hire other people to dream for them. Bands like **The Creatures Of The Golden Dawn** load pennies into their piggy banks, add extra blankets to their beds, and keep their dreams alive themselves. They knew all along that macaroni and cheese isn't so bad.

*(Note: This band should not be confused with the late '80s U.K. disco band of the same name.)*

## THE CREEPING CANDIES
*(Germany)*

A psychedelic-beat band with at least two LPs: *Flesh* from 1986 and *The Stories Of...* from 1988, both produced by Nikki Sudden.

## LOS CREEPLE PEEPLE
*(Berkeley, CA USA)*

A 12 song demo cassette exists; some members went on to form **Wonderwall.** Russel Quan went on to **The Mummies.**

## THE CREEPS
*(Sweden)*

*Enjoy The Creeps* 12 song LP, 1986
    Tracks On Wax, Sweden

**The Creeps** gave us one fabulous album, only to then apparently fall victim to the lure of the big-money record industry. Their *Enjoy* LP was a real shocker, full of blues-based torch songs, fuzzed-up garage, and unrelenting sweat and style. The recording is intense, dense and fiery, with Robert Jelinek screaming some of the most powerful vocals of the decade. The LP was later issued in Canada and also on CD.

This record was deceiving, however, because in

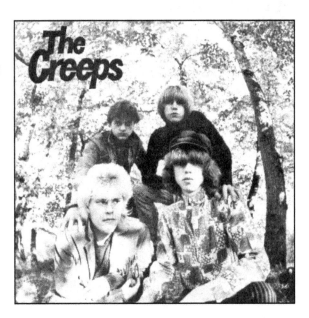

the space of a few years the band would cut its hair, flaunt tattoos and produce funk-metal along the lines of the **Red Hot Chili Peppers**. A circa 1990 MTV video I saw of these lame **Creeps** displayed them shirtless in velvet bell-bottoms — acting "funky" and shaking their "booties."

The first great LP, of course, was an independent product. Soon after it caused a stir they were swept off to a major label — and musical destruction.

I should note that there is nothing wrong with getting signed to a major record label. It is possible for good music to appear with corporate backing. **The Creeps** proved with their debut LP what they were capable of achieving musically, and then showed us they had nothing left but image — and *that* is the problem.

**The Creeps** were one of the most promising of the 1980s garage bands. At least they left behind one fabulous album before committing musical suicide.

## THE CRICKLE
*(Chicago, IL USA)*

This duo circulated a three song cassette in 1985, displaying a knack for slick '60s-tinged pop; one song even sounds like early **Nazz**. They based their name on the mid-'60s pop band **The Cyrcle**. The only release I know of their's can be found on the *Garage Sale* cassette, also from 1985.

## THE CRIMSON SHADOWS
*(Sweden)*

"When I'm Goin' Away" b/w "What I Want" 45, 1985
 Far Out Records, Sweden
"Even I Tell Lies" b/w "You Can't Come Down" 45, 1986
 Sunlight Records, Sweden
*Tales From...* 4 song 7" EP, 1987
*Hangin' Out!* 8 song 12" EP, 1988
 Mystery Scene Records, Germany
"Out Of My Mind" b/w "What I Want" 45, 1995
 Weed Records, France

**The Crimson Shadows** are one of the finest European examples of the reborn 1960s punk spirit. They only released a few records, and two of those are impossibly rare, but their influence swept far and wide in the garage world.

The band formed in October, 1984, and lasted until March, 1986. During their short tenure they

*THE CRIMSON SHADOWS, 1986*

only played a handful of club dates, yet established a great reputation and following based on their two early 45s and an appearance on the essential *Declaration Of Fuzz* compilation LP.

Even I have never seen these early 45s, but their lofty reputation seems to be deserved, based on the second pair of records that are more readily available. (One of those four early rare tracks, "When I'm Going Away," is included on their 12" EP, so I guess I have heard one of the earliest songs after all.)

**The Crimson Shadows** basked in the '66 punk spirit, yet rose above many of their competitor's limitations through better musicianship, especially the effective use of shimmering organ. They had style, forceful yet raw musical sensibilities, and were simply very cool.

Peter and Johan Maniette would later help form the also essential **Wylde Mammoths**, as described later. (The lineage of the Crimson Shadows also can be traced to **The Stomachmouths, Highspeed V** and the **Peter Maniette Group**.)

Weed Records was reportedly set in 1995 to release a compilation LP of all the out-of-print **Crimson Shadows** recordings, including unreleased tracks. This would help another generation of garagers hear the brilliance of **The Crimson Shadows,** and help *me* finally hear those other early legendary songs. Weed did release a 45 with the previously unreleased "Out Of My Mind" shortly before this book went to press.

## CROAKERS
*(Genova, Italy)*

A garage punk combo, featured with **The Others** on a 7" EP, as described in the compilation chapter.

## THE CRUSADERS
*(Sydney, Australia)*

*Wylde Tymes At The Castle* 5 song CD, 1992
 Zero Hour Records, Australia
*Yeah Yeah* 3 song 7" EP, 1994
 Dionysus Records, USA

Beginning as the wonderfully named **Purple Knights,** these Australians debuted with a scorchingly upbeat CD-only EP. *Wyld Tymes At The Castle* bursts with a party atmosphere, and chugs along on plentiful spit and fuzz.

The CD insert states **The Crusaders'** pledge: *"To crusade against the mire of drab and heartless music wherever it exists; to restore fuzz-tone, heavy reverb and extended tail-fins to their rightful place at the forefront of Australian music, and above all, to promote the consumption of fine ale in the quest for merriment and fun. Join the crusade."*

This debut CD is an amazing little nugget — considering the relatively late date of its release — and it's among the best of the Australian garage output.

Their subsequent 7" for Dionysus is rougher, more punk-ish, and less '60s garage sounding. There is a hint of fuzz-surf, but I sense a basic change in attitude and style.

Nevertheless, it is our duty to join their crusade, wherever it may lead us.

## THE CRY BABIES
*(Orleans, France)*

Their *Pop Goes The Cork* LP disproves the contention that the French can't rock, because this collection of pop-punk gems shreds from beginning to end. **The Ramones'** feel is there, but with some good, strong vocals and even some harmonies to give the production a slicker edge. Guitars spit everywhere, making this a solid punk effort. Again, this is not really a '60s sound, but with enough of the same influences to merit its inclusion here.

## THE CRYPTICS
*(Tucson, AZ USA)*

4 song demo, 1986 (As **The Tumors**)
Unreleased 3 song 7" EP, 1986
*Live At The Cavern* unreleased cassette, 1986

This foursome began in 1985 originally as **The Tumors,** then switched to the slightly more palatable **Cryptics** moniker in '86. They began as a hybrid of sloppy punk and noise, and soon added touches of garage and '66 psych. The main component of their sound was Geoff Puhl, whose vocals and **Doors**-ish keyboard tone elevated the band above the pack.

I managed to interest Voxx Records in pressing a 45, and in the spring of 1986 I produced three studio tracks, including the blistering psych/punk classic "This Fatal Peace." Voxx managed to lose the tapes and cover art, however, and the 45 never appeared! (Voxx managed to lose more than a few of my tapes over the years. **The Cryptics'** tape did show up several years later, but remains unreleased.)

A credible tape of their performance at Hollywood's Cavern Club in June of '86 also shows that the band had a versatile nature, as they steam through **The Music Machine**'s "People In Me" and their own excellent instrumental "Snowshoe." After the disappointment of the unreleased 45, though, the band limped on and was gone by the end of the year.

Some video does exist, including a set done for a local "live" TV show — broadcast from a living room! Bassist Matt Griffin would be yet another musical refugee who would later join **The Marshmallow Overcoat.**

*(Note: this band should not be confused with several other Cryptics, including those in Los Angeles, Canada and Europe.)*

## THE CRYPTICS
*(Montreal, PQ Canada)*

*You're Evil* 3 song 7" EP, 1992
    Primitive Records, Canada

Canadian garage show radio host "Amazing Larry" wrote in a 1992 edition of CFUV's Offbeat Magazine, *"They have been described as 'uncensored **Paul Revere and the Raiders'** and 'snarly in voice and guitar like mean **Monkees,'** but what they really are is the coolest garage band to come out of Canada since **The Gruesomes."***

These **Cryptics** started in 1990, and scored national Canadian airplay for their "You're Evil"

*THE CRYPTICS, 1992*

music video. That track is certainly a worthy successor to **The Gruesomes'** sound, with a driving beat, tasteful fuzz and twang, and the requisite snot filled vocals. All in all, that's a formula for garage success. **The Cryptics** follow through in winning style with the two B-side tracks, the organ tinged anthem "Back To Me" and the fuzz laden "Ricordam."

The high quality of this debut whetted the appetite for a long player. There was talk of an LP in the works in 1992, though I have no word if it ever appeared — I have an idea that is was scrapped, and the band dissolved.

Their lone vinyl outing is highly recommended.

## THE CRYPTONES
*(Marseille, France)*

11 song unreleased "live" cassette, 1990
8 song cassette, 1990
3 song unreleased cassette, 1990
    no label, France (all demos)
*Teen Trash #1* 15 song LP & CD, 1993
    Music Maniac Records, Germany

Also "Lolita" on a French fanzine 45; "Don't Forget" and "Cryptones Theme" on the *Girl With Guitars* compilation LP, "Freaks" on the *Electric Carnival* compilation.

**The Cryptones** remain one of my favorite French bands. They mix the snot of **The Miracle Workers,** psych verve of **The Fuzztones,** and European flavor of **The Sick Rose** together into some meaty teen-punk.

The four-track recordings on several of their demos from 1990-1992 are powerful, with driving arrangements, tasteful fuzz and an omnipresent organ. I wouldn't normally include this band in the same class with other, more well known groups

*THE CRYPTONES, 1990*

with several releases, but **The Cryptones** are just too good to relegate to secondary status.

Their "live" demo shows a well-oiled performing machine, showing that regardless of their singing in French or English, they still sound very good, indeed.

The Music Maniac LP gathers together many of these demo tracks together for their deserved release. The first seven songs are blistering studio tracks, while the last eight give another glimpse into their "live" sound. All are nitro-fueled excitement and document what could be one of France's best garage-psych bands of all time.

The band broke up in the summer of 1992, and evolved into a **Ramones**-meets-**The Hard-Ons** punk trio called **The Greedy Guts** by the time this author met up with them for several weeks in late 1992. Along the way we hooked up with several other ex-**Cryptones**, including the immaculately dressed organist Maki and extremely intoxicated drummer Franky.

We can laugh now at one memory, though it was less than hilarious at the time: Lost in Paris late one night after a **Greedy Guts/Overcoat** concert, Franky volunteered to drive the bands' equipment van through the winding narrow city back alleys — blind drunk and at 80 kilometers an hour, of course! At my suggestion that he pull over and let a less stewed member of the entourage drive, he calmly looked back (while we

**52**

were still flying down the street), smiled, and calmly said *"Don't worry — We'll all die!"* My muffled laughter of incredulity couldn't hide the fact that we all thought, indeed, we were all about to die.

We didn't crash, of course, and Franky, Maki, Jerome and Nathalie remain some of my favorite Frenchmen.

The spirit of the fuzzed-out, sweaty, danceable garage combo lived on in Europe, and in France of all places.

Vive Les Cryptones!

## CRYSTALIZED MOVEMENTS
*(Hartford, CT USA)*

The *Mind Disaster* LP, 1983, on Twisted Village Records (and Psycho in the U.K.) is reportedly of worth — described as being similar to **Dimentia 13**. A second and third LP also exist, though I believe their sound drifted off into guitar heaviness without appeal to a garage listener.

## THE CUNTS
*(Chicago, IL USA)*

*It Came From Out Of The Garage* 12 song LP, 1984
*Midnight Party* 12 song CD (only), 1993
   Disturbing Records, USA

My first exposure to this very odd midwestern group came completely by accident in 1983. It was about 3 a.m., and I was flipping through the graveyard of cable TV — the "public access" local production channels. There **The Cunts** popped up in all their glory, abusing an audience at what appeared to be a wild party.

An interview with one bandmate after the show confirmed that they played more often than not to hostile crowds, and even their girlfriends hated the name of their group! Their sound was a mixture of '70s punk, '60s psych, noise and humorous absurdity.

Their legend started in 1978 with the release of their "Chemicals In The Mail" 45, which was followed by at least four more demented singles and the *It Came From the Garage* LP in 1984.

The titles of their ditties should clue you into the mindset here: "There Are Electrical Filaments On My Hamburger," "There's A Mouse In My Hair" and "Penguins Addicted To Molasses" tell the story.

A European pressing of the first LP has helped the band to escape total obscurity, and we can only guess if the outbreak of "Cuntmania" will yet grip the globe with the release of their CD-only follow-up.

As they say on the cover of their debut LP, *"remember — have fun."*

## CURLETTES
*(Germany)*

Ingo Schittko told me that **The Curlettes** were *"an all-girl-band from Berlin who made at least one wonderful 45 — 'Waitin'' b/w 'Just For You' on the Twang! label. This contains two very nice, melodic and a little bit garagey beat songs. I like it very much."*

## THE CUSTOMS
*(Cincinnati, OH USA)*

"Let's Get It On" b/w "Bring My Cadillac" 45, 1979
"She'll Always Be Mine" b/w "Long Gone" 45, 1980
    Shake It Records, USA

A four track 1980 demo displayed a flair for R&B tinged rock; not rave-up material, but likable, with covers of "Boss Hoss," a fabulous version of "I Dig Your Mind" and "Riot On Sunset Strip." They were around from 1978 to '81, and played throughout their native Ohio — even blasting my native Columbus with a version of the classic "Never Alone" in 1980.

Their 1980 45 was described to me by fan Siegfried Kalus as *"an absolute classic of the garage scene. 'Long Gone' has been covered on vinyl by **The Lyres, Devil Dogs** and **Bottle Ups**, and by literally dozens of garage bands in their live sets. The flip side is about the best song **The Lyres** never wrote! The genius behind all that was obviously Peter Greenberg, from the great, great **DMZ**, which had just broken up."*

I find the track enjoyable, but short of Kalus' classic status. I can hear in my mind **The Lyres** doing the song — it fits right in with their sound. Their debut 45 is also a solid R&B-tinged release, but more of interest to collectors because of its late '70s appearance than its garage sound.

The band really shines in their live set, where blistering versions of "99th Floor," "Girl, You Captivate Me," "Hey Little Girl" and "He's Waiting" show their true colors as an energetic, Farfisa-filled garage combo. What could the lame new wave locals have thought at the time of these fuzzed out weirdos?

While their vinyl outings are less spectacular than their reputation, **The Customs'** live sound more than merits their place in the garage band hall of fame — especially considering the time and place of their existence.

## THE CUTBACKS
*(Norway)*

"Tired Of Hanging Around" & "Came To A Party" 7" flexi, 1990
    Rock Furore Magazine, Norway
Untitled 4 track 7" EP, 1992
    That's Entertainment Records, Norway

**The Cutbacks** contained a vocalist from **The Cosmic Dropouts**, I believe, with a two-song 1990 flexi of garage tinged noise — and both songs are pretty cranked up. "She's A Murderer" and "Walk With Me," from the 7" EP, are also upbeat distorted rockers, with some thick organ thrown in for good measure.

## THE CYBERMEN
*(Cincinnati, OH USA)*

"She's Raining" b/w "Insideoutsideupsidedown" 45, 1988
    Whaaam Records, USA
*Everyday And Night* 3 song 7" EP, 1990
    Get Hip Records, USA

From the ashes of **The Buzz** and **El Kabong,** this fivesome began in June 1987 and lasted until February '89. "She's Raining" shows a healthy reverence for **Creation**-styled mod pop, which is also explored on their second and last 45. Can anyone tell me which **Yardbirds** song serves as inspiration for the flip side of the debut 45!?!

Their second 45 appeared a full 18 months after the band's demise. The title track is a stomping fuzz garage monster, much more meaty than their debut. The flip's "Someday Will Come" is a soaring upbeat pop-fuzz number, with an excellent melody and chorus. "Losing You" closes out **The Cybermen's** story, though they also have a track on a local Cincy compilation, *Where The Hell Are The Good Scissors?*

Drummer Michael Grimm and guitarist James Grapes would go onto **The Mortals,** with many other releases.

## THE CYBERMEN
*(Helsinki, Finland)*

*Paint The Subway Blue* 4 song 7" EP, 1989
"House Of Wax" b/w "I'm With You" 45, 1989
*New Thrill* 12 song LP, 1990
*From Beyond* 4 song 7" EP, 1992
   Destination Uranus Records, Finland

Video: "Bag Of Tricks" from the *New Thrill* LP.

This Finnish trio (and later a foursome) shared a certain mod influence with their Cincinnati namesake, though the Europeans also delved into a bit of fuzz, soul and pop as well. Crude recordings and an energetic giddiness pervade the three seven-inchers, mixing some moody organ with the otherwise simple and direct arrangements. All of these 45s are now rare and out of print.

The debut LP expands on the band's formula, with extra back-up vocals and instrumentation. The crude feeling still exists, though, and this helps to keep the band from sounding anything like a wimpy mod band.

Instead they have a distinctive, very European mod-garage sound, and the listener can detect the obvious enjoyment the band had while making the music. This infectious upbeat attitude helps separate **The Cybermen** from many other contenders.

They also managed to tour around the Arctic Circle(!) and down south to Germany and Belgium.


## THEE CYBERMEN
*(Dyfed, U.K.)*

*Got A Groove* 4 song 7" EP, 1994
   Vendetta Records, U.K.

I guess it makes some kind of sense that one of the bands which call itself **"Cybermen"** would actually come from England — the home of the *Doctor Who* TV show where **The Cybermen** name originated.

Doctor Who's **Cybermen** were diabolical robots (who looked like silver vacuum cleaners with legs), but **Thee Cybermen** are anything but mechanical or threatening. In the best **Milkshakes** & **Prisoners** tradition, these latest **Cybermen** deliver an earthy, danceable R&B garage meal.

The trio's plate is filled with cool organ, crunchy guitar and smooth soulful vocals. The recipe is mixed accurately in beautiful mono at Toe-Rag Studios in London — the origination point for some of England's best '80s/'90s beat-garage efforts.

"It's All Gone" is smooth and soulful,

**54**

"I Hate This World" is distorted in the best **Billy Childish** tradition, while the title track earns its title in driving fashion.

My guess is that **Thee Cybermen** are lurking in the shadows with more sounds. The Doctor and I will be waiting.


## THE CYNICS
*(Pittsburgh, PA USA)*

"Painted My Heart" b/w "Sweet Young Thing" 45, 1985
"No Place To Hide" b/w "Hard Times" 45, 1985
   Dionysus Records, USA
"Lying All The Time" b/w "Summers Gone" 45, 1986
   Full Sail Records, USA
"Friday Night" b/w "69" 45, 1986
*Blue Train Station* 12 song LP, 1986
"Smoke Rings" b/w "I'm In Pittsburgh And It's Raining" 45, 1986
"No Way" b/w "Dancing On The Wall" 45, 1987
*12 Flights Up* 12 song LP, 1988
"Way It's Gonna Be" b/w "Roadrunner" 45, 1988
"Get My Way" b/w "Goin' Away" 45, 1989
3 song "Live" 7" EP, 1989
*Rock 'N Roll* 14 song LP, 1990
"Girl, You're On My Mind" b/w "I Don't Need You" 45, 1990
*VPRO Radio Broadcast* 12" EP, 1991
"Right Here With You" b/w "Learn To Lose" 45, 1992
*Learn To Lose* 12 song LP, 1993
"I Got You Babe" (split) 45, 1991
"I Live Alone" b/w "Hand In Hand" 45, 1993
"Private Suicide" b/w "All These Streets" 45, 1994
*Get Our Way* 17 song LP & CD, 1994
*No Siesta Tonite* LP/CD, 1994
   Get Hip Records, USA
*Stranded In Madrid* 13 song Live LP, 1991
   Impossible Records, Spain
*Cynicism* 24 song CD (only), 1992
   1+2 Records, Japan
"Buick McKaine" b/w "Born To Lose" 45, 1992
   S.F.T.R.I., USA
"I Want It All" b/w "Brother The Man" 45, 1992
   Screaming Apple Records, Germany
"Dirty Trick" b/w "Lose Your Mind" 45, 1994
   Mind Cure Records, USA
"Two Rooms" b/w "Jealous Man" 45, 1994
   Weed Records, France

Other compilations: "Be True To Your School" on the *Brian Wilson Tribute* LP, "I Got You Babe" on the *Sonny Bono Tribute* LP(!) All of their Get Hip vinyl albums have been re-released on CD.

Video: "Girl, You're On My Mind" from the *Rock & Roll* LP, 1990

(This author wrote the following feature piece on **The Cynics** in 1994, just as they set out on tour with the release of their *Get My Way* LP.)

Touring the club circuit is no luxury cruise for a band without major label backing. Transportation usually consists of a crowded, beat-up van, a fan's

**THE CYNICS, 1987**

living room floor serves as the night's accommodations, and cheap warm beer seems to be the only ample nourishment for weeks at a time.

After almost seven years of such pampering, **Cynics** vocalist Michael Kastelic can think of nothing he'd rather be doing.

*"I like touring more than being at home or in any one place,"* Kastelic says. *"I love the different people every night, different place every night, different hotel room or floor to sleep on, I love it."*

The wiry, frenetic Kastelic is the stage-show focal point for **The Cynics,** a Pittsburgh-based four-piece that's played in every corner of the globe since their inception in 1984. Veterans of countless European jaunts, they've recently returned from Japan, and are now covering the U.S. West Coast for the first time since 1991.

*"I enjoy playing much more than recording,"* Kastelic says. *"It's a one of a kind special thing. You only get one chance at it, and sometimes people will never see you again, or it'll be the next year, or in the case of the West Coast, it's been three years. It's our one chance to relate to an audience and have them relate to us. It's a special time that won't happen again."*

Kastelic attacks the stage with a possessed fury. He usually hangs from the ceiling, climbs on tables, crawls through the audience, and generally exhausts every calorie of energy for the sake of performance.

*"I'm a mild mannered, quiet, shy kind of a guy,"* he contends with mock

**55**

innocence, then comes clean and admits, *"I can get pretty crazy."*

Kastelic simply doesn't know what its like to hold back for a show. *"I just want to give it all I have. I love doing it more than anything else, and I find it a good release — It's cathartic,"* he adds.

*"I'm pretty much a zombie of the living dead between shows, but the hour and a half that we're playing it just all comes back."*

Kastelic and **The Cynics** will test their endurance during their current 30-shows in almost 30-nights tour, including their first shows ever in Arizona. After that it's back to Europe before finishing the East Coast leg of yet another U.S. club tour.

The almost constant touring has had its casualties. *"We've probably had about five different drummers and six or so different bassists,"* notes Kastelic. Guitarist Gregg Kostelich is the only remaining original band member; Kastelic joined up in 1987.

*"For the first time we now have somebody on bass (David Vucenich) who's interested in the same kind of music we are, and Max (Terasauro) is a young pup, only 20 years old, so he's full of energy. Pretty much all he does is sleep and play drums."*

**The Cynics'** sixth LP, *Get Our Way*, is the first significant document of the revamped group. Besides the new musical blood, Kastelic and Kostelich also sought an outside producer for a fresh take on the band's patently identifiable garage-punk sound. Kostelich has produced most of the band's previous output (as well as releasing records for several dozen other independent bands on his Get Hip Records label).

Enter Boston eccentric and long-time independent producer and musician Erik Lindgren. The resulting studio marriage spawned a staggering 23 songs, 18 of which ended up on the just-released LP. Kastelic says affectionately of Lindgren that *"He's a crazy man. We recorded almost 15 hours every day. The last day was almost 26 hours, and our friends thought we died in the studio."*

Their previous *Learn To Lose* LP *"took so long to complete, it was dragged out over a long period of time, as opposed to this new record which was recorded and mixed in just over a week,"* he says.

Kastelic's obvious satisfaction with Lindgren's recording process is reflected in the album itself. Full of the band's customary stripped-down garage rawness, *Get Our Way* also sports some spirited gutsy pop and trippily tough psychedelia. It might well be the most thoroughly powerful **Cynics** release to date.

"I'll Wait" is a centerpiece for the LP — a combination of **Beatle**sque melody, garage punk sentiment, and Kastelic's emotional, distinctively identifiable vocals. There's a goldmine for fuzz fans as well, since searing punk blastings like "No Reason" and "Dave V's Car" could rattle the dead.

The variety doesn't end there. A demented mood permeates "13 O'Clock Daylight Savings Time" and the burning "Lose Your Mind," while the chemically induced "Beyond The Calico Wall/STP-00117" utilizes a theremin with bizarre results.

Whether blasting fuzz anthems or folk-rockish ballads, **The Cynics'** timeless punk delivery is a blast of fresh air that rivals the best breezes out of Seattle. Major label A&R departments haven't seen it exactly that way.

*"We've gotten letters back from them saying 'We don't really see this as college break-through material,'"* though the band charts high on college radio and has regularly packed East Coast campus-area clubs for years. *"That shows you how little they (A&R people) know."*

Kastelic is neither surprised nor disappointed that the majors haven't bitten. *"They're still looking for another Seattle band,"* he snickers. *"I think it's the majors plot to lull everyone into another '70s complacency, and pretty soon, bam!, there'll be a new **Peter Frampton**,"* he giggles. He adds only somewhat jokingly, *"That actually might be good, because then there'll be another big backlash, and we'll have another punk rock explosion."*

**The Cynics** are doing their best to be ready if and when the commercial marketplace opens up for some honest punk rock. Besides their six LPs (five studio and one live-concert), they have over a dozen 45s available.

In the meantime, the fire-cracker vocalist will be readying himself for yet another blistering garage rock show. *"I'll start shaking, and I could throw up,"* he says of his nerve-racked pre-gig state. *"It helps me keep my energy up."*

Kastelic declines, however, to fabricate stories of ridiculous theatrics or stage gimmicks to sell their shows. He breaks into a spirited laugh, declaring, *"I don't think I could make something up that's worse than what might really happen!"*

---

This author has been lucky enough to tour with **The Cynics**. They are one of the most consistently powerful bands I've ever heard, and the combination of Kastelic and Kostelich is one of the most creative ever in garage rock.

Their Tucson debut was predictably blistering, retaining all of the magic and grit that make **The Cynics** one of the

best rock bands of all time — in any category.

Some final thoughts: In an interview I conducted on March 21, 1986, guitarist Gregg Kostelich told me, *"I was maybe four or five years old when I started collecting garage records, and I've been listening to that type of music ever since.*

*"And I was lucky enough to see a couple of shows when I was a little kid... my parents would bring me to see bands like **The Sonics** and **The Blues Magoos** and **The Who**, when I was about seven or eight! I didn't know what was going on really, but it was really exciting. I was kinda embarrassed in a way because I was with my parents."*

When I mentioned that this early exposure to garage music explained **The Cynics'** style, Gregg responded, *"Yea, maybe I got brain damage from all the noise!"*

## THE DAGGERMAN
(U.K.)

The *Introducing* EP is on Empire Records from mid '80s. Their *Dagger In My Mind* LP is reportedly strong and loud in the vein of **The Prisoners**.

## D.A.I.S.Y.
(Athens, GA USA)

*The Hum Of...* 11 song CD, 1993
Planned Obsolescence Records, USA

They formed in 1990, with three 45s released since 1991. Their debut long player has a few tracks produced by **REM**'s Michael Stipe. It's a feedback-fueled swirling bit of psych noise, punctuated with lots of fuzz. It kind of reminds me of **Spacemen 3** mixed in with **The Smashing Pumpkins**, if that comparison helps at all. **D.A.I.S.Y.** is only somewhat associated with the meat of this book, but worth a listen to the more adventurous.

## DAISY CHAIN
*(Germany)*

A 12" EP, *Do What Thou Wilt* exists; it's a mixture of garage grunge and attempted moodiness with mixed results. Another LP is out on Germany's Unique Records, along with several collaborations with France's **Vietnam Veterans**; these LPs are dubbed **The Vietnam Chain.**

## DARK CELLARS
*(Newtonville, MA USA)*

*Heavy Syrup* 11 song LP, 1986
    Alien Cactus Records, USA

This is a curious LP, indeed. Collecting tracks recorded from 1984 to 1986, it constantly changes mood and direction, from garage pop to psych and back again. The engaging "Everybody's Girl" kicks things off with a foot tapping garage-melody; this is the type of fun song that'll show up on future compilations explaining what that '80s garage thing was all about.

The love of **13th Floor Elevator**-styled dementia is inherent, and the lads even throw in a five-and-half minute version of "Roller Coaster" to drive the point home. I especially like the band's imitation of **The Elevators'** "electric jug" sound — this time it's the vocalist making squeaking noises into a microphone!

Adding to the weirdness is the front cover photo, with one guy in a kilt and another holding a large rock on his lap. Liner notes extolling the virtues of LSD and air-fried borsk complete the off beat trip.

New England had some fine garage outfits, and some of them weren't afraid to delve into the guitar-driven world of psychedelia as well. Hats off to **The Dark Cellars** for giving us a dose of both.

## THE DARKSIDE
*(Rugby, U.K.)*

*Highrise Love* EP, 198?
*All That Noise* 10 song CD, 1991
*Melomania* 9 song CD, 1992
    Beggars Banquet, USA
*Jukebox At Munsters* 45:
"Fate Deals Its Mortal Blow" b/w "Frankie Teardrop", 1992
    Munster Records, Spain
*Lunar Surf* 3 song 7" EP, 1993
    Bomp Records, USA

Many observers credited **The Spacemen 3** with being one of the most important and innovative of the English '80s "noise" groups. They served as a well-known connection between '60s sounds and "modern" sensibilities, but they never seemed to capture my total attention. That band split ironically while on the verge of signing to a major label and spreading their influence above-ground.

Instead, two-thirds of **The Spacemen** signed with RCA as **The Darkside,** and subsequently released the album I always hoped **The Spacemen** would create. **The Darkside** actually formed in 1986, but it was the inclusion of Ex-**Spacemen** Pete Bassman and drummer Rosco in 1988 that undoubtedly made the major label signing possible.

Here we have all the **Byrds, Electric Prunes** and **Beatles** influences without **The Spacemen 3**'s manufactured (ultra-serious) attitude. While many of its English brethren copped spaced-out expressions and danced to a drum machine, **The Darkside** returned to the '60s diet of Farfisa, real drums, bass and jangley guitar.

The results are somewhere between **The Strawberry Alarm Clock** and **Jefferson Airplane** — mixed in with that elusive "modern" sensibility — and to me that's pretty damn good. They're a real surprise, and very pleasant at that.

The *Mellomania* follow-up also has some bright spots, but it veers away from the bright jangley sound into less interesting generic "alternative" stylings at times. The two 45s listed above are pure disappointments, made up of outtakes and ambient drivel.

Stick with *All That Noise* and enjoy what could be called the culmination of **The Spacemen 3**'s legacy.

## DAS FURLINES
*(New York, NY USA)*

This was an all-female group from the mid to late '80s featuring Deb O'Nair of **The Fuzztones** and Wendy Wild of **The Mad Violets**. Their live set reportedly consisted of the entire infamous 1966 **Monks** LP — performed in order from beginning to end! The only recorded output I know of is their rendition of **The Monks'** "Oh To Do Now," transformed for Midnight Records' second Christmas compilation as "Oh Tannenbaum Now." Simply brilliant.

## DATE BAIT
*(Washington, D.C. USA)*

"I'm Outta Here" 45, 1989
  DSI Records, USA
*I Spit On Your Grave* 18 song LP/CD, 1989
  New Rose Records, France
"Dragster Of Ghostrip Hollow" 45, 1990
"What Kind Of Trip Are You On?" b/w
  "Do The Mummy" 45, 1992
  DeCeased Records, USA
"Wild Woman" b/w "Head In the Shed" 45, 1994
  Get Hip, USA

I saw **Date Bait** perform in their native D.C. once in the early 1990s, at a New Year's show in downtown Washington. Their set was fun and whacky, reminding me a bit of **The Cramps** with a less serious demeanor — and a much more party-like attitude. I also found band leader Kim Kane to be intelligent, friendly and a great stage performer.

I asked Jim Maher, who writes about music for the weekly Baltimore area *City Paper*, to contribute entries on several U.S. East Coast acts, including **Date Bait.** He picks up the story:

*Former **Slickee Boys** guitarist Kim Kane, former **Beatnik Flies** guitarist John Stone and drummer Brian Horrorwitz (also singer/drummer of **The Ubangis**) put together **Date Bait** in 1988.*

*They took their name from a 1960 grade-Z flick directed by O'Dale Ireland. Like **The Slickees**, **Date Bait** makes trashy garage/psych rock. Their original singer was called Gutter Boy Baiter, but he left the band a few years ago, and former drummer Brian Horrorwitz took over lead vocals. They've been through a number of drummers and bassists over the years.*

*When I interviewed Horrorwitz a few years ago for Foster Child fanzine, he described the **Date Bait** sound as "Mixtures of '60s garage/punk and surf, '50s sleaze, '70s punk, psychedelic stuff with a definite influence from B-movie/pop-art/rat-fink type culture."*

*The band's live shows are a hoot, with outrageous costumes and props, and sleazy go-go dancers grinding on stage.*

*Date Bait's first album — recorded with original singer Gutter Boy, and only available as a French import — is lots of fun, but it doesn't quite capture the live **Date Bait** experience. In addition to original songs (mostly by Kane and/or Horrorwitz), they cover an eclectic grab bag of songs by **The Dictators, Eddie and the Hot Rods, Iggy Pop, The Troggs, Screaming Lord Sutch** and even **Gary Glitter.***

*Since that first album the revamped*

*Date Bait guys have released three great singles, and have recorded another full-length album, which is set to be released by Get Hip in 1995.*

*— by Jim Maher*

## DATELINE DIAMONDS
*(Germany)*

**The Dateline Diamonds** were a poppy '60s R&B-mod band which seemed to be very typical of the German groups of the late '80s, reportedly sounding very similar to **The Hawks.** They made a demo in 1989, the same year the three song *Love Tunnel* 7" EP was released by Unique Records in their native Germany. It's very light, polite and inoffensive, but not very stirring to these ears.

## THE DAYTONAS
*(Stockholm, Sweden)*

*Ready Set Go!* 13+ song CD, 1993
  Sunlight Records, Sweden

Ah, the summer sun, the surf boards, the sandy beaches of Sweden. Sweden? These Scandinavian surf-bums (ex-**Livingstones** and **Wylde Mammoths**) exhibit a serious case of California-envy, circa 1964 — though they formed in 1990. **Jan & Dean,**

**The Beach Boys** and **Dick Dale** all crowd their altar, with the giddy "I Love California" serving as their battle hymn.

A sound effect of the ocean's tide hitting a beach starts on the CD soon after the last official song. I weathered about 10 minutes of this, and was then surprised to hear about another half dozen unlisted surf tunes! These are most likely earlier demos — the quality is more crude than the other CD selections — but they are energetic and welcome surprise additions. I only wish that the extra song titles were somewhere in the liner notes.

Pure youthful joy wrapped in a timeless sugar coating, *Ready Set Go!* wasn't made to cash in on the nostalgia market — its only intention is to share the joy of Swedish-style surf music.

As organist Patrick Hammarsten says, *"If this album will reach #1 on the Billboard chart, I'll eat shit."* It's a shame he'll never get the chance.

## DC-10
*(U.K.)*

Their *Hi Jack* demo displays some fine Mersey-flower-pop, with "Judy Moody" a sunny day melodic anthem full of bright acoustic 12-string guitar and impish vocals — a wonderful song. "Isabella" is a more rocking staccato-fuzzed groover, slightly reminiscent of a raw **Dave Clark 5** song.

Is this band's name an homage to the **DC-5**, or taken from a type of jet airplane? Either way, I wish some vinyl had materialized.

## DEAD MOON
*(Portland, OR USA)*

*Live Evil* 28 song double LP, 1991
   Music Maniac Records, Germany

Several 45s and many LPs exist, including *In The Graveyard* (1988), *Unknown Passage* (1989), *13 Off My Hook* (1990), *Dead Moon Night* (1990), *Stranded In The Mystery Zone* (1991) — all on Germany's Music Maniac Records. Almost all of their output is also available on their own U.S. Tombstone label.

The focus of the group is Fred Cole, formerly of the 1960s psych-punk group **The Lollipop Shoppe**. **Dead Moon** isn't strictly a garage band, but more generally a loud and crude rock band with punk and garage influences. I played several shows with them in Europe, and was amazed at their unique style, Cole's focus on stage, and the amount of simple energy that his trio was able to exert.

I don't list their extensive discography because **Dead Moon** isn't strictly a '60s-styled garage act, but the double "live" LP listed above certainly qualifies as a powerfully gritty effort.

Cole and **Dead Moon** encompasses almost the entire history of aggressive rock music, which of course does include '60 punk. **59**

Fred Cole commented in 1990 with amazement on his resurgent popularity, saying, "Even *I* thought I was dead!"

## DEADBEATS
*(USA)*

Nothing known.

## THE DEADBOLTS
*(Tucson, AZ USA)*

This was an odd combination of musicians, feeling their way through the mid '80s — not sure if they wanted to be a garage or mod or pop band. They ended up being a little of all three, as their self-released seven song cassette from 1986 suggests. "Watcha Gonna Do" is still their finest garage moment. This author recorded it and several other **Deadbolts** tracks for the *Sounds From LSD* compilation cassette.

Sensing the commercial mood(s) of the day, the band eventually mutated into a metal-funk band, then a hard-rock band, then ... you get the idea. Their "garage" period was sweet and brief.

## DEADLY TOYS
*(Lyon, France)*

**The Deadly Toys** formed in 1987, releasing several slabs 'o sounds, and are reputed to be fiery on stage. The tracks I've heard were very cool, indeed, with plenty of organ and fine bass.

## DEEP SIX
*(origin unknown)*

The *Garage D'or* LP is on Coyote Records.

## DEJA VOODOO
*(Montreal, PQ Canada)*

*The Worst Of...* 24 song LP, 1987
*Big Pile Of Mud* 18 song LP, 1988
*Live At The Backstage Club* 17 song "Live" LP, 1989
   OG Records, Canada

With releases including *Big Pile Of Mud, The Worst Of, Live In Finland,* plus several others, this dynamic duo invented the musical genre of "Sludgeabilly." Their sound consisted of a guitar and drums with no cymbals, with a mixture of R&B,

rockabilly and weirdness. Not exactly '60 punk — but they really don't fit into any musical category, so we'll take them. Tracks like "Monsters In My Garage" and "Feed That Thing" certainly rub up along side the garage ethos.

This Canadian pair was popular on the college circuit throughout the 1980s, and also established the cool OG Records label for other Canadian artists. They were true originals in a world of cheap copies.


## THE DEL MONAS (see "Billy Childish")


## DEL NOAH & THE MT. ARARAT FINKS
(Los Angeles, CA USA)

*The Big Sounds Of...* 4 song 7" EP, 1995
    Dionysus Records, USA

Please forgive me for getting a bit confused here. I think that this combo was yet another offshoot of **The Finks**, but I also I see that bassist Steve of **The Swamp Zombies** and **Tiki Tones** is in the fold as well.

The constant mixing of the same small pool of cool L.A. musicians sometimes creates convoluted band family trees — note that this group probably has ties also to **The Witchdoctors, Bomboras** and **Swinging Fezmen**. They at least share the genre of instrumental surf-hot rod music.

In any case, the wonderful Rat Fink-ish drag race artwork should clue one into the turbo-charged sounds here. As the liner notes say, *"Drop your phonograph needle on this record and experience the sounds and smells of nitromethane 'pop' exploding in the belly of an Enderle-supercharged 392 Chrysler Hemi mill...the aroma of composite rubber burning off a set of M&H Racemaster slicks!"*

'Nuff said!


## THE DENTISTS
(Kent, U.K.)

*Strawberries Are Growing In My Garden* 3 song 7" EP, 1985
*Some People Are On The Pitch They Think It's All
    Over It Is Now* 13 song LP, 1985
*You And Your Bloody Oranges* 6 song EP, 1986
*Down & Out In Paris & Chatham* 5 song EP, 1986
*Writhing On The Shagpile* 5 song 12" EP, 1987
    Spruck/Tambourine Records, U.K.
*Beer Bottle And Bannister Symphonies* LP, 198?
*The Fun Has Arrived* 4 song 12" EP, 198?
*Heads And How To Read Them* 11 song LP/ 16 song CD, 198?
    Antler Records, Belgium

*Naked* 7 song 10" EP, 1991
"Charms And The Girl" b/w "Leave Me Alive" 45, 1992
    Independent Project Records, USA
"Box Of Sun" b/w "I Can See Your House From Here" 45, 1992
*Powdered Lobster Fiasco* 10 song CD, 1993
    Homestead Records, USA
"Outside Your Inside" b/w "All Coming Down" 45, 1992
    Bus Stop Records, USA
*Behind The Door I Keep The Universe* 12 song CD, 1994
    EastWest Records (Atlantic), USA

The feeling one gets from these **Dentists** is neither fear nor agony — but instead melodic joy. This decidedly British guitar band spread bright cheerful psych-pop throughout Europe from 1984 until at least 1995, creating a bright jangley sound that finally — amazingly — poked its way into "the big time."

Their debut 45 only hinted at their promise, which was realized with one of the decades finest LPs, *Some People Are On The Pitch They Think It's All Over It Is Now*. Say that one five time fast, it gets better with every attempt.

**Beatle**sque pieces like "Mary Won't Come Out To Play" and "I'm Not The Devil" certainly stand the test of time, and remain two of this author's favorite tracks from any decade. The entire 13 songs are gems, leaving one gasping with the final seconds of "One of Our Psychedelic Beakers Is Missing."

Their subsequent 12" EPs occasionally rise to the LP's charms, but also sometime stray a bit in style and mood. A cheerful edge permeates all of **The Dentists** original material, however, along with a melodic yet muscular guitar presence.

A series of U.S. 45s appeared in 1991 and 1992 — all of which are collected with extra tracks on the *Powdered Lobster Fiasco* CD. Underground attention lead them to a major label deal, and the resulting *Behind The Door I Keep The Universe* LP. The label apparently left the band alone to do what it is best at — bright fresh guitar pop songs with twists of irony.

From total oblivion to a major label record deal, all in only *nine years* — wow, that was easy! It remains to be seen if there's any more steam left in the band's drills after so many years of hard labor, but their big label "debut" certainly points in the right direction.

Lets hope there are a few songs left in them. **The Dentists** do more to make me smile than any doctor ever could.

# THE DERELICTS
*(Burke, VA USA)*

A 1986 four song demo of unheard proportions exists.

# DESPERATE BICYCLES
*(U.K.)*

The *Remorse Code* LP, 1980, is on Refile Records.

# THE DIED PRETTY
*(Australia)*

3 song 12" EP, 1984
"Mirror Blues" 45, 1984
"Out Of The Unknown" 45, 1984
*Next To Nothing* 12" EP, 1985
*Free Dirt* 10 song LP, 1986
"Stoneage Cinderella" 45, 1986
"Winterland" 45, 1987
   Citadel Records, Australia
"Out Of My Hands" b/w "When You Dance" 45, 1988
   Blue Mosque Records, Australia
"From A Buick" 45, 1988
   Festival Records, Australia
*Whitlam Square* 3 song 12" EP, 1990
   Beggar's Banquet Records, U.K.
*Lost* 10 song LP, 1989
*Every Brilliant Eye* 9 song LP & CD, 1990
*Doughboy Hollow* 11 song CD, 1992
   RCA Records, USA
*Trace* 11 song CD/Cass., 1994
   Columbia Records, USA

The manner of psych created by **The Died Pretty** is a much moodier, darker beast than most other groups in the genre. The band itself probably doesn't even consider itself a psych band, but nonetheless they do share many of the same characteristics — **The Pink Floyd**-esque slide guitar and **Doors**-ish organ, plus Ronald Peno's brooding vocals all evoke dark visions, if not in a strict "1960s" sense. These stylings are most evident on their first disc, where the dramatic **Doors** influence is most apparent.

Subsequent releases (including many 45s and flexis) showed the maturing band trying their hand at sparse introspective ballads along with their cacophonous epics, with many interesting moments along the way. About one-half of their breakthrough *Free Dirt* LP is among their best material, while the rest succumbs to a bit of self importance and epic pretension.

The band caught on in Europe and they later signed to a major label, with much of their character amazingly intact. If not

always musically successful, **The Died Pretty** remained worthy of a listen for the occasional gem poking through the smoke. Their subsequent *Lost, Every Brilliant Eye* and *Doughboy Hollow* albums all contained flashes of brilliance, and added up to an impressive output of solid material.

Twelve years and five albums down the line, Australia's **Died Pretty** remained an enigmatic, untouched resource. The passage of time and continued big-label backing haven't eroded their moody, somber and stately appeal, but it hasn't brought them commercial success either.

1994's *Trace* deserved to be their breakthrough, but then so did their other four LPs. Ronald Peno remained one of the planet's most passionate and identifiable vocalists, reaching emotional depths on epics like "A State Of Graceful Mourning" that few other singers ever attempt. The quiet, evocative trademark church organ and piano was also retained, countered by Brett Myers' shimmering guitar.

Australian music fan Milly Muleskinner told me in 1995, *"They lost their '60s hues early on and now appear to be middle of the road try-hards... admittedly I am a weeny bit prejudice because Peno licked my mate Stephen's ear at a club in Perth, ruining his bowl cut."*

I'll go ahead and forgive the vocalist just this one time.

All the elements are present — have been present since 1983 — but will anyone ever hear the **Died Pretty**?

# DIMENTIA 13
*(Cleveland OH/Chicago, IL USA)*

*Dimentia 13* 10 song LP, 1985
*Mirror Mind* 11 song LP, 1986
*Disturb The Air* 12 song LP, 1989
*TV Screen Head* 12 song LP, 1990
*Flat Earth Society* 12 song LP, 1991
   Midnight Records, USA

Vocalist and guitarist Brad Warner essentially *is* **Dimentia 13.** He assembled various accomplices for the decade's most demented forays into psychedelia, and wrote and sang all of the warped material.

Named after an early Francis Coppola low budget slasher-film, **Dimentia 13** slices up the psych genre, taking what it wants and creating whatever else is needed. One can hear snatches of Warner's inspirations: **Syd Barrett, Mothers Of Invention, Roky Erikson** and **Hendrix**, but these are merely shadows. The sound is distinctly Warner's, a combination of warbly off-key vocals, ultra fuzzed

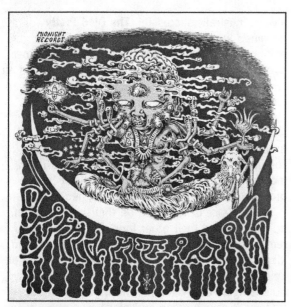

**DIMENTIA 13, 1985**

guitar and weird backing instruments.

The earliest **Dimentia 13** creates one of those rare instances where a studio-only status actually benefits the songs. The sometimes rambling, spacey compositions seem to float to their heart's content — an element that would disappear from a rehearsed full band. Lysergic anthems and epics like "I Am A Whale" and "The Lizard" could only be created by one swirling mind, and in this case the sounds ooze from Warner.

The *Mirror Mind* LP shows improvement in recording and composition, with "20 Years Ahead Of My Time" a sly comment on the psychedelic "revival," and "Psychedelic Mushroom Cloud Explosion" very much self explanatory. The cover of the LP's first pressing was on foiled paper, so you could see your own reflection on top of the scrambled sleeve art.

*Disturb The Air* found Warner and Co. under the wings of **Plasticland**'s Glenn Rehse, and for the first time in a "real" studio. The results are magical, with **Dementia 13** sounding more like a "band" than ever before. The title track is an exhilarating mess of emotion and hushed mystery, while "Samantha" recalls **The Byrds** jamming with **The Electric Prunes**! There's even a tribute of sorts to Rehse's pre-**Plasticland** band **Arousing Polaris**. The development of **Dimentia 13**'s sound had reached full maturity on this LP, without losing the psychotic edge that made it so appealing.

*TV Screen Head* is a collection of Warner solo tracks and demos — probably appreciated best with the knowledge of Warner's past output, rather than as an LP in its own right.

Rehse was back behind the board for

1991's *Flat Earth Society*. Here Warner is at his most coherent, with tight arrangements augmenting his always twisted vocalizations. "You Tickle Me Pink," "Whisperer" and "Pleasant Shoes" joins Warner's best previous work, but much of the material seems directionless. It seemed as though the spontaneous quality that made the early records so interesting was slowly stripped away by the time of *Flat Earth Society*. Nothing else saw release.

Still, **Dimentia 13** proved to be an essential dose of psychedelia for the decade, exhibiting once again what just one mind can do when stimulated correctly.

### DIRTEE SHAMES
*(London, England)*

Another garage band which frequently played live in the London clubs in the mid-'80s. They reportedly featured a wild lead vocalist named Sean who jumped and thrashed about.

### THE DIRTY LOVERS
*(Geelong, Australia)*

A reportedly thrashy styled garage band which has a few releases on Dog Meat Records.

### THE DIRTY SAINTS
*(Giannena, Greece)*

This gritty quintet began in August, 1988, and released the *Hi!* 4 song 7" EP in 1990 on Fifth Dimension Records. Their '60s punk roots are noticeable, but a mainstream rock style is more prominent on the debut disc.

### THE DISPOSSESSED
*(East Hartford, CT USA)*

"Being For The Benefit Of Mr. Kite" b/w
　"Circus Nights" 45, 1988
　Dionysus Records, USA

Doom and gloom are the best ways to describe the stylings of **The Dispossessed,** and they also managed some dark psych on their 1988 debut 45, a unique **Beatles** cover of "For The Benefit Of Mr. Kite" —and culminating with the subsequent *Sister Mary* LP. The somber band came to an end when their guitarist Jeremy Guenter committed suicide in 1988.

## DISTORTED LEVELS

*(Rochester, NY USA)*

Apparently a late 1980s side project by Greg Prevost of **The Chesterfield Kings**. Bona Fide has re-issued a 7" EP that features the tracks from the **Distorted Levels** original 45 on one side, and a track from the **Tar Babies** on the flip, featuring Prevost and Andy Babiuk from **The Kings**. Another side-band, **The Paisley Zippers**, is reportedly associated somehow with **The Chesterfield Kings**.

## THE DIZZY SATELLITES

*(Berlin, Germany)*

They have many LPs out on Germany's great Music Maniac label, including the 1986 six song *Orbit Drive* 12" EP, the 1987 *Crisis In Utopia* LP — plus the "Ain't Comin' Back" b/w "Seven Up" 45 on the LSD label in 1987.

A 14 song cassette (with tracks from these previous releases) on Acid Tapes is a good introduction to the group's gritty take on psychedelia with the wonderfully titled tracks "I Will Hate My Life," "You're Shit" and "You Better Fuck Off Baby." The 12 track *Dizzneyworld* LP also appeared in 1990 on Music Maniac after some major personnel changes.

This brand of garagadelia takes some time and repeated exposure to sink in and make a lasting impression. It is perhaps more challenging and less formulaic than the more obviously '60s groups — which means it's full of trippy surprises and unexpected turns.

They are well worth the effort needed to comprehend their dizziness.

## THE DM3

*(Australia)*

*1 x 2 x Devastated* 3 song 7" EP, 1994
   Screaming Apple Records, Germany

Dom Mariani's repertoire contains some of the best pop-garage of the 1980s. **The Stems** and **Someloves** are discussed at length elsewhere, so I'll just recap by stating that Mariani's pop song writing, arrangements and vocals were rivaled by a precious few throughout the mid to late 1980s.

It is with this knowledge that my expectations for his new band, **The Dom Mariani 3**, were perhaps artificially high. The title track of the debut EP isn't exactly a disappointment — it just doesn't live up to Mariani's past material. More like a

Ramones song with catchy chorus, it doesn't have the intricacies or original style of his best work.

The two B-side selections waver off into some rather wankish lead guitar excursions — the opposite of the lean, stripped down compositions that made his name one of the brightest in the re-emerging power pop scene.

**The Garden Path**'s Vic Conrad told me that this disc was just an advance taste of their debut LP. I can only hope it shows more diversity, maturation and restraint, with songs worthy of the Mariani name.

Conrad also says that a total of three 45s are out as of this date, as well as an excellent EP titled *Soul Top*. Conrad saw a 1994 **DM3** show in Australia, where they shared the bill with **Jellyfish** and **The Died Pretty**. He said that the band was very enjoyable in concert.

That's the type of good news I wanted to hear.

## DMZ

*(Boston, MA USA)*

Untitled 4 song 7" EP, 1977
*Relics* 9 song 12" EP, 1981
*When I Get Off* 18 song CD, 1993
   Bomp Records, USA

**DMZ** is a well known (in underground circles) and influential late '70s rock act featuring Jeff Connolly, later of **The Lyres**. They arguably ruled the active Boston rock scene from 1976-1980, creating a reputation that found its way to the major labels.

They recorded first for Bomp, however, and their debut EP showcased the searing vocals and garage beat that Connolly would make famous with **The Lyres**. It was also the first waxing of the Connolly classic "Busy Man."

The band was then picked up by Sire and delivered a disappointing LP, after which they predictably self-destructed. The debut EP and five other early tracks were then released by Bomp as the *Relics* 12", followed a dozen years later with the addition of nine more outtakes as the *When I Get Off* CD.

Many other bootlegs exist, fueled by the subsequent interest in Connolly and **The Lyres**. To these ears they are an interesting footnote, with **The Lyres** story the culmination of **DMZ**'s spark.

**65**

## DOC AND THE PODS
*(Cincinnati, OH USA)*

Untitled 4 song 7" EP, 1985
  HoHo Records, USA

These **Pods** formed in late '84 and lasting until late '88, with several releases: a four song 7" EP in 1985, a flexi in early '86, a five song 7" EP entitled *Touch The Unclean Thing* in late '87, and the six song *That Is Rare* 7" EP in 1989 — all on Ho Ho Records.

The later discs offered much more garagey tunes, including cool versions of "Hard Times" and "Mr. Nobody." The other tracks mixed sloppy surf and garage. **The Pods** later re-formed in 1990 without "Doc," who was the drummer.

## DOC AND THE RODS
*(Vire, France)*

"You're Gonna Miss Me" b/w "Carry On" 45, 1993
  Weed Records, France

A very '77- punkish attitude combines with a '60s garage mentality — as is evidenced by the energetic stab at the **13th Floor Elevators'** "You're Gonna Miss Me." An interesting start — but I can't venture a guess as to the future direction they might take.

## DOCTOR EXPLOSION
*(Gijon, Spain)*

Untitled 4 song 7" EP, 1990
Untitled 4 song 7" "Live" EP, 1992
Untitled 4 song 7" EP, 1994
  Thunder Pussy Records, Spain
*Vivir Sin Civilizar* 14 song LP/CD/Cass., 1993
  Romilar-D Records, Spain
*El Loco Mundo De Los Jovenes* 14 song LP/CD/cass., 1994
  Subterfuge Records, Spain

Plus: two songs on the Italian *Born Loser* compilation; a track on the *Waco-Zine* compilation, 1993; and a song on the 1991 *Munster Dance Hall Favorites Vol. 4* compilation.

**The Doctor Explosion** explores reverent R&B stylings, with a teenager's exuberance and wide-eyed appreciation for beat music. Their debut EP contains three originals, all loosely based upon countless other R&B standards, but with enough energy and enthusiasm to hook the listener. Clear production and some spirited vocals also give the disc an edge — and how could one resist the hormone driven "Sex At First Sight"?

The "Live" EP contains four well-worn covers, also done up in hip-shaking fashion. This is gritty

*DOCTOR EXPLOSION, 1994*

music made for the fun of it — which is one of my highest recommendations.

Their third EP — containing four cover songs — features a version of the **Village People** disco song "Y.M.C.A." It's a hilarious punk-pop cover re-make, sounding closest to vintage **Ramones**. The original song is so awful that I don't know if I should laugh or cry at this great cover version. Probably a bit of both.

The *Vivir Sin Civilizar* LP is also excellent, with zany humor, powerful playing and a good song selection.

Their *El Loco Mundo De Los Jovenes* LP — which I believe translates into "The Crazy World Of The Young Girls" — show a maturing group, branching out into more garage, surf and trash. **Thee Headcoatees** even sing some back-up vocals on a song, and the band's "Eres Feo Chaval" sounds distinctly like a **Billy Childish** exercise.

This feeling is helped by the appropriately mono recording — made at the now infamous Toe Rag Studios in London. The package is completed by a hilarious cover photo of the band in Catholic girl-school dresses and wigs, walking in a courtyard with teenage girls.

The best garage bands always have a sense of humor.

**64**

## DOG AND THE ACID BUNNIES
*(Boston, MA USA)*

With members of **The Trodds**, a 1984 single was released described by one catalog as being *"courtesy of **Syd Barrett** and that band from Liverpool who went by the name of **The Beatles**."* That sounds like a winner to me, though I haven't been able to uncover it.

## THE DOGS
*(France)*

They might be the longest continually active rock band in France, with at least four albums since their 1978 debut — which is reportedly stocked full of Rickenbacker guitar. They've apparently strayed through other styles, but still conjure up the garage spirit now and then. The tape I heard — sung in English — was energetic and pop-punkish with professional playing and good sound production.

I get the idea that **The Dogs** might be at their best on stage — and this is common with many bands who never quite catch their essence in the recording studio. It's not that I thought **The Dogs'** studio tracks were lacking — I just think I hear a spark of something that ignites under the glare of stage lights.

Sweat can change everything (for the better) when it comes to playing rock music.

## THE DOGS
*(Tucson, AZ USA)*

This author's first band was called **Jacket Weather**, and its drummer was Howie Salmon. By 1984, however, Howie had found his true calling — as guitarist and frontman for his own band **The Dogs**. It didn't matter that he didn't know how to play guitar or sing. Details like that never stopped Mick Jagger.

Howie recruited his brothers and sisters for additional instrumentation, and the band was born. They managed to record two cassettes of **Velvet Underground**-inspired noise: the seven song *Rock 'N Roll Over 'N Play Dead* in 1984 and the five song *Goin' Thru The Mill* in 1985.

In the liner notes to their first release, Salmon explains some of their technical difficulties: *"I had a grounding problem with my amp. It's an old practice amp from the '60s that I bought at a swap meet. Whenever I turned up the volume, the amp would start buzzing very loudly. This was alleviated by* fastening an alligator clip to the treble switch... a wire then led from the clip to another clip, which I kept in my underwear. It sounds kinda uncomfortable, but it worked!"

This was a band put together strictly for fun — a goal fulfilled as well when Salmon briefly joined **The Purple Merkins** almost a decade later.

## DOUBLE DECK 5
*(Torino, Italy)*

A garage-psych band with several releases: "Looking Down" b/w "The Sorcerer" 7" on Toast Records, 1986; *Umbilicus* LP on Cobra, 1988 (with the bonus 7" "Yeah"/"L'uomo Ragno").

## THE DOUBLE NAUGHT SPYS
*(Branford, CT USA)*

*Goin' Nowhere With...* 14 song LP, 1992
 Rockadelic Records, USA
*Teen Trash #5* 16 song LP & CD, 1993
 Music Maniac Records, Germany

Formed in late 1986, this New England combo blasted garage-punk in the time-honored traditional way, loud, fast and crude. The band's curious name comes from the *Beverly Hillbillies* TV show, where the character of Jethro often wanted to be a "double naught spy, like James Bond, 0-0-7!"

The band went through many member changes, at one time even including former **Not Quite** member Joe Guidone. Apparently, as **The Not Quite** went off into a more psychedelic direction, Guidone joined **The Spys** to continue with his garage affection. He left the band in October, 1988.

The guys managed to record several sets of raw demos, and in November, 1988, recorded 11 tracks for a supposed LP or 45 on Crypt. Reported squabbles between Tim Warren and the band prevented the LP's appearance, so a vinyl debut finally came for these garage-punks on the Canadian *Oh My God...* compilation.

An LP did finally appear, limited to 500 copies on the tiny Dallas based Rockadelic label. The 1992 LP was later re-issued by Music Maniac in Germany with extra tracks. It is possibly one of the ten best garage LPs of all time — including the 1960s. Its raw, gutsy playing and inspired teen-angst songwriting makes it a true classic — and a rare collector's find if one can score a copy of the initial Rockadelic pressing. The fact that is was recorded "live" in the studio, without overdubs, makes it all the more impressive.

Ever snotty, band leader Mike Markesich is the

definition of a garage true-believer. *"No girl will ever satisfy me like a 45,"* he told an interviewer in 1992. *"If things were really cool, we wouldn't be so philosophical and introspective. We're all losers."* He also summed up his appraisal of the band, saying, *"We're one of the few bands still playing this kind of music. It's not retrospective or imitative or copying. It's what we are!"* Amen to that.

Markesich finally disbanded the group in March, 1993. *"We can't compete in this square, trendy world,"* he told me then. *"We've proved the legend is bigger than the myth!"*

A video chronicling '87-'92 has been assembled.

## DRAGSTERS
*(Columbus, OH USA)*

They reportedly had one 45 and an LP of garage-surf-rock from the early 1990s which was a little harder-edged than most '60s influenced groups.

## THE DREAM SYNDICATE
*(Los Angeles, CA USA)*

*The Dream Syndicate* 4 song 12" EP, 1982
   Down There Records, USA
*The Days Of Wine And Roses* 9 song LP, 1982
   Ruby Records, USA
*Tell Me When It's Over* 4 song 12" EP, 1983
   Rough Trade Records, U.K.

To say that the early 1980s underground scene in Los Angeles was bursting with talent is a gross understatement, and it is of interest that many of what would become the decade's most popular bands all began as "garage" or "'60s-inspired" outfits.

Steve Wynn had kicked around in several of these attempted bands, rubbing shoulders with musicians who would later inhabit **The Rain Parade, Opal, The Unclaimed** and **Long Ryders**. His own entry into the scene, **The Dream Syndicate**, would turn into one of the most notable U.S. guitar bands of the era.

The initial vinyl offering was recorded only three weeks after Wynn formed the band's first and best lineup. Its addled energy and warped feedback are hardly contained, and while this is obviously a peek at a band still in its embryonic stages, it is compelling nonetheless. The roughest edges were polished a bit by the time of the stunning *Days Of Wine And Roses* LP, which gained deserved worldwide critical praise.

The most obvious benchmark for comparison was **The Velvet Underground**, right down to Wynn's **Lou Reed**-ish spoken voice imitation. The band also shared the **Velvet**'s ability to balance artistic introspection with some very loud and abrasive rock music. This debut LP is simply a classic of any era, and remains the band's high point.

The mounting critical attention would bring the band a major label, and with it a couple subsequent god-awful self-indulgent albums. The spiral hit bottom when guitarist Karl Precoda was replaced by Paul Cutler, who would strangle the last vestiges of interest out of the band.

It was about this time circa 1988 that this author witnessed the sagging band in concert. All high expectations were dashed, as Wynn and Cutler impatiently raced through their time-worn set, with little interest in the audience or their own music. The crowd predictably stood silent and unimpressed — it was obvious that the inspirational creative abilities of **The Dream Syndicate** had evaporated.

Back stage Cutler was surly and boorish — the perfect picture of a rock 'n' roll jerk. The band made a good bit of money that night, and I'm certain the crowd scratched its collective head and wondered why. I was doubly sorry I wasn't able to see them at their peak in '82 or '83.

Wynn would go on to a somewhat interesting solo career, attempting to leave the specter of **The Dream Syndicate** behind him.

## DREAMTIME
*(Piacenza, Italy)*

This is a reportedly psych band with a privately pressed, self-titled LP from 1989.

## DR. NO
*(Barcelona, Spain)*

Nothing is known about **Dr. No,** but this James Bond-inspired band would have been fun on a bill with fellow Spaniards **Los Agentes Secretes.**

## DR. YOGAMI
*(Sweden)*

"Plastic Surgeon" b/w "Flamin' Groovies" 45, 1985
    Third Train Records, Sweden

The 1985 "Plastic Surgeon" 45 is only partially in this genre, but does crank out some distorted noise. Subsequent releases lost their flavor within a few listenings.

## DRIVE TRAIN
*(origin unknown)*

At least one 45 exists on the U.S. Tombstone Records label.

## THE DRIVING WHEELS
*(San Diego, CA USA)*

Original **Crawdaddy** Ron Silva put together this R&B-based outfit, which also put in a forceful appearance on the *It's Happening* TV show. A live tape shows them ripping through "Daddy Was A Rolling Stone," "A Shot Of Rhythm & Blues," "Don't Lie To Me" and "Let's Make It" — all in fine rave-up fashion. I don't think any vinyl materialized.

## THE DROOGS
*(Los Angeles, CA USA)*

"He's Waitin'" b/w "Light Bulb Blues" 45, 1973
"Set My Love On You" b/w "I'm Not Like Everybody Else" 45, 1974
"Ahead Of My Time" b/w "Get Away" 45, 1974
"Overnight Success" b/w "Last Laugh" 45, 1975
"As Much As I Want" b/w "Off The Hook" 45, 1979
"Only Game In Town" b/w "Garden Of My Mind" 45, 1981
*Heads Examined* 4 song 12" EP, 1983
    Plug-N-Socket Records, USA

The first six 45s are compiled as the 1987 *Anthology* LP on Germany's Music Maniac Records.

**The Droogs** could be credited as one of the first 1960s garage revivalists, since they began their assault almost a decade before the rest of the world — and only a few years after the '60s ended.

Cover versions of **The Sonics**' "He's Waitin" or **The Shadows Of Knight**'s "Light Bulb Blues" are unremarkable — except for the fact that they were released in *1973!* The garage-niks of the 1980s felt out of place and neglected by the public, so one can imagine the isolation **The Droogs** must have felt throughout the drab and absolutely lame 1970s.

The 1983 *Heads Examined* EP features a powerful version of **The Lollipop Shoppe**'s "You Must Be A Witch" — but this exercise in good taste is tempered with another lame cover version of the geekish "Born To Be Wild." It should also be noted that none of the few band originals throughout their history stand up to the classic covers that dominate their releases.

The band lasted in several incarnations through at least the late 1980s with several long-players of more pedestrian generic rock, so it is the early 45s that form the backbone of their legacy.

This author saw them perform in Los Angeles in 1989, and while I tip my hat to them for their perseverance and musicianship, their sound was less than inspirational.

Still, their role as a connection between the '66 and '86 garage generations cannot be underestimated. **The Droogs** had the fortune of good taste in music, and the misfortune to form at the worst time — I wouldn't wish a 1973 debut on anyone.

## THE DUKES
*(Germany)*

"She'll Be Mine" b/w "If You Really Love Me" 45, 1987
    Kavern 7 Records, Australia
"I'll Come Back" b/w "Tobacco Road" 45, 1990
*Get The Dukes* 12 song LP, 1991
    Mystery Scene Records, Germany

compilations: *Tant Qu'il A Rock* LP, France, 1988; *Tribute to The Outsiders*, Screaming Apple, Germany, 1992; *Electric Carnival*, Kinetic Vibes, France, 1993; *Sounds Like Fun* cassette in Snap Magazine, Spain, 1993; *Larsen* CD Magazine #8, France 1994; and a three track 45 on another *Larsen* compilation slated for 1995, with songs recorded in November, 1991.

**The Dukes'** debut 45 displays a reverent awe of mid-'60s Euro Beat and white R&B. They even have the legendary **Downliners Sect's** Terry Gibson write the liner notes for a final authentic touch.

Gibson writes, *"Take a trip with me now, back to those halcyon days of the Star Club, enjoy the atmosphere of a bygone age with this, the first record by The Dukes. These are four young men so inspired by their predecessors and German Giants of Beat, The Boots, Kentuckys and Phantom Brothers, that they intend to continue that fine tradition by playing the wildest Beat/R&B music possible."*

Their lone LP mines the same R&B stockpile, with classic numbers like "Rosalyn," "Roadrunner" and "Sticks And Stones" getting a very German interpretation. Half of the 12" is made up of band originals, with the plaintive "It Would Have Been In Vain" and "I'll Come Back" (also on their second 45) as the high points.

They played their last gig in May, 1993.

## THE DUKES OF STRATOSPHEAR
(London, U.K.)

*25 O'Clock* 6 song 12" EP, 1985
*Psonic Psunspot* 10 song LP, 1987
"You're A Good Man Albert Brown" 45, 1987
   Virgin Records, U.K.

The members of **XTC** didn't intend it at the time, but when they unleashed **The Dukes of Stratosphear** on the world they had also released their best music ever.

**XTC** created the persona of **The Dukes** as a little in-joke; a tribute to their favorite psychedelic-era sounds. Unfortunately for them, this "side-project" proved to be more interesting and musically accomplished than any of their "official" releases.

They made a point of recording on vintage 1960s recording equipment and with vintage instruments, and this certainly adds to the absolute authenticity of the *25 O'Clock* EP. These truly sound like *Sgt. Pepper*-era **Beatles** outtakes (with **Syd Barrett** sitting in on the sessions), with more mellotron, backwards guitars, sound effects and fuzz than any psych head ever deserved. Complete with the absolutely freaked out cover art, *25 O'Clock* is a psych-pop fan's

dream come true.

I once announced on my radio show that the track "Mole From the Ministry" was a newly uncovered **Lennon** song from 1967, and the audience ate it up — the record's production is that convincing. The music video for that song is also reportedly very psychedelic.

The record garnered healthy sales and critical response, so the boys tried to milk it with a follow-up LP, *Psonic Psunspot*. These tracks sound much more conventional, in fact, they sound simply like **XTC** album outtakes — a quite disappointing attempt to re-capture the spontaneity of the debut. (Early pressings of the LP sport a cool gatefold cover, however.)

Still, The *25 O'Clock* EP was a shining moment in 1985, proving that even "real" overground musicians understood the appeal of the original psych sounds.

## THE DUM-DUM BOYS
(Nice, France)

Described by others as a sound somewhere between **The Scientists, Spacemen 3**, '60s punk and **The Velvet Underground**! They have at least two LPs.

## DUNDRELLS
(Toronto, ON Canada)

Glynnis Wilson remembers, *"I saw almost every single show this band played, and that is no small feat — I must have seen them at least 90 times! The only band I've seen more are the Gruesomes who I've seen a total of 95 times! Their early releases are the most '60s styled garage. The first, a self-titled cassette, is a humorous combination of '60s punk, soul, '77 punk and sloppy power pop. 'Nothing On T.V.' typifies their warped suburban senses of humor."*

There was also a later 45.

## DURANGO 95
(Ventura, CA USA)

*Dreams & Trains* 7 song 12" EP, 1986
   Stone Garden Records, USA

I was lucky enough to see these guys in action several times in 1986 and '87. They had an American guitar sound somewhere between **The Plimsouls** and **The Long Ryders**, with smooth vocals and a concise pop style. They didn't consider themselves a '60s band, but they exhibited the best tendencies of fun garage pop.

I thought they had commercial possibilities, yet their 1986 12" EP, *Dreams And Trains,* went totally unnoticed. Further tracks were recorded, and I remember them to be of high quality, but nothing else ever materialized.

Interestingly, all but one of the members of the band were Hispanic, and I think this could have retarded their commercial appeal — because of bigotry within the music business.

They were a fine pop group, regardless of their lack of commercial impact.

*(Note: don't confuse this group with a hard-rock Canadian group of the same name which existed at about the same time.)*

## DUST COLLECTION
*(Adelaide, Australia)*

Untitled 3 song 7" EP, 1986
   Greasy Pop Records, Australia

I was browsing through the Rhino Records' "reject file" in Los Angeles one day, and up popped this little record from Australia. The sly smiles on the band's faces — plus a lead singer named Travis Underdog — made me give it a listen, and sometimes we are rewarded for our leaps of faith.

The sound is sparse and plaintive, with Travis and Co. sounding a bit like the best of mid-period **Kinks**.

A little research showed that this was actually a side project of the excellent **Garden Path** — "Travis Underdog" is none other than **The Garden Path**'s vocalist Vic Conrad. He told me during his 1995 visit to Arizona that the **Dust Collection** played live shows consisting mainly of their favorite '60s pop songs like **The Zombies**' "Just Out Of Reach." The EP was simply a fun novelty for them — but consisting of three quality original songs.

**The Dust Collection** also shows up on two separate Greasy Pop Records compilation LPs. I can find no trace of these LPs, of course, so all I have is three marvelous songs on a little round record. I'm happy that I stumbled upon that.

## THE DWARVES
*(Chicago, IL/San Francisco CA USA)*

*Horror Stories* 14 song LP, 1986
*Horror Stories* 12 song LP, 1990
   Voxx/Coxx Records, USA

What can one say about a bunch of losers like **The Dwarves**?

Well, O.K., I'll give you some facts before making more fun of them. Firstly, they began their twisted lives as the **Suburban Nightmare** with one 12" on Midnight Records. Then they changed their name to **The Dwarves** and location to San Francisco.

***THE DWARVES, 1985***

There they reportedly managed to annoy everyone until finally capturing the attention of the mostly lame Seattle Sub Pop label. Seeing the absolute lack of quality in **The Dwarves** — who by this time had thrown away their '60s punk affections — Sub Pop went on a campaign in 1990 promoting a subsequently stupid record with moronic cover art to idiots throughout the world.

But that's not what I'm going to write about.

Instead, I'll discuss their one LP done earlier with Voxx that shows **The Dwarves** still in love with the '60s sound, though in a most perverse way. On *Horror Stories* the band twists every garage convention on its ear, while still managing somehow to sound like a garage band.

Since the fuzz box is an integral part of any garage band, **The Dwarves** use it liberally — on the vocals, on the drums, and even sometimes on the guitar. **The Standells**' "Sometimes Good Guys Don't Wear White" becomes "Sometimes Gay Guys Don't Wear Pink," so you can make a guess about the tilted attitude of the remainder of the LP.

The band was unhappy with Voxx's choice of cover art, (even though their own version was late getting to Voxx by over a year!), so Voxx re-released the LP in 1990 with several other tracks and with the band's equally bad cover. (Voxx also wanted to cash in on **The Dwarves** sudden publicity as bad boys, so for the re-issue they called their label Coxx. Ha ha ha! — that's supposed to be funny.)

Now this author met the boys on several occasions, and it took them approximately four minutes to break my turntable on their first visit. Their second time though town I booked them into a local club I was managing — because it was my last night there. I knew they would destroy the place, and they didn't let me down.

It was truly fun to see the big-hair posers and leather jacket boys getting spit on by **The Dwarves**, not to mention having pitchers of water thrown at them, and ultimately, being literally pissed on by them.

I think I've said enough about **The Dwarves**.

### THE ECTOMORPH
*(U.K.)*

An LP of heavy psych appeared in 1991 on Woronzow in the U.K.

### THE EFFERVESCENT ELEPHANTS
*(Alice Castello, Italy)*

*Radio Muezzin* 3 song 7" EP, 1986
*Something To Say* 10 song LP, 1987
  Electric Eye Records, Italy
*Another Summer Of Grass* 7 song cassette, 1990
  Acid Tapes, U.K.
3 song 7" EP, 1990
  Face Records, Italy

Plus the private cassettes *Radio Muezzin*, *16 Pages*, and *Garage Tracks* in 1985-1988, plus the *Indian Corn Expansion*

cassette on the U.K.'s Acid Tapes in 1989, and also a split 45 with **The Backdoor Men** in *Lost Trails Magazine* #4, 1986.

Quality garage bands outnumbered psychedelic bands by a wide margin in the 1980s, with only a few dozen top-notch practitioners of the pure psych style releasing records. The very Italian **Effervescent Elephants** were one of those bands proudly carrying the psych banner, depositing moody stylish songs in their wake.

**The Elephants** constructed their attack in the best **Syd Barrett**-era **Pink Floyd** tradition, with slide guitar, plenty of echo and a general sense of

mystery. Some more up-beat rock material is also present on their LP, but it is the slower moodier material that defines this band the best. Egyptian and eastern Indian sounds creep in as well, but this is no lame hippy trip band. The compositions are focused and concise, with just the correct amount of mysticism and structure.

Their "All Tomorrow's Parties" almost single-handedly defines their sound, with gentle vocals and a floating atmosphere.

Acid Tapes was the perfect vehicle for several of the band's cassette-only releases. Without economic concerns of pressing records or CDs, **The Elephants** could stretch out their musical ideas on the cassette format. *Another Summer Of Grass* shows that freedom, full of extended guitar interludes and elongated trippiness.

## THEE EGGHEADS
*(Tucson, AZ USA)*

Members of **The Overcoat** and **Thee Flypped Whigs** recorded in 1989 a crude one-off session of several garagadelic songs which remain unreleased.

## EGO ON THE ROCKS
*(Germany)*

A studio project with members of the band **Eloy**, making the *Acid In Wonderland* LP in 1981 — described to me as being very experimental and psychedelic. This is reportedly now extremely rare, changing hands for around $100. There is also a rare promo-only one-sided 12" single, with a song from the LP.

## THE ELECTRIC FLIES
*(Eugene, OR USA)*

*Ain't No Humans On Us* 5 song 7" EP, 1988
    Moxie Records, USA
"Get Stoned" b/w "Devil's Churn" 45, 1992
    Tombstone Records, USA

These cats earn extra points for the title of their lone EP, plus the graphic of the band with giant fly heads — truly inspired. This is real garage music, done for the love of it, with no pretension or self-importance. The trio of **Flies** bang out simple, no-frills rock, the type that hits the spot late on a Friday night.

Guitarist and vocalist Randy Haines wrote "Lonesome Tears" back in '66, but it managed to remain unrecorded until he tackled it for this EP. It's a moody sad love story, complete with enough dripping teen angst to form a million pimples.

*These are compliments.*

The second 45 sports a garage anthem — "Get Stoned." Explains Haines, *"In 1966 I wrote a song with band mate Phil Kramer called 'Get Stoned,' which was about splitting an eight-pack in a parking lot. A lot of kids liked it when our band played it and said we should record it. Now, 25 years later here it is."*

Both sides of the 45 are also on the *Fieldburn* compilation CD, and are well worth a listen.

## THE ELECTRIC NUBIANS
*(Philadelphia, PA USA)*

"Sunshine And Marigolds" b/w
    "Memories Of The '60s" 45, 1993
Self Titled 10 song LP, 1994
    Distortions Records, USA

Not many African-Americans were involved with the garage and psychedelic revival, which alone makes the wonderfully named **Electric Nubians** of special interest. It's the band's music, however, that merits the most attention.

Their debut 45 sports one of the most colorful, creative and psychedelic sleeves of the era, and the A-side, "Sunshine And Marigolds," remains their signature tune, full of positive flower power sentiment and abundant pulsating energy. Flanged vocals tell of "beautiful people everywhere," while a loping rhythm pushes the song along. The standout track also appears on their debut album.

The long-player perhaps showcases the band's overall sound more accurately, which is based on a rougher late '60s archetype. Fuzz, wah-wah and plentiful lead guitar solos show an obvious **Jimi Hendrix** affection, but unlike most of the **Hendrix**-metal clones, **The Nubians** take the best of that sound and make it their own.

"Ladybus Driver," "Going To N.Y." and "Butterfly Queen" all owe an obvious debt to **Hendrix,** but as a worthy inspiration rather than as a pale imitation.

The trio, which included Distortion Records' Dave Brown on drums for the LP, also stands apart from many of their garage relatives by tackling some social concerns. "Dead Meat" discusses government control and our loss of humanity, while "Blood On Your Hands" shouts *"Uncle Sam — I ain't your man, don't ask me to spill my blood for you....March! Suckers!"*

**The Electric Nubians** stand out from most other bands for many reasons, the most important being their solid musicianship and risk-taking self expression.

## ELECTRIC PEACE
*(Los Angeles, CA USA)*

*Rest In Peace* 6 song 12" EP, 1985
    Enigma Records, USA

The L.A. Cavern Crowd never caught on to what **Electric Peace** was all about, mainly because they were a music band, not a fashion show. The bombastic, dramatic band recalled the angst-driven sound of **The Doors**, while remaining contemporary in context.

This band had an angry sound, and its brooding style certainly didn't set well with teeny-boppers out for a few laughs. That's a shame, because **Electric Peace**'s debut EP is a powerful and thoughtful dark-psych record, worthy of attention — and certainly different than any other out at the time.

The band tipped over into a hard-rock style, however, and further recordings lacked the original balance that made their sound so effective.

## THE ELECTRIC ROACHES
*(Montreal, Canada)*

"1-2-5" b/w "Don't Wanna Know" 45, 1985?
   Aller-Retour Records, Canada

This is a bit of a mystery group. I found their (apparently) lone 45 while my band was on tour in Canada, and no one has really been able to tell me anything about the group — except that it's believed that they performed only a handful of live dates. The disc itself is a credible exercise in replicating that late, great 1966 punk sound, with an accurate reading of The Haunted's "1-2-5" as the A side.

It's the B-side that raises a few eyebrows (and smiles), as the trio bashes out a tune they call "Don't Wanna Know." It only takes about five seconds, however, to realize that the song is actually the classic "I Can Only Give You Everything." They simply changed the title and the lyrics, then performed the song note for note like the original. One has to admit that garage groups have guts!

The band loses points, however, for

not having big roach heads in their group photo. See the entry on the **Electric Flies** for details.

## THE ELECTRIC SHADOWS
*(Whitby, ON Canada)*

This was an effort by hipster Glynnis Wilson of *Feline Frenzy Magazine* to form an all-girl garage combo. Wilson told me that they only managed two practices — in their bass player's basement — then gave up "because we couldn't find a cool girl drummer."

## ELECTRIC SHIELDS
*(Chiarano D'Arco, Italy)*

*Cry Baby Cry* 4 song 7" EP, 1988?
   Electric Eye records, Italy
"One Hundred" on Lost Trails #10 split 45, 1989
*White Buffalo County* LP, 1991
   Direct Hit Records, USA

These Italians started as a promising garage punk-folk band, then evolved into a **Long Ryders**-type country-rock tinged outfit by the time of their LP. I found it to be a let down, and it is not recommended.

## ELECTRIC SUICIDE
*(France)*

7 song demo cassette, 1990
*Ekstasy* 6 song demo cassette, 1991
   no label, France (demos)

also tracks on two compilations: *Teenage Rock 'n' Roll From Blouse* and *Underground Vol. 2.*

Here's another French band that merits an entry, though they only have a couple compilation appearances to their credit. Like their countrymen, **The Cryptones**, the high quality of their demos have merited attention here, though they reportedly don't have any vinyl of their own.

Interestingly, the band had already changed styles somewhat from one demo to the other, though a few of these original tracks made it onto the aforementioned comps. This first demo is very garagey, indeed, with densely distorted guitars and snotty vocals mixed in with an infectious and danceable drive.

Their second demo leaves the more structured garage behind, opting for a much more hard-rock-ish guitar style, and a less '60s approach. A bit more like late '70s punk, but one can't complain about the energy. I'll have to track down those compilations that include the early material, and consider the book closed on **Electric Suicide.**

## ELLENA LODOVICO
(Alice Castello, Italy)

A reportedly psychedelic band featuring ex-**Effervescent Elephants,** with three cassettes: *Cats In Love* 1990 (on Acid Tapes in the U.K.), and the private releases *1990-1991* and *La Devastazione Continua* in 1992.

## THE EMBRYONICS
(Solingnen, Germany)

*My Problems Are Bigger Than Your Tits* 4 song 7" EP, 1994
   Unique Records, Germany

Lutz Rauber went on to form the excellent Soundflat Mailorder record service — after performing with **The Embryonics**. They released three 45s, played many dates in Europe, and even came to the U.S. to play in Los Angeles with kindred spirits **The Tommyknockers.**

It's no wonder that they appreciated **The Tommyknockers'** high-octane rock — **The Embryonics** display the same fire power on the only 45 of their's I've heard, the hilariously titled *My Problems Are Bigger Than Your Tits*. That 45 also features another wonderful cartoon picture sleeve by Darren Merinuk. Amongst naked girls, the sleeve says *"100% super-primitive music! 200% super-stupid lyrics!"*

They split in April, 1994.

## THE EMPTIFISH
(Southsea, U.K.)

*Branksmere Sessions* 4 song 7" EP, 198?
*I Want That Girl* 3 song 7" EP, 198?
   The Crystal Rooms Records, UK

Weeds Records honcho Darren Ross says that **The Emptifish** existed from 1982-'86, and were *"Probably one of the finest garage bands to have ever existed. They actually caused riots and were banned by the Houses Of Parliament! No joke or lie."*

I haven't heard a note of this band, but I really dig the **Count V**-like cover photo of their debut EP, complete with a Victorian house as a backdrop and the drummer wearing a cape.

## THE END
(Winter Park, FL USA)

"No No No" b/w "I Know What You Are" 45, 1985
   Friendly Ghost Records

The "No No No" 45 from 1985 is a pleasant mod-pop effort, full of jangley Rickenbacker guitars, with some nice vocals and clean production. Vocalist and guitarist Jeff Jacks would go on to the power-pop outfit **The Immediates**.

## ENEMIES
(London, UK)

Darren Ross says that this 1977 group "Was from London, and probably had the best ever version of **(The Count V's)** 'Psychotic Reaction.'" The A-side of this punk band's 45 was titled "The Radiators From Space."

## LOS ENEMIGOS
(Spain)

Nothing is known except the possible English translation: **The Enemies.**

## THE ENIGMAS
(Vancouver, Canada)

A very locally popular early '80s group, with the *Strangely Wild* six song EP their most known effort. While some fans believe them to be an important inspiration for later Canadian garage bands, I found their sound to be only marginally of interest. I have seen a fun video for their song "Windshield Wiper," circa 1983.

## ETHEREAL COUNTERBALANCE
(U.K.)

A nine song LP appeared on Woronzow in 1990, featuring Rod Goodway and Nick Saloman of **The Bevis Frond**. It features a variety of heavy guitar styles and distorted vocals prevail, tied together by a droning sitar between tracks.

## THE E-TYPES
*(Sacramento, CA USA)*

*Teen Trash #8* 13 song LP & CD, 1993
  Music Maniac Records, Germany

This Northern California trio mines the mod and power pop sound of the late 1970s, with **The Buzzcocks** and **The Jam** as their admitted influences. The result is tame and predictable — with some lame horns adding in to make sure that I never play it again.

This is easily the weakest entry in the usually dependable *Teen Trash* series.

## EVAPORATORS
*(Vancouver, Canada)*

I've seen a pretty crazy live performance on video of these goofy Canucks, and they have a four song 7" EP called *Welcome To My Castle*, circa 1993. They are fronted by a local character who calls himself "Nardwaur The Human Serviette" — a "serviette" is French for "napkin."

Nardwuar promoted many fine shows in the late 1980s, compiled several garage LPs and generally promoted himself as some kind of local media figure. In person he just won't shut up, and that is my enduring — not endearing — impression of him.

## THE EVENT
*(San Diego, CA USA)*

*This Is...* 10 song LP, 1989
  Voxx Records, USA

**The Event** opened for one of this author's bands in 1988, displaying some wild teen energy, sloppiness and a generally excitable nature. They leaned more towards an English mod-pop sound than American rough garage, but the spirit was there, somewhere, ready to come forth.

Within a year of my exposure their debut LP was hurled upon the world, again showing a debt to **The Who** and **Creation**-styled pop, but with a much tighter, focused band delivering the goods.

The lead track, "Pop Think In" is a truly memorable tune, though I swear the melody comes directly from another song, the title of which escapes me. Nonetheless, these teens did crank out the energy, even if they hadn't figured it all out yet. That's what teen garage rock is all about, anyway — the confusion, excitement and wonder of growing up.

**this IS the EVENT** — VOXX — mono

FINALLY, THESE FOUR LADS BRING YOU THIS VINYL SPECTACLE OF SOUND, WROUGHT WITH THE RAW ENERGY OF SONGS LIKE: BETTER RUN, POP — THINK — IN, THE GAME, AND TOM THE IMAGEMAKER!

They played many shows since their 1986 inception, including several appearances on the *It's Happening* cable-TV show.

At least one member went on to join **The Loved Ones**.

## THE EYE CREATURES
*(Melbourne, Australia)*

A garage combo made up of many staples of the Melbourne garage scene. They began in the late '80s.

## THE EYES OF MIND
*(Los Angeles, CA USA)*

*Tales Of The Turquoise Umbrella* 6 song 12" EP, 1984
  Voxx Records, USA

**The Eyes Of Mind** are most often compared with early **Three O'Clock**, and while I understand the comparison, it doesn't do the band much justice. Drummer Troy Howell was also in the pre-**Three O'Clock** group **Salvation Army**, so I suppose this helped fuel such comparisons.

The two bands do share a light sense of melody and some clean studio production, but **The Eyes Of Mind** managed to do what **The Three O'Clock** couldn't — they produced an almost perfect record, their sole 12" titled *Tales Of The Turquoise Umbrella*.

Like the best rock records, this disc is able to bring back vivid memories; for me it is a soundtrack for a summer visit I took to Los Angeles in the mid 1980s, reflecting the mood and timbre of

74

the times perfectly.

Though only six tracks make up this EP, each is a perfect piece in the band's sound-puzzle, adding up to a magnificently achieved whole. It was also released in Europe with an extra track, I believe.

Weaving, rolling keyboard work is ever-present, as well as a larger-than-life drum sound and Jamie Phelan's angelic vocals. The topper is the song "Alice," with its lilting melody, introspective instrumentation, and beautiful arrangement.

The lion's share of credit should go to producer Marc Wirtz, who was a staff engineer at Abbey Road when *Sgt. Pepper's* and *Piper At The Gates Of Dawn* were recorded. He also produced pop psych acts like **Tomorrow** and **Keith West**. His experience is obvious and wondrously deposited throughout the proceedings.

In better times this record would have been a major radio hit, but in the real world of the 1980s it sank without a trace. I once asked Greg Shaw of Voxx whatever happened to **The Eyes Of Mind**, and he replied with a shrug, *"They just vanished…"*

## THE FABULON TRIPOMETER
*(Milwaukee, WI USA)*

*Padded Lounge* 9 song LP & CD, 1992
    Midnight Records, USA

The *Stellaristations* LP/CD and *Padded Bra* 12"/CD releases are reportedly forthcoming.

The distinctive voice of Glenn Rehse — the cornerstone of psychedelic kingpins **Plasticland** — is instantly identifiable in this trio's very noisy stew. The **Plasticland** comparison is appropriate for much of this CD, because many of the same elements that made that band so spectacular are present here.

The heavily echoed vocals, twisting fuzz guitar and angular, trippy arrangements of **Plasticland**'s best work are all in evidence throughout *Padded Lounge* to good effect. If anything, this is a more out of control, noise oriented, completely bonkers version of **Plasticland** — perhaps it's like **Plasticland** on a *double* dose of acid.

The lysergic qualities aside, it's Rehse's vocal and lyrical presence that is the most commanding. It's been said before that he's one of those performers that leaves no middle ground — the listener either hates him or loves him. **Plasticland** fans will eat this up, while the uninitiated will need a few passes to get in sync with Rehse's own brand of reality.

Don't let the amateurish cover art be a detraction — the sounds inside are worth the leap of faith.

## THE FALLING SPIKES
*(Eugene, OR USA)*

*My Head Explodes* 4 song 7" EP, 1986
"Big Blue Wave" b/w "Clam Dippin'" 45, 1990
    Moxie Records, USA
"The Twitch" b/w "Don't Crowd Me" 45, 1990
    Chaos Records, USA
*Teen Trash Volume 10* 13 song LP & CD, 1994
    Music Maniac Records, Germany

In concert **The Falling Spikes** deliver a pulsating aural swirl, twisting such classics like "Baby Please Don't Go" into their own volcanic image. Frontman John Barley looks a bit like **Van Morrison** and sounds a bit like **Captain Beefheart**, and even this description doesn't capture his unique presence. (Barley once served a stint with the eternal nut-bar **Screamin' Jay Hawkins**, and apparently some of the dementia rubbed off).

**The Falling Spikes** also have a secret weapon in the form of vocalist Molly B., whose soaring moans remind one of **Grace Slick** at her early best. This said, it's easy to realize that their early crude vinyl offerings don't fully capture the band in full color.

Their debut EP features two covers and two originals, including the finely titled "My Baby Hurt My Head." **The Spikes** also tackle other classics like "7&7 Is" and "You're Gonna Miss Me" with energy and style — but these songs have simply been heard too many times before to have much impact.

It was almost a full four years (and some lineup changes) before their "Big Blue Wave" 45 appeared, also on Moxie. This time out the band displays its love of surf instrumentals, with Molly B. offering only a few lines here and there.

Their next release was also the finest of their early output. "The Twitch" is an original in the tradition of the best R&B punkers, and the flip is even better — "Don't Crowd Me" is full of snot and warbled organ, cranked up to an incredible pressure that's ready to blow.

In 1994 their debut long-player finally materialized. It contains most of their early tracks, plus previously unreleased studio material. "Lost World" is especially mesmerizing, while the slow grinding version of **The Seeds'** "Pushin' Too Hard" is one of the most interesting interpretations I've heard. (It certainly beats the reggae version I was once subjected to in Texas!) The surf-ish instrumental "Glass In The Sand" originally appeared on the Moxie *Try One Of These* compilation EP, compiled by this author.

I was also lucky to play a few shows with **The Falling Spikes** in their native Oregon. Their recorded output doesn't fully reproduce their fire and spit, nor John Barley's unpredictable personality.

My experience with him was not done, however — Barley served as guitarist for **The Overcoat** on one extended European tour. While in France, I was summoned from the relaxation of the bathroom by my anxious bandmates. *"He's dead!,"* blurted our bassist. I walked into the room to see Barley laid out flat on his back, unconscious. The rest of the band, and some Frenchmen as well, watched for a sign of life.

I reached down to touch his clammy skin. He didn't look like he was breathing. *"Yeah, he's dead,"* I muttered without surprise. Just then, as if on cue, Barley popped up like a marionette, coughing and gasping for air.

That isn't my enduring memory of this character, however. One night in Italy, after apparently drinking massive quantities, Barley was passed out in an alley. No one else would help him get up — so unknown to him — this author carried him several floors of stairs up to a bed. The next morning he awoke complaining, as usual, to everyone about everything — especially me.

That's how I'll always remember John Barley.

## THE FALL-OUTS
*(Seattle, Washington)*

A garage\mod\'6os punk band from Seattle that's reportedly very melodic and musically adept. They performed at the 1992 "Garageshock" mini-festival in Bellingham, Washington, and have the song "Greed" on a 1990 Regal Select Records 7" compilation.

## FASTEN BELT
*(Rome, Italy)*

A reportedly punk & acid group with several releases: the "No Dice" b/w "On The One Hand" 7" on Lilly Records, 1987; the "Your Tears (I'll Kiss Away)" b/w "Without Dreams" 7" on High Rise Records, 1989; the *No Escape From Acid Hysteria* LP on High Rise Records, 1989; and the *My Blood My Sin My Madness* LP on High Rise Records, 1990.

## FERRYBOAT BILL
*(Germany)?*

I've only heard one song from this mystery group — "Upstairs Party" is an upbeat moody pop tune in a mid-period **Kinks** and **Who** fashion. It's not spectacular, but of some interest.

## THE FIENDS
*(Vancouver, Canada)*

Untitled 3 song 7" EP, 1993
    Primitive Records, Canada
*Teen Trash #12* 13 song LP & CD, 1994
    Music Maniac Records, Germany

also a 1995 45 on the Green Label, Greece; and a second LP due late in 1995.

Frontman Greg Johnson of the wonderfully warped **Worst** uses **The Fiends** as his depository for ideas that are even too strange or whacky for his regular band. Tracks like "Zombies Have Feelings Too" and "My Ghoul Friend" grace **The Fiends'** *Teen Trash* outing.

The sound really isn't far at all from **The Worst's** formula of fuzz 'n Farfisa, topped off by Johnson's screeching, blurted vocals. That means that this is top-notch garage stuff, full of graveyard mood and black turtleneck style. And finally a garage band has done a rightfully fuzzy version of the Beat classic "Come See Me," without even a hint of its R&B roots.

The Primitive EP is just that, much more crudely recorded, but with a faithful rendition of **The Electric Prunes'** "Ain't It Hard" as a highlight. The original "Zombie A-Go-Go" hits the creepy spot as well.

By 1995 **The Fiends** had become Johnson's full-time band, carrying on in **The Worst's** tradition.

With **Fiends** like this, who needs enemies?

## THE FINKS
*(Los Angeles, CA USA)*

*Fill 'Er Up And Go!* 14 song LP / 18 song CD, 1994
*Dirty Rotten Finks* 7" EP, 1995
   Dionysus Records, USA

The side-genre of "surf & drag" wasn't explored much by revival groups in the 1980s. It found more popularity by the mid 1990s, however, as '60s aficionados searched for new sounds outside the usual vocal-garage mayhem.

**The Finks** are veterans of other previous garage combos, and together they make some of the best SoCal surf & drag music of any era. Their lone LP was recorded — in authentic manner — live to mono, with plenty of warbly spring reverb and twangy guitar, plus some cool organ.

Tracks like their "Haunted Fink" theme, "12 Miles To Oblivion" and "The Eliminator" take the simple sunny fun of surf music and combine the grit and grease of the drag-car mentality. The results are reverent, but not tame, revved up, but not overly trashy.

As their own liner notes say, *"The sound of waves crashing. The sight of cars smashing. The smell of sweat-drenched cardigans draped casually over the tops of superheated amplifiers...Girls, beer, mystery, and madness — all here in the high octane sound of* **The Finks.***"*

## FISH EYE LENS
*(Texas USA)*

I believe this interestingly named band had some vinyl on the Rockadelic collector's label in the late 1980s. The only track I've heard, "Take Another Ride," was a slow, moody fuzz and echo trip-like excursion complete with reverbed fuzz solo — all the ingredients to make one search out for more of this first-class stuff.

## FIT AND LIMO
*(Germany)*

*Play Incredible String Band* 4 song 7" EP, 1993
   Lollipop Shop Records, Germany
*Folly Is An Endless Maze* 2 CD set, 1995
   Strange Ways Records, Germany

"Limo" is the **Shiny Gnomes'** singer and guitarist Stefan Lienemann, and his wife is "Fit." They've made at least three LPs described to me by a fan as "soft and mellow psychedelia." The first LP, *Retrospective 1983-1988*, is predictably a compilation of early tracks. They also released the seven song *Revisited* LP in 1988 on Bouncing Head Records. Their third release was the 1991 *That Totally Tore My Head Off* LP on Hurdy Gurdy Records.

There is also the *Angel Gopher* LP on Kickside Records, which was re-issued in 1995 with the 7" listed above, along with the *Autre Monde* LP as the second disc of the set. This mammoth collection is impressive in its scope of acoustic folk-psych, with equally mesmerizing instrumental and vocal offerings.

Autoharp, mandolin, sitar, dulcimer, clarinet, tabla drums, violin, kettle drums, glockenspiel and kazoo(!) are just some of the varied instrumentation used by **Fit & Limo**. The result is a gentle trance-like fairy tale ambiance. I recommend their output highly to anyone who wishes to relax and slow themselves into an almost meditative state.

I've also heard the tracks "Everybody Is" and "Tripping Mind." These two exhibit heavy reverb, a dreamy atmosphere, and an aggressive ambiance that perhaps only the Germans can achieve.

## FIVE FOR GARAGE
*(Cagliari, Italy)*

A fuzz punk band with the *Garage One* private cassette, 1987.

## 5,6,7,8's
*(Japan)*

The first single of this all-female outfit was reportedly recorded in the mid-'80s, and just after this they appeared on national Japanese T.V. where they rode in on a motorcycle singing "Fruit Bubble Love." They now have various singles and CDs to their credit, and sing in both English and Japanese.

## THE FIXED UP
*(France)*

All I have by this trio of cats is a shared-Live EP with **The Nomads**. They sound pretty charged-up there, and they have several other discs out in a more '77 styled buzz-punk-pop mode.

## LES FLAMINGOS
(France)

Nothing known.

## THE FLAMIN' GROOVIES
(San Francisco, CA USA)

"You Tore Me Down" b/w "Him Or Me" 45, 1974
   Bomp! Records, USA
*Shake Some Action* 14 song LP, 1976
*Don't Lie To Me* 3 song 7" EP, 1976
"Shake Some Action" b/w "Teenage Confidential" 45, 1976
"I Can't Hide" b/w "Teenage Confidential" 45, 1976
*Now* 14 song LP, 1978
"Paint It Black" b/w "When I Heard Your Name" 45, 1978
*Jumpin' In The Night* 13 song LP, 1979
*Absolutely Sweet Marie* 3 song 7" EP, 1979
   Sire Records, USA
"Let The Boy Rock 'N Roll" b/w "Yes It's True" 45, 1976
"Shake Some Action" b/w "I Can't Hide" 45, 1976
   Phillips Records, France/Holland
"I Can't Explain" b/w "Little Queenie" 45, 1977
*The Gold Star Tapes*, LP, 1983
   Skydog Records, France
*Live At The Whiskey A Go-Go 1979* LP, 1985
   Lolita Records, France

It is not an exaggeration to call **The Flamin' Groovies** one of the few bands that everyone talks about, that few ever really heard, yet one that has actually had a lasting influence over the last 20 years of pop music. They've nurtured their obscurity as an unintentional art form, with a half-dozen attempts at commercial success, only to fall back down between the cracks of consumer consciousness.

I won't go into great detail about their 30 year career — there are plenty of magazines and books that have detailed their checkered history. (The excellent magazine *Cream Puff War* is the best place to start.) I'll just focus on the three mid-1970s LPs that constituted the band's major label "comeback," and to this listener, their most fruitful period.

Their re-emergence actually began with Bomp! Records' first ever release — the magical "You Tore Me Down" 45. This track encapsulates **The Flamin' Groovies** at their best — an amalgamation of **Byrds** jangle, **Beatles** harmony and pure pop sensibility. That track also shines on their Sire debut, along with the sparkling classics "Shake Some Action," "Yes It's True" and "I Can't Hide."

I cannot over-emphasize how out of place **The Groovies** were in the void of the mid-1970s, stuck between the golden '60s era and the new punk movement. They covered songs that were top-40 material a full decade

**78**

earlier, dressed like the **Rolling Stones** circa 1965, and made pop music like the world still wanted to hear it.

The world, of course, had moved past Mersy pop into a haze of '70s lameness, so it should be no surprise that these LPs did not blaze up the charts. In (financial) retrospect it's actually quite amazing that the band was able to squeeze out three LPs on Sire.

The ironically titled follow-up *Now* was also solid, with "Take Me Back" and "When Blue Turns To Grey" rating with their best material. 1979's *Jumpin In The Night* finished the band's mini-Renaissance, with the title track and several fine **Byrds** covers as the centerpiece.

The band also spit out truck loads of aural curiosities from its ever-changing mouth over the years, captured on countless bootlegs. The most interesting are the five 1971 rehearsal-room demos that sparked the second-coming of the band — they're a balance between their initial '60s pop and later '70s rock/R&B formula. They also boast the best sound quality of the material usually offered on the boots; much of the unofficial product consists of raw audience concert recordings and European TV appearances, and only give a glimpse into the true quality of the performances.

A best-of CD also appeared in the early 1990s, so it's reassuring to see **The Flamin' Groovies** presented again for hopeful consumption. They have soldiered on in various lineups throughout the '80s and '90s, seemingly waiting for a public to finally give them a home.

Find some tattered old vinyl versions of their three best LPs and hear why they continue to be deservedly influential.

## THE FLASHBACK V

*(Barcelona, Spain)*

Untitled 4 song 7" EP, 1991
   Flash Records, Spain
*Ugly Thing* 3 song 7" EP, 1992
   Merry-Go-Round Records, U.K.
"Forever Young" b/w "I Have Seen A Woman" 45, 1995
   Mojave Records, Spain

The first two slabs of '66 garage listed above are beautifully constructed teen-a-rama lab experiments. Add five hipsters, some long hair, crude musicianship and a recording studio — and wham! — you get two EPs full of energy and fun. (I haven't seen the third release.)

The sleeve for the debut even states, "For best results play on cheap 'n' primitive equipment at full volume!" and "Surface noise is groovy!" The tunes are full of harmonica wailings, tambourine, cool organ, and a grooving party atmosphere. "Bad Love" is especially toe-tapping, while "Nothin' In The Shadow" is a perfect fuzz stomper.

The follow-up continues their beat-garage mission, with the title track a grooving rave-up. The flip features the organ dominated original "Trouble, Misery and Pain," and a cover of the beat-pop classic "From Above."

The sleeve again shows a sense of humor. Laszlo Loszla writes, *"They pretend to be hip and modern, mentioning old fashioned trends such as '60s punk,' 'R&B,' 'Garage' or 'Eurobeat' as their influences. But that's nothing but a curtain behind which they try to hide their scarce talent. In fact, if they play this kind of 'music' it's because they're fully unable to play their old instruments in any other way."*

**79**

The band actually does a fine job on both discs — and proves that fun and good music should never go out of style.

## THE FLESHTONES

*(New York, NY USA)*

"American Beat" 45, 1979
   Red Star Records, USA
*Up Front* 12" EP, 1980
*Roman Gods* 11 song LP, 1981
*Hexbreaker* 11 song LP, 1983
   IRS Records, USA
*Blast Off!* 13 song cassette-only LP, 1982
   ROIR Cassettes
*Speed Connection Live* 12" EP, 1985
   New Rose Records, France
*Fleshtones Vs. Reality* 11 song LP, 1987
   Emergo Records, USA
*Powerstance* LP, 1991
   Big Beat Records, U.K.
"Take A Walk With The Fleshtones" b/w "One Of Us" 45, 1994
*Beautiful Light* LP, 1994
   Naked Language Records, USA

An official LP of outtakes and in-between record contract tracks from the 1980s has also seen release, titled *Angry Years.*

It seems in hindsight that The Fleshtones should have been major commercial "stars." They were signed to the hottest "New Wave" label, IRS, appeared in the influential *Urgh!: A Music War* film and even showed up on Dick Clark's *American Bandstand* TV show.

They weaved a loose and soulful party ambiance with driving garage rock, and always had their tongues planted firmly in cheeks. This formula should have landed them in the top 40 along side **The Go Gos** and **The B-52s**, selling millions of records worldwide.

This was not the destiny for **The Fleshtones**, however, as they had only a brief moment in the sun before being passed by.

They have managed to leave some incredible rock records in their wake. Their first long-player, *Roman Gods*, is a garage freak's dream come true, with Farfisa and fuzz mixed into a danceable stew. Their follow up, *Hexbreaker*, strayed a bit into a kind of '60s "frat rock" with some saxophone ramblings, but kept their party image intact.

Reports of drug problems, erratic performances and the passage of time helped to scuttle the band's momentum, and their shot at the "big time" seemed spent. They returned with a new studio LP in 1987, however, showing off more of a soul and dance influence. The revved up "Too Late To Run" is one of their most accomplished tracks, with a driving beat and catchy progression. Like many of the band's best tracks, it too should have raced up the charts, but was left at the starting line.

This author saw the band in 1992, during their tour in support of the *Powerstance* LP. Despite years of road wear and a small audience, Peter Zaremba and company belted out a world-class performance of sweat drenched groove-action fun. They definitely still had the fire of rock in their bones, and new tracks like "House Of Rock" sounded as powerful and identifiable as any of their now classic '80s originals.

**The Fleshtones** are as much of an attitude as a musical group; an attitude of fun that should have had a greater impact. It is obvious from their years of relative obscurity that **The Fleshtones** never needed chart success to continue playing — all they've ever needed is a stage and a place to plug in.

## FLIES
*(Rome, Italy)*

*On The Other Side Of The Tracks* 7 song 12" EP, 1990
    High Rise Records, Italy

also "She's A Love" on a split *Lost Trails* 45 #10, 1989.

Their sound had been described to me as a European combination of **The Byrds, Love** and **The Long Ryders** — and upon finally hearing their 12" EP, that sounds like an almost perfect description to me. Excellent sound production and powerful playing by this 6 piece combo also highlight the EP, which has plentiful 12-string guitar and blasts of harmonica.

## THE FLIPS
*(Edinburgh, Scotland)*

Another '60s punk type group of unknown dimensions from the mid-'80s.

## FLOR DE MAL
*(Catania, Italy)*

A reportedly psych/pop band, releasing the "Cover Of The Mind/Sweet Tarantella/Speedy" 7", Cyclope Records, 198?; and a self-titled LP on Cyclope Records, 198?

## THEE FLYPPED WHIGS
*(Washington, D.C. USA)*

**Thee Flypped Whigs** are a proudly crude combo begun by garage radio host Richard Ward late in the '80s, determined to carry the torch of East Coast U.S. garagemania. They began like many of the original '60s combos — performing at parties — before landing some actual club dates by 1992. **The Whigs** then recorded several sets of demos in preparation for a planned 45, the A-side slated to be an ultra-trashy original titled "Caveteen."

*THEE FLYPPED WHIGS, 1993*

An advance slick seven page promotional bio featured psychedelic graphics and "whigged-out" descriptions of the foursome, who were also proud to bill themselves as "the last of the all-Vox combos!" I'm sure that they would wear Vox underwear, if it indeed existed.

This reporter flew to D.C. in the summer of 1993 to produce their first "real" recording sessions. The basement studio recordings were full of spunk, dribble, cheap beer and pizza, fuzz and Farfisa — and were remarkably powerful for a band's first venture into the realm of the recording process. The originals "Girl With The Mixed Up Mind," "Cheshire Girl," and "Man From W.H.I.G." stand with the grittiest, loopiest and most fun of the genre.

The half-dozen tunes were slated to pop up on compilations and as 45s in 1995 — just as this book was being finished. I recommend fully tracking down anything with the **Flypped Whig** name on it — come to think of it, even their socks were made by Vox!

## THE FLYTE REACTION
*(U.K.)*

An eight song LP entitled *Songs In A Circle* appeared in 1991 on Woronzow Records. It has been described by music fan Mick Crossley as soft psychedelia with some fine guitar work. They also have the 10 song *Strawberry Lip Salvation* LP on their own Splendid Label from 1992. It is reportedly excellent as well.

## FOLLI DI DIO
*(Alice Castello)*

A reportedly psychedelic band with two cassettes: self-titled, 1989; *Inediti & Live* 1990; and a self-titled CD on Mellow Records, 1993.

## FORBIDDEN DIMENSION
*(Calgary, AB Canada)*

Big Black Hearse" b/w "Shivs & Shrouds,"
   "Stairway To The Starz"
   Homo Habilis Records, USA

A wonderfully dark yet colorful picture sleeve of hearses and jet fighters is the real winner of this release. The sounds are a bit too "heavy" and lead-guitar oriented for my tastes. Noisy and bombastic, this disc would appeal more to those interested in hard rock tinged garage.

## LOS FOSSILS
*(Barcelona, Spain)*

This band reportedly began very crudely in the late '80s, and have since become an excellent original sounding garage band.

## FOUR BY ART
*(Milan, Italy)*

A '66-inspired garage punk band with several releases: the *My Mind Is Four Sights* 7" on Art Records, 1982; a self-titled LP on Electric Eye, 1985; and the *Everybody's An Artist With...* LP, Electric Eye, 1986.

## THEE FOURGIVEN
*(Los Angeles, CA USA)*

*It A'int Pretty Down Here* 12 song LP, 1985
*Testify* LP, 1987
*Salvation Guaranteed* 10 song LP
   Dionysus Records, USA
*Voila!* LP, 985
   Lolita Records, France
*Songs Of Ordinary Madness* LP, 1986
   LSD Records, Germany
"She Shines" b/w "Be My Lover" 45, 1987
   Mystery Scene Records, Germany

Video: "Anything" and "live" cuts on the *Obnoxious Rock & Roll Video Hour*, Dionysus Records, USA, 1987

Guitarist/vocalist Rich Coffee began his musical journey in the infamous 1970s Indiana punk band **The Gizmos**. ("Rich Coffee" is his real name, by the way. He once told me that if he had been named something different, he would have changed it to Rich Coffee anyway!)

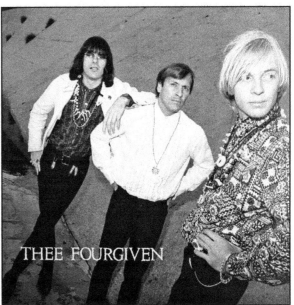

THEE FOURGIVEN

He served a stint with **The Unclaimed** in the early 1980s after moving to L.A., then took the rhythm section with him to form **Thee Fourgiven**. Their debut LP is an exploding collection of guitar-driven numbers. Coffee is a truly gifted guitarist, able to adapt to a song's changing needs, and his vocal delivery is identifiable and expressive.

With bone necklaces around his neck and wild specs in place, the diminutive Coffee projects a striking and energetic stage persona. This public view is tempered by his very friendly, quiet off-stage behavior. He'll gladly go on about his affection for 1950s teen trash movies, or guitars, or girls, or anything that's fun. He fueled these passions into his music.

**Thee Fourgiven** released several other LPs, both in the U.S. and Europe, but their best moments are on the first album. The track "Anything" especially holds up as a stunning moment of guitar-fueled madness. Like many of their peers, **Thee Fourgiven** quickly dismissed the label given to them of being a "revival" band, and their style purposely veered off into several directions. Upon seeing an end to the band's creative output, Coffee disbanded **Thee Fourgiven** in 1989 and formed **The Tommyknockers**, who are detailed elsewhere in this book.

Both of these bands have toured Europe successfully — but have failed to ignite the same loyalty at home.

Rich Coffee remains to be one of the most creative yet unappreciated rock madmen of the L.A. underground. His records exists, however, as proof of his passion, expertise, and love of everything that makes up rock music.

## THE 14th WRAY
(Kingston, ON Canada)

*Wig, Man! Wig!* 10 song cassette, 1991
  Totally Weird Productions, Canada

Alan Wright of the *What Now* magazine drummed for these garage-heads. They circulated a 10 song cassette of 1990 demos, all in the crudest of garage styles. These tracks were recorded in the fuzziest of conditions, and I did like the kazoo solo on their cover of "99th Floor." It would have been interesting to see what this band could have done in a "real" studio after a bit of rehearsal. They certainly had the correct wild attitudes and an atmosphere that reflected their cool band name.

They released the 1991 *Wig Man! Wig!* cassette, produced from more living room 4-track sessions. It is full of crazy fuzzed garage anthems like "Psycho Girl," "I Married A Witch" and the biting "Yuppie Deadhead Party."

I was so enthralled that I picked the swirling song "Your Face Is In My Mind" for the 1992 *Try One Of These* compilation EP (along side the vinyl debut of **The Worst**). It was their only waxing, and they now have one CD appearance as well, on the U.K. *Psychedelic Psauna* compilation.

The band dissolved in 1992, as Alan Wright moved west to continue his garage mission with the excellent *Cryptic Tymes Magazine*.

## FRANKENSTEIN V
(London, ON Canada)

Another fuzzed out garage outfit that stuck to the ('60s garage) classics, but never released anything. Members later went on to **The Evil Hoodoos**.

## JOHN FRANKOVIC
(Milwaukee, WI USA)

*Under The Water Lily* 7 song CD, 1993
  Midnight Records, USA

Many consider Milwaukee's **Plasticland** the 1980s most accomplished practitioners of pop-psych — John Frankovic was one of its creators and life forces. Here, on his debut solo LP, Frankovic mines some of the same rich netherworld veins for the magical tracks "Your Telling Me," "Here We Stand" and the hymn-like "Amen The End."

He also explores less structured and more improvisational moods on the 31-minute dreamy title track, which was "recorded in a pine forest in Northeast Wisconsin." Sitars, tabla, cello, bouzouki and trombone augment the usual rock instrumentation, including some fiery fuzztone guitar.

**Plasticland**'s memory might be melting, but the promise for Frankovic's continued development is blossoming.

## THE FRANTIC V
(Thessaloniki, Greece)

*These Are The Weird Sounds Of...* 12 song demo cassette, 1994
  private pressing

Full of spring reverb twanged guitars, warbly organ, snarled vocals and surf-garage inspiration, **The Frantic V** sound like they stepped out of a 1966 California time-warp.

Their "Haunted Melody" is especially evocative — I can see TV's Herman Munster grabbing the microphone away from the lead screamer and yelling "Oh yeah, baby, now let's hear some of that fuzz guitar!" These cats know how to swing, if you know what I mean, man.

## THE FROGGIES
*(France)*

From what other country could a band called **The Froggies** possibly emerge? I don't know if they managed to release anything — but the tape I heard showed a proficient combination of power pop, some surf melody, and **Ramones**-ish energy and buzz. "Lisa Child", "Love At First Sight" and "Bang Bang" were all credible pop-punk tunes with enough of a garage feel for inclusion here.

## FROSTED FLAYKES
*(New York, NY USA)*

"Waste Your Time" b/w "Rockin' Rhythm" 45, 1984
   Midnight Records, USA

I can't resist a drawing of the cereal-box cartoon Tony The Tiger with sunglasses and a guitar, saying "They're Grrrreat!" That's the cover of this one-off single, featuring two members of **The Outta Place**. The sound is a hybrid R&B, rockabilly, garage, trash stew, with plenty of fine harp blowing. The duo of short songs aren't really that exceptional, but they definitely will bring a smile.

I especially like the caption on the back of the sleeve: *"Okay, here's how it works - if it puts me to sleep, it's folk; if it's played by black guys, it's funk; and if I don't understand it, it's jazz."*

**Frosted Flaykes**, indeed.

## THE FUDDS
*(Victoria, Australia)*

*Meet The Fudds* 15 song CD, 1994
   Lavish Records, Australia

**The Fudds** are an uncannily authentic '60s R&B band especially inspired by **The Pretty Things**, early **Kinks** and **Easybeats**. They existed from 1992 to September '94. Their debut CD is a sweaty and gritty mono-recorded walk through the R&B songbook — while also depositing nine originals. Ex-**Masters Apprentice** Jim Keays also contributes vocals and harmonica to one track.

They recorded a second LP, but to date this has remained unreleased.

The band included artist Stewart MacFarlane on vocals & harmonica, Rob Lovett, Chris Dyson, drummer Peter Robertson, and rhythm guitarist Vic Mavridis. They must have been quite a blast in a pub after a few pints — the way a good beat band should always be heard.

I managed to spend some time with MacFarlane during his jaunt through the U.S. in 1995. He was a humorous, mischievous fellow — whose love of music was obvious and encompassing. He put up with all of my stereotypical Australian jokes, and even taught me a real South Australian accent. (Well, he tried anyway.)

As he would say, *"No worries, mate."*

## THE FUGITIVES
*(origin unknown)*

This entry isn't for the Erik Lindgren studio project that this author included on the 1985 *Beasts From The East* compilation — that much I know. Who these **Fugitives** were or where they came from is another matter. I was sent an eight song cassette of a "live" **Fugitives** show — but without any information other than the song titles.

I can tell from the tape that they were a very gritty garage combo, fitting in toe-tapping covers of "Dirty Old Man," "Be A Caveman" and "I Ain't No Miracle Worker" along side what I believe to be fine originals like "Wolfman" and "Spy Hunter."

It sounds like a party with **The Fugitives** would be a sweaty, beer drenched evening — if we knew where to find them.

## FUNHOUSE
*(Siena, Italy)*

Reportedly a hard punk & acid act with a couple releases: the "Your Rules" b/w "Screamin' Eyes" 7", 1988? and the *Way Things Will Be* LP, 1989, both on Electric Eye Records.

## FUNNY UNCLES
*(Floral Park, NY USA)*

This fivesome entered late in the latest garage explosion, with their first demo tape crossing my desk in mid 1991. They honor the three chord and noise garage structure and add some tongue-in-cheek vocals and a general sense of fun. Like **The Fugitives**, these cats would especially bring a smile after a few beers at a party, that's for sure.

85

## THE FUNSEEKERS
*(Minneapolis, MN USA)*

*We Is...* 4 song 7 EP, 1986
*The Special Sound Of...* 4 song 7" EP, 1987
*Frenzyfying* 14 song LP, 1989
"Psycho Daisies" 45, 1990
   Treehouse Records, USA

Video: 15 minute featurette, entitled *A Northwoods Holiday*.

    **The Funseekers** were perhaps the most artistically successful combo of the decade in merging various mod, beat and garage influences into their own vision. The look of these lads includes neatly trimmed and combed hair, along with suit jackets and turtlenecks in a thoroughly 1965-ish teen manner. They kinda remind me of a cross between **The Zombies** and (early) **Manfred Mann** in looks. The sounds follow accordingly with enough nervous energy to fuel any high school shindig.

    Their rare first EP is a hot little disc, and their other slabs 'o wax also display a group less concerned with the intellect than the movement of the lower parts of one's body.

    Following in the footsteps of **The Zombies'** version of a Gerswhin classic ("Summertime"), **The Funseekers** offer us their own particular cut at "It Ain't Necessarily So" on the appropriately entitled *Frenzifying* LP. It's a good example of how these lads treat their music — with little reverence and a whole lot of energetic fun.

    The band was gone by the early 1990s, with at least one member going on to **The Spectors**.

## THE FUZZTONES
*(New York, NY/Los Angeles, CA USA)*

"Bad News Travels Fast" b/w "Brand New Man" 45, 1984
*Leave Your Mind At Home* 7 song 12" EP, 1984
*Screamin' Jay Hawkins w/ The Fuzztones* 12" EP, 1985
   Midnight Records, USA
*Lysergic Emanations* 10 song LP, 1985
*She's Wicked* 3 song 12" EP, 1985
*Bad News Travels Fast* 4 song 12" EP, 1986
   ABC Records, U.K.
*Lysergic Emanations* 12 song LP, 1986
   Pink Dust Records, USA
*Live In Europe* 13 song LP, 1986
   (includes "Gloria" 7" flexi)
*Nine Months Later* 4 song 12" EP, 1988
*Creatures That Time Forgot* 13 song LP, 1989
*Braindrops* 12 song LP & CD, 1991
*Romilar-D* 4 song 12" EP, 1992
*Teen Trash Volume 4* 12 song LP & CD, 1993
*Lysergic Ejaculations — Live In Europe 1991* 22 song LP & CD, 1994
*Creatures That Time Forgot #2* 21 song LP, 20 song CD, 1995
   Music Maniac Records, Germany
*Hurt On Hold* 3 song 12" EP, 1989
*9 Months Later* 12" EP, 1989

*Action* 4 song 12" EP, 1990
   Situation Two Records, U.K.
*In Heat* 12 song LP, 1989
   Beggars Banquet, U.K.
*Monster A-Go-Go* 13 song LP/14 song CD, 1992
   Screamin' Skull Records, USA
*Lovely Sort Of Death* "live" LP, 1985
*Blues Themes* "live" LP, 1987
   Bootlegs

Video: "The Witch," 1982; "Ward 81," 1983, Live Fan Club Tape, @60 min. circa 1985; "Hurt On Hold," 1988; "9 Months Later," 1989; "Girl, You Captivate Me," 1989 on the *Slipping Through The Cracks* compilation, Skyclad Records.

    Perhaps no psychedelic-garage group from the 1980s is simultaneously loved and hated as much as **The Fuzztones**. Fronted by the irrepressible Rudi Protrudi, **The Fuzztones** helped to elevate the visibility of garage music throughout the western world, sometimes at the cost of support from the remainder of the "garage scene." In retrospect it appears that the 1980s was a war of **The Fuzztones** vs. The World, and the end result of that battle is some incredibly enjoyable music.

### THE FUZZTONES, 1984

    The band's roots were in an awkward Pennsylvanian "New Wave" band called **Tina Peel**, whose several 45s are an odd start indeed. Rudi Protrudi and Voxx keyboardist Deb O'Nair then migrated to NYC at the dawn of the '80s, and began the decade-long trek of **The Fuzztones**.

    The band was one of the first in New York to re-embrace the classic sounds and looks of the '60s garage-punk heydays, and they took it seriously. Protrudi and band adopted the **Music Machine** look: black turtlenecks, long dark hair, leather and a menacing stage persona. They combined their polished sense of style with excellent musicianship — a combination that would lift them far above most of their competitors.

    Protrudi has contended that the band never set out to be a period piece, but

**84**

instead was attempting to revitalize the sorry state of rock music in the early 1980s. I tend to agree. **The Fuzztones** were a breath of fresh energetic air in the midst of an electronic robotic music industry. Garage rock was simply the medium for defiant expression, not the message itself.

**The Fuzztones** were also among the first of these new garage-niks to release vinyl. Their debut 45, "Bad News Travels Fast," has established itself now as a classic in its own right, with a sound and execution sounding not unlike the best of early **Steppenwolf**. (Protrudi would increasingly look like **Steppenwolf** leader **John Kay** as well, with wrap-around Ray-Ban sunglasses and jet black hair.)

Overseas exposure followed, and a steady stream of vinyl began to pour out from 1984 onward. Their debut LP, *Lysergic Emanations*, is a landmark of the genre, again holding its own with the best work of original the 1960s punks.

*Trash Beat Magazine* described **The Fuzztones** in the mid-'80s, *"For those who've never had the experience, a* **Fuzztones** *show goes something like this: Incense is burned and bodies move like a heap of flesh. The music gets louder, it's always getting louder. Rudi protrudes his manhood into the audience; the girls egg him on, the guys egg him on, things get strange. Black leather is everywhere; it looks like some Sixties movie. The crowd is full of paisley and sunglasses, feedback rips through your spine, and are those really human bones around his neck? Things are getting strange!"*

Is it any wonder that original bassist Michael Jay's nickname was "Helmut Head, because of his mushroom-shaped nest of black growth?

**The Fuzztones** began a series of seemingly endless European tours which resulted in enthusiastic crowds and several "live" LPs (both official and bootleg), selling well over 20,000 copies. The relative success of the band soured many other bands back home — Rudi Protrudi was reportedly not the most humble of guys — and the resentment took its toll on the group as well, as dissension eventually worked its way inward.

By 1985 Protrudi had dissolved the original NYC lineup and moved west. It took over a year, but he eventually reconstructed a lineup which included members of **The Morlocks** and some newcomers. Surprisingly, the sound had not gone "metal" — as was the rumor — but instead kept course with the aggressive '60s punk/psych with which the band had been so closely identified. If anything, this new lineup was more professional and dynamic on-stage.

Even more surprisingly, the band landed a deal with mega-major Beggar's

**85**

Banquet/RCA (thanks to the help of the band **The Cult**), and recorded a new LP with famed producer **Shel Talmy** of **Kinks** and **Who** fame at the controls.

Once again the word was **The Fuzztones** had bowed to commercial concerns and had drifted into becoming a dreaded heavy metal act. Once again our fears were put to rest, as the *In Heat* LP blistered with more classic '66 psych-punk. The production hits bullseye, tightening the sound, yet allowing the raw energy and exuberance of Protrudi and Co. to shine through.

**THE FUZZTONES, 1989**

While most of the "garage scene" had written them off, **The Fuzztones** never sounded better. (Interestingly, Protrudi voiced his dissatisfaction with this LP's sound, and later released demo or re-recorded versions of many of the LP's songs in the form he preferred.)

When listening to this band, however, one can make a whole list of other bands' songs that were "borrowed" for **Fuzztones** originals — and in his defense, Protrudi never hid the fact that many of his best moments are derivatives of others'.

Another criticism of Protrudi was his reported tendency to live his on-stage macho personality off stage. He was quite personable to me when I talked to him during the shooting of the band's 1989 "Nine Months Later" video in Hollywood, but stories of his indiscretions are commonplace amongst his fans and detractors alike.

The Beggar's Banquet LP didn't hit paydirt — Protrudi continues to be less than enthralled by Beggar's Banquet royalty assessment — and after one more enjoyable 12" EP he was apparently ready to put **The Fuzztones** name to rest.

But not so fast. The 1991 *Braindrops* LP, back on Music Maniac, proved to be one of **The Fuzztones'** finest, with guest appearances by **Sean Bonniwell** (of the **Music Machine**) and **Arthur Lee** (of **Love**). Yet another European tour ensued, eventually documented in the wonderfully titled *Lysergic Ejaculations* double LP — which included nude photos of female fans on the inner sleeve!

This seems to bring a close to the **Fuzztones** name for now. Rudi Protrudi continues to release albums with the fuzz-instrumentally based **Jaymen**, and a "solo" LP appeared late in 1994.

His crossed-Vox guitar tattoos will obviously never fade, and neither will the legacy of a band called **The Fuzztones**.

I interviewed frontman Rudi Protrudi for *The Psychedelicatessen* in 1986:

TG: It seems that many American groups are getting more attention overseas than here in the U.S.

Rudi Protrudi: *That's pretty much the case with us too. I think the main reason is because American teenagers seem to be really jaded. We always go over well here in the U.S., but there's no comparison to Europe. Places like Germany, France and Italy are really repressed and when they get a chance to see a band that really rocks, the kids go crazy. In Italy we had people jumping up on stage and biting our legs...just really crazed things that would never happen here.*

TG: What do you see as the purpose of garage rock in the 1980s?

RP: *Rock 'n' Roll - the whole idea of it is to rebel - to have something to say as youth instead of having the world shove morals down your throat. The thing that I think is so sad now is that kids sit in front of the TV and watch all this (music) video that their parents can watch with them. There's no separation between the kids and adults. Here I am, older than kids now-a-days, and I'm saying, 'I don't know what's wrong with this generation. They're lame!'*

*(Note: **The Fuzztones** fan club "Cult Of Fuzz" is still active as of 1995, selling **Fuzztones**-related merchandise including live concert cassettes, and also follows all of Rudi Protrudi's other projects. Contact: La Donna at PO Box 381395, Duncanville, Texas, 75138-1395, USA.)*

## GAME FOR VULTURES
*(Bellingham, WA USA)*

Untitled 3 song 7" EP, 1990
  Estrus Records, USA

Here's another combo I was able to enjoy "live in concert" a few times while in the beautiful Northwest U.S. This odd trio sported a real big guitarist, a wildman drummer and female bassist, all spewing out really loud, sloppy '60s-tinged punk. I especially like their version of the **Kinks'** seminal "I Need You," complete with atonal back-up vocals and super-cheezy guitar glop. They were straight ahead, unpretentious and fun.

## THE GARBAGES
*(Rome, Italy)*

Another entry into the "Garage Band Name Hall Of Fame," this acid-punk combo released the *Where The Alien Is?* 12" EP on Arresto Cardiaco Records in 1988.

## THE GARDEN PATH
*(Adelaide, Australia)*

*5 Reasons* 8 song 12" EP, 1986
*Blue* 10 song LP, 1989
  Greasy Pop Records, Australia
*All The Things* 11 song LP, 1989
"Just Like You" b/w "Take It All Back" 45, 1989
  CC Music, Australia

**The Garden Path** evoke the mystery and epic grandeur that few bands can match. Light years away from the 1966 punk ethic that encompasses much of this book, they somehow still remain connected to the moodier side of psychedelia — while also mining their own quiet brand of muted pop.

The band formed in 1984, and have an unreleased four song EP, presumably of their earliest material. Their official debut, 1986's *5 Reasons*, is a stunning slice of a band hitting its musical stride. The fivesome sculpts careful, intricate almost delicate compositions — led by the wistful and plaintive Victor Conrad vocals. (He's the character who called himself "Travis Underdog" in his side-band, **The Dust Collection**. There was also a **Garden Path** offshoot called **The Acid Birds** that did nothing but **Robyn Hitchcock** covers.)

"This Place," "Into The Clouds" and "What Do You Want To Hear" stand along the most appealing and alluring of the 1980s Australian output — quite a feat for a band's debut.

### *THE GARDEN PATH, 1988*

It would be several years before their follow-up long-player. *Blue* showed a much more mature fivesome, with a darker brooding atmosphere tempering their quirky pop approach. The epic opening track "In The Dark" could be their signature tune — with a slowing building crescendo and an expertly sparse production. The remainder of the LP is consistently restrained and understated, demanding attention and involvement from the listener. The obvious comparison might be

to their countrymen **The Died Pretty,** but the similarities are superficial, and don't do justice to **The Garden Path**'s own ability.

Their final LP melds the pop sensibility of the debut and the emotional drama of *Blue*. Stripped down to a four-piece, sans the organ, the guitars shimmer and duel — the stirring opening track "Don't Stand By Me" remains a highlight. "Just Like You" was pegged as a single, and its slow jangle sits comfortably in contrast to Conrad's sinewy vocals. "The Madman" is also an upbeat *Revolver*-ish standout, and to these ears would have served the band much more effectively as a single.

Bands such as this one must fight doubly hard to find an audience. Their challenging, sometimes difficult music isn't easily digested by teens eager for mindless wanking. Regardless, the treasures waiting for the patient listener are bountiful and apparent throughout **The Garden Path**'s releases.

They broke up sometime late in 1991, and Conrad then formed an initially nameless band that is now tentatively called **The First Third**. Their 1995 demo displays the same excellent songwriting and pop sensibility that made **The Garden Path** one of the best bands from the 1980s. A debut release should appear by early 1996.

Vocalist Vic Conrad visited Arizona in the spring of 1995, and I was lucky enough to spend a few days talking with him about music. He said that **The Garden Path** was helped along by other friendly major Australian acts — they played occasionally on bills with **The Died Pretty,** as well as in front of 12,000 **INXS** fans in 1989 — but that the small Australian scene made it almost impossible for an independent band to gain a commercial foothold. He understands that artistic quality most often doesn't equal financial success — but also that he won't stop trying to create top-notch music.

Friendly, intelligent, humble and talented, Vic Conrad is the type of musician that keeps my faith in music alive.

### THE GARGOYLES
*(Richmond, VA USA)*

Another short-lived group which became **The Organ Grinders**; these **Gargoyles** are not related to the short-lived ex-**Plasticland** offshoot.

**87**

## THE GIRLS
*(Sweden)*

Several releases exist: the 1988 *So Be It* three song EP, the "I'll Be Gone" single, the *Don't Say No* three song EP, and the *It's Not For The...* LP/CD. All are from the late 1980s, I believe. They also appear on a Fab Records compilation LP with the Hamburg-tinged pop beat grinder "More Than Enough."

The *This Must Be Hell* demo I heard sounded strangely like (good) *White Album*-era **Beatles**, though some of their other material is reportedly reminiscent of early beat and mid-period pop **Beatles**. An unreleased demo I have has those tendencies, heavy on a power pop mentality and toe-tapping Mersey vocal melodies.

## GIRL TROUBLE
*(Tacoma, WA USA)*

"Riverbed" b/w "She No Rattle My Cage" 45, 1987
"Old Time Religion" b/w "Tarantula" 45, 1987
*Hit It Or Quit It* 12 song LP, 1988
   K/Sub Pop Records, USA
*When Opposites Attract* 3 song 7" EP, 1989
*Cleopatra And The Slaves* 3 song 7" EP, 1990
   Wig Out! Records, USA
"Batman" b/w "The Truth" 45, 1989
   K Records, USA
*Stomp And Shout And Work It On Out* 6 song 12" EP, 1990
   Dionysus Records, USA
*Thrillsphere* 12 song LP, 1990
   Popllama Records, USA

also *New American Shame* LP, circa 1992; a track on the Estrus *Lunch Bucket* box set, and a Regal Select Christmas 45, as well as a Sub Pop compilation LP, plus several other 45s.

The media made much of the exploding Northwest (grunge) rock scene in the late '80s. My band made several tours through the area during this commercial explosion, and **Girl Trouble** was one of the best bands we performed with.

They are perhaps the least pretentious rock musicians I've ever come across — this foursome are best buddies, kindred spirits and musical brothers in arms. If there's any music that is cool, funny, friendly, fierce or campy, they know about it, love it, and very often perform it. In short, this band made music for the pure joy of it, and they succeeded on all counts. They also take seriously the legacy of the Northwest 1960s scene, and so they are also highly identifiable with that regional sound. **The Sonics** and **Wailers** are the obvious comparisons — with a heavy dose of party atmosphere heaped on.

They came together in 1984, have toured endlessly, garnered only modest

**88**

attention, and look to be able to sustain themselves forever on inspiration alone.

I interviewed drummer Bon Von Wheelie for *The Psychedelicatessen* in 1990:

TG: How do you respond to people who attempt to put your music down by dating it in a specific period or style? (Example: "'60s garage" or "'50s instrumental")

Bon: *Once in a while someone will try to put us down with the 'stuck in the '60s' line. I vividly recall an incident on a tour where this little 19-year-old creep got a ride with us after a show. He told us what he thought of our band and called us "'60s throwbacks.' Kahuna, who was driving the van at the time, took him on the 'Girl Trouble Auto Thrill Ride.' It was scary for the rest of the band, so I'm sure this kid was petrified. You should never call us "'60s throwbacks' when Kahuna is driving!*

## THEE GLOOMIES
*(Rennes, France)*

*Don't Try To Resound...* 6 song 7" EP, 1993
   Guess Who Records, France

The insert says "100% back From The Gravin' Wild Garage Punk," and these frogs deliver in a big way. London's Toe Rag Studios is once again the scene of the crime, capturing **Thee Gloomies'** crude, over-amped blurting style.

"Hang Up" gets a thorough beating, while the misleadingly titled "Love Song," "No Reason To Complain" and the rest are sonically destroyed then put back together in glorious mono.

Writes Baine Watson in the liner notes, *"From the vast array of talent passing through Toe Rag, **Thee Gloomies** are unique in their decency to purchase enough whiskey to sufficiently fuel Toe Rag's artist manager Liam Watson to the highest level of recording debauchery and filth."*

The band also has a vicious sense of humor. Besides the half-naked insert band photo, they feature at the beginning of the EP about 30 seconds of the worst funk crap known titled "Disco Thrash."

I suggest that you hide when **Thee Gloomies** come to town. Their kind of fun could be dangerous, and that's why they're one of the best French garage combos.

## THE GLORIAS
*(Basel, Switzerland)*

Music collector Andreas Wunderlin calls them *"Switzerland's best and most authentic garage band."* They have three LPs on Sonic Service Records, and are reportedly influenced by **The Troggs, 13th Floor Elevators, Seeds** and **Chocolate Watchband.**

Their cover of "Don't Need Your Lovin'" certainly pays homage to **The Watchband,** and they do **The Elevators'** "You're Gonna Miss Me" as well. The best track I heard was the wonderfully titled original "Baby It's Time To Come" — full of fuzz and a thumping beat. Other fine songs included the buzzing "Get Blue" and "Baby, You're On My Mind."

Wunderlin also recalls, *"In April 1992 The Glorias played together with The Cynics for 30 people."* No one ever said that having good taste in music would make you popular.

## GOD
*(Australia)*

The only track I've heard is a fuzz-laden grinder called "Strutter." It was on a limited edition (of 500) *Going To Au-Go-Go* compilation EP, but I've no idea when in the '80s it appeared. **God** only knows.

## THE GODS
*(California USA)*

I know nothing of this little joke project except for one track, the goofy "I Like God." With the lyrics, "I like god/he's so mod/he's got a really cool haircut," how could it not become a cult classic?

## THE GOLDEN HORDE
*(Ireland)*

These Irish lads had at least two EPs and two LPs circa 1984. Their *Dig That Crazy Grave* EP liner notes explain, *"This is The Golden Horde...the sound of today, the most, most, exciting, psychedelic, rock n roll band ever!!! Five young people who are dedicated to blowing your mind."*

This sounds like a good time to me.

## THE GORE HOUNDS
*(MA USA)*

"Necrosis" b/w "Voodoo Priest" 45, 1986
*Halloween Everywhere* 14 song LP, 1987
    Alien Cactus Records, USA

I get an idea that the guys in the **Gore Hounds** like dead things.

They even wrote a song of that title on their *Halloween Everywhere* LP, whose title is a pun about **The 13th Floor Elevators'** LP *Easter Everywhere* — get it? This band shares many stylistic tendencies with **The Elevators,** right down to the use of an "electric jug."

Other slightly gloomy, doomy tracks (in a '60s garage/psych sense) include "Corpse Worm" and "Am I Dead Yet?," but perhaps I shouldn't over-emphasize this death fixation. Did I mention that their 45 included songs entitled "Necrosis" and "Voodoo Priest"?

Seriously, I get the idea that the band is having a good time with all of this, playing up the dark, moody psychedelic band image to the hilt. The music is creepily well done, with plentiful fuzz and well constructed moodiness. While many bands of the decade chose to pursue either strict garage or psych formats, **The Gore Hounds** were cool enough to try both and the merging is quite enjoyable.

Besides, a couple of the guys smile on the back cover of the LP, and there isn't a dead thing in sight.

## THE GORGONS
*(Paris, France)*

"I Still Love You" 45, 1991
    Smegma Records, France
*The Fab Four* EP, 1989
*Number One* 13 song CD, 1992
    Dig! Records, France
"I Want My Woman" b/w "No Good To Me" 45, 1995
    Weed Records, France

*"This strange quartet formed in 1989, and continue to surprise their audiences with raw, filthy, primitive rhythm and blues. These four kids love sixties garage punk — especially stuff comin' right from Back From The Grave — and they are also involved with modern music bands such as Thee Headcoats, Thee Mighty Caesars, Sting Rays,* and *The Cramps are among their favorites."*
— from the band's 1992 press kit

Those admitted influences are all evident on their debut CD, which is one of the most grittiest French releases of the early 1990s. "Carnou's

Creamed Cannelloni" is a twisted little moody instrumental, while they also deliver a solid version of "Cry, Cry, Cry." "Lovin' Man" is an interesting R&B slug-fest — made more interesting because it sounds like the lead guitar passage is in a different key than the rest of the song!

The sci-fi inner sleeve art, featuring the beautiful Zsa Zsa Gabor from *Queen Of Outer Space,* is a nice added trashy touch.

I believe another LP is now out, as well as an excellent 45 on Weed Records, which by the mid-1990s became one of the best new garage rock labels.

## THE GOTHICS
*(Milwaukee, WI USA)*

"Richie's Back In Town" b/w "Little Goldfish In A Bowl" 45, 1991
  Susstones Records, USA

John Frankovic and Victor Demichei, formerly of the inspirational **Plasticland,** head up this trio that described itself as "gothic metal." They also talked about using "medieval scales and chord progressions" in their music, but I must admit that I found neither metal nor medieval influences in their debut disc.

Instead we find two appealing psych pop-rock numbers somewhat in the **Plasticland** mold. The guitar in places is a bit "heavier" than **Plasticland**'s sound, but we need not worry of any heavy metal monstrosity here.

This trio initially called themselves **The Gargoyles** before adopting their other moniker in 1990.

## THE GRAVEDIGGER V
*(San Diego, CA USA)*

*All Black And Hairy* 13 song LP, 1984
*The Mirror Cracked* 15 song LP, 1987
  Voxx Records, USA

I just finished with a band called **The Gore Hounds,** who seem to dig dead things, so now we have **The Gravedigger V** to bury them under. To many enthusiasts, **The Gravedigger V** are the ultimate '80s Californian garage band — they were certainly one of the first of the West Coast's new breed. They also exemplified the nasty, snotty, sometimes inept but energetic attitude of the teen garage mentality.

Their first LP is a mortuary of punk madness, pumping life into obscure classics while unleashing some new sounds as well. The recording sounds loose and fun, with the band cracking jokes at each other's expense between tracks. **102**

*THE GRAVEDIGGER V, 1984*

They certainly had no illusions of rock stardom, as Ron Rimsite (of the *99th Floor Fanzine*) noted in the liner notes that *"The V actually slept inside their car in an alley and ate nothing but Tail o' The Pup chili-dogs during the three day (recording) session!"*

The band broke up soon after the release of *All Black And Hairy,* and as fate would have it, found more popularity after their demise than when they slaved away in small Southern California clubs. Voxx scraped together outtakes from the LP, some rehearsals and a live show, and released the posthumous *The Mirror Cracked* LP. The results are spotty to be sure, but the four studio outtakes reaffirm the band's status as supreme garage-niks.

Members from the **Gravedigger V** would stay active throughout the remainder of the decade, popping up in countless other bands like **The Morlocks** and **Manual Scan,** keeping that Californian spirit alive and well.

## THE GREENFISH
*(Breteil, France)*

*Hang On* 8 song cassette, 1992
*Grignou's Garage* 4 song CD, 1993
  self-released, France

Four songs from the cassette demo also show up on their CD, displaying a crunchy garage attack with plenty of swirling organ and gritty vocals — and as much '70s punk energy as '60s garage influences.

A live concert tape from 1992 also shows off the band's garage roots. Dutiful covers of "Action Woman", "Psychotic Action," and "You're Gonna Miss Me" sit well along side the upbeat punkish originals.

## GREEN HORNETS
(U.K.)

Untitled 3 song 7" EP, 1994
  Vendetta Records, U.K.

There is an earlier 1980s 7" EP titled *Come And Love Me* by what I believe to be another unrelated **Green Hornets**. Its origin is unknown.

A plethora of good mono vinyl seems to have poured out of Liam Watson's Toe Rag studios in the 1990s. The common elements of the recordings are a loud full raw sound — and **The Green Hornets** are no different.

A pounding rhythm backing and thick warbling organ highlight **The Hornets'** primitive attack. All three tracks from the EP pulse with a gritty atmosphere, aided by the live to mono recording process.

This fivesome kicks out the grizzled garage with the best of the U.K. outfits, which leads me to believe that more vinyl will have appeared by the time of this book's publication.

Let's hope so.

## GREEN ON RED
(Los Angeles, CA USA)

Untitled 5 song 12" EP, 1981
  Green On Red Records, USA
Self-titled 7 song 12" EP, 1982
  Down There Records, USA

**Green On Red** became popular long after they produced their best work, which consists of the two EPs listed above.

The story starts in Tucson, Arizona, where a band of teenagers formed the late '70s sloppy punk group **The Serfers**. This outfit was very crude, indeed, but brought a much needed energy to the sleepy desert college town. (**The Serfers'** only recordings can be found on a local radio station compilation LP, where they perform two songs in front of a studio audience. One of the songs is titled "Green On Red.")

The aspiring rockers then moved to L.A., changed their moniker, recorded some demos at the same studio that **Bobby Fuller** cut "I Fought The Law," and released them on their own label. Surprisingly we found the punk edge of **The Serfers** refined with a smoother guitar tone and **Doors**-ish keyboards.

Only 500 copies of this EP were ever pressed, and it received absolutely no attention. Still, it is arguably their finest hour, and commands big dollars on the collectors' market. (I suppose I shouldn't mention the copies I saw regularly for less than a dollar in Tucson record stores.)

Steve Wynn of **The Dream Syndicate** subsequently released **Green on Red**'s self-titled seven song 12" on his own Down There label, and this is when the public began to take notice. This EP is also a fine effort, with the creepy **Doors** influence and psychedelic flavor blossoming into full force.

The magical "Dark Night" became an underground L.A. radio darling of sorts, and soon after **Green On Red** would begin its journey from major label to label — releasing some of the absolutely most self-indulgent vinyl of the 1980s and '90s. The band conveniently dumped their "psychedelic" aspirations as the prospect for record company money came closer.

This author remembers a Tucson performance from 1982 where the band was apparently so intoxicated that they could barely stand on stage, then blundered through a twenty minute set before stumbling off to the hushed dismay of the audience. It was hardly a triumphant homecoming.

One engineer who recorded several of the later horrendous albums told me about how **G.O.R.** vocalist Dan Stuart would assemble a make-shift line-up, "jam" in the studio in an attempt to create songs on the spot, then throw darts at a map of the U.S. for song titles and lyrics. Now that's quality!

Band leader Stuart even commented to the *Arizona Daily Star* newspaper in 1993 that he was surprised at how long he had been able to survive by making music. As music fan Karl Taylor commented to me, *"**Green On Red** is a case of The Emperor's New Clothes for too long. And I thought I was the only one who could see through it."*

(A funny end note: both Stuart (using the name "Danny Ray-Ban") and guitarist Chuck Prophet called separately in 1993 seeking to audition for my band, **The Overcoat**. We declined the requests.)

## THE GREEN PAJAMAS
*(Seattle, WA USA)*

"Kim The Waitress" b/w "Jennifer" 45, 1986
*Book Of Hours* 12 song LP & Cassette, 1986
"Sister Anne" 45, 1988
    Green Monkey Records, USA
*Summer Of Lust* 12 song LP, 1989
    Ubik Records, U.K.
"Such A Lovely Daughter" flexi, 1990
    Unhinged Magazine, U.K.
*Ghosts Of Love* 10 song LP, 1990
    Bomp Records, USA
"Song For Christina" b/w "I Have Touched Madness" 45, 1993
    Endgame Records, USA

Band leader Jeff Kelly also has many cassette releases of "solo" material to his credit, including *Baroquen Hearts* (1985), *Coffee In Nepal* (1987 — finally released as an LP by DiDi Music in Greece, 1992); *Portugal* (1990); and *Private Electrical Storm* (1992).

This wonderfully **Beatle**sque outfit started in 1983 when Jeff Kelly and Joe Ross began 4-track

*THE GREEN PAJAMAS, 1988*

living room recordings. The results saw limited release on home made cassettes, and then finally as the *Summer Of Lust* LP in 1989. Its crude atmosphere doesn't mask the wealth of original songwriting, creative arrangements and memorable lyrics. It was recorded about as far away from Abbey Road Studios (distance and soundwise) as possible, but it might be the best **Beatle**sque pop record since *Rubber Soul* and *Revolver*.

I'm getting ahead of myself, however. Their debut 45, "Kim The Waitress" b/w "Jennifer" was released in March 1986, though their first vinyl appearance was actually the melodic "Peppermint Stick" on the Green Monkey Records 1985 sampler LP titled *Monkey Business*.

Their first "official" LP, *Book Of Hours*, contained 12 songs, although overseas versions have been bolstered by various combinations of extra tracks.

Despite the critical acclaim and obvious performance acumen of the band, **The Pajamas** never managed to gain a substantial following in the competitive scene of their native Seattle. Guitarist Steve Lawrence once told me, "The people here never understood what we were trying to do."

Their subsequent — and long delayed — *Ghosts Of Love* LP also failed to spark momentum for the group. The somber, slow and introspective album was again appreciated by critics, but wider recognition eluded Kelly and **The Green Pajamas**. "Walking In The Rain" is the obvious pop stand-out track — a magically wistful and hauntingly beautiful song in the best jangle tradition.

From the Bomp! Records' *Psycho Babble Newsletter #2*, fall, 1990, Kelly states, *"I've been doing this for a long time, and I do it because I have to write songs, I have no choice. It's an obsession and it's all I know how to do well. And the thing that makes you continue on, even after you haven't received any $23 royalty checks from BMI in half a year, is the letter from a guy in some town that I've never heard of in some country I've never been in. It's a very rewarding feeling — better than money really, and it makes me very happy."*

Kelly's royalty checks probably gained a few additional zeros in 1994 — both **Material Issue** and a band called **Sister Psychic** recorded and released major label versions of his composition "Kim The Waitress." **Material Issue**'s stab is a soaring, powerful interpretation, retaining Kelly's original awkwardness while injecting an upbeat punch. It reportedly reached #20 on *Billboard's* "Modern Rock Tracks" chart, and even popped up on MTV.

I'm sure it's gratifying for Kelly and the band to gain recognition through their songs — now it's time for audiences to hear them straight from **The Green Pajama**'s own mouths.

## THE GREEN TELESCOPE
*(Edinburgh, Scotland)*

*Two By Two* 4 song 7" EP, 1985
  Imaginary Records, U.K.
"Face In A Crowd" b/w "Thoughts Of A Madman" 45, 1986
  Wump Records, U.K.

I remember clearly the day in 1985 when the lilting tones of "Make Me Stay" drifted from my stereo. It was the first song I ever heard from **The Green Telescope**, and it was a beautiful moment indeed. The remainder of that initial *Two By Two* EP sealed my love of this band's sound, a combination of Euro-beat and pop with magical production and a sense of wonder.

Lenny Helsing is the man behind **The Green Telescope** (and several other noteworthy U.K. acts), and his vision of the music world melded the best possible '60s influences into a delightful package.

The follow-up 45 took a decidedly more U.S. '60s punk attack, but is no less successful. The fuzz guitar on "Thoughts Of A Madman," for instance, is perhaps the *most* fuzzed fuzz guitar I have ever heard. That's quite an accomplishment in the garage world!

They did a session for BBC Radio One's Andy Kershaw in January 1986, *"where we played covers of 'X+Y= 13' and 'Horror Asparagus Stories',"* Helsing told me, *"and a photo of us was duly printed in the Radio/TV Times national magazine."*

Helsing was afraid that the band's somewhat "psychedelic" moniker would confuse the public, so he changed it to the more beat-like **Thanes** and released a slew of fine records, as we'll discuss later.

I still have a special place in my heart for these two early releases, however. There's a certain human warmth and passion to them, and these are welcome emotions in any decade.

## THE GREEN TODAY
*(Orlando, FL USA)*

A very folk-rock oriented act, sounding very much in the **R.E.M.**-meets-**The Byrds** school. They had a melodic two song flexi in a 1986 edition of *Kaleidoscope Magazine*, and some members would later join forces with *Kaleidoscope's* Dennis Dalcin for the wonderfully **Byrdsy** band **The Lears**.

## THE GRETSCH
*(Hamburg, Germany)*

This was another Markus Steenbock led band, circa 1991. No known studio tracks exist, but a March 1991 concert has the excellent original garage ballad "Always On My Mind," among other R&B-tinged garage. The band is presumably named for the brand of guitar that was popular with garage bands throughout the 1960s.

## THE GRIP WEEDS
*(New Brunswick, NJ USA)*

*See You Through* 3 song 7" EP, 1992
  Ground-up Records, USA
"She Brings The Rain" b/w "Strange Bird" 45, 1993
*House Of Vibes* 12 song LP/CD, 1994
  Twang Records, Germany

Advancing their power pop chops since a 1987 inception and cool debut 45, the dozen home-recorded blasts of their LP explains all that is good and pure about an indy group before they get mucked up by marketing and money.

"Salad Days" and "Close Descending Love" take everything infectious about old **Badfinger**: **Beatle**sque melody with more guitar guts — and then leave us wanting more. Some of the lead guitar is a bit heavy-handed in spots, though, so it's a bit foggy which way this New Jersey combo

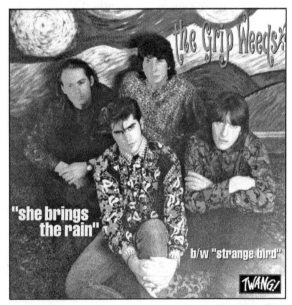

will go next — up to sweet harmony, or down to the depths of guitar wankdom.

Their "She Brings The Rain" 45 gives hope that the band won't lose its pop sensibilities. It's a shimmering slab of sunshine — showing that their best vibes are perhaps to come.

## THE GRIZZELDERS
*(U.K.)*

The mid-1980s *Making It Real Gear With...* cassette is the only release known to me, though I haven't heard it.

## GROOT VALOURS
*(Hamilton, ON Canada)*

Notes Glynnis Wilson, *"Using a German name for 'Good Boys,' the **Groot Valours** played in Hamilton for most of the mid-'80s. Their only recording was a great snot punk original 'Hysterical' for the London, Ontario What Wave fanzine tape compilation* What's All The Fuzz About. *Covers included stuff ranging from the **Velvet Underground** to the **Stooges** as well as '60s punk classics. They definitely took their cue from the **Miracle Workers**."*

## PAUL GROOVY
## AND HIS POP ART EXPERIENCE
*(U.K.)*

They did have an eight song cassette in 1984 titled *Crash The Blue Bus*, and I'll assume the excitable vocalist is Paul Groovy — he excels in belting out an echo-warbled style somewhat reminiscent of **The Cramps'** Lux Interior. The instrumental backing is the standard '80s guitar-bass-drums stuff, nothing remarkable to these ears. I have an idea that this was an act to catch on stage, where the wackiness could take full flower.

They also has a 1986 45, the A-side apparently titled "Andy Watch Out."

## THE GROUP IMAGE
*(Rochester, NY USA)*

"Sonic" Mike Pappart of the **Chesterfield Kings** & his brother recorded one 45 and released it themselves in an effort to reportedly attract members and complete a full line-up. The record, which was heavily British influenced, was a free give-away.

## THE GROVELLERS
*(Boston, MA USA)*

Another Stanton Park New England product; a 45 exists, featuring a two-sided tribute to the band **Love.**

## THE GRUESOMES
*(Montreal, Canada)*

*Jack The Ripper* 4 song 7" EP, 1986
*Unchained* 6 song 12" EP, 1987
   Primitive Records, Canada
*Tyrants Of Teen Trash* 13 song LP, 1986
*Gruesomania* 14 song LP, 1987
*Hey!* 14 song LP, 1988
   OG Records, Canada

Video: "Way Down Below," 1988; "Hey!," 1989, and many live tapes.

**The Gruesomes** were arguably Canada's most popular "underground" band of the 1980s. They built a college-aged audience from coast to coast, packing them in at every imaginable venue north of the border. They appeared on the Canadian version of MTV — Much Music — charted high on Canadian alternative playlists, and were generally accepted as that country's hottest rock group for the second half of the decade.

It comes as some surprise that a larger record label never signed the group, and that the band remained totally unknown in the U.S. **"Gruesomemania"** ended at the American border, and they would never make that all-important

***THE GRUESOMES, 1986***

breakthrough into the U.S. indy consciousness.

**The Gruesomes** did leave behind several of the most enjoyable discs of the decade, and should be considered in the higher echelon of the world garage movement. **The Gruesomes** expertly mixed the looks of the dressed-in-black **Music Machine** with that clean-cut British Invasion-suit style. Then they added pure '66 garage-R&B punk — and the result was four guys with bowl-haircuts, black suits, Vox equipment and a sense of humor.

Alan Wright of *Cryptic Tymes Magazine* notes, *"The Gruesomes had a limited edition demo out before their first LP called 'Garbage Pail Kids' with early versions of tunes that ended up on the LP. Later they also released the excellent 'Live In Hell' cassette — available at gigs and by mail-order. It has a few unreleased tunes that they only did live, and is real fun."*

Perhaps **The Gruesomes'** greatest asset (and liability) was their purposeful lack of seriousness. They were a fun band, designed to get sweaty drunken mobs to dance and laugh, and they never attempted to be anything different. No "heavy" or "psychedelic" influences ever crept into their sound, as they remained a cheerful **Monkees** (dressed in black) type of band from beginning to end. Their final music video for the song and LP entitled "Hey!" showed the band on a hilarious episode similar to the best *Hard Day's Night*/**Monkees** concepts. It's one of the best clips I've ever seen.

Still, that apparent lack of "seriousness" may have cost the band any real chance of gaining a wider non-Canadian audience. Remember, the music business is one big excuse for pretension — an attitude **The Gruesomes** certainly couldn't cultivate.

For teen-inspired garage punk trash, however, **The Gruesomes** are unparalleled. Each and every one of their discs burst with energy and fun. Already their live shows have gained legendary status in their native country, and the rest of the world continues to snap up their vinyl.

It is safe to say that **"Gruesomania"** will live on for many years to come.


## THE GRUFF MEN
(U.K.)

A Medway band from mid-'80s, presumably associated with the prevalent "trash" rockabilly/garage movement.


## GUNPOWDER
(France)

Nothing known.

## THE HALF BACK FLANKERS
(Australia)

This was an early 1990s band featuring a member or two from **The Dust Collection**, doing covers of **Masters Apprentices, Yardbirds, Pretty Things,** and **Remains.** They were reportedly a fine R&B/garage outfit which played about 20 gigs.


## 1\2 LINGS
(Colchester, England)

A '60s punk band from 1986 reportedly made up of teens aged 15. They played songs like "Strychnine" and "Wild Thing." Their first gig was in a monkey cage at the Colchester Zoo — a friend's dad worked there and arranged it! The lead singer reportedly played up the monkey bit to the hilt, scratching his arm pits and checking his bum for fleas, hanging from the bars etc. Brothers Martin and Richard went on to join **The Bugs.**


## THE HAIRS
(Australia)

The circa 1992 *Subcutaneous* 12" EP on Zero Hour is described by them as *"a slice of **The Smithereens**, a dash of **The Someloves**, and a piece of **The Stems**."* Now that sounds like some interesting power-pop to me — if I ever could get my hands on a copy of the EP!


## THE HALIBUTS
(USA)

A "traditional" surf band from California from the early 1980s. They released the *Halibut Beach* LP (with a 3-D cover), and the *Gnarly* LP — both reportedly feature some acceptable pop-surf tunes.

## HAMMERSMITH GORILLAS
*(U.K.)*

"You Really Got Me" b/w "Leavin' One" 45, 1974
 Raw Records, U.K.

Described to me by Darren Ross as *"Mental garage stuff from England, 1974 — but they looked like **Slade** or **T-Rex**!"* I hope that the sounds were indeed cool, because I don't like those visual comparisons!

## LOS HAMSTERS
*(Tucson, AZ USA)*

Only a few rough "live" cassettes remain of this pioneering trash/garage band, circa 1984-85, which featured a future **Marshmallow Overcoat** member.

## THE HANGMEN
*(Australia)*

Yet another mystery group.

## THE HANGMEN'S BEAUTIFUL DAUGHTERS
*(U.K.)*

Untitled 6 song 12" EP, 1987
 Constrictor Records, Germany
*Trash Mantra* 6 song EP, 1987
 Dreamworld Records, U.K.
*The Hangman's Beautiful Daughters* 11 song LP,
 Voxx Records, 1989

The self-titled LP collects tracks from the first two EPs listed above, displaying this British act's love for folk rock, '80s pop and some garage noise as well. The soaring mesmerizing "My Love Is Blue" is the obvious highlight, with its emotional vocals and throbbing delivery.

## HARLEY DAVIDSON PHILOSOPHISTS
*(Milan, Italy)*

A reportedly hard punk psych, with the strangely titled *Virgin Mary Speaks To America* LP on Tambourine Man Records, 198?

## BO HATZFELD AND THE HEADHUNTERS
*(Germany)*

I think there are a few discs out by this band, but the only one I came across was a four song 7" EP recorded in Chicago! The sound here is R&B and roots fun, especially the version of **The Standells'** "Dirty Water," where Bo substitutes *"Dusseldorf, you're my home!"* (instead of Boston).

## THE HAWAI CITY FIVE
*(Brussels, Belgium)*

Vocalist Ivan Andreini says, *"We started in 1989, and as you can tell by the name, it was a mix of surf and motor city influences. As you can see from our 45 ('Hey Baby' b/w 'Cruisin On The Boulevard,' 1990 on Surfin' St. Gilles Records) we're not a 100% garage band. Like **Date Bait**, for example, we do anything we like."*

## LES HAWAI MEN
*(France)*

self-titled 7 song cassette, 1990
 private pressing
Untitled 4 song 7" EP, 1991
 CineLux Records, France

This is really energetic stuff, and it again destroys the idea that the French don't know how to rock — these guys and gals certainly do. I especially like the live version of "Gloria" from their demo cassette where the vocalist screams, "I'm a Shadow Of Knight!" Four of the five members are related somehow, and three of them are women, which certainly makes their lineup different than most others.

I only know of one vinyl outing, a four song EP. The tracks are all upbeat fuzz-filled affairs, with an addled enthusiasm and some snotty soulful vocals and thick organ.

All of the songs have a movie or TV connection — "Beyond The Valley Of The Dolls," "U.N.C.L.E." and "Mrs. Peel" are band originals, with the fourth song being the much covered "Blues Theme."

Pretty cool stuff, and I hope to hear some more.

## THE HAWKS
*(Germany)*

Glynnis Wilson tells me, *"Even though their first release was a recent CD, **The Hawks** have been around for a very long time. I got a very good R&B demo in a '60s-mod vein in 1988. Now they are kind of rock & blues (yikes!)."*

An LP does exist, *Down On My Knees* on Twang! Records. The label describes it as a cross between **Deep Purple** and **The Doors**!?!

## HEAD AND THE HARES
*(Rome, Italy)*

Self Titled 12 song LP, 1992
"Two Tymes" b/w "Lost" 45, 1995
   Distortions/Moulty Records, USA

The excellent track "She Loved Me" is also on the Distortions *Tribute to The Rising Storm* double-45, 1994.

There was a U.S. garage band of this name in the 1960s, and that is where these Italians got their inspiration — and their own band name. Their wistful folk garage style sounds like a long-lost original 1966 session, not the warblings of a modern outfit — and that's perhaps their greatest strength.

*HEAD AND THE HARES, 1992*

The production of their only known LP is minimal but sufficient, the instrumental prowess effective but not overly impressive — but it all adds up to a mesmerizing, atmospheric, beautiful whole. "Try To Forget," "Tomorrow Never Ends" and "Love If You Can" are engagingly naive and hushed, with enough **Byrds/Nightcrawlers/Love** nods to raise goosebumps — while the remainder of the LP is a gem without exception.

Their follow-up 45 is equally essential, with "Two Tymes" a priceless folk rocker and "Lost" a more bombastic garage thumper. A second LP was also reportedly in the works in 1995 — no word on its possible release date.

Lord only knows how this Italian fivesome ended up on the small U.S. Distortions label. I'm just thankful that their sounds somehow found their way out into the world.

## THEE HEADCOATS *(see "Billy Childish")*

## THEE HEADCOATEES *(see "Billy Childish")*

## THE HEADHUNTERS
*(Eugene, OR USA)*

Untitled 3 song 7" EP, 1993
   Tombstone Records, USA

A crunchy distorted sound, not unlike the best of **Billy Childish**, graces this crude punk garage outing. Lots of "Ohhh-Ahhs" pop up in "Jungle Law," which also has a catchy chorus and a general sense of mayhem.

"Headhunter" features some good organ and guitar work alongside the shredded vocals, while "Still At Large" adds handclaps and lots of screaming to the distorted stew — reproduced in mono like all of Tombstone's product.

## THE HEADLESS HORSEMEN
*(New York, NY USA)*

*Can't Help But Shake* 12 song LP, 1987
"Hotel Cadillac" b/w "Tallahassee Lassie" promo 45, 1987
*Gotta Be Cool* 4 song 12" EP, 1988
   Resonance Records, Netherlands

Ex-members of **The Tryfles** and **Fuzztones** combined their mutual talents into this pure pop party band. **The Headless Horsemen** give their sonic treatment to just about every cool style of '60s rock, from ballads to fuzz punkers, to dance groovers to rave-ups.

The vocals and guitar work are superb, and at times the sheer exuberance of the band sends chills up one's back. "It's All Away" is one of those exquisite tracks from their debut LP — a certifiable classic that gains worth with each passing listen.

The title track acts as a roadmap for the remainder of the LP, with a bouncy rhythm and gutsy professional arrangement and performance. There's also a version of the song "Cellar Dwellar," later altered slightly by Rudi Protrudi for **The Fuzztones**.

The 12" EP is disappointing only in it's brevity. The listener is just getting warmed up after the four tracks. The title track "Gotta Be Cool" sums up the plight of **The Headless Horsemen** — they just can't help being one of the coolest acts of the decade, despite their limited output.

## THE HEADSTONES
*(Brisbane, Australia)*

James Peirce, bass player with **The Apaches** and editor of the *Era Of Sound Magazine*, says, *"The Headstones were a wild '60s R&B combo in the early to mid-1980s playing*

small clubs to big crowds — until they went to Sydney and got all fucked up on the heavy guitar thing. Their first 45, 'When You're Down' b/w 'All The Things You Do' is pretty good, but after that they went downhill."

I heard a later 45, and the "heavy guitar thing" had definitely buried any garage intentions. The lead singer later went onto the pop-hard rock band **The Dubrovniks** (along with **The Hoodoo Guru's** first drummer), I believe.

I played a couple shows with **The Dubrovniks** in Germany in 1992, but that's another funny story.


## THE HEADSTONES
*(Matera, Italy)*

*Stone Voices* 9 song Cassette, 1993
    Misty Lane Records, Italy

A garage punk outfit, with a private cassette of live performances, 1992, and also an EP with **The Others,** as described in the compilation chapter.


## HEARTBEATS
*(Germany)*

"Don't Tolerate" b/w "I'm Walkin'" 45, 1989
    Universe Records, Germany

Glynnis Wilson notes, *"The Heartbeats have been kind of left out of the international garage scene, even though they have a very good single out (and I think they have had more records since). They play kind of a sophisticated **Beatle**sque R&B style of '60s pop."*

"I'm Walkin'" is a fine upbeat pop song, with good vocals, jangley guitar and forceful playing. "Don't Tolerate" is less thrilling, sporting a fast shuffle and rushed feel, but with a nice guitar break.

And while their 45 is worth a listen, I also like the raw **Beatle**sque sound of their early demos and some live tracks, with "Don't Look Back," "All I Want" and "Be By My Side" showing that they were a swingin' live combo.


## THE HEARTLESS
*(Barcelona, Spain)*

Another '60s punk band from Spain, circa 198?

## THE HECKLERS
*(Tucson, AZ USA)*

13 song cassette, 1983
    self-released, USA

The multi-demented **Al Perry** headed up this trash band shortly before forming the much longer-lasting **Cattle**. The format here was a combination of thrash punk, '60s garage and some distorted R&B rave-up for good measure. They produced two demos of uniformly fine quality, mixing frantic originals with inspired covers.

They give the energetic **Heckler** treatment to "The Munsters' Theme" and "You're Gonna Miss Me," but their best interpretation has to be **The Beatles'** "I Am The Walrus." The entire song is sped up beyond comprehension, with vocalist Craig Schumacher spitting out the lyrics in gasps. A backward guitar completes the demolition, along with the buzz saw rhythm section (which included this author's brother, Scot Gassen, on drums).

Originals of note included the biting "TV Woman," "Boredom And Anxiety" and "Lobotomy." **The Dead Kennedys'** Jello Biafra even selected the **Hecklers'** demo as one of the best releases of 1983, though none of these tracks have ever seen the light of day on vinyl or CD.

That's a real shocker considering the incredible performances and material at hand; this is truly one of the great un-released efforts of the '80s garage decade.

I guess we'll have to wait for the compilation series *Pebbles* to get to #154 or so to finally document some of this classic stuff.

## THE HENTCHMEN
*(Detroit, MI USA)*

Untitled 3 song 7" EP, 1993
    Happy Hour Records, USA

Another entry into the 1990s American "trash-rock" movement, this poorly recorded trio delivers some predictably crude stabs at frat-rock garagedom. I don't find any of this terribly remarkable — or really terrible either. It just isn't that interesting.

They also have several other 45s and at least one LP, I believe.

## THE HERBS
*(Southampton, U.K.)*

*At Play* 10 song cassette, circa 1992
   Peeved Records, U.K.

   **The Herbs** grow bright, sprightly delivered Mersey pop with melody, teenage emotion and a twinge of naive charm. The lads don't take themselves too seriously either, as the tracks "Surfin' Druid" and "The Man Who Had His Hair Cut Short" attest.

   The gentle jangle of a tambourine and a bright shimmering guitar should never be underestimated — and should never go out of style. I don't think anything else appeared besides this cassette. That's a shame.


## THE HERMITS
*(Italy)*

*Teenage Trash* 4 song 7" EP, 1992
   Flintstone Records, Italy
*Supermegaengine* 11 song LP, 1994
   Destination X Records, Italy

   The term "fun" is most applicable to these six Italians. Their mono-recorded *Teenage Trash* EP bursts with teenage enthusiasm, whirling organ, frantic tambourine — and an overwhelming spirit of energy.

   "The Hermit's Song" is an unrelenting toe-tapping garage anthem, with requisite cheesy guitar leads and sneering vocals, delivered in their native Italian. The colorful picture sleeve is the finishing touch on this almost perfect '66 garage classic.

   Their follow-up LP carries on, although in a bit more crudely recorded fashion with less '66 reverence. Titles such as "I Was A Chicken Monster", "Scream, Mother Scream!" and "Skeleton From Egypt" should give an indication of the mayhem involved — pictured perfectly with the cartoon rear sleeve depicting race cars crashing!

   Their liner notes about the track "Antanauts Vs. Argonauts" reads, *"I was in my flyin' saucer in outer space, and I heard an alien living mushroom sing this tune: the sad epic history of the extermination of the proud people of the Antanauts. I still cry everytime I hear it."*

   It is reassuring that there are people left somewhere in this universe who know how to have a good time.

## HIDDEN PEACE
*(Los Angeles, CA USA)*

*We All Have...Hidden Peace* 12 song LP, 1986
   Hitch Hyke Records, Greece

   Originally from Sacramento, California, **Hidden Peace** journeyed to the "happening" Hollywood scene in 1985. They then landed a spot on the third *Battle Of The Bands* LP with their anthemic "Summer Of Love," which also kicks off their Greek-only LP.

   **Hidden Peace** exhibited a more intricate sensibility than many of their peers, able to transform themselves from two-chord **Seeds** clones to more sophisticated folk-pop along the lines of **Love**.

   Guitarist and vocalist Paul Halbe was the driving force behind the band, writing the original material, with unabashedly colorful titles like "Peacemaker," "Acid Rain" and "I Still Send Her Flowers." Sometimes the guitar interplay is lysergic, sometimes quiet and intricate, but always of interest.

   It's a shame that nothing else came forth from **Hidden Peace**; they brought a welcome difference to the Californian garage family.

   Their very rare lone LP still stands as one of the finest of the decade. It's so rare that I had to travel to Greece to find it — my sincere thanks again to Hitch Hyke for finding one last copy for my collection!


## HIGH JINKS
*(Germany)*

   A Berlin group, with the 1989 ten song *Talk Dirty* LP and the "1000 Times" b/w "When The Rain Just Falls" 45 on the Twang! label. The "A" side is from the LP, and is an upbeat dramatic pop song with female vocals. Their sound has been described as comparable to the **Black Carnations**, and I can fathom that assessment.


## THE HIGHSPEED V
*(Sweden)*

"Baby" b/w "Sally" 45, 1986
   Super Stuff Records, Sweden
*Get High With...* 4 song 7" EP, 1987
   Mystery Scene Records, Germany
"Bye Bye Baby" b/w "I Don't Mind" 45, 1990
   Rave On Records, Germany

   "Teenagers" is the operative term for this quintet of lads ("from Swingin' Sweden," as it says on one of their records). They were young, indeed, even listing their ages on the back of the debut 45 — the elder statesmen in the group was 19. The boys are decked out in fine mid-'60s Euro-beat fashions, sport vintage hollow-body guitars, and have that "rave-up" look in their eyes. That's right, they're a revved-up R&B beat band, with two-minute ravers their specialty.

They must have taken flak for printing their ages on the first 45, because on their follow-up they attempt to deceive us slightly, listing the same line-up's ages as being years ahead and behind the original stats. (One poor guy ages a whole extra 24 years since their first 45!)

They're having a fun time, and so am I. There are great picture sleeves on the first and third 45s, by the way.

## HIJACKERS
(Sweden)

Nothing known.

## HIPPY WOLFBONES
(Pordenone, Italy)

Reportedly a hard garage act , with the "Take Me To The Mountain" 7" on Electric Eye, 198? Do they know how funny — I mean cool — their band name is?

## THE HIPSTERS
(Germany)

Untitled 3 song 7" EP, 1986
    Glitterhouse Records, Germany
*The First 20 Years* 6 song 12" EP, 198?
    Roof Records, Germany

Here's some very danceable R&B-tinged mod-pop, with tasty harmonica and those attractive German accents. "Sound Of The Young Soul" is a nice teen anthem, moving along at a steady pace and inviting universal foot-tapping.

I have an idea that there were probably a dozen or so other bands called **"The Hipsters"** in the 1980s, but at least these cats spelled the name correctly.

## HOLLOWMEN
(Iowa, USA)

The *Sinister Flower Gift* LP is on Chicago's Pravda Records; several other guitar dominated pop discs also exist. I believe there is a European band with the same name.

## HONEYMOON FLOWERS
(Cagliari, Italy)

A psych band with a self-titled private cassette from 1987.

## HONEY SMUGGLERS
(U.K.)

Nothing known.

## THE HOODS
(San Diego, CA USA)

"You Won't Take Her" b/w "Mystery Train" 45, 1991
    Dionysus Records, USA
*Gangsters & Morticians* 16 song LP, 1992
    Midnight Records, USA
"We Are Your Fear" b/w "Never Got Thru" 45, 1992
    Screaming Apple Records, Germany
*4 Songs To Kill For* 4 song 12" EP, 1992
    Satyr Records, Greece
"Empty Head" b/w "One Difference" 45, 1993
    Get Hip Records, USA

After the supposedly last gasp efforts of the **Tell Tale Hearts** somewhere around '90, Mike Stax joined members of **The Trebels** to form **The Hoods**. A 1991 14 track demo, recorded "live" to two track, displayed a strong, simple, R&B based outfit in the **Crawdaddys** mode. Eleven of the tunes were originals, making this an even more impressive beginning.

Many of these demos would be re-recorded for their 1992 LP, but six of them were apparently never released in any form, so these early nuggets may pop up in the future.

All of **The Hoods'** output is worth a listen, especially the LP and Greek 12", but none really capture the fire and grit of their San Diego predecessors — **The Crawdaddys** or **Tell Tale Hearts**.

Stax was asked in a 1992 Cryptic Tymes interview the difference between **The Hoods** and his past bands. His response, "More energy, more humor, more beer."

The band broke up circa 1994, and Stax would go on to re-form **The Tell Tale Hearts**.

## THE HOOLEY DOOLEYS
*(Perth, Australia)*

A group made up just for fun out of members of the **Stems, Neptunes** and **Bamboos**. They shared a lead singer with the **Breadmakers** and **Cracked Jaffers**. Sounds like they're making fun of **The Hoodoo Gurus'** band name, doesn't it?

## HOPELESSLY OBSCURE
*(Boston, MA USA)*

self-titled 5 song 12" EP, 1984
    Majestic Records, USA

Other records do exist, but I'm unsure exactly how many have seen release. There is at least one 7" EP called *Shoot That Girl,* and I believe another 12".

The very moody 1985 EP features the psych-tinged "Twin Cities Of Your Mind," the tremolo-driven instrumental "Any Kind Of Fish You Like," and the cheerfully titled "Rain Of Death."

Richard Julio released this EP, and then went on to help **The Brood** for their entire career. He notes, *"The Hopelessly Obscure were formed by Kenne Highland and Ken Kaiser. Drummer Bob MacKenzie was recruited from the **Lyres** and Miguel d'Amore was with **The Cryptic Edge** out of Rhode Island.*

*"Kenne Highland had left **The Gizmos** in the midwest when Rich Coffee split for the West Coast. Producer Ken Kaiser later went on to **The Beachmasters** with Bob MacKenzie. Kenne Highland continued using the*

**IPI**

*Hopelessly Obscure name for a while with different groups he'd put together. A 7" later appeared on Stanton Park Records bearing a more '70s **Gizmo** sound."*

## THE HORSELESS HEADMEN
*(San Francisco, CA USA)*

Not to be confused with New York's **Headless Horsemen,** this early '90s band featured Russel Quan (of **The Mummies**) and a young Bart Davenport (later of the **Loved Ones**).

## THE HOWLING MEN
*(San Diego, CA USA)*

This short-lived early 1980s group featured some ex-**Crawdaddys,** and later evolved into the **Tell Tale Hearts.**

## THE HYRDOGEN CANDYMEN
*(Basel, Switzerland)*

One reportedly rare 45 exists on Asshole Records (!), plus three songs on a demo cassette. "Within A Dream" is a moody fuzz and reverb track, with some backwards noise at the climax.

## THE HYPSTRZ
*(Minneapolis, MN USA)*

*Hypstrization!* 15 song LP, 1980
    Voxx Records, USA

A 1981 issue of *Sweet Potato Magazine* says, *"Brash and tough,* Hypsterization *immediately turns into a cretin dance record, the sort of beer-soaked garage rock-off disc where you dance to the death and then dance some more. Even **The Hypstrz'** own 'I Don't' sounds like a re-fried and hyper-ventilated smash from the past."*

This LP was one of the earliest Voxx releases, and it helps to demonstrate the evolution of interest in '60s punk garage. Thirteen of the 15 songs here are cover versions, almost creating a "best of" collection for garage music.

Material by **? And The Mysterians, 13th Floor Elevators, Standells** and **Chocolate Watchband** are all represented in fine revved-up fashion. Add in the fact that it's a "live" concert recording, and you have one of the finest (and most rare) of the early '80s garage discs.

## THE HYSTERIC NARCOTICS
*(Livonia, MI USA)*

*Batteries Not Included* 10 song LP, 1986
  Raffscallion Records!, USA

This is a surprising LP for an unknown indy product — the production is good, the arrangements strong and the material uniformly enjoyable. **The Hysteric Narcotics** were not known outside their native Michigan, though they did reportedly attempt a few out-of-state tours. Their fame rests in this LP, which is a pretty good epitaph.

The lysergic "Electric Children," also featured previously as a flexi, shows the band as capable descendants of **The Electric Prunes**. That comparison (and compliment) is especially fitting, as **The Narcotics** capture **The Prunes'** wonderful pop fuzzadelia better than just about every other '80s attempt. Further evidence includes a **Prunes** touch on "The Devil In You," another excursion into Vox-pop.

A follow-up 45 showed the band attempting to move in a more dance-oriented direction, with tepid results. Dig up their sole LP and catch a glimpse of a band's fleeting moment of glory.

It's a fine accomplishment.

## THE IMMEDIATES
*(Tampa, FL USA)*

*Right Now* 6 song 12" EP, 1990
  Pop Records, USA

The *Right Now* EP is a bright and catchy mod-pop effort. They say in the liner notes, "Cover made with recycled paper, songs made with recycled riffs." I appreciate the honesty — this isn't anything new, just some quality toe-tapping pop songs with simple melodies and a good attitude.

## THE IMMEDIATES
*(Hastings, U.K.)*

Not the Florida band, but another combo, based around ex-**Mortician** John Redfern and ex-**Beatpack** Pete Kemp. They formed in 1988 as **The Wolves**, then added Louis Wiggett (also from **The Beatpack**) and re-named themselves. They've toured the U.K. and Europe, playing what they call *"pop art/psyche pop/R&B in the style of **The Creation, John's Children, and Eyes.**"*

A four song demo was recorded circa 1990. It displays an infectious nod to '80s bands like **The Prisoners** as well as their admitted '60s idols.

## LOS IMPOSSIBLES
*(Madrid, Spain)*

*Marigold Garden* 12 song LP, 1994
  Animal Records, Spain

**Los Impossibles** score big points for their ambition — they try their hand at baroque pop, mod pop, **Beatle**sque pop ... and power pop. They aren't always successful, but not for a lack of trying.

"Ronnie" is an example of the band firing on all cylinders, with clever melody, bright strumming guitars and a bouncy rhythm combining into a concise whole. Another band original, "Not The Time," is one of the best Mersey ballads ever (not) sung by **The Beatles**, expertly constructed and delivered.

"Acid To My Soul" explores *Abbey Road*-era **Lennon**isms, complete with pumping piano and wavering vocals. There's even a reference to "listening to the Eggman." The album closes with another sweet **McCartney**-esque melody, making "I'm Alone" one of the album's highlights.

The misses, however, are way off the mark. "Hot Plot," "The Last Show," "Listen To Me" and "Love & Sympathy" veer off into attempted blue-eyed soul or cabaret-ish eclecticism — which just don't deliver on any level.

**Los Impossibles** should be applauded for attempting to meld so many disparate styles on one disc. The reality, however, is that they really succeed only occasionally.

Perhaps if they concentrate on one musical interest (my vote goes for **The Beatles**), then we could see their obvious talent shine through consistently.

### THE IMPOSSIBLE YEARS
*(Philadelphia, PA USA)*

3 song cassette, 1983
  no label

This power pop trio came to my attention with the inclusion of the wonderfully serene "Attraction Gear" on the *Battle Of The Garages Volume 2* compilation in 1984. A year earlier they had produced a shimmering three song demo, highlighted by the jangley "Flower Girl." I believe that track also appeared on a local Philly compilation LP, and that all four were released by the band as a 12", but both pieces of vinyl elude me. (The 12" EP is entitled *Scenes We'd Like To See*, and was issued in the U.K., I believe).

A live tape shows them to be energetic in concert, able to recreate the delicate vocal harmonies of their studio work. Especially engaging was a revved-up version of **The Monkees**' "Pleasant Valley Sunday."

This is one of the genre's better pop bands; one that should have made it to a higher level. I would settle now for just a few more tracks or a hunk of that elusive vinyl.

### IMPUSIVE YOUTH
*(Milan, Italy)*

A reportedly '60s-sounding band with a private cassette circa 198?

### THE INCREDIBLE HANGOVERS
*(Germany)*

Here's another German party-band with a few discs out (and a great name), but I've only heard their early 1990s *Pleasure! Pleasure!* LP. It's a collection of R&B-tinged pop songs that's pretty lightweight but enjoyable. I like the harmonica riff in "Seat Back," lifted right from **The Beatles**' "I Should Have Known Better." Also, who could resist a song entitled "Marshmallowfever"?!?

They have a CD entitled *Fashion Shop*, but I haven't heard or seen it.

### INFLOWER
*(Messina, Italy)*

Nothing known.

### THE INN
*(Charlotte, NC USA)*

*Psychedelic Schedule* 6 song LP, 1987
  Voxx Records, USA
*Traveling at The Speed Of Life* CD, 1990
*Trippin' Tuesday* Cassette, 1990
"Keep On" 45, 1990
  Third Lock Records, USA

I've only heard the Voxx LP, so it's hard to judge exactly what **The Inn** were up to. It's safe to cite a **Grateful Dead** influence, though, as one side of the Voxx disc is an extended **Dead**-like jam.

The other side features a few pleasant folk-psych numbers, but I'm still uncertain as to the band's dominant style. The remainder of their output is self-released.

### THE INNER SLEEVES
*(Melbourne, Australia)*

This was a very cool looking band from 1986, which recorded and planned to release a 45, but I'm unsure if it ever appeared. I have heard two tracks — "End It All" and "Heartache" — so perhaps these are the mystery songs. They are certainly cool slabs of mid-'60s garage pop, full of thick organ, twangy guitar, head-bobbing thumpy drums and some sing along vocals.

"Heartache" is especially noteworthy, with its fine harmonies, shimmering guitar and solid playing all around — one of the best Australian pop-garage songs of the decade.

Talking about the Melbourne scene, guitarist Bill Darling said in the May, 1986 *Smash It Up Fanzine*, *"There are a lot of young bands who are not very professional but nonetheless have a lot of ambition, and they're all trying to outdo each other. Bands like **Too Much Hair For The BBC**, **The Bo-Weevils**, **Speedaway**, **The Nubiles** and **The Arctic Circles."***

The band reportedly covered songs by **The Byrds** and **Remains**, and sported Rickenbacker and Vox guitars, so one can assume they understood full well their mid-1960s influenced sound.

## THE INSENSIBLE EGGS
*(Caligari, Italy)*

"Insensible Eggs" b/w "False Girl" 45, 1994
   For Monsters Records, Italy

This is a rather odd band name, even by garage punk standards. A cool crude ambiance fills this disc, with a bare-bones recording sound and simple performance. The muttered, grumbly vocals are especially fun and garagey, and both sides of this 45 capture a gritty teen exuberance that helps to define garage rock.

I haven't seen this act in concert, so I can only make a guess at their stage demeanor. They're probably insensible.

## THE INSOMNIACS
*(Englishtown, NJ USA)*

Untitled 6 song 10" EP, 1994
   Estrus Records, USA

The most impressive part of this 10" release is the excellent artwork — I'm especially partial to photos of '50s horror-host Vampira. This brings to mind the fact that Estrus Records goes to great lengths to package most of their product in well-designed and attractive packages — even if the material in the grooves usually doesn't deserve the attention.

**The Insomniacs** are a case in point. Unexceptional mod-ish, pop-ish, punk-ish stuff fills up the vinyl. There's some energy and effort, but it's mostly calculated, predictable and simply ordinary.

If this trio can't get to sleep, at least they could write some better songs.

## IVORY LIBRARY
*(Madison, WI USA)*

A 12" EP, 1986, on Dairyland Records reportedly sounds like **The Rain Parade**. I still have not been able to track it down — nor find anyone who owns a copy!

## JACKIE AND THE CEDRICS
*(Tokyo, Japan)*

"Soyokaze" b/w "Hurry Up" 45, 1993
"Go! Honda Go!" b/w "Velocity Stacks" 45, 1994
   Hillsdale Records, USA
"Scalping Party" b/w "Sukiyaki Stomp" & "Justine" 45, 1995
   Norton Records, USA

**IDY**

This Japanese trio make traditional surf music that could have been spinning on American juke boxes in 1962. The sound is simple and guitar oriented, with lots of spring reverb and the requisite bright twangy sound.

The boys apparently played on the U.S. West Coast in the early 1990s, and recorded these first two 45s while in San Francisco (with the help of those ubiquitous **Mummies** guys). The "Soyokaze" 45 is probably the better of the initial two listed above, but all of their lo-fi mono sounds are recommended for surf and instrumental fans.

The Norton 45 (with a beautiful picture sleeve) is highlighted by a very funny and upbeat surf-instrumental version of the later 1950s novelty song "Sukiyaki." It's a real toe-tapping hoot.

I believe a full LP was due on late in 1995.

## JACKIE STEWART SAID
*(Milan, Italy)*

Reportedly '60s pop with the "I Cannot See You" on a split 45 in the *Vinile zine #4*, Stampa Alternative Records, 1989; and the *Hello!* LP on Vox Pop Records, 1990. I'll assume that this band is named after the Scottish race car driver.

## JACK OF ALL TRADES
*(Greece)*

Reportedly a psychedelic band, but of unknown makeup.

## JACK & THE RIPPERS
*(Verona, Italy)*

A two song 1991 demo features gritty versions of the garage standards "99th Floor" and "1-2-5," with plenty of enthusiasm and fuzz. Here's another great garage band name.

## THE JAYBIRDS
*(Vienna, Austria)*

*Teen Trash Volume #13* 12 song LP, 1994
 Music Maniac Records, Germany

Long-time music supporter and promoter Manfred "The Elk" Breiner notes on the rear sleeve of the **Jaybirds'** debut, *"About three years ago four lads met by accident. They had one thing in common: a desperate love for '60s R & B by the likes of early **Stones**,* **IDS**

*Manfred Mann or **John Mayall and The Bluesbreakers**. Their passion was so strong that they started their own band..."*

And that's how most garage bands are born, out of a desire to add to the legacy formed by their heroes. **The Jaybirds** do a good job of paying homage to their R&B roots fathers, and should be commended for sticking predominately to original material rather than simply regurgitating old standards.

"Give Me Your Love" is especially reminiscent of early **Yardbirds**, with some tasty honking harmonica and grinding rhythm. "Oh Baby" and "51 Mainstreet" were also on the band's debut EP on Ilsa Records — and another five song EP has subsequently appeared, also on Ilsa.

Hearing this LP won't change one's life or altar the course of musical history — but it's always satisfying to hear a young band pay their respects to the old masters.

## THE JEKYLLS
*(Beauvais, France)*

"The Good Time Is Over" b/w "Private Party" 45, 1993
 Dig Records, France

Some powerfully delivered pop-garage-soul comes blasting out of their 45's A-side, reminiscent of **The Prisoners**, complete with thick organ and tuneful vocals and a crashing rhythm section.

A punchy, grooving B-side rolls on energetically as a perfect compliment to the flip. Some nice raw guitar helps push the tune over the top, and makes me believe that this is another band that lives truly on a small smoky stage — covered in sweat and beer.

## JELLYFISH
*(Los Angeles, CA USA)*

A very late entry into the genre, becoming somewhat commercially popular in 1990, this colorful pop-psych outfit specialized in tight harmonies, intricate arrangements and featured a powerful recording on their major label debut LP.

The emphasis here is on pop more than psych, but surprisingly interesting nonetheless. Very trippy music videos accompanied their debut LP, which showed the band in wildly colorful outfits and outrageous hats. There was also some god-awful hippy gear, including dreaded bell-bottoms.

In concert the reports on the band have been mixed, with everything from '70s metal to bland top-40 making up their set. This isn't surprising, I suppose, but disappointing nonetheless.

Their second — and last — major label record was a self-indulgent exercise sounding more like **Queen** (!) than anything associated with '60s pop.

## THE JIGSAW SEEN
*(Los Angeles, CA USA)*

"Jim Is The Devil" b/w "Idol Chatter" 45, 1989
"God Rest Ye Merry, Gentlemen" b/w "Jesus Of Hollywood" 45, 1989
*Shortcut Through Clown Alley* 10 song LP, 1990
*My Name Is Tom* 5 song 12" EP & CD, 1991
   Skyclad Records, USA

Video: "Jim Is The Devil," 1989

The lineage of this band can be traced back to Baltimore's **United States Of Existence**, which deposited one fabulous psych-pop LP in the early '80s.

**U.S.E.** vocalist Dennis Davison and drummer Gary Schwartz headed west in the early 1980s and formed **The Playground**, altering their previous sound somewhat into a more pop-oriented direction. **The Playground** issued one fine (and rare) 45 in 1985, then rearranged members once again and adopted the name **Jigsaw Seen** in the process. The group was then bolstered by guitarists Mark Estes and Jonathan Lea from **Revolver**, a **Beatles**-influenced pop band also from Los Angeles.

With all the puzzle pieces in place, the group spent several years accumulating tracks for their debut LP. The time and patience paid off, because *Shortcut Through Clown Alley* is a remarkable pop record considering the tight budget and restrictions of their inept record label.

The **Lennon**-esque vocals of Estes are especially engaging, along with strong production and performance throughout. One can easily hear **The Byrds, Beatles, Turtles** and a variety of the '60s' best intelligent pop artists within this group's grooves.

Their follow-up *My Name Is Tom* EP continued the band's growth, with a slight psych feel combined with the almost nursery rhyme sing-song vocal approach. A commendable stab at **Love**'s "The Daily Planet" is one of the highlights, as is the ragaesque title track.

The band's sound did not transfer well to the stage, however, where their intricate arrangements and vocal-dominated style seemed tame and rather wimpy. This author witnessed several shows where **The Jigsaw Seen** was swept aside by other more forceful bands.

The band also circulated several

single-song Christmas cassettes, including the wistful "Winterland's Gone" in 1991, the brooding "What About Christmas" in 1992 and the jangley "Candy Cane" in 1993.

A reported move in the direction of funk/pop, plus personnel shake-ups did not bode well for the band, and no further releases are known — though a second LP was reportedly slated for release in 1995.

At least we have one fine LP (and a couple 45s) to remember their initial inspiration.

## THE JIVING GARGOYLES
*(Brisbane, Australia)*

A '60s inspired garage/pop/psych combo from the 1980s, with no known recordings.

## JOE PERRINO & THE MELLOWTONES
*(Cagliari, Italy)*

Reportedly beat garage punk with the "Apricots/Love The Colours/I Had A Dream" 7" on High Rise Records, 1986; and the *Rane 'N' Roll* LP on IRA Records, 1988.

## JOHNNY TEEN & THE BROKEN HEARTS
*(Australia)?*

"She Stinks Of Sex" has to be one of the crudest, funniest and most tasteless song titles of the era, but I admit liking the "fake live" recording complete with canned cheering crowd. This is pretty funny stuff, with sneering frog-like vocals, stupid lyrics, a worthless guitar solo and general stupidity.

"Dig It" and "Stardom Ain't Easy" are perhaps more inane and trash-like, if that is possible. If that's not enough, then there's always "Teenage Love Bitch" to finish things off. I'm certain that the band would consider these comments as grand compliments — if they could find someone to read this to them.

This lovable crap is in more of a '77 punk mode, but I just had to include it here.

## JON AND THE NIGHTRIDERS
*(Los Angeles, CA USA)*

One of the first instrumental surf bands to re-emerge in the late '70s, they released several LPs, including a forceful "live" concert at Los Angeles' infamous Whiskey A-Go-Go. The band included

**ITB**

guitarist John Blair, the author of *The Illustrated Discography Of Surf Music.*

His combo performed very traditional surf music, replicating exactly the feel and style of the originals. Greg Shaw says in his *Destination Bomp!* liner notes, *"What I liked best about it all was that this was real, authentic pre-**Beach Boys** surf music, not some watered down modern interpretation."*

Surf was not a major revival genre in the 1980s — at least not compared to '66 garage punk — but **Jon & The Nightriders** were arguably the best of those few dedicated bands.

Surf, hot rod and instrumental music is just now resurfacing in a major way with young bands in the 1990s. Now **Jon & The Nightriders** can influence another generation.

## JONNY SEVIN
*(Tucson, AZ USA)*

This early '80s power-punk band has popped up on a few comps. The group featured Tim Hupp (who goes by the stage name "Joe Dodge") and Lee Joseph, both later of **Yard Trauma**. An LP does exist, but is outside of this genre, landing more in New Wave territory.

Their best '60 punk studio track, "Hey You," appears on the Dionysus *Sounds Of Now* compilation LP. A blistering "live" version of the '66 punk classic "She Lied" is also on the *Obnoxious Rock & Roll Video Hour* from 1987. It was taped by this author at a concert in 1981.

## JUKON SPEAKERS
*(Sweden)*

A band that began in the late '60s, then reformed in the 1980s for several LPs — including the interestingly titled *Flying Saucers Over Lapland* in 1990 — of guitar oriented garage-art-rock and psychedelia. Their version of Zappa's "My Guitar Wants To Kill Your Mama" from their *We're Curious Yellow* LP is a fiery inspired mess of guitars.

## JUST COLORS
*(Holland)*

A 45 of unknown dimensions exists on Carnaby Coral Records.

## EL KABONG
*(Cincinnati, OH USA)*

Surf and grunge mix on their four song demo. Described as a true *Pebbles* cover-band ('60s punk covers), they never officially released any audio in their existence from 1985-87; some tracks are have circulated from a live video they did in 1986.

## KARTOONS
*(Rho, Italy)*

*That's All Folks!* 4 song 7" EP, 1994
Cave Records, Italy

A fine fuzz-filled '66 garage combo, with strong vocals (sung in English) especially put to good use on the cover of "Cry." "Yours", "Perte Sono Guai" and "Don't Ask Me Now" fill out the rest of this solid disc — which also sports some good back-up vocals and clear production. I'd grab this if it ever pops up at your local shop — it's a meaty winner.

## KAVA KAVA
*(Huddersfield, U.K.)*

Their *Dither* EP from 1993 is a CD-only release with extended hard psych and acid inspired jams, closer to a hippy mentality than anything else. Two LPs were in the works for Delerium Records at last word in 1995.

## KIM SQUAD AND DINAH SHORE ZEEKAPERS
*(Rome, Italy)*

Reportedly garage punk, with the *Young Bastards* LP on Virgin Records (!?!?), 1987.

## KING OF LUXEMBOURG
*(U.K.)*

Several records are available. I believe this is a solo act, somewhat in **Paul Roland/Robyn Hitchcock** territory.

## KING KOEN
*(Brussels, Belgium)*

*No Kicks On The Radio* 3 song 12" EP, 1988
    Punk, Etc. Records, Belgium
*Upfront 'N' Straightforward* 11 song LP, 1989
Untitled 3 song 7" EP, 1989
    Boom Records, Belgium

Former **Spanks** guitarist **King Koen** struck out on his own with several fine releases in the late 1980s. The Rickenbacker fueled "No Kicks On The Radio" expressed the sentiment that many felt in the 1980s — that the mainstream media was not responsive to "alternative" ideas and especially music.

The subsequent LP featured some honking harmonica and driving pop-rock anthems, plus another Rickenbacker jangle fest in "Shape Of A Bottle Of Coke." The LP also included a bonus 7" EP.

## THE KITES
*(Germany)*

A four track EP on SG Records is available, but it is unknown to this author.

## THE KLIEK
*(Holland)*

*When Father Was Away On Beat Business In The Magic Centre*
    6 song 12" EP, 1987
*Valleri EP*, 1989
    Kelt Records, Holland
*Across The Milkyway* cassette, 1989
*Behind Bars* 13 song LP, 1990
    Grabo Records, Holland
"Sandra" b/w "House Of Stone" 45, 1992
    Twang! Records, Germany
"Me Right Now" b/w "Nothing's Changed" 45, 1993
    Twist Records, Germany
*Feel Good* 16 song LP / 24 song CD, 1993
    Screaming Apple Records, Germany
*It's My Pride* 4 song 7" EP, 1994
    Outer Limits Records, Germany

Also on the Fab Records *Bizarre Beauties* LP compilation, the 1989 *Ex-Nexu Magazine* EP compilation, The Twist *My Mind's Eye* EP comp, *Let's Have A Picnic* LP comp on the Noet Lachten label in 1990, the *Linke Soep* LP comp in 1992, and *Misfit: A Tribute to The Outsiders* LP on Screaming Apple in 1992.

The oddly-named **Kliek** has toured extensively throughout Europe since their formation in 1987 — and in 1993 was reportedly the first '60s garage band to perform in Russia with a three week tour.

Their repertoire ranges from beautiful folk-rock to Euro-beat to raw U.S.-styled garage punk, and they seem equally adept at all of them. The Nederbeat style seems most prominent, however, and some fans have voiced their opinion to me that **The Kliek** might be one of the best beat bands of any era. Their live concert reputation rates them as a fiery outfit — even Grabo Records' Ron Martin claims that their records don't do the band justice.

**The Kinks' Ray Davies** even said in a 1990 BBC radio interview that Holland's **Kliek** are a joyful resurrection of his 1960s beat-band days. *"Last summer I was in Amsterdam at The Milky Way and I saw some local kids come up on stage. They were called The Clip or The Kliek or something,"* he explained.

*"To my surprise they started to play that uptight beat we used to do, say twenty five years ago. But*

Sandra     House of Stone

*it wasn't at all like those MTV-bands, that just imitate our hairstyles and our outfits. These guys were able to recreate the original atmosphere. They had so much power and enthusiasm like they invented the music the day before the gig ... That evening I wished I could do it all over again. I just love those guys for it."*

Throughout almost all of **The Kliek**'s records the Rickenbacker guitars chime and jangle — has their ever been a sweeter sound in pop music? — and harmonies warm the room. These Dutch lads make us believe, if only for a couple of precious minutes at a time, that a little harmless toe-tapping and head bobbing is left in the

**120**

world.

The title track of *Feel Good* is the band in microcosm: it could make a dead man smile, it could make the Grinch give back Christmas — and it made **Ray Davies** remember how sweet it feels to sing and sweat and laugh.

## THE KRAVIN' "A"s
*(Kent, U.K.)*

*Krave On!* 14 song CD, 1993
    Get Hip Records, USA
*Pushin' And Shovin'* 4 song 7" EP, 1993
    Screaming Apple Records, Germany

The '80s UK "Medwaybeat" sound never made a dent in the U.S. underground, except for the recent Sub Pop hipster "validation" of **Billy Childish**. Despite (or because of) the lack of attention, rootsy beat combos like **The Kravin' "A"s** continue to crank out crudely recorded (and performed) slabs of distinctively British (white) R&B.

Forming in 1986, a couple ex-**Milkshakes** give the **"A"s** their pedigree, but stand-out tracks on their LP such as "Girls Like That," "Look Back And Laugh" and "Free Girl" sound instead like another unknown '80s fave, **The Prisoners**. It's amazing to me that this band could have existed for seven years without recording — and then finally delivered the goods in an LP.

The four song 7" is even more appealing. "Born Yesterday" is a grooving and grinding fuzz-ballad, complete with "hey, hey hey!" back-up vocals, and a mesmerizing vocal hook. "Trust Me" isn't far behind in quality, with a tight melody and again some meaty background vocals.

It's always a bit strange to hear white kids from London singing with soul, but **The Pretty Things** and **The Stones** got away with it thirty years ago, so why not in the 1990s?

## KRYPTASTHESIE
*(Como, Italy)*

A psych-pop outfit, with several releases: the "Ask The Calendar/Charade Part 2/El Nagual" 7", private pressing, 1989; the *Shaken At The Sun*, double LP, Menbir Records, 1992; and the *Any Water Knows*, private cassette, circa 1987.

"Ask The Calendar" is a bouncy pop number with some carnival-like keyboards and wah-wah guitar work, while "Charade" has more of an upbeat garage feel and a very whigged-out guitar-solo-sound-effect. Some nice vocal interplay also make this one an upbeat

winner. A very strange musical change at the end of this song displays **Kryptasthesie**'s unpredictably psychedelic sound.

This odd band is worth investigation.

## THE KWYET KINGS
*(Oslo, Norway)*

*Need My Lovin' Tonight* 3 song 7" EP, 1994
*Firebeat* 10 song LP, 1994
    Screaming Apple Records, Germany
"Don't Doubt My Love" b/w "Open Up Your Door" 45, 1994
    Weed Records, France
"Don't Put Me Down" b/w "Self Important Girl" 45, 1995
    Get Hip Records, USA

Vocalist Arne Thelin formed this new combo from the ashes of **The Lust-O-Rama**. (Skip ahead to their story if you want this to make some kind of sequential sense).

If anything, **The Kwyet Kings'** *Firebeat* LP sounds like the perfect progression of **The Lust-O-Rama**'s R&B garage sound — I would have thought it was **The Lusties'** new LP unless told otherwise.

"Ain't Nobody's Business," "Can't Go On" and "I Say Yeah" rate up with the best of Thelin's previous bands, and their **Firebeats** tribute song, "Let Me Tell You," is a wonderful burning beat-ballad, complete with vocals from the songwriter, Yngve Bjerke.

This is absolutely essential garage music performed at the highest level of expert proficiency.

"Don't Doubt My Love" is another toe-tapping pop garage winner, with grooving anthemic chorus and gutsy riffing guitar. The 45's flip is an alternate mix of "Open Up Your Door" from the LP.

"Need My Lovin' Tonight" from their debut EP is different than any of their other tracks: more introspective, slower and vocally dominated — a bit like an early **Stones** ballad. "You're Tellin' Me Lies" returns to their more effective formula of upbeat garage pop. "Number One" is the EP's most memorable tune, with cool warbly organ and propulsive guitar strumming.

The Get Hip 45 is another excellent upbeat pop-garage affair. I think a second LP has also appeared in 1995.

Arne Thelin and his fellow musicians have made some remarkable Norwegian garage music — with **The Cosmic Dropouts, Lust-O-Rama** and now **The Kwyet Kings**. I can't wait to hear what he cooks up next.

## THE LADDS FROM BELLEVUE
(Massachusetts USA)

"Relative Distance" b/w "Till The Stroke Of Dawn" 45, 1987
    Stanton Park Records, USA

Here's a studio-only project, combining the talents of several bands on the Stanton Park label, most notably vocalist Chris Horne of **The Brood**. They cover two obscure New England nuggets from the '60s in fun fashion. Another session was recorded but unreleased as of press time.

## LAIKA & THE COSMONAUTS
(Finland)

*Instruments Of Terror* 15 song CD, 1993
*The Amazing Colossal Band* 17 song CD, 1995
    Upstart Records, USA

Instrumental music fan and musician Scott Moody says of their 1995 Tucson show, *"They were just the fuckin' greatest!"* They play a combination of what Moody

calls *"surf instrumental spy movie music. I think they're better by far than most of the other new instrumental bands."*

## LANDLORDS
(Holland)

Nothing known.

## LARRY & THE LEFTHANDED
(Kauhajoki, Finland)

Untitled 4 song 7" EP, 1994
*From 0-20 to 40-116 And Back With...* 4 song 7" EP, 1994
    Trash Can Records, Finland

For some reason it is really strange for me to listen to rock music from Finland. Their culture seem so different than the U.S. "rock lifestyle," so it's odd for me to get such cool Finnish records like this pair from **Larry And The Lefthanded**.

Their debut is a crusty, crude, spittle-driven lo-fi effort, with some suitably warbly organ and distorted shouted vocals. The follow-up is similarly twisted, and as the label says, "Made in Finland, dammit!"

Maybe rock'n'roll and Finland isn't such a weird combination. A Finnish surf band called **Laika & The Cosmonauts** (described just above in this book) are playing in a club down the street (in Tucson, Arizona) right now as I write this.

Maybe the world is a small place after all.

## THE LAST
(Los Angeles, CA USA)

"She Don't Know Why I'm Here" b/w
    "Bombing Of London" 45, 1978
"Every Summer Day" b/w "Slavedriver" 45, 1979
"Objections" b/w "Be-Bop-A-Lula" 12" single, 1979
*L.A. Explosion* 14 song LP, 1979
"L.A. Explosion" b/w "Hitler's Brother", 1980
    Bomp Records, USA

Other discs include the 1982 *Fade To Black* EP, and the 1984 *Painted Smiles On A Dead Man* LP.

One should not underestimate the worth of a pioneer.

The first in any given attempt is usually forgotten as the more successful followers gain success, and such is the case with **The Last**. They remembered the value of melody and lyrical power at a time when many were indulging in the fury of '70s punk. They acknowledged the classics of pop

**122**

history, then took what they needed to form a new sound in their own image. ,

The time was the late 1970s. The place was Los Angeles. The band was **The Last**. The story you are about to read is mostly true.

Bomp released several **Last** 45s into the "New Wave" miasma, but it is their debut LP which caused the real sparks to fly. *L.A. Explosion* is just that, a fury of pop guitars and ideas and frantic teenage voices. Its 15 blistering tracks (14 originals!) journeyed from Mersey pop to guitar ballads to angry rough rock, all in the course of a few songs.

Their lead-off anthem, "She Don't Know Why I'm Here," is one of the most stunning independent label efforts ever, with its searing guitar hook, emotional vocals and identifiable group intensity. It's **The Byrds** meets **The Seeds**, with a late '70s power pop sensibility thrown in — and it captures the era like a time capsule.

Several more records would appear, but **The Last** were never given their due as pioneers of 1980s garage pop. They were there first, and were at least lucky enough to leave several documents of their pioneering efforts.

## THE LAST DRIVE
*(Athens, Greece)*

*Underworld Shakedown* 11 song LP, 1986
*Time* 3 song 12" EP, 1989
   Hitch Hyke Records, Greece
Untitled 3 song 7" EP, 1987
   Voxx Records, USA
*Heatwave* 9 song LP, 1988
   Music Maniac Records, Germany

Much was made in the underground press of this Greek band, though I must admit that I don't find them to be of great interest. They released a 1985 EP, *Midnight Hop*, then gained wide attention for their 1986 LP *Under World Shakedown*. It's arguably their finest moment, with covers of "Night Of The Phantom" and an epic reworking of "Blue Moon."

Their mixture of surf, R&B and heavy guitar noise doesn't quite jell for me, but many Europeans hailed the young band. They toured extensively, released a three song 45 on Voxx in the U.S. and appeared on several compilations.

In 1988 they released their sophomore effort, *Heatwave,* and a "best of" CD on Germany's Music Maniac label in 1989. The much over-rated Paul Cutler (of **The Dream Syndicate**) produced their 1990 effort *Blood Nirvana*.

This author met several of the lads in Greece, and found them to be sincere

good hearted rock guys, with a passion of gutsy guitar-driven music. I can certainly see why they have a loyal legion of fans.

## LAUGHING SKY
*(New York, NY USA)*

This is an early 1990s project of Dino Sorbello, formerly of **The Blacklight Chameleons**. He described their sound as *"Syd Barrett meets Hawkwind at a heavy metal bar."* They played live and recorded, but no word on any releases.

A three song 1991 demo cassette showcased Sorbello's stellar guitar work and a mesmerizing fluid mood. I can hear the **Hawkwind** influence, but luckily none of the "heavy metal bar" wankings.

## THE LAUGHING SOUP DISH
*(New Jersey, USA)*

"Teenage Lima Bean" b/w "Rainy Day Sponge" 45, 1985
*We Are The Dish* 12 song LP, 1987
*Underthrow The Overground* 12 song LP, 1990
   Voxx Records, USA

This enigmatic combo went through many line-up changes since their 1982 inception, but managed to keep its wildly psychedelic status intact. The band name comes from a slang dictionary — "Laughing Soup" meaning an intoxicating liquid — they then added "Dish" to complete the "L.S.D." connection. **The Laughing Soup Dish** shared members with **The Secret Syde**, while **Marc Saxton** left after the first 45 to form the equally excellent **Watch Children**.

That first 7" included the wacky "Teenage Lima

III

Bean," a surreal and drastically trippy exercise in psych pop. Its churningly creative imagery made it a wonderful and unexpected find. The flip, "Rainy Day Sponge," is no less bizarre and beautiful.

It was more than a year before a re-vamped lineup released their debut LP, recorded in glorious distortion in their home studio. The LP is as trippy as the 45, though the lo-fi recording interferes in giving us a clear aural picture of the proceedings. The experience is still pure lysergia, however, complete with acid nightmare artwork on the sleeve.

*B-Side Magazine* noted, *"After a listen or two you'll swear your lava lamp exploded, sending you back into a time warp of jingle-jangle flower-powered energy."*

The band thankfully employed a "real" studio for their follow-up, and the results were markedly improved. My favorite is "Blood Sucking Creatures," which I thought was called "Blood Sucking Preachers" on first listen. Either way the track is loopy fun, and the remainder of the LP is just as twisted, fun and aggressively trippy.

I'll leave the band with a thought from their second LP's liner notes: *"The planet remains in reverberation, and their ruler it seems is tied and bound, because his subjects have succeeded, to Overthrow the Underground."*

## THE LEARS
(Orlando, FL USA)

"I Won't Remind You" b/w "A Flash Of Light" 45, 1993
  Susstones Records, USA
4 X 4 4 song 7" EP, 1994
  Lollipop Shop Records, Germany

Also "You Don't Believe Me" on the Australian **Pretty Things** *Not So Pretty* tribute LP, 1994; and another EP due in 1995 on the German Outer Limits label. They also planned a four song tribute EP to the band **Love**, though no word if that materialized.

**The Lears** formed in 1990 with Dennis Dalcin (former head of *Kaleidoscope Magazine* and Records) and two former members of **Green Today**. They state their influences as **The Byrds, Love, Beatles, Electric Prunes** and **Syd's Pink Floyd** — and all of those classic elements can be found in their own output.

"I Won't Remind You" sounds like the remnant of a long-lost '67 **Byrds** session, complete with **McGuinn's** aggressive Rickenbacker twinkles and his plaintive vocals — simply magical. The flip combines a **Bo Diddley** beat, some **Beau Brummels**-like vocals and an upbeat mood to good effect — complete with trippy 12-string solo.

Their four song EP was originally recorded on a home 4-track recorder in 1991, then later overdubbed and eventually released in 1994. The slightly thin production only somewhat hampers the sweet Rickenbacker recipe. "Then You Want" is another infectious **Byrds**-like jewel, with some nice dual vocals, a snappy arrangement and the requisite "Ricky" solo.

Both discs are highly recommended — and I believe a long-player was in the works for 1995.

## LEE JOSEPH
(Los Angeles, CA USA)

*Four By One* 4 song 7" EP, 1987
  Mystery Scene Records, Germany

**Yard Trauma** and Dionysus head honcho **Lee Joseph** was a master at living-room recordings, and he accumulated a bunch of them over the years. They were so good that Mystery Scene asked for an EP, and **Joseph** delivered.

Especially cool is his sparse treatment of **The 13th Floor Elevators'** "Splash One." It should also be noted that **Rich Coffee** and **Zebra Stripes** both add their talents to the disc, which is a welcome amendment to the best work from **Yard Trauma**.

## LEGENDARY GOLDEN VAMPIRES
(Germany)

Various 45s and a 10" EP exist, including the 1985 "Gone For Good" 45, 1985's "Creeping Poison" b/w "Rebel Woman" 45 and the 1986 four song 10" EP titled *Troublebound*. All are on Exile Records out of the U.K. I remember them to be fuzzed-out with **Cramps**, garage and trash-rockabilly influenced sounds.

## LEMON BABIES
(Germany)

*Fresh 'N' Fizzy* 4 song 7" EP, 1991
  Twang! Records, Germany

I'm admittedly not a giant fan of the typical 1960s "girl-group" sound — sweet, polite adolescent voices accompanied by tame backing tracks. That's the flavor here, hampered by some unfortunate horn excursions and some shrill vocals. This one's a miss — by a wide mark.

## THE LEOPARDS
*(Kansas City / Los Angeles, CA USA)*

"Psychedelic Boy" b/w "If You Come Back" 45, 1986
*Magic Still Exists* 14 song LP, 1987
  Voxx Records, USA

Other releases: *Kansas City Slickers* LP; "I wonder If I'll Ever See You Again" b/w "It Must Be Love"; "They All Play Loud" b/w "I'm Living In A Jungle"; "Don't Go Away" b/w "The Only Girl For Me" — all on Moon Records, previous to those listed above.

One can't help but label **The Leopards** as being an "American **Kinks**." Their attitude is very much American, but their songs are sly and observant stories in the best **Ray Davies** tradition. They

### THE LEOPARDS, 1987

released several obscure records in their Kansas City home, but their real interest starts with their move to L.A. in the mid-1980s.

In SoCal they became darlings of The Cavern Club set, and radio heroes of sorts (on Rodney Bingenheimer's KROQ show) with the release of the "Psychedelic Boy" 45. The lilting melody and biting lyrical message of this song sums up the love/hate relationship that musicians and fans alike had with the resurgent "1960s revival." *("A psychedelic boy never wonders — about the recent past that he plunders...")* This track remains an anthem for the time, an essential document of a fleeting sound and scene.

The *Magic Still Exists* LP soon followed, with a mass of tightly structured and beautifully delivered pop songs. Again the **Kinks** comparison is valid, as the plethora of acoustic guitars and sweet ironic harmonies build throughout the LP.

Despite the solid releases, **The Leopards** are yet another example of a fine underground band being inexplicably ignored by the public and music industry alike.

Track down their vinyl while you can, and pass the word — magic does still exist, and **The Leopards** know where to find it.  **113**

## THE LETTUCE HEADS
*(Springfield, MO USA)*

Reportedly comprised of the **Royal Nonesuch**'s ex-drummer and other locals, this late '80s combo wins points for their moniker alone.

## THE LIARS
*(Pisa, Italy)*

I remember hearing that their *Optical Sound* 12" EP that was mildly interesting, though not completely in the genre. There's a 1988 45 out on Germany's Unique Records entitled "Cold Girl" b/w "Flashin'" and a 1988 LP titled *Mindscrewer* on Tramite Records as well.

## THE LIBERTINES
*(Cincinnati, OH USA)*

"Everybody Wants To Be My Sister" b/w "Swayback" 45, 1984
"Voices From The Past" b/w "Something In The Water" 45, 1986
  Day One Records, USA

**The Libertines** never considered themselves a "'60s band," but their brand of jangley forceful pop certainly owes much to that sound. A more modern comparison might be early **R.E.M.**, with the muted and impressionistic vocal style layered over a bright guitar and driving beat.

The main difference is that **The Libertines** were an unpretentious trio, and a powerful one at that. There was a certain intensity to the group when I saw them perform "live," an intensity that I don't think many in the audiences ever picked up. **The Libertines** were for real; the emotion they displayed was a reflection of their lives, not some stage affectation.

The band did gain popularity with the college crowd in their native southern Ohio, but never ventured much further. They released one LP titled simply *Ohio*, but this didn't open doors for them either, though it did garner well deserved critical praise.

Their 45s are now impossible to find, but still shine as inspired, thoughtful pop.

## LILITH
*(Piacenza, Italy)*

The ex-**Not Moving** singer performs a combination of pop/folk/psych and cabaret-ish torch songs. She has many releases; the "Venus In Furs" b/w "Tombstone Blues" 7", 1991; the ironically titled *Hello! I Love Me!* 12" EP, 1990; and the *Lady Sings Love Songs* LP, 1992 — all on Face Records.

None of this fits strictly in the garage-psych genre, but there are moments that merit attention nonetheless.

## THE LIME SPIDERS
*(Sydney, Australia)*

*Slave Girl* 6 song 12" EP, 1985
  Big Time Records, USA

Video: "Just One Solution," 1987, from the *Cave Comes Alive* LP.

Sure, there are many who count **The Lime Spiders** as one of the top rock bands of the 1980s, though I am not one of them.

They were a passable rock outfit that somehow managed to gain notoriety outside their native continent, eventually ending up on a major label. This original excitement was caused by a few early 45s, which were collected onto the one 12" EP listed above.

I stand alone perhaps in the following assessment, but I believe these early recordings to be the best and only real document of the band worth discussing. They feature a brash, vicarious punk stance, with an obvious debt to the garage sound, though certainly not overwhelmingly so.

They then released a string of very average, unexciting "rock" records, each becoming more mundane and less interesting with time. There was one stand-out track from their major-label LP *The Cave Comes Alive*, which just happened to be made into a big budget music video.

I truly believe that **The Lime Spiders** were — and are — vastly overrated.

## THE LINKERS
*(Bordeaux, France)*

Untitled 4 song 7" EP, 1994
*Voodoo Eyes* 6 song 12" EP, 1994
  Weed Records, France
untitled 3 song 7" EP, 1995
  Vicious Circle Records, France

This author played one show with **The Linkers**, and found them to be enthusiastic garage true-believers, with a sound full of thick organ playing.

Their press sheet says, *"The Linkers welcome you to their creepy world of wicked psychedelic tunes that might tear your flesh apart. Just crawl to the feast of these gurgling cellar dwellars every time the moon* comes up and you'll hear werewolves howl, sneaky whispers sound in your head, more oozing pains in your remains, until you're fuzzed outta your brains, that's when you'll know you're round the bend! Trip on the overload!"

Whoah!

They actually thank this author on the sleeve of their debut EP — which means that I am obligated to say nice things about the record. Actually I get off the hook this time — because the EP really is a fine slab of garagemania. "Suzy" blasts an organ-led stomper, while the fivesome rips through the Creeps' "She's Gone" with demented determination.

Their follow-up 12" is just as good, with plenty of fine guitar and some gutsy vocals — along with the aforementioned stand-out keyboard playing.

France lagged behind in producing 1980s garageheads, but it picked up the pace in the 1990s to be one of the leaders of the continuing movement. **The Linkers** are at the head of that rebirth.

I'd love to see them play one more time.

## LINK PROTRUDI AND THE JAYMEN
*(New York, NY USA)*

*Missing Links* 8 song 12" EP, 1989
  Skyclad Records, USA
*Drive It Home* 16 song LP, 1987
*Hit And Run* LP, 1988?
*Slow Grind* 13 song CD, 1992
*Seduction* LP/CD, 1994
  Music Maniac Records, Germany

Video: "Bandito," 1989, on the *Slipping Through The Cracks* compilation, Skyclad Records.

**114**

This band began as essentially a filler project for Rudi Protrudi in-between the East Coast and West Coast line-ups of **The Fuzztones,** but ended up being a full-time project in its own right. One could guess from the band's name that this trio also began as an homage of sorts to instrumentalist **Link Wray** — and you would be correct.

The sound is often bargain-basement crude, but also always enjoyable, unpretentious, simple and fun. A wide variety of '60s-inspired instrumental sounds were explored, with titles like "Beaver Shot" giving a glimpse of the mentality involved.

The band also toured Europe several times playing this stuff — while establishing a large fan base similar to **The Fuzztones'** — showing that perhaps Protrudi had more to offer musically than many of his detractors believed.

And I just love those stripper photos on the insert for *Slow Grind.*

## LIQUID GENERATION
(Seattle, WA USA)

"I Love You" b/w "1/4 To Zen" 45, 1985
Green Monkey Records, USA

I believe that this 45 is the lone release from these demented garage-niks, and a fine monument it is to fuzzadelia. The A-side, "I Love You," also appears on the *Deadly Spawn* compilation, and is their shining moment.

Recalling a **Paul Revere & The Raiders** anthem, it moves along in head-bobbing, toe tapping fashion, with a frantic tambourine shaking away. The flip, the oddly titled "1/4 To Zen," features fine vocal harmonies amidst a sense of cacophonous noise.

An unreleased cassette contains an album's worth of garage nuggets, including covers of "Out Of Our Tree," "Hang Up" and "We're Pretty Quick," along with a few more originals. It's an awesomely authentic garage collection, and should have made its way onto vinyl.

Raw, crude, energetic and fun — ahh, the virtues of the American garage band!

## THE LIZARD KINGS
(Germany)?

They had some kind of release on Germany's Unique Records, but aren't a **Doors** sound-alike as their name suggests. The only track I've heard is the stomping '66 anthem titled "Kinda Square." It featured a simple beat, hypnotic guitar riffing, some warbly harmonica and a total garage sound production.

As my Grandmother would say when eating something good, "It tastes like more." Is there any more?

## LOKOMOTIVE DRAGSTER
(Toscana, Italy)

Reportedly punk and hard garage, with the "Speed Monster" b/w "Guilty Man" 7" on Vitriol Records, 1989.

## THE LOLITAS
(Berlin, Germany)

A 1980s French band living in Germany, with three LPs, though only the debut is reportedly in the garage genre.

## THE LOMBEGO SURFERS
(Basel, Switzerland)

**The Lombego Surfers'** bassist is a veteran of original 1960s bands **The Dynamites, Sauterelles** and **The Slaves.** His late 1980s band is a very punkish outfit without a surf influence, despite the band's name. They have at least one LP and CD.

## THE LONE WOLVES
(New York, NY USA)

This grungey outfit features garage veterans Orin and Elan Portnoy, something or someone called Hambone Legbone, and Andrea Kusten. Between them they played previously in **The Outta Place, Optic Nerve, Twisted, Fuzztones, Headless Horsemen, Funny Uncles, Blacklight Chameleons** and **Maneaters,** among others! They have several releases in the early 1990s, more in a harder punk sound than straight garage.

## THE LONG RYDERS
*(Los Angeles, CA USA)*

*10-5-60* 6 song 12" EP, 1983
   PVC Records, USA
*Native Sons* 11 song LP, 1984
   Frontier Records, USA
*State Of Our Union* 11 song LP, 1985
   Island Records, USA
*I Can't Hide* 7" flexi, 1985?
   The Bob Magazine, USA

Video: "I Had A Dream," 1984; "Looking For Lewis & Clark," 1986; "I Want You Bad," 1987.

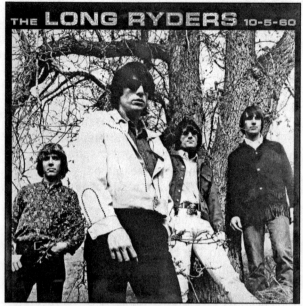

Many people either love **The Long Ryders**, or hate them like the Devil himself. They represented many ideals and evils of the "garage revival," and at the very least are interesting as an example of "the rock musician vs. the music business."

The lineage of **The Long Ryders** can be traced back to mid-period **Byrds, The Flying Burrito Brothers, Buffalo Springfield** and just about any other late '60s "country-rock" group. Back then the term "country-rock" didn't conjure up images of bloated pretentious "super-groups" like **The Eagles**, but instead a progressive set of musicians attempting to form a new musical genre. It is with this more artistic aim that **The Long Ryders** set up shop.

Guitarist/vocalist Sid Griffin is a veteran of the ultra-'60s **Unclaimed**, (leaving the band with bassist Barry Shank in fall 1981), so it's no surprise that much of early **Long Ryders** output owes as much to **The Seeds** as to **Gram Parsons**.

Their first 12" comes off like a great lost **Byrds** session, with expert musicianship and songwriting making it an auspicious debut. What would be identified as **The Ryders'** sound is inherent from the start of this disc, as they alternate "rock" and "country-influenced" tracks, each with great success. (I should note here that I truly dislike most "country" music, so you must believe me when I say that **The Long Ryders** managed somehow to make this work!)

The *10-5-60* EP was later re-issued in 1987 with an extra original track entitled "The Trip;" this is a band original, not a cover of the infamous 1960s Kim Fowley composition. This EP would be their debut and their high water mark — at the same time.

Their *Native Sons* long-player confirmed the band's early promise, though the country and rock influences were beginning to separate. I can imagine fans of either style picking up their stylus to skip certain songs, as did this author. Still, there are some spine-tingling moments, like "Ivory Tower,"

**116**

where **The Byrds'** vocalist **Gene Clark** helps add a perfect touch to the new folk-rock classic.

The band was swept up in the brief mid-'80s critical praise of "American guitar bands," and signed to a major label. This is where **The Long Ryders'** problems really begin. Already in a precarious position with their "underground" fans because of the major-label deal, the band then signed a sponsorship deal with the Miller Beer corporation. The band then shot a Miller Beer commercial, designed to help give them a national image to go with their upcoming LP. (I remember that **The Del Fuegos** shot a similar Miller commercial.)

The commercial proved to be a public relations disaster.

The "hip" underground zines shredded the band and labeled them lame, corporate and greedy. They lost their "alternative music" support at a time when they were totally unknown to the commercial market, and the result was a total void for the band. Suddenly they had their major label deal but no fan support whatsoever!

(This author saw the band in concert during this period. They had just returned from packed houses in Europe, but were now met with a cold and indifferent U.S. public. There were only about a dozen people at the show, and the band was in a surly mood.

I'll always remember the look on their faces as they waited in the small club's kitchen before the show. It was the definition of utter despair, but they somehow collected themselves to put on a professional set for the assembled 12 people.

In the dead silence between songs I asked Griffin for my favorite of their songs, "Join My Gang." He looked at me blankly and replied with attempted humor, "What's your gang called?"

I give them a great deal of credit for playing at all that night, and a live tape of the show proves that they did a pretty good job.)

The idea of a corporate sponsor should not have been a major problem, but the band responded in print to the criticisms with inept rationalizations or snotty retorts, and the damage was done.

The end result was two partially successful albums; partially successful artistically, that is. Both *State Of Our Union* and *Two Fisted Tales* had flashes of **The Long Ryders** sound, but much of the material was pedestrian and uninspired. (The band would later contend that the record company rejected many of the original songs they wished to record, opting for "safer" commercial tracks). Neither LP sold well at all, and the band was eventually dropped by its corporate sugar-daddies.

Sid Griffin later formed **The Coal Porters**, a band that sounded like the product of a bitter, tired performer. At least that's the impression Griffin gave after a 1991 show this author played with them in Hollywood.

Their fan club also released a cassette and CD of concert tracks and outtakes titled *Metallic B.O.* which primarily shows off the band's live muscle. Other outtakes showcase their country tendencies on "Dirty Old Town" and a strained sense of attempted "humor" on **Michael Jackson**'s "Billy Jean." Ironically, the packaging of this CD is better than any of their major label records, though the sound is predictably spotty at times.

It's another rock cliché, but timing is everything. No one would have called **The Long Ryders** big-money whores in the *totally* corporate 1990s — that kind of perceived greed would have sat nicely with their audience a decade later. But in the 1980s **The Long Ryders** were a good idea that simply missed completion.

Not enough listeners ended up joining their gang.

## THE LOONEY TUNES
*(France)*

A demo tape exists of decidedly French pop.

## LOOPOPHORIA
*(Venezia, Italy)*

'60s garage with a private cassette, circa 1987-88.

## LORD HUNT AND HIS MISSING FINKS
*(Los Angeles, CA USA)*

"Rodan" b/w "The Clutch" 45, 1994
    Screaming Apple Records, Germany

An off-shoot band with three of **The Finks**, carrying on in a similar instrumental fashion. The vintage '60s wrestling masks make for some very cool band photos — just dig that cheesy Silvertone

guitar — and you just gotta love that demented laughing throughout "Rodan." Similar nuttiness fills the flipside.

Tack these two winners at the end of your cassette of **The Finks** LP and call me in the morning. It'll all make sense then.

## LORD JOHN
*(New Jersey, USA)*

The *Six Days Of Sound* LP on Bomp has a few worthy tracks, though it attempts to sound mainly like modern British pop rock.

## LORDS OF THE NEW SURF
*(New York, NY USA)*

A part-time group with Dino Sorbello (ex- **Mad Violets** & **Blacklight Chameleons**) on guitar, Chris Cush (ex-**Headless Horsemen**) on guitar, Peter Stuart (ex-**Tryfles** & **Headless Horsemen**) on bass, and Elan Portnoy (ex-**Fuzztones** & **Headless Horsemen**) on drums. (Quite curious that Portnoy would play drums here, since he is usually a lead guitarist!)

Sorbello says, *"We did a handful of New York gigs and toured Canada once. We did mostly covers with a few of my original surf instrumental tunes"* — this was circa summer 1986. The band name is a parody of the somewhat popular early '80s doom and gloom band **Lords Of The New Church**, in case you hadn't figured it out.

## LOST PATROL
*(Windsor, Canada)*

A 7" EP appeared on their own label in 1986, a French LP in 1988 and a LP-length cassette in 1990. All are rather bland efforts, with just a tinge of garage-ness.

## LOST TRADE CO.
*(Italy)*

Reportedly punk/acid with the "Desolation Land" b/w "Somebody Killed Jinny" 7" on Mantra Records, 198?

## LOTUS STP
*(Rochester, NY USA)*

*Million Dollar Ring* 11 song LP, 1987
    Jargon Records, USA

Described simply to me by collector Karl Taylor as "a fairly straight ahead garage band."

"Rockslide Rock," "I Got Questions" and "Broke Down" from the LP are exactly that — passable but not terribly interesting or exceptional garage tunes.

## LOVE CIRCUS
*(San Francisco, CA USA)*

*Love Circus* 5 song 12" EP, 1984
    Broken Records, USA

This is a curious one-off disc from the northern California Bay area. I don't believe that these folks consciously aped a '60s pose, but the product certainly evokes some of the attitude of vintage folk rock. A **Credence Clearwater Revival** comparison might be more accurate, but a folksy psych sound is also in there somewhere. "Live Forever" is an especially fine track, mesmerizing in its own way. **Love Circus** is a strange entry into this field, but worth a listen.

## THE LOVE CRAFTS
*(Germany)*

Featuring **Swinging London** members, so I can guess that this is pop-mod oriented.

## LOVE DELEGATION
*(New York, NY USA)*

*Spread The Word* 11 song LP, 1986
    Moving Target Records, USA

The **Fleshtones'** Peter Zaremba seemed to always have two passions: garage and dance rock. He combined the two into a series of studio sessions, proving that even garage rock can make its way onto a disco's turntable. He didn't employ sampling, drum machines or stupid chants, however, like the accepted "modern" dance formula.

Instead, he simply arranged the songs into straight-forward dance anthems, and gave them a good kick in the pants with tight production, real performances, and a general party atmosphere.

Ex-**Mad Violet** Wendy Wild is especially engaging in duets with **Zaremba**, and the whole mess is an unpretentious day-glo bucket of fun.

Garage "purists" will drop dead at the sound of this record, which leaves more fun for the rest of us.

## THE LOVED ONES
*(Oakland, CA USA)*

*Untitled* 4 song 7" EP, 1992
    Get Hip Records, USA
*The Price For Love* LP/CD, 1993
*Better Do Right* LP/CD, 1994
    HighTone Records, USA

**The Loved Ones'** press material sounds pretty fishy. They claim that this is the members' first band, but I distinctly remember several of them in a San Diego band called **The Event** — they opened a show for **The Marshmallow Overcoat** there in 1990.

**The Loved Ones'** sound isn't really that much different than their **Event** days. There's that blue-eyed mod soul thing, some R&B flashes, and strictly purist mod fashion on stage. Nothing is out of place, everything is as expected, and while their musical chops are good, there just isn't a spark of originality anywhere in the mixture. I'll play my early **Animals, Downliners Sect** or even first couple of **Stones** LPs instead of this stuff.

For the uninitiated, perhaps, **The Loved Ones** take the place of the real thing.

## THE LUBBERS
*(Holland)*

I've only heard the song "Now's Not Then," an upbeat folk-pop number with subdued vocals, energetic drumming, and an interesting arrangement. I've no idea if anything appeared on vinyl.

## THE LUST-O-RAMA
*(Moss, Norway)*

4 song 7" EP, 1990
*Low Budget Live* 5 song 7" EP, 1993 (only 25 made)
    That's Entertainment Records, Norway
*The In-Crowd E.P.* 4 song 7" EP, 1991
    Screaming Apple Records, Germany
*26 Screams* 17 song LP, 1991
    Skyclad Records, USA
*Smells Like Teenage Psychosis* 4 song 7" EP, 1992
    Pure Lust Productions, Norway
*The Dark Side* 4 song 7" EP, 1992
    Estrus Records, USA
*Why?* 4 song 7" EP, 1993
    Twist Records, Germany
*Loose Ends* 24 song LP, 1993
    Wild Weed Records, France

Also have two songs on the *Shit Too Early* compilation LP on Norway's Big Ball records.

As I mentioned before, vocalist Arne Thelin left **The Cosmic Dropouts** to form this outfit in 1990. Crude garage and R&B is their game, with the early EPs in a style similar to Sweden's **Wylde Mammoths**. The maracas shake and the drums boom, the guitar squeals, and Thelin lets out a moan; these boys want to share a good time!

As their promo sheet puts it, *"The Lust-O-Rama is a raw and frantic garage band, a pounding R&B combo and soulful deliverer of sleazy love songs, and they're really shakin' it when they hit the groove."* I couldn't have said it better.

A string of fine 7" EPs then began to pour out, with a more U.S.-styled garage sound sitting well next to their R&B blasts. There were more than enough tracks to combine for an LP, but the band instead went back into their Norwegian caves to record all new material for their debut long-player.

Their *26 Screams* LP is a culmination of the band's power, with "Another Mistake," "I Want You" and "Won't Be Running" a sample of their solid stompers. **The Lust-O-Rama** is one of those few precious bands that delivers 100% meat on every release — there is no filler, only quality well produced and performed material.

The *Loose Ends* LP is a collection of demos and outtakes — many of which

**THE LUST-O-RAMA, 1991**

appeared on compilation LPs — plus a side of "live" recordings. Any **Lust-O-Rama** fan will find it of great interest.

**The Lust-O-Rama** eventually ran down, and by 1994 Thelin would go onto another quality outfit, **The Kwyet Kings**, as described earlier.

## THE LUTON ARCHIES
*(U.K.)*

A Medway band from mid-'80s.

## THE LYRES
*(Boston, MA USA)*

*Lyres* 4 song 12" EP, 1981
*On Fyre* 11 song LP, 1984
Untitled 4 song 12" EP, 1985
*Touch* 3 song 7" EP, 1988
    New Rose Records, France
"I Really Want You Right Now" b/w "Help You Ann" 45, 1983
*Lyres Lyres* 12 song LP, 1986
    Ace Of Hearts Records, USA
*A Promise Is A Promise* 21 song 2 LPs, 1988
    Star Records, Canada
"We Sell Soul" b/w "Busy Body" 45, 1992
*Some Lyres* 12 song CD, 1994
    Taang! Records, USA
*Happy Now* 13 song LP, 1992
    Impossible Records, Spain
"Ain't Goin' Nowhere" b/w "100CC" 45, 1992?
    Butch Records, USA? (Bootleg)
"Baby (I Still Need Your Lovin')" b/w "Gettin' Plenty Lovin'" 45, 1992
"Boston" b/w "Shake It Some More" 45, 1993

*Those Lyres* 26 song CD, 1995
"Give Your Love To Me" b/w "Security" 45, 1995
   Norton Records, USA
"Self-Centered Girl" b/w
   "What's A Girl Like You Doing In A Place Like This?"
   45, 1993
   Telstar Records, USA
"Stay Away" b/w "Grounded" 45, 1993
"7" b/w "Feeling No Pain" 45, 1995
   Moulty Records, USA
Untitled 3 song 7" EP, 1994
   That's Entertainment Records, Norway
"Baby It's Me" b/w "I'll Make It Up To You" 45, 1994
   Chunk Records, USA

Also *Last Live Show* LP, *Let's Have A Party, Live 1983* LP, *Live At Cantones* LP, *Live In Madrid* LP, plus various other bootlegs and 45s.

**Jeff Conolly** has been known as the "Mono Man" since 1978, spitting out countless slabs of garage mayhem with a revolving door of capable back-up sidemen. He could very well be the most recognizable single figure in the 1980s garage movement, and his legendary tendency toward public drunkenness, fiery vocals and wild stage shows helped bring attention to his string of consistently fine records.

Not quite a best-of collection, *Some Lyres* does gather their debut 45, three live-on-the-radio tracks, four songs not available anywhere else and three other recently vinylized blasts. **Conolly**'s soulful pipes and wheezing Vox Continental keyboards

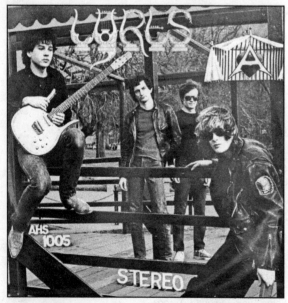

dominate the grooves, along with the patented tremolo guitar and the ever-steady 4/4 beat. An accurate introduction, *Some Lyres* should lead the listener to the used vinyl bins in search of more "Mono Man" madness.

**IZD**

The madness of **The Lyres** is fully the story of **Conolly**, since he alone survived the several dozen back-up musicians in the group's decade-long history. (A somewhat humorous "family tree" of the band takes up the entire inner sleeve of the *A Promise Is A Promise* LP. I doubt that there is a musician in Boston who *hasn't* been in **The Lyres** at one point or another!)

Quite simply, **Conolly** *is* **The Lyres**.

His greatest talent is his ability to inject passion into garage-pop anthems. Whether self-penned or an interpretation of a long-forgotten cover tune, **Conolly** can wring the sweat out of a song like a soul-starved shaman. One could always rely on a **Lyres** record to have that precious balance of garage grit and torch-song emotion.

Joe Longone noted in his *Great Rock 'N' Roll Survey*, however, *"As a performing band, **The Lyres** were less reliable. Depending upon Jeff's mental and physical health, their current lineup, or the place they were playing, they could be one of the best or one of the worst acts to catch."*

It is this volatile personality that made **Conolly** legendary, and also ironically prevented him from breaking into the commercial mainstream. **The Lyres** would break up and reform with new members almost monthly, it seemed, and that instability would take its eventual toll. By 1990 **The Lyres** apparently could not muster any more magic, and **Conolly** seemed a doomed actor without a stage.

Remarkably then, in 1991, **Conolly** and Co. were suddenly back in business, headlining a comeback show in their native Boston. There was talk about a major label record deal, and another round of touring. Some music figures can appear invincible, and it appears that **Jeff Conolly** has fooled the reaper once more.

This author saw **The Lyres** in concert for the first time in the summer of 1993. **Conolly** stumbled into the afternoon sound check already intoxicated, swiped the opening band's pitcher of beer, and fell to the ground in a heap. To say he looked like death warmed over would be kind — and an understatement.

**Conolly** stayed in the corner of the Washington, D.C. club throughout the opening act's set, rolled up on the floor like a ball of clothes. There was some nervous talk amongst the club's manager and the conscious **Lyres** about the show going on, when — almost uncannily on cue — **Conolly** popped to his feet, sprang on stage, and led his band on an hour-long parade of the most powerful garage rock exhibition I've ever witnessed. Amidst the deafening cheers and ringing of the last cymbal hit, he stumbled off the stage and right back into his corner — and was out like the lights.

I've never seen a performance like that — and I can't wait for the next **Lyres** record.

*(An interesting side note: Conolly had his band use Dan Electro brand 1960s guitars and basses on stage and in the studio. One especially cool gold Dan Electro "Lyre" Longhorn guitar was used extensively for the early years of recording and playing — and was featured on the band's first two 12" picture sleeves. It was later sold to a guitarist named Oz — who ended up in Tucson, Arizona — and the guitar would grace another record's cover and grooves:* **The Purple Merkins'** *third 7".)*

## LOS MACANA
(Spain)

Nothing known.

## LA MACCHINA DEL TEMPO
(Verona, Italy)

*Non Ti Votero Mai!* 4 song 7" EP, 1993
    Destination X / AVT Records, Italy

I believe the English translation for the band would be "The Time Machine," which is appropriate for this act's excellent '66 garage reproduction. The title track is the classic cover "Ain't No Friend Of Mine" sung in Italian, and a fine instrumental version of the **Max Frost** track "Shape Of Things To Come" is also a highlight.

The flip side has presumably two originals, the tuneful "Vivo" and also their self-titled theme song. This EP gets a big thumbs up from me — and I was excited to get my hands on the vinyl.

## MAD TURKS
(Australia)

Power pop is belted out in fine fashion on the two tracks I've heard — most probably from a late 1980s 45. "Lolene" features a fine vocal melody and chorus, pretty guitars, and a gentle soft quality pushed along by forceful playing. "Seeing Is Believing" is a more aggressive punk-pop number, without the intricacies needed to separate it from the pack of similar sounding groups.

## MAD VIOLETS
(New York, NY USA)

*World Of...* 5 song 12" EP, 1986
    Lolita Records, France

Vocalist Wendy Wild's on-stage (and offstage) antics are the stuff of legend: she would often undulate in flowery outfits, hurling psychedelic mushrooms into the audience, while wailing away to the sonic backing of her band. Guitarist Dino Sorbello was the other essential ingredient of the **Mad Violets,** and he would later also prove his psilocybic expertise with **The Blacklight Chameleons.**

Together they formed one of the East Coast's best-ever psych-pop groups. Their early demo efforts are scattered on an assortment of compilations, and if collected together they would make an impressive LP. (A cassette of other un-released demos and live material also displays the band's strength, showing that this was one of the most important '80s bands never to release a well-deserved LP.)

Their lone 12", however, is a French issue documenting the band's later lineup which included guitarist Keith Streng from **The Fleshtones.** (Interestingly, the credits for the LP have Streng playing just about everything but guitar!) These tracks have a slicker, more professionally produced polish about them, but don't lose any of that

*MAD VIOLETS, 1985*

Wendy Wild magic.

The first side of the EP is especially strong, with all three tracks exhibiting the difficult combination of both danceability and trippiness. Once again, a collection of these tracks plus some live and demo material would make one of the most lysergic, essential documents of the decade.

For now, find all of their compilations appearances (listed in the "All Together Now" section) and make your own **Mad Violets** "best-of" tape. Some of that magic mushroom power just might rub off on you.

Wendy Wild would go onto to form the all-woman **Das Furlines**, as well as provide strong vocal work for **Peter Zaremba**'s **Love Delegation**. She also sang on a 1994 **Hoodoo Gurus** LP.

I've yet to meet this paisley goddess, but I'm saving my strength.

## MAGIC MINSTRELS
(Belgium)

Nothing known.

## MAGIC POTION
(Rome, Italy)

"I Live With The Monks" b/w "The Mental Traveler" 45, 1986
*Four Wizards In Your Tea* LP, 1988
*Misplaced In Your Perfect World* 10 song LP, 1989
   High Rise Records, Italy

The **Technicolour Dream** lineage is obvious here, with similarly sinewy fuzzed tremolo guitars, trippy vocals and punchy hypnotizing arrangements. The *Misplaced In Your Perfect World* LP delivers all of the above, in an expertly mixed stew of psilocybic pleasure.

"I Feel Possessed" twists and turns with precision, weaving itself into one of the decade's most powerful and memorable psychedelic offerings. The remainder of the *Misplaced* album is equally entrancing, lush and majestically epic in scope.

Their debut 45 is also a special treat, with a pair of extended trippy numbers.

Fans of **Plasticland** or **The Tyrnaround** will find a gold mine of melodic psychedelia after consuming some **Magic Potion**.

## MAJOR DOG & THE GISSUMS
(U.K.)

A Medway band from mid-'80s.

## THE MAKERS
(Spokane, WA USA)

*Hip-notic* 10" EP, 1992
   S.F.T.R.I., USA
"Sometimes Good Guys Don't Waer White" 45, 1992
*Here Comes Trouble* 3 song 7" EP, 1993
3 song 7" promo EP, 1994
*Howl* LP, 1994
   Estrus Records, USA
untitled 3 song 7" EP, 1995
   Dionysus Records, USA

Also *The Devil's Nine Questions* 10" EP/CD (Estrus); "Bust Out" 45 (Rip-Off); "Witchdoctor" 45 (Bag Of Hammers); "Marrianne" 45 (S.F.T.R.I.), *All-Night Riot LP*; and "This Is The Answer" 45 on Get Hip.

Their promo sheet exclaims, *"Surly yet suave. Dashing yet deadly. Fun lovin' yet fierce. These very qualities have made The Makers a fan favorite worldwide. The Makers deliver tough, real, angst-ridden rock'n'roll in the vein of Northwest forefathers The Sonics.*

*"Since forming in late 1991, The Makers have dedicated themselves in giving the bloated corpse of rock with a much needed lipo-sucking. Hailing from Spokane, Washington, a suffocating blue collar town easy of Seattle, The Makers have elevated rioting to an art form."*

Many Northwest bands have attempted to raise the corpse of **The Wailers** and **Sonics**, but none has succeeded like **The Makers**. Their purposely crude recordings are as authentic as any Buck Ormsby session (though he was trying

to make his '60s bands sound good!), while still letting through enough real sound to keep one's ears from bleeding.

The *Here Comes Trouble* EP could have been a long-lost session from '65, with equal doses of frat-rock, garage and R&B squeezed into its dreadful recording. A beautiful color picture sleeve completes the nugget.

The *Howl* LP picks right up with more basic mayhem. The sound and style of this fivesome is more important than any one song, so it's no use trying to pick favorites. Like **The Trashwomen**, most of this stuff ends up sounding alike because of the simplistic recording. The listener either likes the whole idea or not.

And like **The Trashwomen**, I make an exception for this band — the no-fi recordings perfectly reflect these boys' punk garage attitude, and they're just good enough sounding to make it through a side of an LP at a time. Barely.

I know there's at least another album and a few more 45s out as of this writing, but I've been waiting since 1990 for any kind of promo shipment from Estrus Records.

I don't think it's coming!

## LES MANDIES
*(France)*

Nothing known.

## LES MANIACS
*(Geneva, Switzerland)*

Several LPs are available in an aggressive punk style, but with a touch of the requisite garage mentality.

## MAN OR ASTROMAN?
*(Auburn, AL USA)*

*Is It...* 16 song LP, 1993
Estrus Records, USA

This Alabama combo created a stir in the "hip" underground (for a few minutes) in 1993 with this and some subsequent releases. Their basic surf-inspired instrumental formula is augmented by a cheesy 1950s-'60s science-fiction movie ambiance, including aural snippets from obscure movies and cartoons.

The sci-fi theme permeates down to the cover art and song titles: "Invasion Of The Dragonmen," "Journey To The Stars" (a Ventures song), "The Human Calculator" and "Alien Visitors" should give a glimpse into the mindset here.

The playing is competent throughout, with some creative arrangements — and the movie sound bites are funny — but all of this extra stuff is designed to detract the listener from the fact that this music has mostly been done before. Now this isn't necessarily a negative critical assessment — almost all of the sounds described in this book are based somewhat on several generations of pop culture that came before.

More specifically, **Man Or Astroman** could be the perfect definition of a "post-modernist" rock group. Without getting too intelligent here, what I mean is that they take a widely known genre of music — "the surf instrumental" — and infuse it with other influences and media, creating a new whole.

The creation of "media about media" is not a new concept, but it has become increasingly more prevalent in the 1990s, so much that almost all commercial subject matter today — movies, television, music — is an exposition of *itself*, or is a combination of media.

An obvious example: this book is a "post-modernist" reflection of the "garage music revival," which is itself a regurgitation of many types of past media.

O.K., O.K., I'll stop now. Give me a call if you need a further explanation. Quite simply, go buy some of the many **Man Or Astroman** records if you like surf music and strange instrumentals.

They're really cool, dude.

## MANUAL SCAN
*(San Diego, CA USA)*

*Plan Of Action* EP, 1982
    Dance And Stance, USA
2 song flexi, 1986
1 song flexi, 1991
    In The Crowd Magazine, U.K.
*One* 17 track LP, 1986
    Hi-Lo Records, U.K.
*Down Lights* 17 track LP, 1988 (re-issue of U.K. LP)
*Days And Maybes* 5 song 7" EP, 1991
    Susstones Records, USA
*The Lost Sessions* 4 song 7" EP, 1989
    Get Hip Records, USA

This long-running mod-oriented band formed in July 1981, starting with a focus on covers of **Yardbirds, Zombies** and **Beatles** classics. They weathered innumerable member changes throughout the decade, with Bart Mendoza and Kevin Ring remaining as the only original members as the '90s dawned.

Although they somehow kept a very low public profile for the entire decade, they did manage to play shows opening for **The Bangles, Three O'Clock, Rain Parade, Plimsouls, Fuzztones, Marshmallow Overcoat, Lyres,** etc., as well as landing a song in the major studio *A Girl To Die For* motion picture. The film flopped, but is available in video stores, so go rent it and listen closely for their track.

Other performing highlights included a couple visits to England, where they even played at the infamous mod-mecca The Marquee.

As for their recorded output, their LP *Down Lights* is an energetic collection of mod-garage, with a cool version of the *Wild In The Streets* movie song "Shape Of Things To Come" a personal favorite of mine. (This obviously is not to be confused with **The Yardbirds'** "Shape Of Things"!)

Their two subsequent EPs are even more appealing: "The Lost Sessions" featured some fine outtakes from over the years, while "Days And Maybes" featured new band originals plus a spirited rendition of the "James Bond" movie theme. Bart Mendoza's bright vocals and gentle guitar stylings are the highlights, along with some very melodic, sunny songs.

By 1991 Mendoza had adopted for his group the name **The Shambles**, with his personal sound and vision remaining intact. I witnessed several shows during this period, and found the band to be musically adept, lighthearted and enjoyable.

Rarely do hard-working musicians attain their earned success, but these lads deserve continued appreciation because of their dedication to "real" songs in the finest melodic-pop tradition.

## MARBLE ORCHARD
*(Eugene, OR USA)*

"Something Happens" b/w "Ever Think About Me?" 45, 1990
*Savage Sleep* 11 song CD (only), 1991
"It's My Time" b/w "Agent Invisible" 45, 1992
    Estrus Records, USA
*Agent Invisible* 13 song LP, 1992
    September Gurls Records, Germany

Their debut 45 shows-off a gutty guitar-fueled trio, with enough pure punk to please any **Ramones** fan around. It's pure garage with that undefeatable spirit, plus a vibrating blue and orange cover.

It's amazing how much energy they could muster as only a trio, and the band's sound became even more intricate with the addition of a fourth member for their *Savage Sleep* CD. The punk influences widen to include some fuzz-garage, folk-pop and psych as well.

A ferocious version of **The Basement Wall**'s anthem "Never Existed" is one gem, while 12-string jangle of **The Byrds** soars on the band original "You Don't Have To Cry," which rates as one of my favorite folk-pop songs of the genre. A beautiful **McGuinn**-esque solo completes the finely structured pop classic.

Back as a trio, the group also returned to their grungier roots for the *Agent Invisible* LP. Of less interest to the purist garage-head, the LP is nonetheless gutsy throughout — and the end track "Angel Of The Night" an upbeat raga-esque rocker that would have fit in nicely on *Savage Sleep*.

Guitarist/vocalist Ron Kleim pops up in a variety of other Oregon groups, most notably the long-running **Surf Trio**. The reader should track down his efforts post-haste.

## MARBLE SHEEP
*(Tokyo, Japan)*

A noisy modern psych band, with emphasis on feedback and long improvisational jams — with at least four CDs, a flexi, a video and countless cassette releases, all on their own Captain Trip Records. They described their music to me in 1993 this way: *"We play a crystal sound!"*

## MARGIN OF SANITY
*(U.K.)*

Nothing known.

## THE MARIGOLDS
*(Perth, Australia)*

Untitled 3 song 7" EP, 1987
   Easter Records, Australia

This pretty light-weight pop garage effort was produced by Dom Mariani (of **The Stems**) and Kim Williams (of **The Summer Suns**). It's pleasant though not startling. Music fan Milly Muleskinner says that this is the band's second release — *"The first 45 is much sought after and goes for $50!,"* she says. Milly also adds, *"These guys did lots of* Pebbles *at live shows, and had mops (mop-top haircuts)."*

## THE MARSHMALLOWMEN
*(Germany)*

The three song 7" EP from 1989 on Soon To Be Rare Records from Germany has been described to me by Ingo Schittko as *"having no unique style. One song is pure garage, one is more R&B, and the third is more Flower-Power."*

Regardless of their musical orientation, I have respect for any band that has the guts to put the word "marshmallow" in its name, as you are about to read.

## THE MARSHMALLOW OVERCOAT
also known as **THE OVERCOAT**
*(Tucson, AZ USA)*

*as THE MARSHMALLOW OVERCOAT:*

"Groovy Little Trip" b/w "Stop It Baby" 45, 1986
*The Inner Groove* 10 song LP, 1987
*Alive* 4 song "live" EP, 1989
   Dionysus Records, USA
"Suddenly Sunday" b/w "Tomorrow Never Knows" 45, 1988
*Try On...* 14 song LP, 1988
*Beverly Pepper* 8 song 12" EP, 1990
*1986-1990* 22 song CD, 1990
   Get Hip Records, USA
*Try On... & The Inner Groove* 24 song CD, 1994
*All You Need Is Fuzz* 22 song CD, 1994
   Collectables Records, USA
*The Baroque Sound Of...* 16 song LP, 1995
   Misty Lane/Helter Skelter Records, Italy

*As THE OVERCOAT:*

*Three Chords...And A Cloud Of Dust!*
   10 song LP / 12 song CD, 1991
   Dionysus Records, USA
"Season Of The Witch" b/w "1000 Years Ago" 45, 1991
   Face Records, Italy
*Fuzz, Screams & Tambourines!* 19 song "live" CD, 1992
   Kinetic Vibes Records, France

*A Touch Of Evil* 13 song LP / 15 song CD, 1993
   Music Maniac Records, Germany

Plus many compilation EPs and LPs, as described later.

Video: "Stop It Baby," 1986; "Suddenly Sunday," 1988; "13 Ghosts," 1990; *Video Ghosts 1986-1990* 45-minute compilation video; "The Mummy" 1991, "Bones Crack" 1993, many live concerts.

I'll always be grateful that I was in a garage band. My experiences making this music lead directly to the creation of this book — and to my efforts to share the appreciation for the garage band culture.

I've written more than 200,000 words supporting *other* groups in this book — so I ask the reader to

**THE MARSHMALLOW OVERCOAT, 1990**

bear with these few more words concerning my own creation.

I also think **The Marshmallow Overcoat's** story illustrates commonalties with *many* bands of the era — hence the amount of details that ensue.

The following is reprinted from the 1995 liner notes written by Marcus Tybalt, Jr. for the *Baroque Sound* LP.

Garage and psychedelic music ignites a passion which takes hold at an early age. *"When I was a little kid, my older brother would play all these great '60s records,"* **Marshmallow Overcoat** founder Timothy Gassen told the *San Diego Union* in 1991.

The singer and songwriter explained, *"I remember* **The Jefferson Airplane** *on the turntable,* **The Doors** *on the radio and* **The Beatles** *on our old black-and-white TV. These things infected me from the time I was five, and the stage was set from that point on."*

**125**

The infection blossomed in the spring of 1986, when Gassen pushed four other kindred cavemen into a Tucson, Arizona living room to cut their first demo. They didn't know it at the time, but they were triggering a chain reaction leading to international tours, MTV video airplay, college radio chart-toppers and a tireless schedule of recording.

That lovably crude demo turned into their debut "Groovy Little Trip" 45 for Los Angeles' Dionysus Records, and suddenly there was no turning back. The records started pouring out, and by 1995 there were already eight LPs (in various combinations of vinyl and CD) and eight 45s scattered on labels throughout the globe, plus innumerable compilation appearances.

Critics were confused, dumbfounded, or happily startled at the band's approach and delivery. *"The best material here is capable of peeling the fluorescent paint off one's walls,"* wrote the *Arizona Daily Star* in response to their first LP, *The Inner Groove.*

Recorded for $250 in a friend's living-room studio, *The Inner Groove* featured fuzzed Rickenbacker 12-string guitars, a vintage Sears toy organ and vocals suitably delivered from the bathroom via a long microphone cable. Like most of their later records, it was also drenched in tremolo, reverb, Vox, Farfisa and the wheezings of a broken old "Kustom Kraft" guitar amplifier.

Bigger budgets and more elaborate studios ensued, with the resulting albums bringing more widespread praise. *"The Overcoat has the roller coaster lilt of sheer pop and the feel of magic,"* exclaimed England's *Unhinged Magazine*, while back in the U.S., *Buzz Magazine* observed that **The Marshmallow Overcoat** *"is the cerebral nugget that blows the lid off the underground!"*

The U.K. psychedelic bible *Freakbeat Magazine* contended their second album *"Try On... The Marshmallow Overcoat should be listened to 1000 times. This LP holds its own with the most revered of classics."* Similar sentiments showered each subsequent LP, especially a crescendo of glowing reviews for 1993's *A Touch Of Evil.*

And as the recording studio became a second home, so did the tour van. **The Marshmallow Overcoat** wore out countless tires on American and Canadian roads, blasting the fuzz and Farfisa throughout the hemisphere.

Along the way they swore they saw **The 13th Floor Elevators' Roky Erikson** in his native Austin, Texas, so they played "Tried To Hide" just for him.

**Arthur Lee** of **Love** stood in the front row at one Los Angeles gig, then came backstage to thank the band for doing justice to his "7 & 7 Is." **Lee** was back the next night to see the combo at another club, leaning on a pool cue, posing for photos with the band. (Gassen later added several more choice **Love** cuts to the set).

The everlastingly-freaky **Seeds** frontman **Sky Saxon** also jumped up on stage with the lads during a San Francisco outing, but they escaped (musically and physically) unscathed.

A two-month 1992 European tour prompted wild shows from Holland all the way to Greece, as the band's infamously sweaty stage show scorched the Continent. France's *Kinetic Vibes Magazine* wrote that the band *"creates an apocalyptic universe of shapes and colours...an alchemy of sounds that subliminally invade the depths of our minds and spin in the unexplored zones of our psyche."*

Italy's *Davy Magazine* also reacted strongly to the European invasion. *"Like a piece of wood left too long in the rain, The Overcoat has assumed weird and twisted forms. Music from the last outpost of the world could hardly be more mysterious."*

Musically, they gladly credit the cream of the original garage/psych crop as their fathers. **The Overcoat's** records are jammed with loving nods to **The Chocolate Watch Band, Blues Magoos, Strawberry Alarm Clock**, and **Music Machine**, among countless others.

Hardly a one-man show, Gassen has enjoyed the fortune of some remarkable collaborators. Studio and concert engineer Randy McReynolds is the techno-wizard behind most of the band's best moments, and video-god Ray Frieders helped produce a barrage of quality video that spread the band's sights and sounds the world over. MTV even picked up on the buzz, airing the "13 Ghosts" clip, while countless other international music shows aired the film-videos for "Suddenly Sunday," "The Mummy" and "Bones Crack."

The most notable musicians in the fold kept the faith and never left — virtuoso keyboardist Debra Dickey signed on in 1988, and multi-instrumentalist/bass specialist Sean Randel jumped aboard in '91. They formed with Gassen a triumvirate of force that kept the band vital, creatively productive and defiantly unbowed.

The lava-lamp anthems of this desert band might be heard as only musical graffiti to the uninformed. Perhaps only true believers can understand these sounds as the indelible benchmarks of a paisley-punk mission.

But **The Marshmallow Overcoat** won't be forgotten — there's a band in a garage down the street right now trying hard to learn their songs.

*— by Marcus Tybalt, Jr.*

## MARYLAND COOKIES
*(Johanneshov, Sweden)*

"Don't Lie To Me" b/w "Into The Primitive" 45, 1986
*Open Up!* 11 song LP, 1988
   Rainbow Music, Sweden

Hot on the heels of **The Nomads** came **The Maryland Cookies**, with their own stab at fuzzed-out garage punk. There's an indescribable Swedish atmosphere to this disc that sets it apart from its American cousins; the nitro-fueled tunes and European flavor are quite enjoyable and unique, and I like the **Buddy Holly**-esque hiccup vocals on the A-side.

The flip, "Into The Primitive," is a pounding anthem about the virtues of garage rock, and closes out this very impressive debut.

The subsequent *Open Up!* LP continued the band's strong showing, with less of an obvious garage slant, and more of a mainstream rock style. It is a professional disc by any standards, and compares favorably to any of the later **Nomads** efforts.

Not merely a **Nomads** clone, however, **The Maryland Cookies** had their own distinctive (and brief) garage taste.

## MATHMOS
*(Melbourne, Australia)*

A 1960s punk style band which never recorded. They were featured in *Feline Frenzy Magazine #7*, began in mid-'87 and lasted until 1992. They have been described as sounding like the fictional **Sacred Cows** band which appeared on the *Get Smart* TV show (i.e.. their music is "trance enducing").

The **Mathmos** derived their name from the movie *Barberella* — **Mathmos** was the liquid-like solution with evil powers which controlled the "City of Darkness."

## MAT & THE GNATS
*(Berkeley, CA USA)*

An R&B garage band which did a couple of shows, featuring members of other San Francisco area bands. They never recorded but live tapes have circulated.

## MAZZY STAR
*(Los Angeles, CA USA)*

*She Hangs Brightly* 11 song CD, 1990
   Rough Trade Records, USA
*So Tonight That I Might See* 10 song CD, 1993
   Capitol Records, USA

You might want to skip ahead to the entry on **Opal** before reading on about **Mazzy Star**, as the two bands are intertwined — and **Opal** came first chronologically, if not alphabetically.

This said, it's eerie how **David Roback** replaced **Kendra Smith** with **Hope Sandoval**, then almost completely replicated Smith's vocal style on **Mazzy Star**'s debut. **Sandoval**'s voice is a bit richer and

*MAZZY STAR, 1993*

more evocative than **Smith**'s, but the phrasing, style and delivery is almost a carbon copy of **Opal**'s best work. This is not a complaint, but a rather strange observation.

**Roback** continues to mine the school of hushed understatement once again, as his muted guitar work and **Sandoval**'s lush vocals are quietly enveloping. The brooding mood and sparse instrumentation sounds more like the **Velvet Underground** than any of **Opal**'s efforts, which once again is not necessarily a criticism.

Like the best of **Roback**'s previous work, this is

mesmerizing, beautifully constructed music. It's obvious that **Roback** knows exactly what he wants to evoke, no matter who the singer might be.

**Mazzy Star** finally broke through somehow into commercial acceptance late in 1994, almost a year after their second LP was released. They even rated several pages in the October 20, 1994 edition of the ultra-commercial *Rolling Stone Magazine*, and gained considerable MTV airplay with several excellent super-8 low budget videos. In 1995 they were even featured on the soundtrack album for the mega-budget *Batman Forever* film.

I guess that miracles can exist.

## MEDFLY INVASION
*(Bologna, Italy)*

A rock & psych act, with the *First Fly* private cassette, 1987.

## THE M-8os
*(Norfolk, VA USA)*

"You've Been Told" b/w "What I'm After" 45, 1989
*In A Fury* 16 song LP, 1993
    Get Hip Records, USA
"That Ain't All" 45, 1989
    Criminal Records, USA
self-titled 24 song CD, 1993
    Reid Records, USA

The debut 45 is ordinary R&B flavored garage-punk, lacking a bit in atmosphere and mood. The harmonica is a nice touch, but it seems that the band can't figure out if it wants to be a blues band, Euro-'60s Beat combo, or an American garage outfit.

The B-side, "What I'm After," has a bit more emotion to it, but still doesn't answer many questions as to what this band is really all about.

Their first LP followed a 45 on Estrus. **Gregg Kostelich** of **The Cynics** was in the producer's chair, and the album does share some similarity to early **Cynics** — though not quite as dirty or fuzzy.

The band released their own CD of material recorded from 1988-1991, without much overlap from the previous releases. Once again this seems like a band that would pack more of a punch in a small smoky club than on disc.

This band isn't a bomb, just a firecracker that hasn't quite exploded.

## MELTED AMERICANS
*(Brooklyn, NY USA)*

I have no idea what their LP on Mad Hat Records sounds like, but I love that band name.

## THE MEMORIES
*(Germany)*

I've only heard one track, the Merseybeat-ish "Run Run Run," which featured smooth vocals, fine harmonies, bright guitar, and an infectious chorus. If this ended up on vinyl it is a must-have.

## MERIK TROUT PACT
*(Montreal, Canada)*

A local mid-1980s band that reportedly played in a heavier late '60s style.

## LOS MESCALEROS
*(Lyon, France)*

I heard a very cool track, "No, No, No," that might signal other worthy sounds to come from these Frenchmen. They also have at least two LPs.

## THE METEORS
*(U.K.)*

An influential band with a psycho-rockabilly & **Cramps** sound from the mid to late -'80s. The U.K. psychobilly "trash" scene was associated somewhat with the garage revival, though it probably should be considered a sub-genre all to itself — and outside the scope of this book.

## THE MICE
*(Ontario, CA USA)*

"Winter Ocean Mary Go Round" b/w "I Can Fly" 45, 1987
    Voxx Records, USA

**Greg Shaw** told me that **The Mice** sent him a demo tape exhibiting a variety of styles, from metal to pop to electronic. The idea was to get Shaw to like at least two songs for a 45! Well the ploy worked, and Voxx released two psych pop numbers in the finest (1967) **Pink Floyd-Beatles** tradition.

Backwards guitar, dreamy vocals and a general trippy atmosphere make this a surprise bulls-eye hit.

I don't care if this was just a one-off attempt at a record deal; both songs are very cool, indeed.

*(Note: there were several other groups of Mice scurrying through the 1980s.)*

## MIDNIGHT MEN
*(Belgium)*

*Mondo Teeno Experience* 12 song LP, 1990
    Punk, Etc. Records, Belgium
*Midnight Confidential* 12 song LP, 1990
    Wipe Out Records, Greece

Their debut LP of loud guitars falls closer to **The Ramones** than '60s punk, but the garage sound does pop up in revved-up covers of "Night Of The Sadist" and "Invisible Creatures" — which is *actually* the song "Invisible People." You see, the band changed the title and some words, and then took writing credit for the classic '60s song!

The promo stuff (and LP cover) wants you to know that there are two women in the band, although this fact does not necessarily make the band any better.

Their second LP is a reissue of their 1987 six song debut EP and other assorted outtakes — and is actually the better of the two. The energy is more out of control and less calculated, and some of the stuff is simply awful and weird — "Kill Paul McCartney" and "Sidewalk Surfin'" fall into that category. Some other well-worn garage covers are thrown in, but I'm just not impressed.

Just watch, **The Midnight Men** will probably be my favorite group by the time that the third edition of this book rolls out. I've changed my mind before.

## THEE MIGHTY CAESARS (See "Billy Childish")
*(U.K.)*

## MILKSHAKES (See "Billy Childish")
*(U.K.)*

## THE MIND SET
*(Whitby, ON Canada)*

A four song demo of this psych band, 1989, has circulated. They reportedly became more pop oriented in the early 1990s, but with no known product.

## THE MINERS OF MUZO
*(Holland)*

Several discs are available — some of which include the 1984 six song *In Surf Of Fish* EP, the 1985 *Apogee* LP, the 1987 *Dig Deep For...* LP (all on Eksakt Records), The *Make My Day* 10 song LP, and the 1991 "No One" b/w "Psychedelic Relic" 45 on Silenz Records. They seem only partially related to the garage genre.

## THE MINSTRELS
*(Quebec City/Montreal, PQ Canada)*

*Come Out To Play* 6 song 12" EP, 1990
    What Wave Records, Canada

Dave and Rena O'Halloran of *What Wave Magazine* managed to branch out into releasing a few discs on their own label, with **The Minstrels** being their first (and only) 12" effort. Staunch promoters of the Canadian scene, *What Wave* continually made north-of-the-border music available to world audiences, and **The Minstrels** were a worthy target for their help.

There's a certain naive charm about this young band, dressed in early '60s suits, ties and turtlenecks. Some of the sound here is like a polite Hamburg-era **Beatles**, with emphasis put on melody and harmony rather than R&B bluster. "She's A Real Scream" especially mines this early Mersey style, though lacking real fiery abandon and grit.

**Byrds**-**Beatles**-styled jangle pop is documented on the immediately hummable "Rose Is Gone Away," with its hauntingly beautiful chorus and guitar riff. I especially enjoy the call and response vocal *"Rose Is Gone Away...Bye Bye...."* A 12-string Rickenbacker guitar solo would have made this track an instant classic, but it stands as a fine effort nonetheless.

These young lads understood how to construct toe-tapping hummable pop-garage songs. They just needed to let loose a little and summon up an occasional growl.

They reportedly relocated to New Orleans (?!?) for a brief stint in the early 1990s, with unknown results.

## MIRACLE BIRDS
*(U.K.)*

Unknown, circa 1992.

## THE MIRACLE WORKERS
(Portland, OR USA)

Untitled 4 song 7" EP, 1984
    Moxie Records, USA
*1000 Micrograms Of...* 6 song, 12" EP, 1984
    Sounds Interesting Records, USA
*Inside Out* 13 song LP, 1985
    Voxx Records, USA
*Halloween Wake* 90-minute cassette, 1985
    Miracle Workers Fan Club, USA
"Blue Girl" (split) 45, 1987
    Lost Trails Magazine, Italy
"Strange Little Girl" b/w "Green Fuz" 45, 1989
*Moxie's Revenge* 12 song LP, 1989
    Get Hip Records, USA

The U.S. Pacific Northwest was a teeming hotbed for garage music in the 1960s. The legendary exploits of **The Sonics, Wailers, Paul Revere And The Raiders** and so on are widely known and appreciated.

Portland's **Miracle Workers** now join the ranks of these seminal rock bands as a testament to the

**MIRACLE WORKERS, circa 1986**

enduring power of the garage mystique. **The Miracle Workers** maintained a stable lineup for most of their (garage) existence, and this fact enabled them to become a tight-knit core of songwriters and performers. Their knack for song arrangement and execution is second to none, as they repeatedly produced

tracks to rival those of their own past heroes.

Their 1984 debut EP on Moxie displays raw punk stylings, featuring two covers and two blistering originals. **Fred Cole** (formerly of 1960s bands **The Weeds** & **Lollipop Shoppe** — and now **Dead Moon**) helped out with the gritty production.

A 12" EP followed, with more raw and powerful songs captured via a crude four-track tape recorder. It is their Voxx LP *Inside Out*, however, that cemented the band's reputation as one of the most forceful of the new garage breed. The 13 track monster is a bonanza of fuzz and Farfisa, managing to both pay homage to the past while blazing **The Miracle Workers'** own aggressive sound. (Hard-core punk radio shows even played the LP's frantic opening track, "Go Now," without any mention of a "retro '60s" connection).

The sound is confident and loud, without a single trace of quaintness or nostalgic reverence. *Inside Out* is a classic rock record by any standard; it just happens that it fits in nicely with everything that's exciting about garage music.

Guitarist/organist Danny Demiankow chatted with me about *Inside Out* at The Cavern Club in April 1986, saying, *"After I had joined the band, the sound started changing, and Joel (Barnett) was becoming dissatisfied with the direction we were going in. He thought we weren't as gnarly as before. I knew **The Seeds** was one of his favorite bands, so I wrote (the song) 'Inside Out' for him. I copped the first two chords of 'Pushin' Too Hard,' and at least in my mind it was like **The Seeds**, and...he liked it!"*

Danny D.'s involvement was an important facet in the band's fusing of the '60s punk sound with contemporary stylings. He actually began playing in the mid-'60s as a teen guitarist in a L.A. band called **Aftermath**, but it took his partnership in the early '80s with **The Miracle Workers** to put his garage knowledge to work.

Demiankow left the band a few months after *Inside Out* saw release, and the band never recovered musically. They moved to Los Angeles permanently, and converted themselves into a more commercially fashionable metal-punk band. Gone was the style and careful arrangements, and **The Workers'** string of miracles was over. They apparently disbanded in the early '90s.

A fine 45 (of older tracks) and the *Moxie's Revenge* compilation LP (of previously released and rare tracks) appeared several years later, reaffirming just how important the band was in its prime. A CD of the Moxie 7" and 12" EP tracks has also appeared.

The band's legacy has certainly not been lost, as

**130**

more than several '90s combos have recorded and released their own versions of **'Workers** originals. The resilient garage spirit inexplicably lives on, and **The Miracle Workers'** magic was an integral link in passing it on from one generation to another.

Danny Demiankow himself sums up their experience in the liner notes for the *Moxie's Revenge* LP, writing, *"Like wizards on speed, the band leapt from song to song until the ceremony crescendoed into a frenzy of fuzz-induced-gnarly-mind-warps and colors spewed across the walls and volume knobs broke off as they reached for Nirvana. Mermaids popped up out of the sea and applauded and suddenly — nothing. It was over."*

## MIRRORS
*(Alice Castello, Italy)*

This is another band with ex-**Effervescent Elephants**. They released "Mirrors In Motion/Let The Music Shining In Your Mind/Listen To The Heart" as a split 7" in *Urlo* zine #4, 1992; and the *From Planet Mirror* private cassette also from 1992.

## THE MISANTHROPES
*(Harrisburg, PA USA)*

*Why Do You Treat Me So Bad* 3 song 7" EP, 1988
   Get Hip Records, USA

This is the sound of **The Yardbirds** in the garage, the door locked, with a car spewing exhaust into the band's face.

The title track to this debut EP has been hailed by some fans as one of the most gritty, powerful garage tracks of the decade — and I believe this assessment might be correct. Reverb, fuzz, tambourine and gravely-grumbling vocals crowd the densely mixed track in unrelenting fashion.

The duo of songs on the B-side don't let down, as they clip along at break-neck speed, leaving dented tambourines and drum heads in their wake.

This is aggressive, snotty, out of control rave-up '60s punk rock at its very best (or musically worst, depending on how you look at it). My God, listen to the fuzz on "Waste My Time" — these cats were seriously demented!

A reportedly recorded LP was much anticipated, but never appeared.

## LOS MISERABLES
*(Spain)*

Nothing known.

## THE MISTREATERS
*(London, U.K.)*

*At The River's Edge* 4 song 7" EP, 1988?
   Mystery Scene Records, Germany

The resurgence of European Beat music in the mid-1980s was spearheaded by groups like **The Tell Tale Hearts** and **Thanes**, but **The Mistreaters** are certainly worth a mention as able practitioners of this specific garage accent. Their four song EP sports a beautifully rendered B&W cover, with the music itself aptly crude, energetic and bluesy. The lads are apparently enjoying themselves, and that's worth the price of admission no matter what the style.

As they supposedly used to say in smoky English R&B taverns, "Drive on, gov'ner!"

Glynnis Wilson notes *"Sam, the lead vocalist of The Mistreaters used to be a dead ringer for **Wally Tax**. The band existed for a only short time in the mid-'80s and the single surfaced later."*

## DENNIS MITCHELL AND THE NEW BREED
*(New Jersey, USA)*

"A Teenage Myth" b/w "The Rose Colored Lights" 45, 1986
   Rosy's Records

The 1986 "A Teenage Myth" 45 shows Mitchell and his back-up band mining a mod-pop vein, with interesting melodies and a subdued feel. No further discs appeared, though Mitchell moved to Tucson, Arizona and continued to perform in various power pop bands.

## THE MOCKERS
*(Los Angeles, CA USA)*

The only known appearance for this all-female combo is "Perfect Day" on the *Slipping Through The Cracks* video. It's a pretty catchy **Beatles**-styled pop song, with plenty 'o Rickenbacker and vocal harmonies — the song is much better than the video!

They reportedly changed their name to **The Beat Birds** in the early 1990s, still with no confirmed vinyl.

*(Note: Don't confuse this band with the South American **Mockers** from the 1960s.)*

## THE MOCKING BYRDS
*(Gijon, Spain)*

Untitled 4 song 7" EP, 1995
  Thunder Pussy Records, Spain

One would think that this is a jangle pop band based on the **"Byrds"** appropriation, but these Spaniards follow a crude R&B-based garage archetype instead. Good backing vocals and a shimmering organ track make "You'll Never Realize" the EP's highlight.

Teen energy and a gritty mono recording move the entire disc along — and I'm sure these lads would make a fun night on a bill with their label mates **Dr. Explosion.**

## MOD FUN
*(New Jersey, USA)*

*Hangin' Round* 3 song 7" EP, 1986
  Making Tyme Records, USA

Mick London & Co. gained some popularity in the 1980s mod community, releasing at least the *Hangin' Round* 3 song EP in 1986 plus the *90 Wardour St.* 12" EP and the *Dorothy's Dream* LP. This is pretty light-weight stuff, heavy only on the mod fashions. London would later go onto the even less interesting **Crocodile Shop.**

The 1980s Mod scene only intersects occasionally with the garage sounds that are the focus of this book. It is a matter of arguable opinion and taste to exactly what degree of importance the mods are to the garage and psych "scene" — whether it's from the 1960s or '80s-'90s.

I'll leave a more detailed account of their 1980s and '90s sub-culture to others.

## THE MOFFS
*(Australia)*

"Another Day In The Sun" b/w "Clarodomineaux" 45, 1985
*The Moffs* 5 song 12" EP, 1986
"Flowers" b/w "By The Breeze" 45, 1986
"The Traveler" b/w "Quakers Drum" 45, 1987
*Labyrinth* 8 song LP, 1988
*Entomology* LP, 1988?
  Citadel Records, Australia

Originally formed in 1984, **The Moffs** became one of the most heralded and artistic psychedelic bands of the decade. They began their recording journey with an unreleased six song demo from November 1984, and on the value of their later work this would seem a most interesting look at the band's

**THE MOFFS, 1987**

early development.

Their debut 45, "Another Day In The Sun," gained notable critical praise, and England's *Bucketfull Of Brains Magazine* named it the "Single Of The Year, 1985." Its expert building of mood, joyously restrained yet emotional imagery and melodic structure was a good indication of the band's artistic potential, which would subsequently be confirmed by a series of uniformly superb releases.

Their first 12" built on the 45's artistic momentum, giving the band the space to stretch its formula of Eastern Indian melody, soaring guitar flourishes and mesmerizing rhythmic backings. Vocalist/guitarist Tom Kazas would prove to be the backbone of the band, authoring the bulk of material and remaining the band's focal point through various line-up shuffles.

His brooding, evocative vocal style fit the band's introspective aura perfectly, and would occasionally surprise the listener with dramatic outbursts of volume and bluster. His guitar work is even more impressive, with a distinctive and inviting warm tone and energetic but structured style. There are only a few guitarists able to be identified immediately by their unique style, and Kazas is one of those gifted musicians.

Two more fine 45s would come, but didn't fully prepare the listener for the ultimate accumulation of the band's artistic merit, their *Labyrinth* LP. Kazas once again puts all of the group's trademark mysterious sound to use, also blending oboe, cello and various odd synth sounds into his stew of searing guitar and mesmerizing rhythm.

Tracks simmer in calm murkiness only to leap forward into orchestral crescendo, all in epic

**132** proportion. The crystalline production details every brilliant touch and embellishment — the album displays **The Moffs** at the peak of their powers.

The band was unable to gain a commercial spotlight and follow in the steps of fellow Aussies, **The Church,** who often tread on similar ground. The band disintegrated, but their 45s and one unreleased track are collected on the *Entomology* 12", which is a handy disc, seeing as the original 45s are now impossibly rare.

**The Moffs** elevated themselves into the minds of serious music listeners while evoking all the mysterious power of psychedelic music at its best.

Their output is recommended highly to anyone with an ear for greatness.

## LES MOKOS
*(France)*

Nothing known, except that "Mokos" means "boogers" in Spanish.

## THE MOLE PEOPLE
*(Rome, Italy)*

*It's Eerie* 5 song cassette, 1992
    Misty Lane Records, Italy

Brian and Andy of **The Others** recorded some garage tunes as a side project in a bedroom "studio," capturing the crude essence of American '66 garage. Their vinyl output is described in the chapter detailing compilations.

## MONGOLS
*(Montreal, PQ Canada)*

Glynnis Wilson says, *"This was the first 'revival' band in Montreal, and they have influenced a long line of other fine garage and surf bands. Lead singer Kim Shadow fell to his untimely death shortly after the release of their only vinyl release (the* Sleepwalk *LP) which was the first record on the Montreal garage label Primitive Records."*

## THE MONKS
*(Udine, Italy)*

No, this isn't the legendary 1960s legion of weirdos. These **Monks** are reportedly in the **Stooges** vein, perhaps described as "hard" garage punk, and also perhaps too heavy for some tastes. Their releases include the "You Took Me By Surprise" split flexi 7" in

**133**

*Strychnine* zine #1, 1988, and the *Synapsis* LP on Crime Records, 1989.

## THE MONO MEN
*(Bellingham, WA USA)*

"Burning Bush" b/w "Rat Fink" 45, 1989
"I Don't Care" b/w "Jezebel" 45, 1990
*Stop Draggin' Me Down* 11 song LP, 1990
    Estrus Records, USA
*Remind Me* 3 song 7" EP, 1992
    Screaming Apple Records, Germany

Plus many compilation tracks and later releases.

Originally called **The Roofdogs, The Mono Men** developed in the late 1980s into what some observers termed somewhat accurately "the **Cynics** of the great Northwest."

Like their East Coast counterparts, their guitar-stoked sound is simple and lean, with straight-forward ear-bombs aimed right at the listener's temple. They also thank **The Stooges** on the cover of their debut LP, but they certainly don't fall into the popular **Stooge**-copy band mold. **The Mono Men** keep the guitar solos short and (bitter) sweet, with **The Ramones**-meets-**The Sonics** mayhem a much better comparison.

Guitarist Dave Crider has been the driving force behind the **Mono Men**. It is his Estrus Records that releases their vinyl — plus that of other regional acts. Crider is a determined, committed man (some say egotistical and self-important as well), and his one-mindedness helped **The Mono Men** gain credibility and proficiency when many of his peers fell by the wayside.

This author performed a series of shows with **The Mono Men** in 1989 and 1990, and found them to be a sincere bunch of generous garage punks, dedicated to the tough life of underground rock. Most music fans will never know how difficult it is to tour as a rock band — **The Mono Men** know full well.

Headquartered in the small coastal Washington town of Bellingham, **The Mono Men** would travel often to mix with the best of Seattle's exploding guitar-grunge scene, gaining critical praise and notice in the local music awards.

Their early discs would show consistent quality, and never stray from the enduring two and a half chords of grunge joy. Many other EPs, LPs and compilation tracks — though less inspired — have also been unleashed on the grunge-starved populace.

While it appeared a few years ago that **The Mono Men** could have reached out to a wider audience (via their association with Seattle's grunge world), they seem to have settled at this writing into an underground circuit. Fighting off a rash of personnel changes, Crider & his cohorts continue on, but their sound now seems less inspired and more formulaic. I witnessed a 1993 show which found the band to be tired — and disinterested — before a small and equally apathetic audience.

Several other bands (some on his own label) also have observed that **The Mono Men** gain attention simply because their guitarist runs Estrus Records, assuring them of an advertising and distribution spotlight. This might be an unfair assessment, since the early **Mono Men** efforts certainly deserve attention regardless of their origin.

## THE MOOD SIX
*(U.K.)*

*The Difference Is* 10 song LP, 1985
   Psycho Records, U.K.
*A Matter Of!* 12 song LP, 1986
   Passport Records, USA

The music video for the early 1980s **Mood Six** track "Hanging Around" is one of those magical moments — what appeared to be the birth of a new scene, the kindling of the "1980s garage revival" in Britain. It's a colourful exercise in '60s attitude, complete with Carnaby Street fashions, Vox guitars, and a storyline right out of *Help!* The song itself is a wonderful amalgamation of '60s pop and "modern" sensibilities — and as it turned out, it is also the band's high water mark musically.

The later *Difference Is* LP features a watered-down re-recording of "Hanging Around," complete with thudding disco-like drums and a "commercial" arrangement. Abysmal production and daft cover art makes this a quizzical disappointment — but it can't erode that time-capsule of a music video.

The *A Matter Of!* LP is also a complete waste — full of weak "pop" material without a memorable song in sight.

Perhaps the original version of "Hanging Around" is out there somewhere as a 45?

## SCOTT MOODY
*(Tucson, AZ USA)*

self-titled 10 song cassette, 1994
   Slant Six Sound, USA

Guitarist **Scott Moody** gathered some friends into his bedroom recording studio and cranked out 10 slabs of fuzz and surf instrumental madness. There

are loving nods to **Dick Dale, Davie Allen & The Arrows**, as well as contemporaries like **Billy Childish** and **Al Perry**.

**Moody**'s own compositions stand up to his heroes', with "Theme From 'Gringo'" and "Von Zipper" (remember the character from the Beach movies?) leading the way. This stuff is good enough to be released on disc — let's hope at least some of it pops up for wider distribution elsewhere.

## THE MORLOCKS
*(San Diego, CA USA)*

*Emerge* 8 song 12" EP, 1985
   Midnight Records, USA
"She's My Fix" b/w "You Must Not Be Seen As I Am" 45, 1989
   Earache Records, USA
"Under The Wheel" b/w "Hurricane's A Coming" 45, 1990
   Iloki Records, USA

This was one offshoot of **The Gravedigger V**, but this lineup didn't have the original fire of its predecessor. The *Emerge* EP has a beautiful cover, but the grooves themselves were recorded crudely at a rehearsal session. I enjoy the attitude and energy, but this record is crude even by garage standards!

They followed it up with a fake "live" LP (the dreadful *Submerged Alive*) on Epitaph, which is better left unheard. There is also a Yugoslavian (perhaps I should say Croatian) "live" LP *Wake Me I'm Dead* — limited to 500 copies, and containing nine (actual) "live" tracks from 1986-88 and two studio outtakes. The sound is reportedly comparable to the *Emerge* EP.

The two other 45s are limited editions of 750 copies, and are of unknown makeup.

## THE MORTALS
*(Cincinnati, OH USA)*

*Ritual Dimension Of Sound* 12 song LP, 1992
*Bulletproof* 12 song LP, 1994
   Estrus Records, USA

Two former **Cybermen** contributed to this combo, which formed in 1989 and took a mod-pop approach and dirtied it up quite a bit. (They claim to cover in concert **The Creation, The Partridge Family** and **Captain Beefheart!**)

A demo with at least three also tracks exist, including a cool version of the *Our Man Flint* movie theme.

The *Ritual Dimension Of Sound* LP is **134** quite a bit dirtier and more distorted than I first believed. The cover art is a beautiful parody of 1950s exotic cocktail LP sleeves, but the music inside is a very — dare I say it — crunchy and almost "grungey" — wow, I hate that word.

The dual guitars dominate the proceedings, but like a similarly mis-fired **Woggles** record, a hasty recording produced by Dave Crider hurts the band. The sleeve notes say that the entire LP was "Recorded and mixed in 35 hours," and the lack of time shows — every song has the same mix and arrangement, which quickly becomes dull. Now this isn't necessarily the band's problem — any group becomes monotonous if a record's production betrays it.

The *Bulletproof* LP has another clever sleeve, this time reminiscent of a James Bond movie soundtrack. The production — done in their native Cincinnati — is better, with "Psychlone" an especially effective punk groover. Still, a bit of variety in arrangement would have been a help — the mind wanders after too many hits over the head by over-amped guitars.

Yes, I know, there are some other records out by **The Mortals**. This was all I could dig up.

## THE MORTICIANS
*(Sussex, U.K.)*

*Freak Out With ...* 12 song LP, 1987
    Tin Soldier Records, U.K.
*She's Like Heroin* 8 song LP, 1988
    Distortion Records, U.K.

**The Morticians** came together in 1986 from the remnants of the curiously named **Giant Sunhorse**. Their new name was in homage to Carolyn Jones' character "Morticia" on the 1960s TV show, *The Addams Family*, and they even wrote a song titled "Carolyn" for their first LP.

They said their early gigs were *"played to local crowds, proving to be frustrating affairs complete with fights at the bar, audiences walking out, continual requests to turn-down by management and general apathy for anything that was not top 10 material."*

Their first LP sleeve was not meant to signal a musical imitation of **Frank Zappa**, though the LP cover parodies the **Mothers'** own *Freak Out* LP. (Super obscure collectors' note: The first press of the LP has purple ink on the sleeves; the re-press has a different label and green ink on the sleeves). The disc is separated into "punk" and "psych" sides, with one containing covers of well-known '66 classics such as "Sweet Young Thing," "Blackout At Gretely" and "Action

Woman," while the other features extended original guitar jams.

The second LP is a collection of outtakes, demos and "live" tracks, marking an end to the recordings available, though there is word that a re-formed lineup recorded more material in 1991.

Members went on to form **The** (U.K.) **Immediates**.

## THE MORTICIANS
*(Montreal, PQ Canada)*

This is not the U.K. group — these lads went on to become **The Cryptics**.

## THE MOSQUITOS
*(New York, NY USA)*

*That Was Then, This Is Now* 5 song 12" EP, 1985
    Valhalla Records, USA

Video: "Hang," 1984

They took their band name from the mid-'60s TV comedy show *Gilligan's Island*, (where a hip garage band was briefly shipwrecked with the castaways) so you know these guys had a sense of humor.

They contributed their roughest song, "Darn Well," to the essential *Garage Sale* compilation

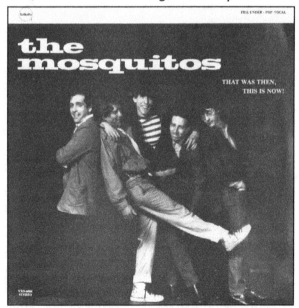

cassette, and a video for the melodic "Hang" showed that **The Mosquitos** were on their way up. (To my knowledge, "Hang" never appeared on vinyl, though it is by far the band's most memorable, melodic and enjoyable track.)

The band then issued their own five song EP, and suddenly the garage edges were smoothed

**135**

away, leaving a less interesting — though accomplished — pop band. The joyously **Beatle**sque "I Know A Secret" is really the only hint at their '60s garage roots, as vocalist/guitarist Vance Brescia shows off his melodic songwriting skills instead of rock muscle.

This proved to be commercially profitable, as the partially reformed **Monkees** had a smash hit in 1986 with Brescia's "That Was Then, This Is Now." **The Mosquitos'** version is on the EP, and is very close to the top 40 version, though thankfully absent of synthesizers! (Brescia long admired the **Monkees'** style of '60s pop, and he said that it was especially rewarding for him to see his idols turn his homage into their hit song.)

This was one rare instance where the '60s garage underground and the top-40 intersected, though Brescia's songwriting talent could well have contributed hits via his own band, **The Mosquitos**.

## THE MOTOR WEIRDOS
*(Nuremberg, Germany)*

A psychedelic-pop act with an untitled 1987 LP, the *Wicked* five song 12" EP (1988), and the 1990 *Cheepo Magic* LP, all on Glitterhouse Records. The first two have been recommended to me — the third has been described as commercial heavy rock.

## THE MOTHS
*(U.K.)*

Self Titled 3 song 12" EP, 1988
  Distortion Records, U.K.

also the *Summer Snow* debut LP.

The EP contains Rickenbacker guitar pop of some interest, though I haven't seen or heard the subsequent LP.

## THE MOUNT McKINLEYS
*(Pittsburgh, PA USA)*

"Drag You" b/w "Degeneration" and one unlisted song, 45, 1992?
  Ape City Records, USA
*Thrill Thrill Thrill* 4 song 7" EP, 1992
*Going To Pieces* 3 song 7" EP, 1993?
  Mummified Sounds, USA

Just a hint to collectors: buy any 45 that has the creature from the *Not Of This Earth* sci-fi movie on its cover. This is usually a sign that the band plays demented surf-garage, recorded in lo-fi with little regard for

**136**

musical conventions or rules.

Well, at least that's how it works with **The Mount McKinleys**. I was first introduced to their brand of light-hearted mayhem by bassist Dave Vecunich — when he was on tour playing in **The Cynics**. He was kind enough to toss the *Going To Pieces* slab my way, and from there I worked my way backwards (what's new?) to their prior discs.

All of the 7"s are highly recommended, but my favorite track has to be the "Thrill Thrill Thrill" title track from the second disc. It's a song from the *Get Smart* TV show — performed in one episode by a group called **The Sacred Cows**. Suffice it to say that it is dementia in a bucket.

The *Going To Pieces* EP features the aforementioned sci-fi cover art, and probably their most proficient sounds. The creepy sci-fi mood is especially appropriate, as the richly evocative instrumentals "Theme From The Killers" and "El Paso Vs. Itself" proves.

Climb any mountain necessary to tracks down these sounds — they won't disappoint.

## THE MOURNING AFTER
*(Sheffield, U.K.)*

*Do Your Thing* 3 song 7" EP, 1993
  Merry Go-Round Records, U.K.
"Doin' Me In" b/w "Out For The Count" 45, 1995
  Detour Records, U.K.

There is also a self-titled LP that was supposedly recorded in 1991, though I think its release was delayed by record company shenanigans until 1995.

I've heard "Creeping Out Tonight" and "Do Your Thing" from the 7" EP listed above — they show a revved-up fuzz combo, complete with cheese-ball organ and some gritty production. The 1995 45 is in a similar vein, though with some "woofy" low-tones marring the pressing somewhat. They band is reportedly influenced by **The Kinks, Remains** and **Swamp Rats**, and those sounds are reflected in the few songs I've uncovered.

Did the LP ever appear?

## THE MORNING GLORIES
*(Ramsey, NJ USA)*

"Smile" b/w "Easy" 45, 1992
  Zev Records, USA

The promo sheet for this band's debut 45 was more interesting than most: *"The use of hallucinogenic plants is the basic philosophy of this new band. Everyone should have at least one* psychedelic experience in their lifetime. Mind expanding drugs such as Mushrooms (psilocybin) and LSD by definition are not addictive. They are not used to escape reality like street drugs are (Crack, Cocaine, Alcohol). The experience that one achieves from a psychedelic encounter is extremely beneficial and fulfilling when done responsibly."

They close with, *"The Morning Glories are not a retro, hippie band. They are not into The Grateful Dead and do not associate themselves with the psychedelic movement of the 1960s. There is a new psychedelic movement happening right now, and The Morning Glories are a part of it."*

The 45 is a very modern trip, showing the musician's obvious affection for psychedelic substances.

## THE MOZELLS
*(California, USA)*

This was another of the few all-female '80s outfits playing '60s tinged pop. Some people would make a sexist and clichéd observation by saying that **The Mozells** *"play their instruments like girls."* I'll put it another way: they play very tentatively and unconvincingly.

It is unknown if any vinyl appeared; they did pop up on the *It's Happening* cable-TV show in the mid '80s, and reportedly have at least three demo tapes.

## MR. SONES
*(Milan, Italy)*

Reportedly folk & '60s pop with a self-titled 12" EP on Crazy Mannequin Records, 1989.

## MR. SUAVE
*(Eugene, OR USA)*

*They Call Him...* 4 song 7" EP, 1995
    Real Records/Vendetta Records, U.K.

This is some kind of **Billy Childish** send-up, with tracks like "You Can Call Me Mr. Suave" and "You Can't Keep A Suave Man Down" leading the way.

The sound is suitably crude, with purposely distorted vocals and silly lyrics, and the cover graphics are a hoot. I've been to Eugene, Oregon, so I understand how that place could produce such twisted mayhem — but I didn't realize that it would be a home for ... **Mr. Suave.**

## MUDGANG
*(Belgium)*

This sounds like a hard rock name to me, but I found this band amongst descriptions of other Belgian garage bands, so who knows?

## MULTICOLOURED SHADES
*(Germany)*

Several discs are available in a harder guitar-oriented style. I found them to be only marginally connected to the garage sound, but some European readers felt strongly that they belong in this book.

Some of their releases include a self titled 12" EP, the *House Of Wax* LP, *Sundown City Exit* LP (1987), The *2000 Light Years From Home* 12" EP, 1987, and the *Ranchero* LP on Virgin Records in 1989. I've been told their first 12" is the most garagey, their latest one the least.

## THE MUMMIES
*(San Mateo, CA USA)*

Untitled 4 song 7" EP, 1990
    Pre-B.S. Records, USA
"Out Of Our Tree" b/w "Tall Cool One" 45, 1990
"Intro To The Mummies Play Their Own Records"
    b/w "High Heel Sneakers" 45, 1992
*Play Their Own Records* 15 song LP, 1992
    Estrus Records, USA
*Shitsville* 4 song 7" EP, 1990
    Regal Select Records, USA
"Stronger Than Dirt" b/w "Your Love" 45, 1992
*Never Been Caught* 17 song LP, 1992
    Telstar Records, USA
*Fuck C.D.s! It's...* 14 song LP, 1989
    Hangman Records, U.K.
*Party At Steve's House* 12 song LP, 1994
    Pin Up Records, Germany

Some of the best punk bands of the 1960s had a gimmick. Some band called **The Vikings** probably wore hats with horns. **The Ghouls** would wear Frankenstein masks. And in the 1980s we had **The Mummies**, who would perform on stage wrapped in rags or toilet paper — dressed completely as **Mummies**.

Their first two discs — like all that would follow — are explorations of crude garage and punk noise, in glorious mono, with no regard for just about any musical convention. Fast, furious, fun.

*(And they dress like mummies!)*

They also released a seemingly endless supply of limited edition 45s — and oh my god — even a dreaded CD. The band once swore they would never make

**137**

one, but hey, that easy money is hard to pass up.

*(And they dress like mummies!)*

Their differently titled LPs actually share many of the same rehearsal studio-recorded lo-fi tracks, and are more notable for the cool album covers of the band in their mummy outfits. The *Party At Steve's House* LP, for example, is a very weak attempt at a fake "live" record — they dub in the same pre-recorded snippet of applause before and after each song! The lack of aural quality is made up by the nice photos on the rear sleeve of two band members hanging by nooses.

*(And they dress like mummies!)*

The band is probably more well known now for their snotty attitude than their admittedly limited musical abilities and purposefully crude recordings. The pinnacle of supposedly cool record labels, Seattle's Sub Pop, approached the band in 1990, and here is their response:

*"**The Mummies** wish to have nothing to do with anything Sub Pop puts out or stands for. We don't go for any of your Heavy Metal (excuse me, 'Punk Rock') crap, or your $12 CDs and $15 picture discs in this catalog you've included. So in closing, I guess I could say that we appreciate the offer, but I would only be lying. So Fuck Off. — **The Mummies**."*

I can appreciate that sentiment. I mean, not many bands would have the guts to turn down an "important" label like Sub Pop. **The Mummies** soon took their bad attitude to an extreme, however, going out of their way in an attempt to make almost anyone and everyone hate them — even their former friends, fellow bands and supporters — and they eventually succeeded.

They might think that they are simply "punks," but I suppose others would see them instead as simply "jerks." Perhaps they aren't smart enough to know the difference.

*(But they dress like mummies!)*

**138**

## MUSHROOM GARDEN
*(Los Angeles, CA USA)*

This was a summer 1984 group which played only one gig, consisting of '60s punk classics; a low-quality cassette exists. The band consisted of **Paula Pierce** and Casey Gomez of **The Pandoras**, **Rich Coffee** of **Thee Fourgiven** and **Lee Joseph** of **Yard Trauma**.

## THE MUSHROOMS
*(Athens, Greece)*

At least two LPs exist; reflecting '80s-styled rock as much as '60s psychedelia, if my memory serves me. Their 1989 *Scarecrow Princess* LP definitely put a premium on harder guitar psych.

I also recall that vocalist "D.P. Mushroom" was pressed in the front row of one of **The Overcoat's** Athens, Greece shows. He seemed rather intoxicated, and continually called for the band to play the **13th Elevators'** song "Levitation." He was already apparently levitating himself!

## MUTANT SWAMP THING
*(Tucson, AZ USA)*

An **Al Perry** (of **The Cattle**) solo project, with the very intoxicating clip "Glue Sniffing Revival" on the *Obnoxious Rock & Roll Video Hour*, 1987. It has plenty o' fuzz, with tongue planted firmly in cheek.

## THE MYSTIC EYES
*(Buffalo, NY USA)*

"My Time To Leave" b/w "From Above" 45, 1988
*Our Time To Leave* 14 song LP, 1988
"I Can't Wait To Love You" b/w "Taste Of The Same" 45, 1991
"I Would Marry You Today" (split) 45, 1993
*The Whole World Is Watching* 14 song LP & CD, 1995
  Get Hip Records, USA

Bernie Kugel wrote some of the catchiest, most memorable garage tunes of the decade. His ability to mix the jangle of **The Byrds** with the snot of **The Seeds** was unparalleled in the genre, and his band, **The Mystic Eyes**, was the lucky recipient of his talent.

The band is named after a **Them** song, but they display much more of the American folk-rock sound than any scruffy British R&B styling. They sprinkled a few gems across several compilation LPs, then unleashed the "My Time To Leave" 45. Densely packed with Farfisa and anthemic vocals, this proved a tasty appetizer for their debut LP.

*Our Time To Leave* combines all of the scattered compilation tracks, the "A" side of their 45, plus some new Kugel compositions. "Baby We're Free" is especially engaging, with its chiming **Byrds** riff and wistful strained vocals. Kugel's vocal style is rough and snotty, planting **The Mystic Eyes** firmly in the finest garage tradition.

In more delicate hands some of **The Mystic Eyes'** love songs would be reduced to standard pop. Under Kugel's direction, however, even the most gentle of love songs retains that certain garage-rock edge. The entire LP is a folk-garage fan's dream come true, let down only by the crude cover art.

Kugel would later give one of his songs to label-mates **The Cynics**, and "Girl, You're On My Mind" became one of their best efforts ever.

The second **Mystic Eyes** LP appeared a full *seven years* after the first, but was worth every second of waiting. Folk-rock anthems such as "So Far Away From Here" and "If I Say I Love You" are instant classics, while the album closer, "One Of The Ones," manages to sound eerily like an outtake from a long lost 1960s **Nightcrawlers** session. Both sides of the band's stellar 1991 "I Can't Wait To Love You" 45 are also included.

Simply put, **The Mystic Eyes** are one of the best groups discussed in this book — find their output at all costs.

## THE MYSTREATED
*(Kent, U.K.)*

*10 Boss Cuts* LP, 1992
"Never Question Why" b/w
   "Take A Look In The Mirror" 45, 1995
   Hangman's Daughter Records, U.K.
Untitled 4 song 7" EP, 1992
"Don't Do That" b/w "I Try So Hard" 45, 1995
   S.F.T.R.I. Records, USA
"You Better Run" 45, 1994
*Looking Right Through* 13 song LP, 1994
"She's Gone" b/w
   "Senses Deceiving Me As Time Goes By" 45, 1994
Live At The BBC 4 song 7" EP, 1995
   Twist Records, U.K.

The press sheet for the *Looking Right Through* LP states, *"Formed around May, 1992, **The Mystreated** are a garage punk band creating an authentic 1966 (U.S.) West Coast sound — hair, clothes, Vox amps, Vox guitar and bass, circa 1965 drum kit, Vox P.A., they even go so far as to never mike their gear up live."*

The U.K. mainstream music rag *Melody Maker* even recognized **The Mystreated's** purity of

***THE MYSTREATED, 1993***

purpose. *"Top marks to **The Mystreated** for the most authentic mono-recorded R&B this side of 1965,"* they gushed.

Lynne Aldridge added in *Lime Lizard Magazine*, circa 1994, *"Authenticity comes naturally to **The Mystreated**. Recorded in Mono, this is raw, young, loud and snotty. All your favorite themes are here — boy likes girl, girl hates boy; boy loses girl, feels inadequate; boy thinks girl is leaving, boy gets paranoid — sung in a rough whiny voice accompanied by thudding bass, scratchy guitars (6 & 12 string) and thunderous drums...everything to make you realize that time is relative and only really exists when you're running late."*

I don't know how much I can add except to say that **The Mystreated** have become one of my favorite English garage bands of all time. Their sense of style never outweighs their musical mission, and they never succumb to wimpy or watered down formulas. They are quite simply a powerful exponent of garage rock at its pinnacle of vibrancy. I recommend all of their output wholeheartedly.

Music fan Julian Levsby is responsible for initially bringing **The Mystreated** to my attention. He sent me a tape and some information about the band, ending his letter with the wonderful motto, *"Always Remember...No Fuzz — No Good."*

Those are words to live by.

## THE NARC TWINS
*(Marlboro, NJ USA)*

Another example of free-form home-taping. Here Buck Quickly and Quick Parkly — dubbed **The Narc Twins** — throw in fuzz guitar, found voices, noises and a general sense of chaos into their 1990 cassette, *Life With The Lemons*. They manage to get 20 short "songs" onto the 45 minute tape release.

## THE NASHVILLE RAMBLERS
*(San Diego / San Francisco, CA USA)*

Made up from ex-members of **The Mystery Machine, Gravedigger V** and **The Crawdaddys**, this group mined a power pop sound, best realized on "The Trains," a beautiful song that always send chills up my spine. I believe its only vinyl appearance is on the obscure British Mod compilation LP *American Heart & Soul*, as described in the compilation section of this book.

This is yet another cool band which appears on the *It's Happening* TV show, providing me with the only visual information I have on the group. They continued to play up until at least the mid 1990s — renamed **The Black Diamonds**, I believe.

## LOS NADYNES
*(Barcelona, Spain)*

Glynnis Wilson reports that **Los Nadynes** were a *"Spanish garage band that played '60s punk & surf and featured two girl organ players. The girls were best friends so they would alternate songs and gigs. The band released a demo in 1990, were the lead singer mumbles lyrics to the songs because none of the band knew any English!"*

## THE NASTIES
*(Brisbane, Australia)*

A '60s inspired mod-pop combo from the 1980s, with no known recordings.

## NAZ NOMAD AND THE NIGHTMARES
*(U.K.)*

"Hey Bo Diddley Man" 45, 1983
   bootleg, U.K.
*Give Daddy The Knife Cindy* 12 song LP, 1984
   Big Beat Records, U.K.

O.K., O.K., I know that this is really **The Damned** doing their '60s garage imitation. Their joke was so convincing that one 1980s rock book listed the record as a re-issue of an obscure '60s original!

All the tracks here are obvious covers, save the brief but hilarious knock on **The Seeds** titled "Call Me Sky." The sound is pretty much accurate to the garage sound throughout, with Farfisa and fuzzbox put to good and reverent effect.

One must love the beautifully constructed cover art, which parodies the movie soundtrack LPs of the mid-'60s. O.K., I know it's a joke, but it's a pretty good one at that.

## THE NEEDLES
*(Genf, Switzerland)*

The band name pricks my interest, but I have no information other than the fact they released the *Never Looking Back* six song 12" EP, produced by Robin Willis of **The Flaming Groovies/Barracudas**, on the Phantas Magoria In Tow label in Switzerland. "Action" is a fine mod-pop guitar & organ effort, while "Back To You" is an upbeat shuffle.

"Nice Guy" and "When You're Gone" are also in the upbeat guitar pop tradition, with tight playing and pleasant production. Nothing earth shaking here, but definitely worth a listen.

## THE NEEDS
*(France)*

*Dyin' On Blue Pebbles* 12 song CD, 1992
   Henri Gauby Records, France
"The Nigger" b/w "Sad Hours" 45, 1993
   Weed Records, France

Perhaps I've already mentioned the emergence of French garage bands in the 1990s. There were a few notable outfits throughout the 1980s, but it seems that by the 1990s

**142**

the French bands were more comfortable in letting loose — and have become much more favorably comparable to their English and American counterparts.

**The Needs** definitely fall into this category of "revived French revivalism." Their debut CD is a meaty affair, with a couple well-placed '60s covers ("City Of People" and "I Can Only Give You Everything") but with an emphasis on gutsy original material.

Not strictly a '66 fivesome, some '70s punk energy and pop sensibility melds together with the garage elements — and guest Maki of **The Cryptones** adds some tasty organ as well.

I liked the French wine and bread very much in my stay there, but I think that bands like **The Needs** might be a more important export — at least for the ears.

## LOS NEGATIVOS
*(Barcelona, Spain)*

*Piknik Caleidoscopico* 14 song LP, 1986
    Victoria Records, Spain

**Los Negativos** sang in their native Spanish, and this helps to explain why they were so popular in their home country and little elsewhere. Their debut LP is a Spanish-language hit-parade of the most enjoyable '60s influences. Mid-period **Beatles, Byrds** and psych-pop all explode from the 14 tracks, with some fine vocals completing the picture.

*LOS NEGATIVOS, 1986*

The cover graphics are also beautiful, making this one of the most professionally accomplished albums of the era. I'm always amazed when a record of this magnitude appears on my doorstep from seemingly thin air and from around the globe.

Popularity most likely brought the temptations of money, however, and their later recordings were much less adventurous, relying on pedestrian compositions, the use of horn sections and a general lack of energy.

Sometimes the first efforts of a band are the best, as is the case here. I'd rank their first LP up among the best 20 or so in the genre.

## THE NEPTUNES
*(Australia)*

*Hydrophobia* 6 song 12" EP, 1988
    Citadel Records, Australia

The *Hydrophobia* 12" EP features wonderfully produced slabs of surf-tinged garage pop. A general **Stems** influence is obvious here (and ex-**Stems** drummer Dave Shaw pounds the skins), with sparkling arrangements, first class guitar playing and a professional gloss which doesn't take away from the music but instead makes it one of the best instrumental and vocal surf-garage efforts of the 1980s.

"Juliane" is an especially sparkling, soaring pop song — but all six tunes are of equally high stature, and I'll be singing along to "My Mermaid" for weeks to come.

This is a definite must-have for lovers of surf-garage-power pop.

## THE NERD BIRDS
*(Sydney, Australia)*

Described as trashy authentic '60s punk from the 1980s, with no known recordings.

## THE NERVE
*(Northampton, U.K.)*

This isn't the early 1980s L.A. power punk band featuring a pre-**Plimsouls** Peter Case.

This **Nerve**'s circa 1992 "Dragonfly" b/w "Take Me To The Other Side" 45 is reportedly influenced by **Kaleidoscope** (U.S. & U.K.), **The Nice, Small Faces, Zombies** and **The Nazz**. I can hear those influences, wrapped up in some fine harmonies and tight upbeat playing and production. Some great backward guitar especially makes "Take Me..." a very trippy pop experience, while "Dragonfly" features a majestic chorus and general colourful feeling.

This is very good, indeed.

## NEW SONGS FROM THE BRITISH SIXTIES
*(origin unknown)*

I actually have no idea of the name of this solo artist, who titled his cassette album *New Songs From The British Sixties*. He sent me the cassette for inclusion in this book, listed the songs and included liner notes, but forgot to include his name!

Classic Mersey-pop is the sound, with "Mr. X" pulling off a wonderful vocal cross of **Ray Davies** and **John Lennon**. (He calls it his *"John Lennon meets The Hollies* voice"). All 11 tracks are sparkling melodic originals, full of lilting harmonies and jangley guitars — **The Beatles, Byrds,** early **Bee Gees** and **Badfinger** are the launching points. One song dates as far back as 1978, but I believe this recording to be from the late 1980s, of U.S. origin, and most probably Californian.

Songs like "All For You," "A Hollow Man," "You're Around," and "Everyday Woman" are some of the best Merseybeat tunes ever conceived — even though they came more than 20 years after their inspiration.

Now if I only knew who wrote and sang them.

## NICK NICELY
*(U.K.)*

"Hilly Fields" 45, 1982
    EMI Records, U.K.

All I have to go on is this one song on cassette, but I believe that it was an early '80s single in the U.K. that even managed to dent the bottom of the pop charts. "Hilly Fields" is a wonderful exercise in the "Strawberry Fields"-era **Beatles** sound, complete with lilting harmonies, lush orchestration and wonderfully daft production.

I was compelled to include **Nick Nicely** in this book based solely on hearing this one beautiful song, so I would be most disappointed to hear that the remainder of his output was lame pop or disco.

I'll gladly take any news offered on **Nick Nicely** with utmost interest, and also a copy of this 45!

## NICK RIFF
*(Zanesville, OH USA)*

He released the *From The Heart of Oblivion* LP as a cassette, 1989, though it was later pressed as a vinyl release by Delerium Records in the U.K. It's a one-man show, with some spacey psych ideas mitigated by the obvious drum machine.

## NICOTINE SPYRAL SURFERS
*(Milan, Italy)*

*I Had A Dream* 4 song 7" EP, 1988
*Untitled* 3 song 7" EP, 1989
    Spiral Joint Music, Italy
"Plastic Sonic Pill" b/w "Dharma Bum" 45, 1991?
    Dionysus Records, USA

Also the track "I Had A Dream" is on the *Kaleidoscopic Vibrations* compilation LP.

I've only heard the Dionysus release, and it's a very slow, moody, trippy excursion — as the title "Plastic Sonic Pill" would suggest. There's plenty of wah-wah guitar and pulsating rhythm, but it drags a bit for my taste. The flip is more upbeat, but still doesn't break out into full flight.

Perhaps some chemical or organic help is needed to prepare fully for this band's full effect?

## THE NIGHT STALKERS
*(Vancouver, Canada)*

*Cloud Nine In Outer Space* 5 song cassette, 1990
    no label, Canada

Video: "Sombrio Beach," 1989.

I was able to play a couple shows with these friendly Canadians, and was pleased to discover a creative, adventurous garage-pop band. They contend that they were *"writing pop songs with a twist: a twist of psychedelia, a twist of white noise, a twist of silence, a twist of harmony..."*

Their five song demo shows this attitude of diversity, with odes to surf, psych, garage and pop. The band claimed to have more than 50 original songs in the wings, waiting for a record company to help them make a disc.

In concert I enjoyed all the authentic Vox gear and especially drummer Colin Raesler's op-art spinning bass drum head — the work of genius! **The Night Stalkers** never made it to disc, though, and reportedly changed their name and direction in 1991 toward a more pop-oriented field.

Groups like this make me wonder how many

garage-psych outfits exist without any word reaching outside their circle of friends. It's probably a good number, and that's a shame, because people should have heard about **The Night Stalkers** as well.

Several members went on to join Greg Johnson in **The Worst** — finally releasing some much deserved vinyl.

## THE 99th FLOOR
*(Torino, Italy)*

*Teen Trash #9* 14 song LP & CD, 1993
   Music Maniac Records, Germany

A split LP with **The Others** and **Sciacalli** is still to be released by the Italian label Destination X, and the "Quelli" b/w "One Night Stand" 45 was set for a 1995 release.

The **99th Floor** note that *"garage music has become a traditional genre like blues, country and folk, and the bands nowadays choose this kind of music do it out of dedication and without any kind of commercial concern."*

They began in 1989, led by garage fan extraordinare Paulo Messina, and then bolstered by the addition of **The Sick Rose**'s dynamic frontman Luca Re. I was very lucky to share the stage with the **99th Floor** on their home turf, and to spend

**THE 99th FLOOR, 1992**

time visiting with the band in their homes.

They are perhaps the most sincere musicians I've come across, because they truly believe in the worth and value of their music. Their faith inspires them to help other kindred spirits, and my band was lucky enough to cross their paths.

On stage Luca Re is an intense ball of concentrated vocal fury, and Paolo Messina an inspired guitar demon in the finest '66 tradition. Paolo has a perfect

**T45**

head of black **Beatle**-esque hair, and he says that even now it is difficult for him to retain a mainstream job because of his looks.

**The 99th Floor** quickly established themselves as one of the top European garage bands — they even have their own sheet music published — I can just see symphony musicians tuning up to "Jungle Stomp" or "Losing Your Mind."

Singer Luca Re's voice is unmistakable, and that's the highest possible compliment for any crooner. This Italian throws his deeply resonant emotional pipes completely into a frenzy, backed on their debut LP with a capable supporting cast of garage true-believers.

Fuzz-rock, folk-rock and pop-rock are the flavors here, all delivered without a hint of nostalgia or revisionist apology. The tambourines are flying, the Farfisa organ (made in Italy, of course) wheezes, and the room fills with addled enthusiasm.

Who else but the **99th Floor** has the guts to cover **The Castaways**' cheeseball classic "Liar Liar" and pull it off with a smile on their lips?

Bravo, Luca, Bravo!

## NIRVANA DEVILS
*(Germany)*

The "Some Foreign Shore" b/w "Pure Fun" and "Secret Agent Girl" 45s appeared in 1985 on Exile Records in the U.K., as well as the four song 10" EP *Twisted Tales*. They're also featured on the Raw Cuts #3 compilation LP. They were from Berlin, and there are conflicting reports about them sharing some members with **The Legendary Golden Vampires**.

## NO FUN
*(Lucca, Italy)*

A punk & garage band with the *Mongolia* cassette, 1985; the *No Escape From Ulan Bator* double cassette, 1986; and the *Personal War* 12" EP on Amtal Records, 1987.

## NO FUZZ
*(Arona, Italy)*

A reportedly acid punk band with the "Sickly Chips In Empty Places" 7" on Distorsion Perla Sordia Records, 1991; and the *Inane Theories, Garble Rounds Of, Whole Solutions* 12" EP on the same label, 1992.

## THE NOMADS
*(Stockholm, Sweden)*

"Psycho" 45, 1981
   Noon Records, Sweden
"Night Time" b/w "Boss Hoss" 45, 1982
   Amigo Records, Sweden
*Where The Wolf Bane Blooms* 6 song 12" EP
*Temptation Pays Double* 7 song 12" EP
   Amigo Records, Sweden / Closer Records, France
*Outburst* 12 song LP, 1984
   What Goes On Records, U.K.
"Live" 2 song EP (w/ The Fixed Up), 1984
   Closer Records, France
*She Pays The Rent* 3 song 12" EP, 1985
   Homestead Records, USA
*Stagger In The Snow* 90-minute cassette, 1984
   Fools Rush In Productions (bootleg), Sweden
*Hardware* 10 song LP, 1987
*16 Forever* 3 song 12" EP, 1987
*All Wrecked Up* 11 song LP, 1989
   Amigo Records, Sweden

also the "Showdown" 7" flexi, date unknown, and at least another LP from 1993.

**The Nomads** was the first band to come from Sweden to make amends for the horrible musical damage of their countrymen **Abba.**

They were a real rock group, in other words, and helped erase the image of Swedes as wimpy bell-bottomed fools. **The Nomads** were actually quite a sensation in the mid-1980s, gaining great underground popularity in Europe, and substantial

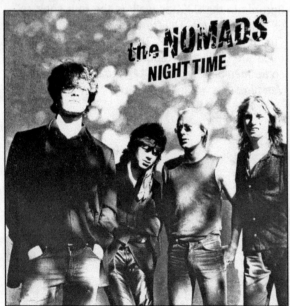

critical acclaim in the U.S. (Their emergence would pave the way for several other top-notch Swedish garage bands as well.)

**The Nomads'** sound was simple: fuzz guitar, fuzz guitar and a little more fuzz guitar. Producer "Four-Eyed" Thomas would make sure the fuzz-quotient was high on just about everything the band recorded, and this sat well with the burgeoning European garage movement.

The band released a few rare 45s and EPs, then broke into larger notoriety with the *Outburst* LP. This battleship of fuzz took the best tracks from their EPs and added a couple more punkers, such as their reckless cover of **The Standells'** "Sometimes Good Guys Don't Wear White." The remainder of the LP is just as good, with a dependence on '60s punk classics, but all done in the highly identifiable **Nomads** style.

**The Nomads** were inspirational — suddenly fuzz-punk seemed new again!

The fan-issued *Stagger In The Snow* cassette showed off some early demo takes and live tracks, proving that these boys could crank-it out in concert. A number of bootleg live LPs appeared as well.

The band then attempted to break into the "big time" commercial market with the *All Wrecked Up* LP, where the '60s punk fuzz was replaced by a more commercial and less interesting hard-rock-metal sound. Several other less inspired discs have subsequently appeared.

Nevertheless, **The Nomads** could be considered the best European garage band of the 1980s, and will surely inspire future generations of Swedes to burn their **Abba** records and crank up the fuzz.

## NO MAN'S LAND
*(Australia)*

"It's Happening Now" is a sprightly performed garage pop song with a moody interlude and some cool organ and guitar interplay, but I know nothing else about these lads from Down Under. This one track was on a free *Going To Au-Go-Go* record label compilation EP.

## NO STRANGE
*(Torino, Italy)*

*Rainbow* cassette
   private press
Self-Titled 5 song 12" EP, 1985
"White Bird" b/w "Fiori Risplendenti" 45, 1986
*L'Universo* 12 song LP, 1987
*Flora Di Romi* LP, 1991
   Toast Records, Italy

Along with **Technicolour Dream** and **Magic Potion**, **No Strange** are one of the finest Italian bands to meld gentle flowing psychedelia in the dreamiest of fashions. The lead-off track from their 1985 12", "Talkin' To The Child," is a wonderfully relaxed instrumental mixture of simple sitar, guitar and pulsing bass — adding up to a mesmerizing mood as thick as any incense. The subsequent vocal tracks are no less entrancing, with tasteful guitar interplay and atmosphere thick enough to scoop up and taste.

The *L'Universo* LP continues the trip, with more staccato guitar plucking, sitar, almost hymn-like vocal lines and a general sense of mystery and majesty.

This is expertly conceptualized and realized psychedelic music with a sense of drama and inner radiance. I remember once sitting in an audience almost hypnotized by the intensely focused performance of Indian sitar legend **Ravi Shankar**, and I get a sense of that same feeling — though actualized with mainly western "rock" instrumentation — from **No Strange**.

## THE NOT MOVING
*(Piacenza, Italy)*

*Strange Dolls* 4 song 7" EP, 1982
    Electric Eye Records, Italy
*Movin' Over* 4 song 7" EP, 1983
*Black 'N Wild* 4 song 12" EP, 1985
*Sinnermen* LP, 1986
*Jesus Loves His Children* 12" EP, 1987
    Spittle Records, Italy
*Flash On You* 10 song LP, 1988
    Electric Eye Records, Italy
*Song Of Myself* 12" EP, 1989
    Wide Records, Italy

This band went through some major musical developments, from odd "New Wave" band to garage psych combo, then to a more gritty rock outfit. The 1982 EP is a stab at addled energy and eerie moodiness; their version of the surf standard "Wipe Out" is certainly unique.

I think their best disc is the *Black 'N Wild* 12", with its thick production and much more developed sense of style. Some searing slide guitar highlights the proceedings, along with a general sense of mystery. This music is dark, almost sinister, and mesmerizing in its way. Some nice shared male and female vocals also set this apart.

I seem to remember that another 12" EP also appeared, featuring a unique version of **The Doors'** "Break On Through," among more originals. The band's sound had really matured by the time of their *Flash On You* LP, however. The sound was more aggressive and guitar-driven than in the past, though their dark atmosphere remained. The band sang in English, although the thick Italian accents sometimes hid that fact.

Nevertheless, this was a polished

**145**

product, and one I'm surprised did not gain more attention in Europe. **The Not Moving** were a fine example of a band taking its 1960s inspirations and shaping them into a contemporary context.

Singer Lilith would go on as a "solo" act (along with Tony Face), singing a mixture of folky torch songs and **Velvet Underground**-ish dirges, including the *Hello I Love Me* 5 song 12" EP in 1990 and the "Venus In Furs" b/w "Tombstone Blues" 45 in 1991.

## THE NOT QUITE
*(Connecticut, USA)*

*The Not Quite* 11 song LP, 1986
"Green Slime" b/w "Circles" 45, 1986
    Resonance Records, Netherlands
*Having A Grunge-Fest With The Not Quite*
    Unreleased LP, circa 1988
*...Or The Beginning* 9 song LP, 1990
    Voxx Records, USA

Video: "Wars Or Hands Of Time," 1986

One does not think of Connecticut when thinking of psychedelic rock strongholds, but **The Not Quite** certainly come to mind as one of the strongest bands in the genre. Their early demos document a band experimenting with all of its favorite influences, from '60s punk to spaced psych. These

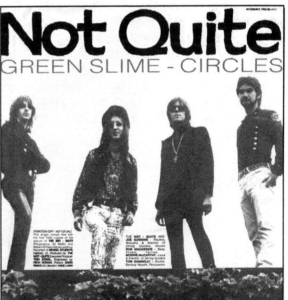

influences would be focused and remain throughout their recordings, to great effect.

Their self-titled debut defines this mixture, with **Byrds**-like ballads and searing fuzzed lysergia sitting side by side. The band gained notoriety for their cover of **The Master's Apprentices'** "Wars Or Hands Of Time," and it jumps from speakers with renewed urgency. A beautiful album cover and clear sound production make this a very fanciful debut, and early pressings of the LP had a bonus 45 with powerful covers of "Circles" and "Green Slime."

A follow-up was recorded, but was reportedly rejected by Resonance for being "too garagey," and so it has never seen the light of day. I can only imagine what treasures wait in these unreleased tapes! Guitarist Joe Guidone then left the band to join the **Double Naught Spys**, citing the usual "musical differences."

This reportedly meant that the band wanted to go in the psych direction, while Guidone wanted to push on into fuzzadelia. This split is not surprising considering the plethora of influences the band had been attempting to encompass.

In any case, with organist Colleen Crane as a replacement, the band finally saw the release of their second LP *...Or The Beginning*. (The master tapes sat completed at Voxx Records for over a year, until finally making their way to the pressing plant — not an unusual event for a Greg Shaw production.)

The psych influence had indeed taken over the band, but with a wonderful effect. The production is lush and mysterious, the vocal harmonies angelic, and the guitar work magnificent. The band's treatment of **The Byrds'** "Draft Morning" far exceeds the original, and their cover of **The Animals'** "When I Was Young" isn't far behind. The remainder of the LP is original, with an emphasis on Morrie McCarthy's lysergic guitar. Only an inept album cover prevents this LP from being a complete classic package.

**The Not Quite** reportedly had another album for Resonance, but I don't think it ever appeared. I'd still like to hear that "rejected" recording, however — I'll bet it's a killer.

## NOUVEAUX RICHES
(France)

Nothing known.

## DAVID NUDELMAN AND THE WILD BREED
(San Francisco, CA USA)

Glynnis Wilson reports, *"This was a '60s garage punk and psychedelic band made up of various members of The Mummies, Phantom Surfers and Wig Torture. The Wild Breed released three 7" EPs in the late '80s and in 1990.*

*"Apparently David Nudelman is quite the character. The Wild Breed's stunt was to become as drunk as possible*

**146**

but still stand and play. (I've never heard of that before — editor) All of their songs are either covers or very weird originals with minimal vocabulary.

*"Their music sounds trashy and lo-fi and is really badly recorded. Records are home made and the record sleeves are just drawn by hand and photocopied. They sound like The Scotsmen or the band that originally does 'Scream Mother Scream.' The band is now called the Three Stoned Men and have a cut on the* Fuck You Spaceman *EP."*

## THE NUMBERS
(USA)

This group managed to release one LP on Voxx in 1983 titled *Anthology '64-'67*. They were attempting to appear as an actual band from the 1960s, with this LP being a collection of tracks supposedly from those years. Well, one listen betrays their plan, because the music just sounds wrong, and isn't very good either. I think they were from Texas.

## THE NUTHINS
(Wiltshire, U.K.)

"Allergic Kiss" b/w "Colour Trip" 45, 1992
    Merry Go-Round Records, U.K.
*Modesty Blaize* 4 song 7" EP, 1994
    Dionysus Records, USA

Also "Why Do I Love Ya?" on a split 7" with the **Slingbacks** for the *Submerge* zine, country of issue unknown.

**The Nuthins** reportedly began as a '60s snot punk band in the mid-'80s, then evolved into the more tuneful outfit that is captured on their two discs.

Their debut 45 is a fun and toe-tapping affair, with some cool organ especially notable. (Organist Bob also plays the glockenspiel — now there's a combination that you don't see everyday in garageland!) "Colour Trip" adds some fuzz and snot back into the proceedings, and is the winner of the two sides.

The follow-up disc is similar in fashion, with the title track possessing a very polished pop feel, while "Ain't Gonna Miss Ya!" shows more grit. The B-side is even better, with "Paid The Price" and "Alternative Medicine" moody combinations of fuzz and verve with a slight psych edge.

Band member Mojo Mills also published the fine *Gravedigger* fanzine, which was one of England's best in 1995.

The band also thanks a chap on their records by the remarkable name of Simon Wigglesworth — ah, the English.

**The Nuthins** were developing into one of Britain's best combos as of mid-1995 — subsequent releases should be of obvious interest.

## OBJECTS
(USA)

The *Live at the Greatwood Cafe* LP, 1978, is reportedly worthwhile.

## THE OFFHOOKS
(U.K.)

*Off The Hook* 6 song 12" EP, 1988
DDT Records, U.K.

Lenny Helsing was one busy beaver during the 1980s. He belonged to at least a half-dozen different musical groups — singing, playing drums, guitar, and I think everything in-between.

**The Offhooks** are another of his projects, and it shouldn't be a surprise that it is also in the Euro-beat school of R&B noise. The performances are energetic and reverent, and once again we see (hear) why this musical form has stood up for so many years; it's fun, simple and has some guts.

Lenny Helsing says, "We also recorded a full LP, *Outside Looking In* for Nightshift Records in 1990, which remains unreleased to this day."

The band split in December, 1991, with band member Calvin Burt heading up a garage outfit called **The Sinister Urge** from February to summer 1993, without any releases.

## THE 1-2-5
(Holland)

**The 1-2-5** is a fine garage outfit which formed in the early 1990s, combining U.S.-styled fuzz garage punk with harmonica driven Nederbeat. They have several fine demos, including a blistering four song cassette from 1993. It included two fiery originals, along with a spirited Tax/Splinter cover, and a

*THE 1-2-5, 1993*

whigged-out fuzz-stab at the **William Penn V** classic "Swami." Another 1993 demo included the grooving original "I Had My Share" and the driving "She's Something Else."

Eric Danno writes in their *Introducing...* cassette, *"Don't expect these recordings to be hi-fi. Don't expect stupid virtuosity either. What counts is the raw energy of the pure garage sound that might hit you right between the eyes. Don't say I didn't warn you."*

They had more than enough quality material to merit a release, but I don't think any vinyl had materialized by 1995.

## THE ONLOOKERS
(London, U.K.)

Julian Levsby reports, *"They formed in 1979 and split in 1982, and were influenced by mid-'60s to late-'60s psych pop bands like **The Smoke, The Creation** and **John's Children**. They were very popular in London — at first by mainly a mod audience — but by early 1981 by the psychedelic crowd as well. Their only vinyl was a 1981 single, 'You And I' b/w 'Please Understand' — which is now something of a collector's item, fetching over 60 pounds (or over $75 U.S.)."*

A 1981 demo displayed sweet harmony vocals, energetic playing and spirited guitar on "How Can You Say That?," "Windsor Castle," "You Know Everything" and "Green Circles." A live tape from a

1981 gig at The Groovy Cellar shows the band tackling a vocally-flanged and revved up version of **The Beatles'** psych-pop classic "Rain."

## ON THE AIR
*(Los Angeles, CA USA)*

An all-girl group which attempted to attract attention through the **Bangles**-style of pop-rock. It's pretty tame actually, without much guts. There is at least one EP extant, and several less-than-professional appearances on the *It's Happening* cable-TV show.

## OPAL
*(Los Angeles, CA USA)*

as *CLAY ALLISON*:
"Fell From the Sun" 45, 1984
*Fell From The Sun* 4 song 12" EP, 1984
    Serpent Records, USA

as *OPAL*:
Untitled 3 song 12" EP, 1985
    One Big Guitar Records, U.K.
*Happy Nightmare Baby* 9 song LP, 1987
    SST Records, USA
*Early Recordings* 12 song LP, 1989
    Rough Trade Records, USA

Video: "Happy Nightmare Baby," 1987.

**Opal** remains to be a special musical entity in my heart.

Guitarist and vocalist David Roback left **The Rain Parade,** and bassist and vocalist Kendra Smith left the **Dream Syndicate** — together they would form in 1983 a magical duo and the backbone of **Opal.**

They recorded an LP worth of material, but only released four of those tracks under the band name **Clay Allison.** (The two tracks from the 45 listed above are included on the 12" EP. Later pressings of the 12" delete the name **Clay Allison,** and simply list the musicians on the front cover.)

One can only wonder why the remainder of the material was not released at that time. A bootleg tape of the entire session shows it to be uniformly strong...but I'm getting ahead of myself — first we must discuss the sound of Roback and Smith.

David Roback is a master at the understated guitar. Lifting a loping slide method right from **Syd Barrett's** fingertips, he is able to transform his guitar into an angelic voice or a growling monster — I suppose that "dynamic" would be the operative adjective.

Kendra Smith brings a gentle, fragile, evocative voice to the duo. Sometimes she seems to be almost whispering, as a velvety reverb encompasses her breath, lushly echoing against Roback's elegant backing. Friend and session-man Keith Mitchell is the other important player, whose precise and orchestral drumming complete the basic form that **Clay Allison/Opal** would take over the years. (Keyboardist Suki Ewers would also contribute significantly to the band's dark and moody sound.)

I was fortunate to witness this lineup perform in the winter of 1984. They played in a small Ohio college bar on a wet and cold night, with a sizable though seemingly disinterested crowd present. The band slid slowly into their set, taking a few minutes to build their sound from a hush before erupted into song. Drummer Mitchell played his tom-toms with the palms of his hands before graduating to mallets and finally drum sticks. I was mesmerized by the brooding tone and presence of the band — and by their total concentration and trance-enducing quality.

The crowd was less than enthralled, however, and squirmed as the band refused to simply kick into a loud beer-drinking anthem. Instead, Roback and Smith slowly fueled their intense and mysterious sound sculpture, even though one could clearly hear the talking of the bar patrons over their gentle tones!

This performance was an affirmation of the belief that music can be emotional and artistic, involving without being boring. The rest of the crowd missed out that night, but I consider myself most fortunate.

A U.K. 12" would follow the **Clay Allison** discs — titled **Opal** for the first time. The three song effort showcases quiet country-folk balladeering on one side, with the psychedelic fuzz monster "Soul Giver" on the flip, all eight minutes and 33 seconds of it. It is here that a certain mystical **Doors** influence began to exert itself.

The usually hardcore punk haven SST issued **Opal's** first long-player, which featured an apparently re-mixed "Soul Giver" and the best song **The Doors** never wrote, "Happy Nightmare Baby." Accompanied by a ghostly black and white music video (shot effectively on super-8 film), "Happy Nightmare Baby" could be the definitive **Opal** "pop" song, as it features the style, grace and power of the band at its best.

Some of the aforementioned unreleased tracks were finally heard on the *Early Recordings* LP, which also collected the **Clay Allison** EP and first **Opal** EP onto one disc. Some of the most cacophonous psych material is still missing from those initial sessions, as the band attempts to paint a quieter, more orderly image for itself on this collection. Still, one listen to a track like "Soul Giver" will give you an idea of what **Opal** was capable of when the volume pedal hit the floor.

Roback and Smith would drift apart, with Roback forming the eerily similar sounding **Mazzy Star**, which was chronicled a few pages back. **Opal** should be considered one of the most artistically successful projects of the decade, however, with my only wish being that they had let out a smile once in a while.

Maybe just a little one.

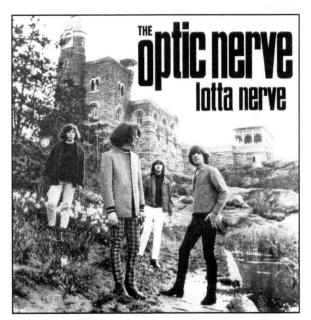

## THE OPTIC NERVE
*(New York, NY USA)*

Untitled 3 song 7" EP, 1986
Untitled 3 song 7" EP, 1988
    Cryptovision Records, USA
*Forever And A Day* 10 song LP & CD, 1993
    Screaming Apple Records, Germany
*Lotta Nerve* 13 song CD, 1994
    Get Hip Records, USA

One might tend to forget that the 1980s garage scene encompassed many separate styles. We've discussed the usual fuzz punk and trippy psych, but **The Optic Nerve** were masters at the art of folk-rock. This was quite a departure for the ex-**Outta Place's** Orin Portnoy, since there are no fuzz boxes or screaming vocalists to be found in **The Optic Nerve.**

This band weaved gentle melodies, harmonies and jingle-jangley guitars in the best **Byrds** meets the **Turtles** jamming with **The Buffalo Springfield** tradition. Their quiet, deliberate songs were an interesting contrast to the rest of the N.Y.C. scene; there were certainly no others adventurous enough to tackle the **Optic Nerve's** stylings.

Two hauntingly beautiful EPs by **The Optic Nerve** escaped unnoticed by almost everyone in the late 1980s. Even their belatedly released LP and CD is from a 1988 session — but the music seems timeless in its appeal and delivery.

Mixing equal doses of early **Dylan, Beatles** and electric country-folk, this New York quintet evokes a gentle, introspective aura. The jangley guitars are balanced with some plaintive harmonica, all topped off with Bobby Belifore and Tony Matura's poignant harmonies — **The Byrds' McGuinn, Crosby** and **Clark** would all be very proud.

The song "What's Been Missing" is the band's crowning achievement, with

its spine-tingling harmonies and hypnotic melody. This would have been heralded as a folk-rock landmark in 1966. In 1996 its simply one of the best pop songs I've ever heard.

The posthumously released *Forever And A Day* LP/CD and the *Lotta Nerve* CD share some tracks, but not all, and feature some dramatically different mixes. *Lotta Nerve* contains all of the EP tracks, which makes it essential. Neither release is a clear-cut winner — the best result comes from taking the best from both discs.

**The Optic Nerve** might only now be receiving the praise they deserved all along — late is better than never, I suppose.

Wonderfully melodic guitar-folk-pop — like **The Optic Nerve's** — is a tymeless flyte.

## THE ORANGE ALABASTER MUSHROOM
*(Kingston, ON Canada)*

Untitled 11 song demo cassette, 1992
    private pressing, Canada

Greg Watson of **The 14th Wray** plays all instruments and supplies vocals to this home-recording dementia. Songs like "I Am The Tree Pie," "Rainbow Man" and "Sidney's Electric Headcheese" should give you an indication of Watson's mindset — somewhere in the area of **Dimentia 13** and **The Laughing Soup Dish.** Plenty of backward warbly guitar, dreamy vocals and general loopiness abound. No vinyl appeared, but their theme song showed up on a *Cryptic Tymes* compilation cassette.

## ORGAN GRINDERS
*(Richmond, VA USA)*

A five song demo exists circa 1986-1987.

## ORIGINAL SINS
*(Bethlehem, PA USA)*

Several LPs and 45s exist, though as the band wore on into the '90s the product became 'heavier," and of less interest. I witnessed one performance at the "South By Southwest Festival" in Austin, Texas, 1990, and was impressed by their volume. They were loud.

## OZRIC TENTACLES
*(U.K.)*

A festival-scene band with many members; their sound was described to me by Ingo Schittko as *"Ethno-Space-Freak-Jazz-Psychedelic. I've never heard anything else like it."*

They have at least four LPs since 1989, including *Pungent Effulgent* (1991), *Erpland* (1990), *Strangeitude* (1991) and *Afterswish* (1991).

## THE OTHERS
*(Rome, Italy)*

"You Better Know Why" b/w "Girl" 45, 1992?
*Teen Trash Volume 7* 15 song LP, 1993
    Music Maniac Records, Germany
*Lost In Time* 18 song LP, 1994
    Misty Lane Records, Italy

Also many promo cassettes, from 1989 to 1995; several split 45s described in the compilation chapter.

Massimo Del Pozzo — aka "Brian '66" — is one of those dedicated archivists who will not let the spirit of garage music die. He operates the Misty Lane record label releasing authentic slabs of '60s pop, garage and psych, while also publishing the *Misty Lane* fanzine of cool music, B-movies and '60s fashion.

His band **The Others** also just happens to be one of the top garage acts in the world.

In person, "Brian '66" is a humble, serious hipster, wearing his **Beatle** boots, leather vest and button-down shirt with stove pipe pants on even the most casual of visits. He was kind enough to show me and my band around Rome a few years ago, casually pointing to The Coliseum or The Vatican as we gawked wide-eyed.

On stage he is a sweating, frantic frontman,

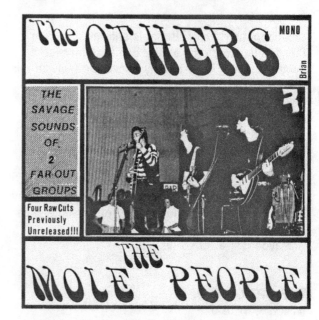

belting out powerful vocals and commanding a sweet tone from his Vox guitars. He is also a generous fellow — putting my band up in a downtown hotel for our duration in Rome. We soon found out why he could afford the rates — it was a well-known hotel for transvestite hookers, and I guess there were a few rooms empty! (It was funny to see our one-time friend Phillippe surrounded by transvestites each time we left or entered the building. Why do transvestite hookers prefer Frenchmen?)

"Brian '66" worked for several years with various lineups of **The Others** before getting any vinyl released. His hard work and dedication paid off — he's released some of the finest garage records described in this book.

Radio host Amazin' Larry says in the liner notes of their *Teen Trash* LP, *"Everything about this band is vintage (the equipment, the clothing, the haircuts) and they've absolutely mastered all the meanest '60s snarl songs that the* Pebbles *or* Back From The Grave *compilations have to offer."*

The tracks from their excellent debut 45 are also on the *Teen Trash* LP, as well as the wonderful "It's Eerie!" and "Fallin' Off My World," which are on another split EP with **The Headstones**. "Brian '66's" expert originals dominate the disc, and are supplemented by cool versions of **The Chocolate Watchband**'s "Loose Lips Sync Ship" and **The Lil' Boys Blue**'s "I'm Not There." It's important to realize that unlike many bands, **The Others** use covers simply as additional tastes — Brian's songs are the meat and main meal.

The second LP is even better, chocked full of shimmering originals and Brian's distinctive vocals. The liner notes explain, *"With* these new cuts **The Others** try to explain their love for the whole '60s decade ... well ... at least until 1967! The folk-punk vein inspired by **The Squires** and the Psychedelic Unknowns, surf combos like **The Vaqueros**; early **Stones** and **Shadows Of Knight** R&B, primal garage-psych à la **The Seeds** or **We The People**; Texas gods like **The Zakary Thax** and obscure comp-only treasures."

This obvious breadth of knowledge and good taste oozes from this LP, which is completed with a very cool color cover photo of the band with a happening Italian sports car.

Massimo Del Pozzo and **The Others** deserve international attention and recognition for their faithful dedication to garage music. They're a time capsule of the very best in '66 folk-garage-punk — and they are worthy of appreciation in the here and now.

## THE OTHER SIDE
*(Holland)*

*Haunted House* 4 song 7" EP, 1985
*Two Sides Of...* 4 song 7" EP, 1986?
  Kelt Records, Holland

Here's another band with only few released tracks and a deservedly elevated reputation. The band slipped in and out of the scene between 1983 and 1987, with these two EPs their best testament, though there are also a few other rare tracks on various compilations as well.

**The Other Side** (not to be confused with a Texas band of the same name) traveled between moody garage ("Haunted House"), '60s pop ("Heartful Of Soul") and folky, melodic beat ("Man With Money"), each with an airy and carefree attitude. This was a band having fun, and they were also accomplished musically.

I'd love to see these EP tracks plus the compilation-only songs put together into one monster LP. This was one Euro-garage group which deserved to see an LP backing up their well-deserved reputation.

The guitarist from **The Other Side** would go onto another fine Euro beat band — **The Kliek**.

## THE OTHER SIDE
*(Dallas, Texas USA)*

This is not the Dutch band; these folks have their own 1985 7" EP on Rockadelic Records, which I seem to remember being a bit psychedelically "progressive" — that is,

kinda 1968-ish. The songs were "People Always," "Everywhere" and "I Want You."

## OTTO'S CHEMICAL LOUNGE
*(Minneapolis, MN USA)*

I seem to remember that the 1983 self-titled 7" EP featured some whigged-out guitars and a trippy atmosphere — somewhat associated with the subject of this book. The disc was produced by Hüsker Dü's Bob Mould. This act developed into a heavier, less interesting combo, if memory serves me.

## THE OUTER LIMITS
*(U.K.)*

A Medway band from mid-'80s.

## OUT OF TIME
*(Bra, Italy)*

*Stories We Can Tell* LP, 1985
  Mail Records, Italy

Reportedly a '60s-styled psych pop band — I did enjoy their cover of **Love**'s "This House Is Not A Motel" on a split 45 with **The Sick Rose** in *Lost Trails Magazine* #2, 1985.

## OUTSIDEINSIDE
*(Los Angeles, CA USA)*

Untitled 8 song 10" EP, 1993
Untitled 3 song 7" EP, 1993
*Six Point Six* 14 song LP & CD, 1994
  Hell Yeah Records, USA

Former Tucsonan **Lee Joseph** has left his long-time band **Yard Trauma** in the dust with the enigmatically titled **Outsideinside**. Their debut 7" is a tasty punk grind and burn, while their 10" is an elegant nugget of psych noise, mood and fire. Their version of "A Musical Tribute To The Oscar Mayer Weiner Wagon" is magical — but it is **Joseph**'s original material that cuts to the bone with emotion, grit and lyrical honesty.

These two early efforts were notable, but only paved the way to their debut LP's blast of furor and **Electric Prunes** meets **Sonic Youth** energy.

Noise, punk, psych and anger all combine to wipe away anything that Seattle might want to call rock — this is the real McCoy, with the track "The Truth" a new underground anthem.

### OUTSIDEINSIDE, 1994

**The Outsideinside** was a monument to **Joseph's** ability to grow and flourish in Los Angeles' decaying environment — the record is titled for one of the devastating SoCal earthquakes — and *Six Point Six* is his crowning accomplishment.

The band managed one West Coast tour, then collapsed in early 1995 after crippling personnel defections. That's quite a shame, since the band was just hitting its stride — but I have a feeling that **Lee Joseph** will be back louder than ever.

### OUTSKIRTS OF INFINITY
(U.K.)

Several discs are available, including *Lord Of The Dark Skies* (1987) on Woronzow, *Scenes From the Dreams Of Angels* on Infinity (1989), and the live *Stoned Crazy* LP from 1989. A heavy guitar sound dominates, sounding at times like **Cream**. They tackle "Tales Of Brave Ulysses" on their debut LP dutifully in that style.

### THE OUTTA PLACE
(New York, NY USA)

*We're Outta Place* 7 song 12" EP, 1984
*Outta Too!!* 7 song 12" EP, 1987
   Midnight Records, USA

**The Outta Place** were dubbed "New York's own Caveteens" by a local character named **Ognir**. (**Ognir** is "Ringo" spelled backwards ... get it?!) Orin Portnoy told me *"Og was the guy who was at all the shows, and hung out until it was time to hang out again. He had a big golden bowl (haircut), and said 'man' a lot. Where he came from no one's sure, and what happened to him no one knows! But he was the mascot of the 'scene.' There is a caricature of him at the front of the new Venus Records (store) in NYC. Did I mention that he was a large man?"* Photos of him show a large mountain of a man!

Portnoy continues about the band's moniker, *"The Outta Place got their name because me and Shari (keyboards) went to the same school and some kid said to us, 'Hey, youz guyz looks outta place!' because we were wearing Beatle boots and paisley! So we put together the band; this was all in 1983 and '84. I was only 16 years old."*

Portnoy also remembers, *"Probably the biggest gig for us was 'Fuzz Fest '84,' which me and my brother Elan put together. We wanted to put together the biggest collection of psych bands ever! We rented a place called 240 West, which is now the 'New Lonestar.'*

*"The show consisted of The Tryfles, The Cheepskates, The Outta Place, The Fuzztones, The Vipers and The Mosquitos. (I believe that I have*

*some video of the night, and it looks wild! — Editor.) It was a big success and the last show for The Outta Place. Guess I'll just sum up The Outta Place by saying we were teen punks who loved to get fucked up and play '60s tunes as garagey as possible!"*

Portnoy would go on to **The Optic Nerve, The Twisted** (with brother Elan), **The Lone Wolves** and **The Primeval Unknown.** He also released a demo in 1990 of aggressive rock tinged with blues and garage called *Out Orin.*

## THE OVERCOAT (see *Marshmallow Overcoat*)

## THE PAINTED AIR
*(Germany)*

*"We're into the harder distorted sounds of psych-rock,"* noted the former co-editor of *Rave On Magazine* and band member Markus Steenbock in 1992.

I don't think they ever recorded.

## PALE DAWN
*(Rome, Italy)*

"Mesmeric Moon" b/w "Before The Faint" 45, 1986
    High Rise Records, Italy

Former **Technicolour Dream** vocalist Marco Conti mined a similar '60s psych-pop field with the only **Pale Dawn** 45 that I know of. It's a quiet, hushed trippy experience, and rates up as highly as the lone **Technicolour Dream** 12".

I think that more releases exist, and I would be keen to hear them.

## THE PANDORAS
*(Los Angeles, CA USA)*

Untitled 4 song 7" EP, 1984
    Moxie Records
*It's About Time* 12 song LP, 1984
"Hot Generation" b/w "You Don't Satisfy" 45, 1984
    (all of the above, plus 3 unreleased tracks are on the Voxx
    *It's About Time* CD, 1993)
    Voxx Records, USA
*Stop Pretending* 12 song LP, 1986
"In And Out Of My Life (In A Day)" b/w "The Hump" 45, 1986
    Rhino Records, USA
*Psychedelic Sluts* 21 song CD, 1994
    Erekta Records (bootleg), USA

Video: *L.A. In* TV show, 1984; *Live At Irving Plaza (N.Y.C.)* concert tape, 1984

*"Talk about authenticity. These girls sound as though they've melted down their **Standells, Syndicate Of Sound, Music Explosion** and **Seeds** singles and are taking them intravenously."*

— Alan diPerna, *BAM Magazine*

Just about everyone connected to the "garage scene" has a story about **Pandoras** leader **Paula Pierce.** The wild blonde Californian reveled in the image of the trashy rock vixen, an image that was certainly based upon her actual experience.

**Pierce**'s musical influences were the cream of the garage crop, and they are apparent in her "original" compositions, many of which are mainly thinly veiled alterations of classic '60s tunes. (The best example is **Pierce**'s "I Live My Life," which is really **The Leaves**' "Too Many People" with new lyrics and altered title.)

**The Pandoras**' debut EP on Moxie is a rare and noisy treat, with an extreme raw edge and abundant energy. It's similar in tone to their first LP, *It's About Time,* with its slightly out-of-tune guitars and sloppy musicianship by **Pierce** and her all-girl back-up band. It should be noted that **Pierce** herself was a fine guitarist, but she at times seemed to surround herself with less than adequate musicians.

Rhino took on the girls for a larger budget effort, *Stop Pretending,* and the band delivered a strong pop garage effort — one of the best for the decade. The songs are more solidly arranged and performed than the debut long-player, **Pierce**'s vocals more aggressive, and the whole package comes across with much more authority. Part of this was due to **Pierce**'s firing of her initial back-up players, and the importing of what she called "thinner" girls. **Pierce** reportedly played all the recorded instrumental parts on the *Stop Pretending*

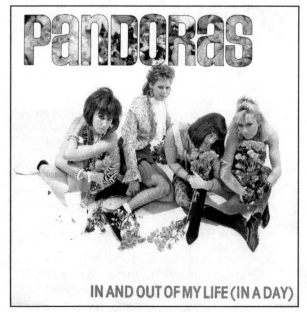

**IN AND OUT OF MY LIFE (IN A DAY)**

record, however, except the drums!

This LP was an example of a "garage" record with possible appeal to the masses, but it did not develop into a hit anywhere along the lines of **The GoGos** or **The Bangles**. It was also overlooked by the garage scene at the time because of its slick production. Still, *Stop Pretending* is a great party record for any decade.

The glory of **The Pandoras** as a trashy garage band ends here, however, as Paula & Co. then tried their hand as an all-gash heavy metal act, releasing two more 12"s full of un-inspired garbage. (This was the opposite of the *inspired* garbage of their heyday.)

A reported eight-LP deal with Elektra fell through when one of Pierce's friends left the label. (A bootleg of demos from this period entitled *Psychedelic Sluts* has since seen release. It fits in stylistically somewhere between *Stop Pretending* and their metal-ish era, with only the slightest garage hint — and is of interest to only the most fanatical of fans.)

Critical barbs and kidding aside, I'm sad to say that **Paula Pierce**'s journey did not end happily — *Goldmine Magazine* reported in the August 20, 1991 issue that she "died of cardiac arrest August 10 in Los Angeles." She was only 31 years old. That's quite a tragic end for one of the decade's best garage groups.

Several **Pandoras** alumni went on to form the very cool pop-punk act **The Muffs**, ironically landing the major-label contract that eluded their former group.

## PARANOIACS
(Belgium)

A later '80s lineup has several releases which are more in the hard-pop-rock genre: the *Sometimes Teenage Is Spelled T.N.T* six song 12" EP, the *We're Teenage Lovers* six song 12" EP, and the *Bananas* 12 song LP — all on Play It Again Sam Records in Holland.

The garage true believer **King Koen** was involved in the band's July 1986 sessions — the eight unreleased garage gems include the wonderful garage anthem "I Know A Boy" and a cover of **The Shadows Of Knight**'s rare novelty commercial for snack food, "Potato Chip." This session is much more '60s garage oriented than the subsequently released **Paranoiacs** material, and to these ears it is also superior.

**King Koen** would leave to form **Some Kinda Weird** and later **The Greenhorns**. His solo releases are also excellent garage-pop efforts.

## THE PARIAHS
(Montreal, PQ Canada)

An early Montreal mid-'80s garage band which featured Mike Nox who later went to London, England to form **The Surrounds**.

## PARTY KIDZ
(Torino, Italy)

An R&B garage/soul group with several releases: "Gimme Your Money" b/w "Lasciati Andare" 45, 1987 on Toast Records; the *Shock Treatment* LP, 1985 on Superbeat Records.

## THE PEECOCKS
(Brighton, MA USA)

"Pussy Minstrel Show" b/w
   "Are You A Boy Or Are You A Girl" 45, 1990
   Arf, Arf Records, USA

The "Pussy Minstrel Show" 45 is another eclectic Arf Arf release. It's included here because of the credible version of **The Barbarians**' '60s oddity "Are You A Boy Or Are You A Girl."

## THE PERVERTS
*(Rotterdam, Holland)*

*(I'm In Love With) The Headcoat Girl* 3 song 7" EP
  Teenscream Records, Holland, 1993
"Down & Out" b/w "Young Man Afraid Of Horses" 45
  Vinyl Vaults, U.K., 1994
*Wildest Men In Town* 3 song 7 EP, 1994
  Out Now Records, Holland

The "Ik ben zo wild, man!" track is on the on the 1994 Demolition Derby Records EP. They also have one track on the *Billy Childish tribute LP* on Vendetta Records in the U.K. 1995 releases include the *For Perverts Only* 3 song EP and a split single with Spain's **Doctor Explosion.**

Heavily inspired by Euro-beat bands of the '60s (**The Kinks** and the "Gods of Nederbiet" — **The Outsiders** — especially), **The Perverts** formed in August 1991. They've since played in Belgium, Germany, France, Spain and the U.K.

They say, *"We prefer to play without large P.A. systems. We mostly use our own back-line including an old 100 watt Selmer voice amplifier, which once belonged to **The Q-65."***

I bumped into a couple of **The Perverts** while in Holland, and they promised to send me their debut 45. About a year later a crumpled box arrived in the mail — there's nothing like getting a package with the return address listed as **"The Perverts"**!

The A-side of their debut is self-explanatory. Not only does this band have a fascination for **Billy Childish** and **The Headcoats**, but also their girlfriends **The Headcoatees**. A good gritty version of "Social End Product" and the **"Perverts** Theme" makes the flip a real winner as well. I also like how they invite the listener over to listen to Euro-beat records and have a drink. Friendly chaps, those **Perverts**.

The follow-up EP's title track is a spunky **Kinks**-like chord grinder, while "My Little Nymphomaniac" has some cool organ and a freakout rave-up section.

The EP's liner notes contend, *"Just when you think you've seen it all, you run up against **The Perverts**. A delirious, trash can juvenile combo from Rotterdam who never learned that drink and music just don't mix!"*

What a bunch of **Perverts**.

## THE PETALS
*(Milwaukee, WI USA)*

"Just Another Flower Song" b/w "Dreamtime" 45, 1989
"The Mushroom Farm" b/w "Energy Panel" 45, 1990
"Cemetery" b/w "Lay Down With Flowers" 45, 1991
*Parahelion* 15 song LP, 1992
*Cadis Center* 15 song LP / 16 song CD, 1994

  November Rain Records, USA
"Blue Bicycle" b/w "Box In The Time" 45, 1993
  Twang! Records, Germany

The song 'Painted Desert" is on the *Adventure 5* compilation on Guiding Lights Records in Denmark; "Teapot" is on the German *Goar* magazine 7" EP, 1994; "Hurry on Sundown" is on the Ceres Records *Hawkwind Tribute* double LP, USA, 1995; "Babe You Know" on the *Women's Homeless Shelter Benefit* LP, U.K., 1995. **The Petals'** fifth 45 and third LP should be out by late 1995.

Folk-psych is a from I can never hear enough of. These beer-town minstrels deliver some very serene, upbeat, smiling mood-folk, with **Plasticland**er John Frankovic most notably at the control board. "Just Another Flower Song" is anything but "just another" stab at the style, with

its gentle arrangement and beautiful execution. The flip, "Dreamtime," is even more glorious in the most relaxed way.

"Mushroom Farm" gets my vote for funniest song about psilocybes ever, and is agonizingly catchy — one listen and you'll drive yourself and your friends crazy singing this one!

The 45s prepared the listener for the stunning debut LP. From the opening magic of "Imaginations Daughter" **The Petals** weave their spell, and draw the listener into a world of castles and looking glasses. "If I Open" is perhaps the best song that **The Rain Parade** never wrote and recorded, but perhaps such a comparison isn't fair to this bunch of talented musicians.

There was no sophomore jinx for these Wisconsin weirdos — their second long-player bursts with mature energy while further developing their mythic based folk-rock. The LP title refers to a Wisconsin ghost town, and the 16 tracks act

**ISS**

almost like an aural equivalent to *The Spoon River Anthology* — instead of biographical prose, we hear the tales of "Old George," "Sheldon's Cavern" and the "Cadis Valley Tinker."

An eclectic mix of old world folk and **Byrds**ian jangle, **The Petals** might be seen by some as merely quaint — but heartfelt words sung with soaring emotion should be the core of any important music.

They're delicate, playful, and sincere, but **The Petals** are anything but quaint.

## PERMANENT GREEN LIGHT
*(Sherman Oaks, CA USA)*

"We Could Just Die" b/w "The Truth This Time" 45, 1992
   Rockville Records, USA

This Michael Quercio project had been heralded as a maturation of his former **Three O'Clock**'s pop stylings. **Permanent Green Light**'s power pop aspirations are muted by one minor obstacle — there aren't any songs of merit here. The melodies and execution are pedestrian, and lack any of the flavor of Quercio's former band.

I think there might be subsequent LP, but I have no interest in finding it.

## PETER SELLERS & THE HOLLYWOOD PARTY
*(Milan, Italy)*

This psych-pop group had a self-titled 12" EP in 1987 on Toast Records, and appeared on several split 45s and compilations from 1986-1989.

## THE PHANTOM FIVE
*(New Jersey, USA)*

*Great Jones Street* 4 song 7" EP, 1986
   Making Tyme Records, USA

What a great unknown treasure this is: a little four song EP full of distorted energy, melody and mood. Everything about this effort is odd, however. Drummer/vocalist Larry Grogan looks to be at least 300 pounds large, one side of the disc is in stereo, the other in mono, the production sounds like it was recorded with one mike set in another room — and yet this is one of my favorite releases of the decade!

I think it's the raw enthusiasm that touches me here, along with the anthemic title cut. I seem to remember an ad for this record in one of the big East Coast college oriented

**156**

papers, stating *"Buy this record now or wait to hear it on Pebbles #94..."* or something to that effect.

I think they're right. Most people won't hear this stuff until the *Pebbles* compilations get to it in a few decades. I was lucky enough to stumble on it the first time around.

In 1995 I saw an ad for a new record by **Thee Phantom Five**, but their surf-trash sounds aren't related to these lads.

## THE PHANTOM GIFT
*(Japan)*

Glynnis Wilson says, *"They were the best and most professional 'Group Sound' revival band from the '80s combining modern guitar techniques with traditional G.S. styles. They had at least one CD release, a self-titled debut in 1985. The CD features some really wild versions of Japanese songs which appear on the* Tokyo Teen Trash *'60s comp trilogy. They sang mostly in Japanese."*

## THE PHANTOM SURFERS
*(San Francisco, CA USA)*

Untitled 5 song 7" EP, 1991
   Estrus Records, USA

A 1991 five song 7" EP provided some simple, crude surf pleasure, very much in a traditional Californian '60s mode. Unremarkable in their playing, **The Phantom Surfers** (they wear "bandit masks") seem more pre-occupied with their costumes, nerdy suits and period equipment than any original ideas.

Several other musicians have also reported to me that **The Phantom Surfers** regularly showed great disdain for almost all other groups and musicians, confirming the obvious — that many musicians are more concerned with their own notion of "cool" and misguided feelings of superiority than any musical expression or sense of community.

Several long-players of little interest have also appeared.

## THE PHASE ONE PSYCHOTICS
*(Long Island, NY USA)*

This was an early '80s group with ex-**Tryfle** John Fay. They had yet another memorable band name; they just don't make them like that anymore!

## PHILISTEINS
*(Australia)*

The eight song 12" *Bloody Convicts* features a two-guitar attack, clean production, and a pop-punk style with a tinge of garagemania. Their energetic version of "You Must Be A Witch" is a highlight. **The Philisteins** transcend a mere '60s garage label, but share the attitude and spittle. I'm unsure of other releases, or when in the '80s they existed.

## THEE PICKLES
*(Nuremberg, Germany)*

A former member of **The Surfadelics** joined some German cohorts in 1992, recording what would become an eight song double 7" at the infamous Toe-Rag studios in London, England. Their sound has been described as beat/garage — but I haven't heard their efforts myself.

## PIKES IN PANIC
*(Siena, Italy)*

*Untitled* 4 song 7" EP, 1986
   Microbon Records, Italy?
*Keep It Cool And Dry* LP, 1987
   Contempo Records, Italy

A '60s garage punk combo — I haven't heard their output.

## THE PINHEADS
*(Sweden)*

*Rot 'N' Roll Live* 13 song LP, 1985
   Garageland Records, Sweden

Formed with Lars Gille'n of the long-standing Swedish band **Jukon Speakers**, **The Pinheads** also made three singles and two other full LPs. Gille'n also runs the Garageland Record label, which specialized throughout the 1980s in re-issuing original 1960s Swedish garage punk.

*Rot 'N' Roll Live* features classic '60s covers like "Strychnine", "Sometimes Good Guys Don't Wear White" and "Pushing Too Hard," along with some '70s punk tunes.

## PINK FLOWERS
*(Belgium)*

They have unknown releases, but are a fine pop group judging by their tracks on the *Belgian Garagemania* compilation albums.

## PINKY SILENCE AND THE MAD HORSES
*(Milan, Italy)*

A beat/psych group with a split 45 on Crazy Mannequin Records, 198?

## THE PLANETS
*(Japan)*

An all-girl '60s-styled beat group that reportedly never recorded. They played in 1989-1990.

## PLAN 9
*(Rhode Island, USA)*

"Frustration" 45, 1981
*Frustration* 7 song 12" EP, 1982
   Voxx Records, USA
*Hideaway* 7" EP, 1984
"Merry Christmas" b/w "White Christmas" 45, 1984
*Dealing With The Dead* 9 song LP, 1984
*I Just Killed A Man, I Don't Want To See Any Meat* 9 song "Live" LP, 1985
   Midnight Records, USA

It is difficult to imagine an eight-member band making garage-psych music, but this is precisely what **Plan 9** were all about. With enough guitarists for at least two bands, **Plan 9** would crowd all but the largest stages in their run through the 1980s. Led by guitarist (#1) Eric Stumpo, this rare Rhode Island representative to the rock world helped to bring a bit of a "heavier" sound to the garage scene.

Comparisons to **The Grateful Dead** were brought on by the intense guitar work and the number of musicians involved, but that comparison is fully unfair. **Plan 9** always played intense rock music, with little room for self-indulgent burnt-out hippy ramblings. Sure, the sound was gruff and dense, but **Plan 9**'s best work always sounded like it was just rehearsed in a garage, not in front of a couple thousand tie-dyed **Deadheads**.

It's not surprising that their most garagey disc is their debut 12" EP. The extremely '66 sound is offset by the title track "Frustration" — an almost 12 minute interpretation of the **Painted Ship**'s classic '66 song — which takes up the entire second side of the EP. Even in their most garagey days, **Plan 9** made sure to be different.

Their first long-player, *Dealing With the Dead*, is undoubtedly their finest hour. The intricate guitars fly all over one another, with vocalist Michael Ripa joining in on guitar #5! The fuzzed garage sound is tempered with a dark psych edge, as the title track stands out

**157**

as a moody, day-glo effort. Complete with R.K. Sloane's nightmare neon cover art, *Dealing With The Dead* is a masterful documentation of **Plan 9** at their peak.

The band's voluminous lineup would ebb and flow for later records, with that magical punch seemingly just out of reach. They recorded a credible "live" LP to fulfill their Midnight Records contract, then split for Enigma Records and a series of thoroughly pedestrian and bland releases.

I was lucky enough to see the band in 1986, however, and they still had the fire in their bones. I believe that they were "only" a six-piece at the time, but were thunderously loud nonetheless. Stumpo's guitar-work was excellent, as well as Deborah D.'s keyboards.

**Plan 9** stood out as a band always looking to try something new, and that alone makes them one of the genre's most unique contributors.

## PLASTICLAND
*(Milwaukee, WI USA)*

"Mink Dress" b/w "Office Skills" 45, 1980
*Vibrasonics From Plasticland* 7" EP, 1981
 "Color Appreciation" b/w "Mushroom Hill" 45, 1981
*Pop! Op Drops!* 7" EP, 1982
"Euphoric Trapdoor Shoes" b/w "Rat-Tail Comb" 45, 1983
    Scadillac Records, USA
*Color Appreciation* 15 song LP, 1984
"Magic Rocking Horse" promo 7", 1984
    Lolita Records, France
"Flower Scene" b/w "In My Black And White" 45, 1985
*You Need A Fairy Godmother* LP (w/Twink), 1989
*Confetti* 13 song "Live" LP, 1989
    Midnight Records, USA
*Plasticland* 15 song LP, 1984
*Wonder Wonderful Wonderland* 12 song LP, 1985
*Salon* 13 song LP & CD, 1987
    Pink Dust Records, USA
*Plasticland* 15 song LP, 1985
    (same as U.S. version, w/different art)
    Bam Caruso Records, U.K.
"Let's Play Pollyanna" b/w "Enchanted Forestry" 45, 1989
*Let's Play Pollyanna* 3 song 12" EP, 1990
*Dapper Snappings* 11 song CD, 1994
    Repulsion Records, Germany
*Mink Dress And Other Cats* 19 song CD, 1995
    Timothy's Brain Records, USA

The band also had 11 separate compilation appearances, with the tracks all available elsewhere on other LP releases. An unreleased studio session with **Twink** exists from 1989, with only a few 7" test pressings extant. The songs are "Seize The Time" and "Iris Of The Waterfall." John Frankovic also contributed to the reportedly psychedelic 1990 LP by **F/I** entitled *Paradise Out Here* on Other Sounds Records in the U.S. and Human Wrechords in Germany.

The wildly colorful **Plasticland** arose from the ashes of the art-noise band **Arousing Polaris,** which formed in 1975 and survived until the end of the decade. Early '80s Plasticland 45s are very rare, and were released on the band's own Scadillac label.

Many of these tracks were collected on the 1984 *Colour Appreciation* LP, released in the U.S. as simply *Plasticland* with a slightly amended track lineup. This LP is startling in its scope and

execution, as every accepted pop rock and psychedelic convention is turned inside out to great effect.

Each song evokes its own lysergic world, with studio tricks well designed into the mix. Glenn Rehse's moaning, surreal vocals are instantly identifiable and are one facet of the **Plasticland** experience that sets the band apart from its competitors.

The band was able to follow up this brilliant debut with *Wonder Wonderful Wonderland,* an effort that was later listed in *Spin Magazine*'s poll of the 25 most important albums of the 1980s. **The Dream Syndicate**'s Paul Butler produced the disc, making sure that the guitar dominated the mixes, and in retrospect the band was less happy with the results. Still, it is an incredible sophomore effort, and certainly an evolutionary step forward.

Next was **Plasticland**'s pinnacle of studio production, titled *Salon.* The psychedelic swirl is a bit darker and menacing in tone, and Rehse's lyrics even more obtuse and bizarre. The band contended that they had been listening to a lot of 1960s Motown soul at the time of this album, but these influences are mutated into **Plasticland**'s own, and don't detract at all from the final product. (I

**158** suppose one could hear a Motown soul influence on "Go A Go-Go Time," but the track is so demented as to blur such stylistic distinctions.)

These albums all failed to become big sellers, and it seemed that **Plasticland** had reached its peak without cracking the underground's consciousness. A few more 12"s would appear, all in the best **Plasticland** tradition, but by 1990 the band had dissolved, with bassist John Frankovic leaving to form **The Gothics** with drummer Vic Demechei.

The *Dapper Snappings* LP appeared in 1994 — though the sessions were actually several years old — and found the band still vital, experimental, noisy and strange. The appearance of the belated album also helped to foster momentum for the group to reform.

By 1995 it was reported that an original lineup had reunited and were set to record and tour. A compilation titled *Mink Dress And Other Cats* then appeared, containing early and unreleased rare tracks. It is a goldmine for **Plasticland** fans, since it offers up the rarest of the band's output with countless surprises and brilliant sound throughout. Excellent packaging by Aram Heller also make this *the* Plasticland CD to find. (Surprisingly, as of this writing, neither of the band's first two LPs are available on CD.)

It is without dispute that **Plasticland** was the 1980s' finest pop psych band, and one could argue for their position as the best pop psych outfit of all time.

## LES PLAYBOYS
*(Nice, France)*

They formed in 1977 as a punk band called **The Dentists** (not to be confused with the U.K. band of the same name), then switched to **Les Playboys** in 1980. They released at least four LPs from 1980 to 1990, some supposedly very '60s-ish, and also reportedly featured a group of eight "very beautiful and well dressed '60s go-go girls" called 'Ginettes,'" which is French slang for "chicks"! The *Encore* LP does have a '60s R&B energy, with some fuzz and (unfortunately) some horns as well.

Their singer reportedly replaced **Peter Zaremba** of **The Fleshtones** for one show in the 1980s, when **Zaremba** was stuck in Mexico during an airline strike. The comparison holds between the two groups, with their combination of upbeat party music, R&B and pop.

Have I mentioned that I once sat behind **Peter Zaremba** at an ice hockey game? He looks more at home sweating on stage. **IS9**

## THE PLAYGROUND
*(Baltimore, MD USA)*

"These Are The Days" b/w "Cordially Invited" 45, 1985
 Carnival Records, USA

This rare 45 is an interesting taste of vocalist Dennis Davison between his stint with **The United States Of Existence** and his to-be-formed **Jigsaw Seen**.

The A-side is a jangley pop effort with equal parts **Turtles, Byrds** and **Love** — and an innocent mood above all. Like all of Davison's compositions, a sing-song nursery rhyme feel pervades, and this is an acquired taste for some.

The B-side is a more engaging amalgamation of these pop influences, and sounds remarkably like an outtake from the **U.S.E.**'s lone LP. It's one of Davison's best songs, and it's a shame that it is buried on this limited edition release.

I actually played on a bill with Davison and his Los Angeles version of **The Playground** in late 1986, shortly before they were compelled to change their name because of a legal claim by several other groups. This proto-**Jigsaw Seen** was bright and jangley, but lacked stage power.

## THE PLAYMATES
*(Sweden)*

I once had a very melodic 12" EP from these Swedes, but I can't find it now for the life of me. It contained good jangley pop, if memory serves correctly.

## PLAYN JAYN
*(U.K.?)*

A highly rated (in some circles) early to mid 1980s garage-pub band with two LPs: *Friday The 13th* and *Five Good Evils*. They struck me rather blandly, but some readers seemed to think them of interest.

## THE PLIMSOULS
*(Los Angles, CA USA)*

*A Million Miles Away* 3 song 12" EP, 1982
 Shaky City/Bomp Records, USA
*Everywhere At One* 11 track LP, 1983
 Geffen Records, USA

While Peter Case and Co. are better known for their Rickenbacker fueled power-pop anthem "A

Million Miles Away," their major label debut *Everywhere At Once* features the Farfisa-driven garage standout "Lie Beg Borrow Steal."

**The Plimsouls** admittedly don't merit a large entry in a book that emphasizes garage fuzz and psychedelic madness, but at times they did veer off into that intersecting musical world. Their *A Night In America* live concert LP especially shows their garage-pop-rock muscle.

Incidentally, I witnessed a 1994 Peter Case solo show — which held none of the magic or songwriting skill of **The Plimsouls**' early '80s work.

## THE POINT
*(Los Angeles, CA USA)*

untitled 4 song 10" EP, 1981
  Radlab records, USA
*Magic Circle* 10 song LP, 1983
  WarfRat Records, USA

Guitarist Jon Stebbins of **The Point** wrote to me in 1992 with recollections about his band and the Los Angeles scene of the early 1980s:

*"Now the fun really started — we played shows all over L.A. in 1982 and '83. We shared the stage with the gamut of the garage/psych scene — **The Last, Rain Parade, Wednesday Week, Dream Syndicate, Crawdaddys, Unclaimed, Long Ryders, Leaving Trains, 100 Flowers, Fleshtones, Pandoras,** etc.*

*"I remember a show with the **Leaving Trains** where we were dropped from the bill because we missed our sound check. When we arrived someone had taken our name off the marquee and replaced it with '**The Beatles.**' So when we were given 15 minutes by the club owner we played (**The Beatles'**) "And Your Bird Can Sing" five times and walked off!*

*"We also played a big outdoor party up in Laurel Canyon that summer (1982). We were frying on mushrooms as a unit that day, and fearlessly meandered through our set complete with hallucinations both visual and aural. By the end of the night we had no idea what our Play-Do/marshmallow guitars were playing, but the crowd (also on mushrooms) thought the 60-year-old drunken Mexican man on crutches screaming at them in Spanish was just a guest vocalist, so I gave him the mike and fell off the stage."*

**The Point** also released a self-made four song 10" EP in 1981, described by *The L.A. Times* in early 1982 as *"A surprisingly strong piece of pop craftsmanship. Combining crystalline guitars and gently earnest vocals, the band has the purity of intent that* **TGD**

*recalls the haunting resonance of pre-psychedelic California groups like **The Beau Brummels**."* The band was unhappy with the EP's production, however, and only 500 copies were pressed, all on white vinyl.

There are two especially stand-out tracks on their *Magic Circle* LP. The first, "All My Life," also made an appearance on the *Rebel Kind* compilation. It's a gentle folk-ballad in the finest mid-'60s mold. The mushroom-induced "Magic Circle" is the album's other undisputed highlight, bringing forth images of an intricate band like **Love**.

They survived until May 1985, leaving some fine music and garage memories behind them. A tape of four unreleased songs showed that there was still some magic left in the band to the end. The original tracks "94550," "Look To The Stars," "The Right Thing" and the **Monkees** cover "Circle Sky" would all fit right in on a CD re-release of *The Magic Circle* LP, along side their debut EP.

Stebbins noted that some of his best memories come from many of the great bands he was able to see and know personally. The idea of one fine band valuing respect for fellow musicians is a testament to the positive nature of garage music at its best.

They got **The Point**.

## THE POINT OF DEPARTURE
*(Surrey, U.K.)*

"Magic Circles" b/w "Magic Circles (reprise)" 45, 1993
  Susstones Records, USA

This is a studio project headed by Stuart Farnden, with a distinctly British psych-pop feel. Backward guitars, mellotron and loping bass bring to mind *Magical Mystery Tour*-era **Beatles** or early **Pink Floyd**, though the melody is far less structured or engaging.

The flipside is a re-working of the same song, and is actually a bit less meandering, more cohesive and interesting — though without vocals. This one's a close miss — all the best elements don't add up to a realized whole.

An interesting footnote: the disc was mastered at the infamous Abbey Road Studios.

## POLVERE DI PINGUINO
*(Carrara, Italy)*

"Open My Hands" b/w "Alabama Song" 45, 1986
  Lilly Records, Italy
Self-titled LP, 1988
*Electric Tribe* 12" EP, 1989
  Cobra Records, Italy

A reportedly psychedelic outfit.

## THE POLYESTER EXPLOSION
*(Toronto, ON Canada)*

Glynnis Wilson remembers, *"Forming in 1990, **The Polyester Explosion** sounded like a mid-'80s snot punk band. Their slow hypnotic playing is reminiscent of early **Ultra 5** but they also play surf instrumentals."*

## THE POPPEES
*(New York, NY USA)*

"Jealousy" b/w "She's Got It" 45, 1978
   Bomp Records, USA

Greg Shaw notes in his *Bomp! 20th Anniversary* double CD liner notes, *"**The Poppees** were a throwback to the Liverpool scene, circa '61. They played authentic beat music with uncanny exuberance, as cocky as though they'd just stepped off the boat from Hamburg."*
They were officially Bomp's first signing, and had at least two singles released in 1975 and 1976, far before anyone thought of a "'60s revival." (The fine 1978 effort listed above is the only disc I could uncover.) **The Poppees** obviously were inspired by their own muse, unaffected by the musical trends around them.
"Love Of The Loved," from their first 45, shows their admiration and reverence for the **Beatles**-beat period. There's a certain charm, gentle smile and unpretentious fun about **The Poppees** that makes them one of the purest of the bands who looked back into their record collection — and found a goldmine of inspiration.

## POW
*(Milan, Italy)*

*Net Wt. 4 Oz.* 12" EP, 1989
   Crazy Mannequin Records, Italy
*The Sidescenes* 12" EP, 1991
   Vox Pop Records, Italy?
"Maximum Punk 'N' Beat" 45, 1992
   Face Records

A mod-beat combo, with the emphasis more on the mod end, I believe.

## THE PREACHERS
*(Sweden)*

There were several other **"Preachers"** of the period, but I haven't heard any of them.

## LE PREHISTORIC POP
*(Toulouse, France)*

I've heard a very melodic, enjoyable garage pop cassette of demos from 1989/90, complete with beautiful harmonies and some sunny organ. Unlike some European pop bands that overdose on sweetness, **Le Prehistoric Pop** manages to avoid a sickly sweet sound while still retaining a very pop edge.
Sparkling songs like "Everybody Else" and "Boy After Boy" make this a very appealing demo, and I can only hope that some of these sounds have found their way onto vinyl. Hearing tapes like this reminds me of how many fine unknown bands there are out there — somewhere.

## PRESCRIPTION
*(Edinburgh, Scotland)*

A mid-'80s mod/beat band which reportedly later went folky. There are no known records or demos.

## PRESSION X
*(Milan, Italy)*

Self-Titled 5 song 12" EP, 1986
   Electric Eye Records, Italy

A '66 styled garage-surf-punk outfit. I've only heard the excellent "Jenny Is 17," which features a rave-up section, cool organ, and a driving syncopated beat. Crude and energetic in the best of ways, I can only assume the remainder of the EP is of similar stature.

## THE PREYTELLS
*(Australia)*

From what I can piece together, this was an R&B- based fivesome, existing from at least 1986 to 1988.

## PRIMAL SCREAM
*(U.K.)*

The enticingly titled *Sonic Flower Groove* (!) LP is on Elevator Records; at least two 45s and a double LP exist on Creation Records. They apparently drifted away from the genre quickly and into the quagmire of disco "house music" by 1991.

## THE PRIMATES
*(Los Angeles, CA USA)*

*We Are...* 12 song LP, 1986
   Voxx Records, USA

These apes quickly became favorites of the Cavern Club crowd. I met them in 1986 at that club, and they pondered my ingenious question:

Q: Where do you guys get your inspiration?
A: *Uh...Curious George!*

Unable to answer any of my other queries with anything but a grunt, one member made this case for their sole LP, "If you've ever made a monkey noise in your life, you'll like this album!"

The LP did resemble a monkey's efforts, with extremely crude musicianship (and ironically good

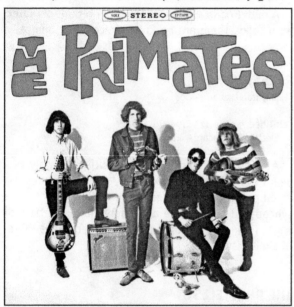

sound production) throughout. There is fuzz, fuzz, and more fuzz, along with snarling vocals, dumb lyrics, and a general sense of anarchy.

In other words, this was one of the most fun records of the garage-rock decade!

## THE PRIME MOVERS
*(Boston, MA USA)*

"Change For The Better" b/w "1-2-5" 45, 1983
   Moulty Records, USA
*Matters Of Time* 6 song 12" EP, 1984
   Throbbing Lobster Records, USA

The debut 45 is very much a do-it-yourself independent production, with the tentative

sounding A-side bettered by a crude version of the garage standard "1-2-5."

I first heard the band, however, on the seminal *Battle Of The Garages Volume 2* LP. The anthemic "Come To Where It's At" could certainly be recovered by future generations as a symbol of the entire 1980s garage "revival," as it encapsulates many of the genre's best attributes. Like all **Prime Movers** material, grizzly guitars and blurting vocals spew forth, recalling long lost garage punk forefathers. The track is also on the excellent EP.

Word has it that **The Prime Movers** were only topped by **The Lyres** for early 1980s Beantown popularity, and one can see how they could have been quite a live act to see and hear. Energy abounds throughout the 12" EP, leaving the listener hungry for more, though I don't believe that any other tracks were ever issued.

Members went on to form **The Slaves** and **The Voodoo Dolls**, both with a "heavier" sound. The band apparently had a reunion in 1989, where they played a gig at The Rat. A home video shows a fiery version of "You're Gonna Miss Me."

## THE PRIME MOVERS
*(U.K.)*

This isn't the Boston group, but another U.K. group with connections to **The Prisoners, James Taylor Quartet** and **Makin' Time**. They have two LPs out on Unique Records, and again, I haven't seen a trace of them in the U.S. What scraps I have heard sound very much in the **Prisoners** vein, with an emphasis on mod-soul, with a tinge of garage.

The 11 song *Earth Church* LP certainly fits into **The Prisoners** category, with plenty of mod melodies and choruses, some flanged vocals, some heavy and slightly funky guitar — and plenty of syncopated toe-tapping rhythms. The end result is very professional and tightly performed, but a bit too slick for these ears.

## PRIMETEENS
*(Bologna, Italy)*

"I'm Gonna Love You" b/w "Good To Me" 45, 1988
   Electric Eye Records, Italy
"Rock 'N' Roll" b/w "By My Side" 7" flexi, 1990
   *Urlo Magazine*, Italy
*Bikers From Hell* LP, 1989
   Lakota Records, Italy

They also have track "Halloween Night" on split 45 for *Lost Trails* #10, 1989, and are reportedly a garage punk outfit.

## LES PRIMITIVES
(Caen, France)

Don't confuse these Frenchmen with the U.K. pop band **The Primitives**. These guys really are primitive, as their "Adult Sickness" 45 shows. This is revved-up punk-pop, once again disproving the notion that the French don't rock. I believe that some other discs are available, including a flexi with a photo of *The Munsters* on the cover.

## THE PRISMATICS
(Barcelona, Spain)

Nothing known.

## THE PRISONERS
(Kent, U.K.)

*A Taste Of Pink* 12 song LP, 1982
*The Last Fourfathers* 12 song LP, 1985
    Own-Up Records, U.K.
"There's A Time" b/w "Revenge Of The Cybermen" 1983?
    Skydog Records, France
"Hurricane" b/w "Tomorrow (She Said)" 45, 1983
*The WiserMiserDemelza* LP, 1983
*Electric Fit* 4 song EP, 1984
*Four On Four* compilation EP
    (with **Milkshakes, Sting Rays** & **Tall Boys**), 1984
    Big Beat Records, U.K.
*Revenge Of The...* 13 song LP, 1984
    Pink Dust Records, USA
*Farewell To The Mic* "Live" 7 song LP, 1985
    (also w/7 songs by **The Milkshakes**)
    Empire Records, U.K.
*In From The Cold* LP, 1986
"Whenever I'm Gone" b/w "Promised Land" 45, 1986
*Whenever I'm Gone* 3 song 12" EP, 1986
    Countdown Records, U.K.
*Rare And Unissued* LP, 1988
    Hangman Records, U.K.

They also appeared on at least 10 compilation LPs, including all of the Hangman Sampler LP's.

Many music fans believe that **The Prisoners** should have become extremely popular internationally. Their unique combination of '60s pop, garage, soul and mod is infectious, but strangely never grabbed a commercial foothold. This foursome also sounds distinctly British, a quality that would have aided the band in 1965, but was perhaps too quaint for American audiences in 1985.

Their debut disc is arguably their best, with vocalist/guitarist Graham Day having a hand in writing all of the 12 original compositions. The LP is a wonderful mixture of **Byrds**-jangle, soulful

*THE PRISONERS, 1982*

vocals and a pure pop sensibility. **The Prisoners** achieved a great feat: they managed to sound instantly identifiable, with their own individual stamp. One could hear snatches of inspiration of other bands in their sound, but it came out distinctively as **The Prisoners**.

The oddly titled *WiserMizerDemelza* continued the band's progress, though my copy seems to have vanished! Some tracks from these two LPs and previous EPs were combined for the U.S. release *Revenge Of The Prisoners*. It's a good introduction to the band's sound, but unfortunately failed to spark much U.S. interest.

1985's *The Last Fourfathers* shows off more of an R&B-meets-the-garage (in England) styling, with a thicker Leslie organ sound dominating. There's some strange moody pieces juxtaposed with upbeat stompers, but it's a solid if not a completely consistent effort.

The band itself seems to totally discount the subsequent 1986 *In From The Cold* LP, which was reportedly wrecked by record company interference and band squabbles. Buckling from internal problems and a lack of commercial success — the lads played their last gig on September 18, 1986 at the 100 Club on Oxford Street in London.

Distinctly British in approach and style, **The Prisoners** were yet another accomplished band that should have broken the garage sound to a wider audience.

It's a shame they didn't have a chance to find out about "#1" — the top of the charts, that is.

## THE PROJECTILES
*(Rochester, NY USA)*

"Some Things Never Change" b/w
   "I Need Somebody" 45, 1986
Untitled 3 song 7" EP, 1987
   Jargon Records, USA

I would think that it was difficult for **The Projectiles** to be a '60s garage band in **The Chesterfield Kings'** hometown. **The Kings** had almost single-handedly given rebirth to the garage sound, and **The Projectiles** were most likely hidden in their shadow.

Still, **The Projectiles** held their own musically with their two 45s. Mining a bit more of the garage-psych sound than **The Kings'** R&B garage style, **The Projectiles** tempered snot and grunge with a bit of tremelo and mood.

Almost one billion garage bands (that's my informed estimate) have covered the classic "I Wanna Come Back From the World Of L.S.D.," but

this band somehow manages to breathe new life into it. The crude production work and delivery doesn't detract at all from this version's appeal — they're a garage band, after all!

The lads subsequently contributed a fabulous original song to one of the *Kaleidoscope Magazine* compilation LPs, but I'm not sure if anything else ever appeared.

If anything, I consider Rochester to have been the birthplace for *two* fine garage outfits: **The Chesterfield Kings** *and* **The Projectiles.**

## THE PSYCHEDELIC KLEPS
*(France)*

I believe this is just a different name for **The Klepstones,** featured on the *Battle Of The Garages Volume 4* compilation.

## THE PSYCHOTIC PETUNIAS
*(North Versailles, PA USA)*

Darren Ross says that this band's circa 1978-'79 single features the *"Most mental version of 'Louie Louie' I've ever heard. The singer is singing on helium and it's just so fuckin' cool."* The B-side features a cover of "Surfin' Bird" — on Mayhem Records, of course.

This band was probably a one-off fun side project. Regardless, They make it into the "Garage Band Name Hall of Fame."

## PSYCHOMOTOR PLUCK
*(Siena, Italy)*

Untitled 4 song 7" EP, 1987
   Kanguro Records, Italy
*Everyone For Himself And The Devil Takes The...* LP, 1988
   Tambourine Man Records, Italy

Reportedly a garage punk and hard psych act.

## PSYCHOTIC REACTIONS
*(Los Angeles, CA USA)*

Mike Snyder (former writer for the underground *Ben is Dead* magazine) was in this L.A. garage band '84-'85. He says they sounded "like **Stooges, Seeds, Cramps** and **Pretty Things.** Definitely primitive." They recorded an EP worth of demos which remain unreleased. Snyder went on to join the more straight-punk **Kings Of Oblivion.**

## PSYCHOTIC TURNBUCKLES
*(Australia)*

This band's early 45s display a wild garage atmosphere. Their 1985 debut "The Creeps" b/w "Energy" 45 possesses driving basslines and anthemic choruses, along with some crazy wah-wah and fuzz guitar. The follow-up 45 continues in the fuzz direction, with the buzzing "Psychotic Situation" and a cover of the trash classic "The Crusher." Though it doesn't touch the **Cramps'** supreme version, it is a worthy effort complete with handclaps and a cool knuckle-dragger guitar solo.

I found their later efforts to be a rather bland and generic hard rock, with the 1988 45 track "Good Times" a prime uninspired example. A later EP and LP also exist.

## PSYCHOTIC YOUTH
*(Sweden or Norway?)*

They released the *Devil's Train* EP on Garageland Records in November 1985, including covers of "I Wanna Come Back From the World of LSD" and the **13th Floor Elevators'** "You're Gonna Miss Me."

## PSYCH OUT
*(France)*

Several demo cassettes exists, along with appearances on a 1986 *What Wave Magazine* cassette compilation and a couple tracks on the French *Fireball* compilation LP from 1983. They existed from 1982-86, and opened for visiting luminaries such as **The Barracudas** in 1982 and the **Sting Rays** and **Prisoners** in 1983. They also have at least four unreleased studio cuts from 1984. Several readers cited them as one of the best unknown garage groups from the beginning of the movement.

## PSYCHO'S MUM
*(U.K.)*

At least one LP of unknown sounds is out, *A Sibilant Sin,* on Woronzow Records.

## THE PSYCHOVIOLETS
*(Lawrence, KS USA)*

*Teen Trash #2* 10 song LP & 20 song CD, 1993
    Music Maniac Records, Germany

This is the same band that released an album under the name **The Ultraviolets** for Music Maniac. A dispute over their second album caused a split with the German label, and the band apparently issued their next record in the U.S.

Music Maniac then took that release — which it contends it paid for in the first place — and combined it with the previous **Ultraviolets** LP for a CD release in the *Teen Trash* series. The vinyl version of this **Psychoviolets** LP has only the newer 10 songs. Get all that?

**165**

I really can't figure out what all the fuss was about — none of the music seems all that interesting to me. It's kinda a trippy **Velvet Underground**-like thing, with lots of obvious drug references, but nothing to get lawyers up and shouting at each other about.

## PSYLONS
*(U.K.)*

Two 45s and a 12" EP of unknown quality are on Iron Lung Records.

## THE PURDINS
*(Seattle, WA USA)*

The *My Girl Hopefully* EP reportedly fits the genre.

## THE PURITANS
*(Victoria, Australia)*

*The Puritans* 6 song 10" EP, 1988
"Grace Hotel" b/w "Moral Crusader" 45, 1990
    Mr. Spaceman Records, Australia
"101 Johnston St." b/w "One Way Train" 45, 1989
    Rave On Records, Germany
*(My Baby's Mind Is Like A) Beach House* 10 song CD, 1991
    Shock Records, Australia
*Have An R'N'B Party With...* 11 song LP, 1993
    Corduroy Records, Australia

**The Puritans** produce fine slices of white R&B, very much in the Euro-beat school of **Pretty Things, Downliners Sect,** etc. Since they're a few generations away from their original inspiration, starting in 1985, perhaps comparing them to the 1980s' **Tell Tale Hearts** is more accurate — and this is high praise, indeed.

The "Grace Hotel" debut is a fine stomper, with stand-out organ and slashing guitar, especially the fuzzed staccato solo. The harmonica and buzzed guitar are all there, along with **Jagger**-esque R&B vocals and that general beat atmosphere — pretty gritty, human and cool.

Their 10" EP might be their most solid effort. "101 Johnston St." kicks off the disc — and a different mix also graces their German 45. It's another snotty harmonica driven grinder, complete with the requisite snarling attitude. A beautiful duo-tone purple and black cover completes the package.

A much fuzzier, less purist feel permeates the *Beach House* CD, with the title track grinding away, but a much less focused and generic sound all around.

The band regains its legs with their next long-player. The cool thick organ and wailing harmonica of "2120 S. Michigan Ave" signals a return to their R&B roots, followed by the steamy "Rack My Mind" and "Can't Judge A Book." All of the tracks are covers of R&B standards, except the nice instrumental take off of "Green Onions" titled "Luna Onions" — their all-original *Beach House* CD would have benefited with the addition of a few of these covers.

The hilarious cover art — of two parents about to walk in on their naked daughter and her boyfriend — is a playful compliment to the grooving music.

That playful atmosphere is probably the most accurate assessment (and compliment) for this fine R&B party outfit.

## PURPLE FLASHES
*(Rochester, NY USA)*

This is reportedly an offshoot band of the **Chesterfield Kings** featuring Walt O'Brien. Their style was reportedly anything from power pop with **Beatle**sque harmonies to mod-psych & folk-rock. They played together under various names from the early to late-'80s.

## THE PURPLE HELMETS
*(U.K.)*

*Ride Again* 15 song LP, 198?
New Rose Records, France

**The Damned** did their '60s impostor gag with their side-band **Naz Nomad & The Nightmares**, and **The Stranglers** got in on the act with their own alter egos **The Purple Helmets**. (Any schoolboy knows what a purple helmet is. Girls, just ask.)

Really the best thing about this joke is the band's phallic logo and the photos of the band in '60s biker outfits (complete with WWII German army helmets.)

There is some music involved — it was recorded live in the studio, and displays what sounds like a competent '60s cover band — and not much more. There isn't much adventurous material here — all are covers — and some of the songs like "Louie Louie" and "Tobacco Road" have been heard about 1000 times too many by this author.

Still, I like the attitude and the band's appreciation for the genre. Now tell me, the title of this LP suggests that there is more out there by **The Purple Helmets**. Are there any more lines to this joke?

**166**

## THE PURPLE KNIGHTS
*(Sydney, Australia)*

This is a high energy R&B-based band that formed circa 1990. The only known recordings are four tracks on a *Born Loser Magazine* compilation cassette. They are driving upbeat efforts, complete with rave-up freak-out sections and snotty vocals. I'd like to think some of this cool stuff made it to vinyl somewhere, somehow.

## THE PURPLE MERKINS
*(Tucson, AZ USA)*

"Purple Merkin Power" b/w "Get On This Plane" 45, 1992
    *What Wave Magazine*, Canada
"Ain't Got Enough" b/w "The Wind Blows Your Hair" 45, 1994
    Rockadelic Records, USA
*Dig It!* 4 song 7" EP, 1995
    Dionysus Records
*Under The Covers With ...* 4 song 7" EP, 1995
    Weed Records, France
*Baby's Got Kinks!* 4 song 7" EP, 1995
    Dr. Vinyl Records, Belgium

Also two tracks on Italy's Misty Lane Records compilation, 1995.

This "side-band" soon ended up with the same line-up as **The Marshmallow Overcoat** — but with a slightly different musical attitude.

While this author's band **The Overcoat** was becoming more proficient and varied musically, **The Purple Merkins** were purposely crude and an absolutely *purist* '66 garage punk combo. We made a point of rehearsing only once — or not at all — before our recording sessions, and we were adamant about avoiding "quality" at all costs.

The debut 45 is as notable for the Darren Merinuk cartoon cover as for the fuzz in the grooves, which borders on the silly and ridiculous — as we intended.

A few microphones, lots of cheep beer and a living room was all we needed to produce the next two 7"s, which sound remarkably like long-lost '66 sessions. The playing and production are also improved on these releases, which despite our best efforts teeter close to achieving musical "quality."

Ironically, these are some of my favorite tracks I've ever produced, compared to my scores of "real" studio sessions! (Several major labels also approached us after these releases — more proof that the music industry really *is* degenerating.)

We also recorded ten songs for the *Peyote Stomp* series — a "live" radio broadcast recorded in a local studio. These songs are set to be released as part of the band's debut long player early in 1996, titled *Merkinmania!*

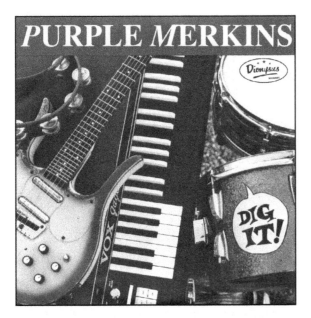

We've also performed on stage, complete with purple fur on the drums and keyboards. Perhaps I should have mentioned this already — a "merkin" is a pubic toupee. Look it up in a good dictionary.

And get ready for "Merkinmania!"

## THE PURPLE ONION
*(Washington, D.C. USA)*

Another short-lived early 1980s group featuring Bobby Belifore, later of **The Optic Nerve**.

## PURPLE OVERDOSE
*(Greece)*

*Exit #4* 10 song LP, 1988
*Indigo* 7 song 12" EP, 1990
   Pegasus Records, Greece
"2008 Old View" b/w "You Lose It" 45, 1993
   Fifth Dimension Records, Greece

Forming in 1987, their debut LP of the next year is a combination of trippy tunes, jazzy instrumentation and stretched arrangements. Their *Indigo* EP is even more accomplished, with a more confident delivery of their mellow, dreamy sound, and some silky smooth vocals. An excellent touch of cello and dual vocals make the record's closer, "Magic Forest," an especially pleasant trip.

**The Purple Overdose**'s brand of quiet introspective psychedelia will be too muted for some, but they are one of the more sophisticatedly "musical" acts covered in this book — and also worth the time needed for their world to come into focus.

## PURPLE PEOPLE EATERS
*(London, England)*

A simple '60s-styled psychedelic band from the mid-'80s. They had two cuts on the British *Raw Cuts* compilation LP: "Nightmares" & "I'm A Woman."

## PURPLE THINGS
*(U.K.)*

*Out Of The Deep* 5 song 12" EP, 1986
*Deep In The Mind Of...* 5 song 12" EP, 1985
   Media Burn Records, U.K.

These cats were originally **The Vibes**, formed in 1985 (with a bland 45), and as **The Purple Things** have at least the two EPs listed above and an LP — which is reportedly sub-par.

The first EP is an average garage-noise exercise, reminiscent of **The Cramps** sensibility in spots, but without a vital spark. I do like the title "Insect Bones & Astronauts," but the sounds don't match up with the kooky imagery.

The second EP features almost identical cover art (but with different ink colors), and the sounds are as similar. "Shadowed Room" is a good fuzz stomper — again in **The Cramps** mode — while a cover of the ever-popular '60s psych gem "Suzy Creem Cheese" is a demented echo-drenched blast that isn't half bad.

I suspect that **The Purple Things** fit more comfortably in the U.K. "trash-a-billy" scene than the '60s garage arena — or maybe they just don't fit in anywhere at all.

## PURPLE TOADS
*(Oshawa, Canada)*

Two LPs exist on the Star Label: a self-titled effort and *Love Songs For The Hard Of Hearing*. They featured several '60s punk covers, played in a sloppy '77 punk style, and were reportedly much better in concert than on record.

Glynnis Wilson says, *"Made up of mainstays from what was Canada's most thriving garage scene in the mid-'80s. They also contributed many, many songs on the What Wave compilation tapes."*

167

## THE PYRAMIDIACS
*(Australia)*

The "Can't Keep A Hold On You" b/w "Out Of Sight" 45 on Zero Hour Records is described by the label as having *"tons of Rickenbacker jangle and melody in the true Groovies/Plimsouls style."* Their second 45 for Zero Hour, "No Soul" b/w "Forever Gone" was produced by Rob Younger, and is also reportedly in the power pop style, circa 1992.

## THE QUAGMIRES
*(Fresno, CA USA)*

Yet another late-'80s short-lived California R&B-based band, reportedly in style similar to **The Yardbirds**. They tapes several episodes for the *It's Happening* cable-TV series, and a live tape showed them plowing through such standards as "Route 66," "Little Red Rooster" and "The Train Kept A-Rollin'."

## QUARTERED SHADOWS
*(Catania, Italy)*

Reportedly '60s pop, with a self-titled 12" EP, 1989 on Crazy Mannequin Records in Italy.

## RAINY DAY
*(Los Angeles, CA USA)*

*Rainy Day* 9 song LP, 1983
  Enigma Records, USA

I suppose that this should be included in the compilation section, since **Rainy Day** really wasn't a group, but instead a gathering a friends. In this case it was the cream of the crop of L.A.'s early 1980s "Paisley Underground," featuring members of **The Three O'Clock, Bangles, Rain Parade** and **Dream Syndicate**.

Produced like the initial **Rain Parade** releases at the infamous Radio Tokyo studios, the bare-bones recordings are understated, regal, moody and simply beautiful.

Kendra Smith and Susanna Hoffs are velvety on "Flying On The Ground Is Wrong," Michael Quercio is playful on "Sloop John B.," and Hoffs is again stunning on "I'll Be Your Mirror." Why did **The Bangles** have to end up being so bad, when their singer was capable of being so good?!?

"All-star" records of this type almost never work, but this collection was made before any of the leading characters had tasted the "big time." Our reward is an un-self-conscious and honest collection of hearts and minds.

As the title suggests, save this record for a rainy day, close your eyes, and enjoy.

## THE RAIN PARADE
*(Los Angeles, CA USA)*

"What She's Done To Your Mind" b/w "Kaleidoscope" 45, 1982
  Llama Records, USA
*Emergency Third Rail Power Trip* 9 song LP, 1983
*Explosions In The Glass Palace* 5 song EP, 1984
*Behind The Sunset* 10 song "Live" LP, 1985
  Enigma Records, USA
"Sad Eyes Kill" 7" flexi, 1985
  Bucketfull Of Brains Magazine, U.K.
*Crashing Dream* 10 song LP, 1985
  Island Records, U.K.

**The Rain Parade**'s recorded output is some of the most enjoyable of all that is discussed in this book. Their attention to musical detail, impeccable vocals, arrangements, songwriting and production make them a candidate for "band of the decade, 1980-1990" — and I hereby cast my vote.

This band reminds me of how my sister would wait in 1965 for a record store to open so she could buy a new **Beatles** LP on its first day of release. This loyalty and high expectation is the same feeling I had with **The Rain Parade**.

(And I'll never forget the day in 1982 when I heard their debut 45 at a friend's record store. It featured a beautiful photo sleeve of **The Bangles'**

Susanna Hoffs, plus two of the **Rain Parade**'s best-ever songs. I could have bought it for $1.50, but I didn't have the cash. I came back the next day, the record was gone, and now it sells for $25 and up.)

**The Rain Parade**'s sound was the wringing of a sponge that contained the 1960s best pop sensibilities. Out pour **The Byrds, Jefferson Airplane,** *Revolver*-era **Beatles,** and oddly **The Doors,** plus any number of folk-psych ancestors. Those influences are not the end of the band's appeal, but simply a starting

point, to which they've added their own unusual pop touches.

This was a mysterious, thoughtful, intelligent and introspective group, at a time when self-realization and humanity was strictly "out." **The Rain Parade** was not sterile, but instead gushing with emotion, so it is of little surprise that it fell short of staggering commercial heights.

They began in October 1981, playing their first show at Hollywood's Cathay De Grande the following May. The set at this time featured their own hushed originals — along with covers of **Syd Barrett**'s "No Good Trying" and **The Left Banke**'s "I've Got Something On My Mind."

Their debut album was released in October 1983, is a low-budget classic by any standards, and sits well along side its more heralded 1960s counterparts. *"They were the trippiest, most hypnotic of all the paisley bands,"* recalls Steve Wynn, leader of the now-defunct **Dream Syndicate**, in the October 20, 1994 edition of *Rolling Stone Magazine. "All the other bands in the scene felt some obligation to rock now and then. But the early Rain Parade played at three speeds: slow, slower, and slowest."*

Guitarist David Roback left after the debut LP's promotional tour — (or was expelled, depending on who tells the story) — to form **Clay Allison**.

The band's follow-up EP, *Explosions In The Glass Palace,* doesn't noticeably suffer for Roback's loss, and is perhaps even a greater accomplishment than their stunning debut. This time out the production is lush and evocative, with some of the most beautiful drum and guitar production of the decade.

This EP rightfully garnered major critical praise, and they even went on to sign with a major label, though that experience would be bittersweet at best. The 1985 "Sad Eyes Kill" flexi then appeared, featuring a demo version of a song that would grace their upcoming major label LP.

The subsequent LP, appropriately titled *Crashing Dream,* could also be called their finest hour. Again the production to these ears is picture perfect and the songs elegant and powerful. (Interestingly, vocalist and guitarist Matt Piucci was less than enthusiastic about the production of the album. He told me in 1992, *"A little tip on production — never do anything that doesn't feel right to your tunes."*)

Island Records seemingly sensed a critical backlash against "American guitar groups," and dropped the band from its roster reportedly the week the LP was released! Needless to say, little or no promotion or attention was afforded the LP, which was pressed in limited quantities and buried like a dead dog. The band disbanded and reformed several times in the coming few years, but their moment had passed.

The debut LP & the *Explosions* EP were later combined onto one CD, with the early track "Look Both Ways" added as a bonus. (It previously had been available only on the U.K. version of the LP.)

I believed in the mid-1980s that **The Rain Parade** was the finest "pop" rock band on the planet, and years later I stand by that judgment. My proof is in timeless songs such as "You Are My Friend," "This Can't Be Today" and "Don't Feel Bad."

They're indisputable proof, if they ever needed any.

Note: While I'm neither a fan nor collector of bootlegs, I have made an exception with the three **Rain Parade** boots listed above. The first is an audience tape from an October 12, 1983 show at CBGB's which includes the never-released original "Whatever They Say" and also a cover of **The Beatles'** "Revolution," which is ruined with the guest appearance of "vocalist" Dan Stuart from **Green On Red**. The sound quality is fair at best.

The second boot is a sound-board tape from the November 13, 1985 Turin, Italy show with no new tracks and a more sterile sound. I've been told that this was a "fan club" release, but I can't believe that it was sanctioned by the band due to its pale sound — the picture disc is nice, though.

I haven't heard the *No Easy Way Down* bootleg. It is reportedly a live recording made in Riverside Studios on May 5, 1985 while the band was in England on tour.

A live tape of a show at Boston's Rathskeller on November 11, 1984 shows the band in fine form, and also features an unreleased song titled "Boy In The Bubble" — which would have fit in perfectly on any of their studio records, with its pulsating raga-esque tone and swirling guitar work. The band even calls the song on microphone "a preview of what's to come on our next record." Pity it didn't make it.

I'm sure there are several others bootlegs out there as well, but stick with the officially-released *Behind The Sunset* for a listenable peek at the band's pulsating "live" sound.

## THE RAMBLERS
*(Avignon, France)*

"Ramblin Back..." b/w "Rainy Days" 45, 1995
    Weed Records, France

From the South of France come these lads, forming in 1983 doing covers like "I Wanna Come Back From The World Of L.S.D." and the like. They have at least one LP out, and another in the can, though they reportedly split just as their debut was released.

French music fan Jean-Marc Rimette told me, "When I first heard them, I really thought they were Americans!" This is a compliment — when talking about garage music.

Weed Records released a **Ramblers** 45 in 1995, and it's a blistering garage-

punk winner, with a mixture of **The Seeds** and **Sonics** sound filling the grooves. I have an idea that this band is definitely a hidden gem.

## RAVING MANIACS
*(Belgium)*

An early '80s garage band that played '60s punk.

## THE RAYBEATS
*(New York, NY USA)*

*Guitar Beat* 11 song LP, 1981
    PVC Records, USA

**The Raybeats** were an all instrumental foursome which played into the mid 1980s. **Purple Merkins** guitarist Oz said in 1995, *"I saw them in 1982 on a bill with **Plan 9** and **The Chesterfield Kings** at The Peppermint Lounge in New York. They were a great live band."*

The debut LP combines a New Wave ambiance with traditional surf influences, and throws in an AceTone organ for a garage touch. "B-Gas-Rickshaw" is an especially cool organ and twang surf ditty, with a cheezy fake oriental flair.

A follow-up LP is reportedly of less interest.

**The Raybeats** were not consciously at the forefront of the coming garage scene, but in retrospect it's obvious that they helped pave the way for the New York combos that were just around the corner.

## THE RAZORBLADE
*(Vienna, Austria)*

Self Titled 11 song LP, 1987
    T.U.T. Records, Austria

This fivesome formed in 1986, and they also have a cut on the T.U.T. compilation LP of Vienna bands, *The Third Man*, from 1987. Their 11 song LP of the same year features some mod, pop and garage sounds, marred a bit by some horn work. Still, this was another cool effort from the Austrian Ton Um Ton label, which was unknown to me until researching this book.

## REAL IMPOSSIBLES
*(Los Angeles, CA USA)*

Nothing known.

## REACTION
(Luzern, Switzerland)

They reportedly released two exceptional EPs in 1986/87. I've heard "Fire And Ashes," a passable organ filled pop number, and the much gutsier fuzz stomper "Turn The Clock Back."

## REBBLE PEBBLE
(Belgium)

They were reportedly an all girl-garage rock band modeled after the **Stooges**.

## REBELS WITHOUT A CAUSE
(Cervia, Italy)

"God Damn Boys" b/w "Cramps Of The Moon" 45, 198?
*Naked Lunch* 12" EP, 1987
*Why Don't You Die?* LP, 1988
   Electric Eye Records, Italy
*Jones Comin' Dawn* LP, 1991
   Ultima Uscita Records, Italy

Reportedly an R&B garage act.

## RED ROSES IN THE SAND
(Milan, Italy)

"Love Song" b/w "Play With Fire" 45, 198?
   Crazy Mannequin Records, Italy

An unknown act.

## REEFUS MOONS
(York, U.K.)

*The Art Of Slow Traveling* cassette, 198?
*Moon Dust* cassette, 198?
*World In A Droplet* cassette, 198?
   Acid Tapes, U.K.
*Reach For The Sundial And Kiss For The Hits* 10 song LP, 1990
*The Word Raven* 10 song LP, 1991
*Uptight Sound From The Message Tree* 11 song CD, 1993
   Insect Eye Records, U.K.

Also the track "The Watch Keeper" on the Denmark *Adventure Magazine* compilation LP, circa 1992.

Ross Stephens peeked through the window to see the ghost of **John Lennon** jamming with **Robyn Hitchcock, Paul Roland** and **Syd Barrett**. He took notes, literally, then retired to his cave in York, England.

Three albums later, his sonic stew of quirky psych-pop is still as energetic, whimsical and bright as ever, and Stephens (calling himself **Reefus Moons**) still plays all the sounds himself, probably all at the same time.

I wrote to Reefus for information, and he replied, *"You said you'd like some bio material — I just came back with a load of leaves and branches — when I twigged what you meant."*

His privately pressed debut album is chocked full of insanely catchy melodies, warm vocals, shimmering guitar — and above all else a wealth of imagination. The entire collection is deserving of a much wider audience — and rates with me as one of the most accomplished releases of the entire period. The irony does not escape met that Stephens released this album at his own expense, at a time when indy labels thrust so much dreck upon us.

It's difficult for me to sort out individual tracks for praise, but special kudos should go to "Space Garden 9," "Strawberry Sunset" and "Monkey Valentine Revolution."

The follow-up LP is as eccentric as the first, with "Salamander Raincoat," "Gardening The Mind" and "The Dinosaur Of Truth" added to **Reefus Moons'** considerably individualistic output. Both of these vinyl-only releases were pressed in extremely small quantities, but are well worth the high price of admission they will assuredly command in collectors' shops.

The *Uptight Sounds From The Message Tree* CD continued his aural trip. "Acid House Sergeant" explains the plight of a tripping policeman, while "Love Bomb" could be a Valentine Day's card from **Timothy Leary**.

*"This album was made on earth, under the influence of cats,"* contends the man who plants several tongues firmly in cheek.

Cheerio!

## THE REFUGEES
(Lyon, France)

A demo tape exists, circa 1991. They are reportedly good on stage, but I'm unsure of their musical orientation.

## REPTILE HOUSE
(Columbus, OH USA)

"Reptile House" & "Room For Hate" 7" flexi, 1984
   Testube Magazine, USA
Untitled 5 song cassette, 1984
   Testube Distribution, USA

This author formed this band while in college with future **Marshmallow Overcoat** keyboardist Debra Dickey. Enamored with the burgeoning garage sound, we bashed through our own early garage-trash efforts — mainly originals.

Our story is unspectacular, I suppose, except as an example of the somewhat amusing trials and tribulations that most similar bands at the time would suffer through.

On January 1, 1984, for instance, we headed to southern Ohio to record some demo tracks. We had heard of an inexpensive studio down there, so we figured it was worth the 150 mile drive from Columbus. Timing it perfectly, we just happened to leave as the worst ice and snow storm of the decade hit. It was so cold and stormy during the trip that we had to hold our hands against the car windshield — to melt the ice — so we could see the road!

We then found out why the studio was so cheap — it was housed literally in a barn! The sound of the tracks reflects this, matching the crudeness of our musicianship perfectly.

Two songs found their way onto a magazine's flexi, and several others were released as a limited cassette later that year. Several videos of the band exist, including rehearsals and a live show on February 22, 1984.

Our guitarist, a Philippino named Elmer Laos, was convinced he was really **Carlos Santana**, and in early 1985 left to "find himself" in California. He was never heard from again, and neither was **Reptile House**.

*(Note: This band was (and is) constantly confused with the hardcore band of the same name from Maryland.)*

## THE RESONARS
(Tucson, AZ USA)

*"My brother was in a Tucson band called **The Resonars** in the '60s,"* says rhythm guitarist and vocalist Matt Rendon. *"I thought it was a cool name — it had something to do with 'resonating.'"*

The re-claimed name also accurately describes this young foursome's vibrating, undulating brand of music. Comparisons come to mind to the best U.S. West Coast bands of the

mid-1960s — **Jefferson Airplane, The Byrds, Buffalo Springfield** and especially **Love**.

*"Mostly the* Forever Changes *album,"* says Rendon of the **Love** fixation. *"It sounds like Arizona, that album, it strikes me like that anyway."*

*"That's a big influence,"* says lead guitarist and vocalist Eric Royer, *"but that's not what we're trying to do."* Royer notes that folk, country and power-pop also blend into the lysergia, eliminating any hint of nostalgia or retro-rock pigeonholing.

Hardly a new Tucson act, these latest **Resonars** formed in 1992 and deposited a cassette-only four song cassette EP the next year. They've also weathered the ebb and flow of line-up changes and countless low-key club dates in Tucson, Phoenix, Flagstaff and Bisbee (Arizona).

While the '60s guitar fire might be an obvious influence, the group is made up of a variety of other musical interests.

*"I came into the group from a different angle,"* says Royer. *"I'd listened to a lot of punk music. I really like D. Boon's guitar playing in **The Minutemen**."*

Bassist Forest Dunn is the newest member. *"I was totally into 'prog rock' in high school, and I've always liked a lot of '60s psychedelia,"* he notes enthusiastically. Dunn's active and fluid bass style fits right into **The Resonars'** intricate textured approach. *"He fills in a lot of (musical) holes,"* notes Rendon.

Creative vocal harmonies from Rendon, Dunn and Royer also distinguish **The Resonars** from most other underground groups. Their combination of polished vocals and sinewy dual guitars makes **The Resonars** an obviously talented bands — even if no one can agree on what to call their music.

*"Everybody has a different category for us,"* says drummer O.J. Moyer. *"Everybody calls us something different."*

That variety of musical genres is reflected in their 1995 recordings — a full 29 songs constructed in their own back-yard rehearsal studio. The "studio" is actually a converted garage jammed full of instruments, records and a pool table, with a plethora of classic 1960s album covers gracing the walls. The band's sound seems to have bounced off those musical ghosts and been absorbed directly into the recordings.

These home made 8-track sessions are also remarkably clean and professional — saving the band a truckload of money and affording them the time and comfort of recording when and how they wanted. They plan on selecting about half of the songs for release as a full length CD later this year.

*"We mixed it in '**Moby Grape**' stereo,"* laughs

Rendon. *"I was listening to **Moby Grape** a lot at the time, so we ended up mixing it like a **Moby Grape** record."*

Sparkling vocals, bright guitar and the occasional banjo highlight the sessions, which veer from **Long Ryders**-like country rock to **Plimsouls** power pop to the melodious aforementioned '60s psychedelia.

Some interesting titles also pop up, including "Drunk Pumpkin Blues," "Make It Dark and Cold" and "Sleeping Blood." The regal "Your Soul Has Been Neglected" is a chillingly emotional song, featuring warm and soaring harmonies and a tasteful piano passage. **Love**'s **Arthur Lee** would be thankful to pen a piece of such power and depth.

The power pop and acid folk sophistication of their new tape doesn't display one important and vital facet of the band — the strength of their live stage presentation. *"We play a lot harder live,"* Moyer says with a smirk.

*"I think when we play live we can be pretty garagey,"* adds Royer. *"What we really want to do is get our harmonies down live."*

Many bands worry about their stage clothes, hair, fancy equipment and promo photos — then sit down and try to write some songs. **The Resonars** have accomplished the hardest thing first — they've created their own powerful, polished, creative sound.

A debut 45 and CD were in the works as of mid-1995.

## REVELATION CHILDREN
*(Italy)*

The two songs I've heard, "Bike," and the live "Because" are gritty dark garage blasters with some restrained fuzz guitar and nicely placed organ. I've no idea if anything was ever released.

## THE REVELLS
*(Venlo, Holland)*

Darren Ross calls **The Revells** *"Real good Dutch teen Garage from 1986."* Their five song *Swamp City* EP from '86 features a cool picture sleeve and cover versions of "All Black & Hairy" and "Night Of The Sadist," so this one might be worth tracking down.

## THE REVENGE
*(Brussels, Belgium)*

A '60s style garage band from the early '80s, with no known product.

## THE REVERBS
*(Chicago, IL USA)*

*The Happy Forest* 7 song 12" EP, 1984
Metro America/Enigma Records, USA

Here's a record that should teach readers not to take the word of reviewers (like me) as the sacred truth. I read many kind and even raving reviews of this duo's 12" for several years — and then I finally picked it up for a couple dollars in a used bin. I could have saved my money.

All of the descriptions I had read were accurate enough to a degree — the jangley Rickenbacker guitars and classic pop structures are indeed there — but in the most tame '80s pop kind of way. It's just all so calculated and polite and...tame.

This stuff isn't awful, it just doesn't have the spark that makes the subject of this book so interesting to me.

## REVOLVER
*(Los Angeles, CA USA)*

"Some Other Guy" b/w
    "I'm Gonna Sit Right Down & Cry Over You" 45, 1983
    Revolver Records, USA

1964-era **Beatles** is the inspiration for these lads, who sported the vintage instruments and dark suits and ties that made the **Fab Four** infamous. They

only had one 45, I believe, though a track or two also showed up on one of the Radio Tokyo (recording studio) compilation LPs. The 45 sports '60s Capitol Records-like labels and a very **Beatles**-ish duo-tone picture sleeve.

Guitarist/ vocalist Mark Estes and guitarist Howard Lea would go onto **The Jigsaw Seen**, where their pop sensibilities would flourish more completely. Estes is an admitted **Beatles** nut, and I remember being serenaded by his uncanny **Lennon** imitation for hours at after-gig parties in the late 1980s.

## THE RHOMBOIDS
*(Washington, D.C. USA)*

A long enduring local act which kept the spirit of garage-punk alive in the nation's capital in the 1980s. I'm not sure of any releases.

## DUANE RIPLEY & THE GO-GO SET
*(U.K.)*

This looks to be a combined **Cannibals/Sting Rays** effort with one 45 extant circa 1985. The A-side song is "Revenge Of The 50 Foot Go-Go Girls (From Outer Space)," while the B-side is credited to Multicoloured Michael & The Rainbow People. It's apparently the same studio folks, doing the song "The Day The Fish Came Out Dancing In Guru Weirdbrains Mind."

If the songs are as creative as the fake band names and song titles, then this 45 could be worth a listen.

## THE ROADRUNNERS
*(France)*

They have been called by some the best band on stage in France which is influenced by '60s R&B and '60s punk — they also have at least three LPs to their credit. I seem to remember that many bands mentioned recommended them to me when I was in France, and spoke of them with great respect.

The tape I've heard is full of finely crafted pop-rock songs, with expert harmonies and snappy playing. "Who's Behind The Door" is the kind of classic pop song that used to grace the charts when a song's merit — not record company promotion money — would determine success. The song title "A Frog In My Throat" is not only a funny pun for a French band, its a bouncy and melodic number.

## PAUL ROLAND
*(U.K.)*

Untitled 3 song 7" EP, 1987
   Pastell Records, Germany
"Sword & Sorcery" 45, 1987
   Constrictor Records, Germany
*A Cabinet Of Curiosities* LP, 1987
   New Rose Records, France
*Confessions Of An Opium Eater* 13 song LP, 1988
Untitled 5 song 7" EP, 1988
   DiDi Records, Greece
*House Of Dark Shadows* 13 song cassette, 1988?
   Acid Tapes, U.K.

plus *Werewolves Of London* LP, 1980; *Burnt Orchids* EP, 1985; *Gabrielle* 12"; *Dance Macabre* LP, 1987...and many others.

Here's a rare commodity for the 1980s: a talented solo artist. I suppose the tag of "solo artist" is misleading, however, as **Paul Roland** more than not is accompanied by session musicians' backing. Still the music and arrangements were singularly **Roland**'s, and they were indeed creative.

Comparisons to early **Al Stewart** and **Syd Barrett** hold up, as do the similarities to his contemporary **Robyn Hitchcock**. Unlike **Hitchcock**, however, **Roland**'s work is more "serious," epic and dramatic. It is perhaps odd that the more frivolous (but still enjoyable) **Hitchcock** garnered far more attention than **Roland** in the 1980s — but the comparison of the two are only superficial at best.

A plethora of **Roland** vinyl appeared throughout the decade on many different independent labels, but I've only been lucky to find a Greek "best-of" and an odd 7" EP. The *Confessions Of An Opium Eater* compilation is at least a fine start, while The *House Of Dark Shadows* cassette also appears to be a sampler of various releases, and a fine showcase in its own right.

Like **Al Stewart**, **Roland** is a skewed English storyteller, whose tales rise and fall with dramatic grace. "The Great Edwardian Air Raid" is an evocative and haunting epic, just as "Berlin" is a dark and moody bit of emotional memory. Melody and passion are exhibited throughout the work, which is augmented by excellent uses of strings and woodwinds. "Blades Of Battenberg," "In The Opium Den" and "Gabrielle" are all major works, deserving of mass artistic attention.

Much of **Roland**'s output reminds me in tone of the haunting *War Of The Worlds* concept double LP from the late 1970s — a melding of melody, narrative and moody atmosphere.

The *Confessions Of An Opium Eater* LP is a colorful roadmap to a decade of his art, and now I'll follow the directions and dig up the other treasures that await.

174

## THE ROMULANS
*(Madison, WI USA)*

"She's Tara" b/w "Psychedelic Kingbee" 45, 1991
"Alias Lovely" b/w "In The Corner Of Your Room" 45, 1992
    Susstones Records, USA
*Flight Of...* 13 song CD, 1993
    Prospective Records

Kevin Hagen, who also produced a garage music video show for local television, headed this outfit, which started gigging in late 1990.

Hagen's band is difficult to categorize. Owing as much to the '90s grunge movement as the garage sensibility, their very distorted and noisy 45s don't quite deliver a precise picture of the band's direction.

Both tracks from their second 7" are also on their debut CD, which doesn't clear up many of the questions about the band's focus. "In The Corner Of Your Room" — from the 45 and the CD — is one of more traditionally psychedelic tracks, with a raga-esque feel and extended freak-out section. An excellent cover of the **William Penn V**'s "Swami" is also a highlight of the disc.

Much of the CD is uncertain or murky, however. "Paisley Farm," despite its creative title, leads off the album with a dirge-like turned almost hardcore punk mixture that doesn't quite satisfy.

*(Note: This was one of several **Romulans** in the '70s and '80s.)*

## THE ROOFDOGS
*(Bellingham, WA USA)*

*Having A Rave Up With...* 6 song 7" EP, 1991
    Estrus Records, USA

This is really **The Mono Men** in their embryonic late 1980s all-instrumental inception, when some cool organ shared space with the trashy guitars. The tapes sat for several years while **The Mono Men**'s Estrus record label got up and running.

The completely accurate rip-off of **The Yardbirds'** *Rave Up* LP cover could be the best part of the disc — though their version of the always fun "Out Of Limits" is also worth a listen.

*"An impressive feature of this group is its complete lack of versatility,"* says the liner notes. *"They create a kind of excitement that comes from alcohol: they fart, belch, vomit, choke — and do it all with a case of beer."*

Say no more.

## ROTTE KAPELLE
*(Tucson, AZ USA)*

11 song cassette, 1982
    Iconoclast International Records, USA
unreleased LP, 1984

**Lee Joseph** of **Yard Trauma** was the driving force behind this early **Syd Barrett**-influenced combo, which survived the desert heat for 1982 and '83. There really wasn't a supporting worldwide "scene" at the time for the psychedelic doodlings of this group, so they should be regarded as ahead of their time (or a few years behind their time, depending how you look at it.)

This was not a retro-styled psych group, however. The feel and texture of this group was contemporary, but the mood and delivery was identifiably trippy and "psychedelic." They only released one cassette, a self-titled 1982 effort on the locally infamous Iconoclast International label — it remains one of the finest cassette-only releases of the decade.

The 10 song collection features dense instrumentation, aggressive rhythms and almost stream-of-consciousness vocals drifting through the mix. A teenage angst permeates the proceedings as well, cementing the now-classic sound of these tracks.

They also contributed some later songs to the *Town Without Pity* compilation cassette, as described elsewhere. This was one of Tucson's best psych groups from any era, but they remain obscure even by local standards.

A full LP was also recorded, but sadly remains unreleased.

## THE ROUSERS
*(Holland)*

Formed in 1977, described as a mixture of new wave and Merseybeat. They made a few 45s and two LPs, and split in 1982. Several members went on to form **The Thought**.

## THE ROYAL NONESUCH
*(Springfield, MO USA)*

"Something Strange" b/w "You Need Love" 45, 1987
    Unlimited Productions, USA
"Why Should I Care" b/w "Two Can Play That Game" 45, 1990
    Get Hip Records, USA

The group began in 1985 as a combination of **The Limit**, a mod band, and **The Sparrows**, a garage group. They then worked up several sets of mid-'60s pop and began to play at the only local venues available for such sounds: the Missouri "oldies" circuit.

They really wanted to play their own whigged-out originals to cranked up teenagers, but they were in a very tame Midwestern state — the time and place were just not right. They would eventually play the college circuit throughout the Midwest, but the overwhelming conservative times were not conducive to bowl hair cuts and their brand of '60s cool.

**The Royal Nonesuch** did record some stellar tracks, and their un-released version of **The Apparitions**' 1966 stomper "She's So Satisfyin'" is a classic. **The Apparitions**' original bass player was at one gig the band played in Kansas City, and was reportedly amazed that someone remembered a

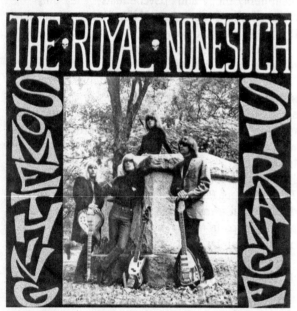

song that he played 20 years earlier. A picture sleeve was even prepared for a 45 to feature the song, but the record never saw the light of day. Oddly, a video of the song was released anyway in 1987, showing the band at its frantic-best.

I was fortunate enough to stay with these hep-cats on several occasions, and I can't think of a cooler set of people stuck in a stranger place. They were like an oasis of style trapped in a desert of opportunity, and this obviously limited whatever success they could have musically. Eventually members moved to California to join a reformed **Tell Tale Hearts,** but this didn't hit paydirt either.

Their two 45s are absolute essential '80s garage, however, complete with perfect picture sleeves and total Vox madness in the grooves. Few groups of the decade matched **The Royal Nonesuch**'s combination of style and musical ability, with their

vinyl as enduring proof.

They deserved attention and acclaim far beyond the scope of their sleepy Springfield home — and garage fans needed more than the few tracks that the band squeezed out before their late '80s demise.

One can only imagine what this group could have accomplished if it had somehow been based in Los Angeles or New York at the height of the garage craze.

**The Royal Nonesuch** are one of the best garage bands that almost no one has ever heard. But they thankfully existed — I can play you the proof.

## RUBBER DOLPHINARIUM
*(Edinburgh, Scotland)*

Yet another Lenny Helsing side-band, this time featuring some female co-conspirators. I believe a cassette exists, with a mandolin version of the classic **We The People** tune "In The Past."

Glynnis Wilson notes, *"Part of a long line-up of incestuous Edinburgh garage bands like the* **Stayrcase, Offhooks, Thanes, Green Telescope,** *etc. They featured Ross (who was in* **The Crypt Kicker V** *in 1992), Dennis, Angus, and of course Lenny Helsing. They mostly played at a club called the Waterloo. They never released any demos or records and if you dare ask anybody about them now all you get is a nod and change of subject! They were rumoured to be very wild!"*

## RUBBERMIND REVENGE
*(Germany)*

They released the wonderfully titled nine song *Hippies Are More Fun Than People* LP in 1988 and the "My Zen" and "Little Lion" 45s on the Vielklang label in 1986-87. I've heard mixed reviews of their sound, which is mod and pop oriented.

## RUNNING STREAM
*(Trieste, Italy)*

*Running Stream* 8 song 12" EP, 1985
  Ton Um Ton Records, Austria
*2nd* 12 song LP, 1988
  Vinyl Savage Records, Italy(?)

I am constantly surprised at the amount of previously unknown groups that pop up from the garage-psych underworld.

**176**     **The Running Stream** had a great cut on the essential mid-1980s *Declaration Of*

*Fuzz* compilation LP, but I didn't realize until years later that they had two 12"s of their own available as well.

The first 12" is half covers and half originals, with the descriptive "She Eats A Mushroom" the best of the lot, though "Acid Head" is also pretty demented. These cats leaned more towards the psych part of garage, if you couldn't tell from their song titles, and their distinctively European flavor helped make the familiar elements of fuzz 'n Vox somehow new.

Their second effort is a full LP, with original material taking the forefront. The psych edge engulfs the disc, and wonderfully so, as Carlo, Zombie, Shorty and Ugly dish out some deliciously

## RUNNING STREAM, 1985

warped noise. (Organist "Ugly" would later go onto **The Woody Peakers**, as you'll read later.)

The cryptic tone of this band only adds to their appeal; sure, we might have heard this type of black turtleneck garage-psych before, but not with the sense of mysterious fun that **The Running Stream** muster.

I only hope that there are a few more records of **The Running Stream** — and of bands like them — that I have yet to discover.

## THE RUTLES
*(Rutland, England)*

*The Rutles* 14 song LP, 1978
  Warner Brothers Records, USA

All right, just a minute. I know that this wasn't a real band — it was Neil Innes (formerly of **The Bonzo Dog Band**) plus Eric Idle (from comic troupe **Monty Python**), plus a couple of other studio musicians. This record was the soundtrack from the *All You Need Is Cash* TV movie; an elaborate **Beatles** parody, if you couldn't figure it out by now.

All elements of **Beatle**mania are lampooned rather effectively in the movie, but it is the expertly

conceived music that makes the greatest impression. Each period of the **Beatles'** music is parodied with infuriating accuracy — Innes composed all 14 tracks, and in them he combines elements from at least 50 different **Beatles** songs!

These songs are incredibly close to the spirit and mood of the originals, but somehow just a bit different here and there. They're so close, though, that one can mistake them for actual **Beatles** tracks after repeated listens. (I've confused myself with songs like "Hold My Hand" and "I Must Be In Love"!)

Now I know it might seem odd that this parody would find its way into a book on 1980s garage-psychedelia. The fact is that this record was unwittingly made at the beginning of the garage "revival," and was one of the few '60s pop records attempted in the late 1970s.

Whether the creators like it or not, **The Rutles** have become an actual part of the post-modernist rock world that they themselves had parodied.

*(Note: Rhino records re-released the **Rutles** LP in 1990 as a CD with several extra tracks. An actual **Rutles** "tribute LP" even appeared in 1990, showing that the world truly is a wacky, zany and strange place.)*

## SACRED HEARTS
*(Guernsey, U.K.)*

A power pop and mod-tinged band with the occasional '60s pop influence — several members were previously in the mod act **The Risk**. Among their output is the 1990 *Love Bomb* EP, the "Lucy Don't Mind" 45 and *Sacred* LP in '91, the 4 *Your Love* and *Prime Time* EPs in '92, the *Broken Dream* LP & CD in '94 and the *Psyche Out* EP in 1995.

Vocalist Mark le Gallez also helps to run (along with Frank Osiewacz in Germany) the Twist record label, releasing a variety of interesting underground and garage sounds.

## SAINT LUCA
*(Piombino, Italy)*

These Italians reportedly have a psych/wave/**Velvet Underground** influence, with *The Name Of This Man Is Legion* LP, label and year unknown.

## SANDOZ LIME
*(Bala Cynwyd, PA USA)*

Self Titled 10 song LP, 1992
   Distortions Records, USA

Also one track on the *Kaleidoscopic Vibrations* compilation, 1991; *Frozen Laughter* EP, 1993; and a second LP recorded late 1994, for release in 1995.

The original name of band was **The Way Back Machine,** when they were reportedly a heavy mod-psych band from 1989-1991.

Extremely thick reverb, heavily echoed vocals and wah-wahed guitars dominate their LP, which is rooted in English "freakbeat" sounds and heavy late-1960s psych.

Covers of "Francis" and "When The Night Falls" are especially highlights — but fans of guitar-oriented head psych will find all of this LP a trippy treat.

The sound production is a bit muddled for my taste, but this LP could be an accurate glimpse at the band's loud "live" sound — which would be quite an earful, I'm sure.

## SANTA CASSINE KIDS
*(France)*

Untitled 4 song 7" EP, 1994
   Larsen Records, France

This simple 7" EP is a true do-it-yourself punk effort, featuring some distinctly French punk-pop screamers. I like the fact that one band member calls himself "Luigi Skywalker."

## THE SAPPHIRES
*(Chicago, IL USA)*

A January, 1988 Neal Skok review in *Option Magazine* described these cats as, *"Pedestrian garage rock that's reminiscent of **The Seeds** in its hum-drum tempos and simplistic repetitive riffs."*

This formula sounds pretty good to me, though one gets the idea that Skok was disappointed. I'm unsure if this was a demo tape or a record release.

## SATAN'S CHEERLEADERS
*(Los Angeles, CA USA)*

"Lysergia" b/w "Electric Prunes Theme" 45, 1985
   Living Eye Records, USA

This L.A. group reappeared every few years starting in the mid-'80s, with several 45s out, including "Lysergia" on Living Eye Records. Beginning as a psych-garage styled instrumental combo, they eventually added a vocalist for their noise-trip releases.

## LES SATELLITES
*(France)*

My secret agent in France tells me that their first LP, circa late 1980s, is quite good.

## THE SAUCERMEN
*(Australia)*

James Peirce of *Era Of Sound Magazine* says, *"They're faves of mine — a wild '60s punk/surf/rock combo that should have some vinyl out by 1994."* I hadn't heard of any product by mid-1995 besides an appearance on a 7" compilation EP.

## SCALPERS
*(Belgium)*

Have unknown releases.

## SCARECROWS
*(Brussels, Belgium)*

Reported to be one of the first '80s "revival" garage bands in Belgium, starting in the summer of 1982.

Music fan Ivan Andreini saw them perform and notes, *"They were fueled by their love of bands* like **The Barracudas**, **The Cramps**, **The Plimsouls**, and the French band **The Dogs**. Looking back, they were not a million miles away from N.Y.'s **Outta Place**. They did a total of only about ten gigs, didn't record anything, and split in the summer of '83.

"The drummer Marc went on to **The Lunatic Asylum** — a more **Byrds** and psychedelic music oriented outfit — and he also played one month in N.Y. with **The Optic Nerve** around 1985, then played with **The Bees**.

"I want to add that except for say 15 or 20 enthusiastic fans, **The Scarecrows** were despised by most of the people who saw them. This was 1982 and passionate rock'n'roll was out, my dear, and boring English post-'New Wave' was in."

## SCIACALLI
*(Bologna, Italy)*

"Dimmi La Verati" b/w "Les Cactus" 45, 1992
*Finira* 7" EP, 1993
*E La Cosa Si Ripete* LP, 1993
*In Orbita* 13 song LP, 1994
    Destination X Records, Italy

Several other releases were pending as of press time, mid-1995.

I find it most amazing how other cultures appropriate the distinctly American '66 garage archetype and infuse it with their own regional influences. **Sciacalli**, for example, sings in their native Italian, and add an almost imperceiveable European flavor to the instrumentation. This is something felt rather than specifically heard, but it does exist.

I've only heard the latest LP listed above — but the '66 sound remains mostly intact, with the Vox organ dripping throughout "Balbettando" and the fuzz buzzing in "Yeeeehhh!!" The cross-culture melting hits another level with their cover of the Canadian '60s punk standard "Je Cherche," sung in the original North American French.

**Sciacalli** also does a nice job with an early **David Bowie** track, "You've Got A Habit Of Leaving," though for some reason they take partial writing credit for the 1965 tune, presumably for the translation of the lyrics into Italian!

I'm also not sure what the back cover with a girl showing her underwear has to do with anything — but I like it nonetheless.

## SCREAMING FLOOR
*(Senigaglia, Italy)*

*Village And Woodland* LP, 1986
*Bridge And Ashes* 12" EP, 198?
    Toast Records, Italy

Reportedly a psych/pop group.

## THE SCREAMIN' PIJAS
*(Gijon, Spain)*

*Freakshow* 4 song 7" EP, 1992
self-titled 13 song LP, 1994
    Opus Daemonis/Thunderpussy Records, Spain

A wonderfully aggressive ambiance permeates the debut EP, with the roughly titled "Buttfuck Place" as a driving garage-punk anthem. Mixing equal parts of '60s fuzz and organ with Ramones guitar buzz, **The Screamin' Pijas** create an addled frantic world, which comes into clearer focus with their 1994 limited edition LP.

The 13 tracks are more polished but no less frenetic, with a re-recorded "Buttfuck Place" once again as a highlight. The LP also enables the band to stretch out on their influences, from straight '66 punk groovers to more acoustic and punk numbers.

**The Screamin' Pijas** are another example of a quality band that could very well go unnoticed outside their own circle — and one that the reader should snap up if the vinyl ever passes their path.

## THE SCREAMIN' SPECIES
*(Australia)*

A '60s punk outfit that formed in the late '70s and carried over into the mid-'80s. I'm afraid that's all I know.

## SCRIMSHAKERS
*(Stradella, Italy)*

Reportedly rock/psych with a private cassette, circa 198?

## LA SECTA
*(Spain)*

A garage band with the 1990 *Blue Tales* LP on Munster Records in Spain and Spliff Records in France, as well as the U.S. *Our Kicks* double 7" from 1991 on S.F.T.R.I.

## THE SECRET SERVICE
*(Smithstown, NY, USA)*

A mid to late-'80s mod/garage group, with at least one 12" EP, *It's All Happening Here*. Their slick R&B pop didn't jump off the vinyl at me, but they reportedly had a much more energetic live show. Let's hope so.

Steven Martin of *The Island Ear* newspaper disagrees with my assessment. He wrote in the May 30, 1988 issue, *"Pointy boots, high collared striped shirts, shades, straight bangs, shiny ties and Rickenbackers aside then, their debut EP is a brash, melodic two sides of energy, gimmick-free rock'n'roll."*

You might want to find this one and decide for yourself.

## SECRET SYDE
*(Long Branch, NJ USA)*

*Hidden Secrets* 7 song 12" EP, 1983/1986
    Red Rhino Records, U.K.

The LP *Hidden Secrets* has the reputation as an excellent early '80s psych gem. I found it to be a muddy, self-indulgent and poorly produced effort — heavy on the guitars and thin on melody, craftsmanship or interest. But I've been wrong before, once or twice at least.

## THE SEDGWICKS
*(Minneapolis, MN USA)*

Another successful Susstones Records production, this pleasant melodious effort recalls the smile that power pop once brought to our lips. Not overly drenched in the '60s tradition, but cool enough to be included here.

## THE SEEING EYE GODS
*(Los Angeles, CA USA)*

Untitled 5 song 12" EP, 1985
    Epitaph Records, USA

O.K., so this was just a studio project of **Bad Religion**'s Brett Gurewitz, complete with — gasp — a drum machine, but it also boasts a red and green paisley picture disc that looks pretty cool.

The music? Mild psych-pop, with the original "Psychedelic Suzie" the most interesting (poor Suzie Shaw of Bomp Records had to endure the wrath of being called "Psychedelic Suzie" for years to come), though their treatment of "Pictures Of Matchstick Men" isn't bad either. Classify this as a novelty disc of enjoyable proportions.

## THE SEEN
*(State College, PA USA)*

The *Under The Sun* LP, 1986, on Red Dog Records is an extremely lightweight mod-pop effort. A follow up 45 was a bit better, but still a bit too fragile for my tastes.

## SETTORE OUT
*(Torino, Italy)*

"Iceberg" b/w "Uomini Di Fronttiera" 45, 1986
*Citta* 12" EP, 1987
*Un Grido Nel Cielo* "Live" cassette, 1988
    Private pressings
"Ragazzo Di Strada" b/w "Gente" 7", 1987
    Tramite Records, Italy
"Un Altra Volta" b/w "Quello Chemesta" 7" flexi, 1990
    Urlo Magazine, Italy
*Un Altra Volta* LP, 1990
    Diva Records, Italy

Reportedly a mod/beat band.

## SEXICOLOR
*(Mestre/Venezia, Italy)*

"Don't Hang on Me" b/w "The Quest" split 45, 1992
    Urlo Magazine #2

Reportedly a psych pop band.

## SEX MUSEUM
*(Madrid, Spain)*

*Fuzz Face* 10 song LP, 1987
"Sexual Beast" b/w "Ya Es Tarde" promo 45, 1987
    Fidias Records, Spain
"Get Lost" b/w "Free Living" 45, 1989
*Independence* LP, 1989
    Romilar-D Records, Spain

**Sex Museum** must be one of the oddest names for a band with a garage allegiance. It certainly isn't very typical, but then a garage band by any name from Spain certainly isn't typical.

The *Fuzz Face* LP delivers on the promise the band spread through several compilation LPs, as it collects all of the teen garage energy together — reflecting the band's love for (tough) mod, garage-psych and trash.

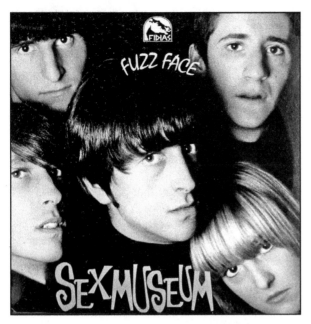

A "fuzz-face," for the uninitiated, is a famous brand of guitar fuzz-box, and **The Sex Museum** uses it liberally throughout the record. (It even is pictured on the back cover of the LP, along with photos of **The Doors** and **Small Faces**.)

Keeping with their unusual moniker, there are a few oddly titled songs on the LP, like "Big Cock" and "Sexual Beast." These turn out to be true-blue '66 garage tracks, despite their names, and I suppose one must credit the songwriters for thinking a bit differently. The pure garage mentality would erode, however, and after this LP the band drifted toward hard rock like many of its contemporaries.

The subsequent "Get Lost" 45 showed these tendencies, with an extended B-side that edged into the self-indulgent. Several other discs would appear as well, but the fun and fuzz-filled debut LP is still the best exhibit in their museum.

## THE SHADES
*(St. Petersburg, FL USA)*

"Time For Change" b/w "Shake It" 45, 1980
    Direct Hit Records, USA

The "Time For Change" 45 is a good example of the new sounds that started to spring forth with the new decade. Mod-pop-garage is the style, done up energetically.

Dennis Dalcin would later revive the Direct Hit label for releases through his *Kaleidoscope* magazine — and then go onto the highly recommended **Lears**.

## SHADOW CIRCUS
*(Lancaster, PA USA)*

A three song demo exists.

## SHADOWLAND
*(Scotland, U.K.)*

"She" b/w "She Sells" 45, 1994
    Twist Records, U.K. / Germany

Forming circa 1989, they released the 1991 eight song *Kaleidoscope* 12" EP and the *Oldies, Live & Rarities* demo. Their sound has been compared to the pop-garage-mod style of **The Prisoners**, and that's a fair comparison to these ears.

"Throw A Six" from their 12" features fine vocal harmonies, and a solid groove (hampered by the "anti-Farfisa" — that pesky Hammond B-3 organ).

"She Sells" is a smooth effort, with a trippy slide guitar, dreamy lead vocal and hummable hook. The 45's A-side, "She," is a less remarkable tune, though professionally delivered. Like in the 1960s, a band often is better represented musically by their B-side, as is the case here.

The band also reportedly sports a stage show full of acid inspired lighting and op art — some of it is featured on the "She" picture sleeve.

## THE SHAMBLES
*(Boston, MA USA)*

A late 1980s band which featured ex-**Lyres**.

## THE SHAMBLES
*(San Diego, CA USA)*

"Fire" b/w "Louise" 45, 1993
    Prospective Records, USA

This Bart Mendoza-led combo formed in 1990 out of the long-running **Manual Scan**. They soon accumulated appearances on the compilation CDs *Staring At The Sun Volumes #1-2,* and contributed "Might as Well" for the *Raspberries Tribute* LP in late 1994:

They also contributed "Nothing Can Be Everything" on the dreadful 1994 *Fish Sauce* compilation, one of the worst collections of supposed "rock" music I've ever been subjected to. **The Shambles'** bright pop sound sticks out like a sore thumb among the dreary ramblings of the other participants.

A May 1992 four song demo also included the usual **Manual Scan** mod-pop melody, but with a little more guitar muscle on "Original Tangent" and some sweet Mersey-mod atmosphere on "Of Heart And Soul" and "Stuck On The Inside."

The A-side of their 45, "Fire," is a pleasant if unremarkable mod-pop tune, while the version of **The Raiders**' "Louise" is a killer — full of groove with a sprite organ and fine back-up vocals.

A long-player was reportedly in the works for 1995.

## THE SHAMEN
(U.K.)

Many records exist; often described as the 1980's **Electric Prunes**, but with a modern approach to recording. Their 1988 LP *Drop* is a good example. Some of their later recordings, however, seemed little more than disco "house" blathering.

## THE SHEDS
(London, England)

Reportedly a side-project garage band — made up of members of other groups — who played infrequently during the mid-'80s but then fortified a lineup in the late-'80s to play more regularly in London clubs. Their *Stepping Stoned* cassette features 13 mono cover versions of garage classics like "You Burn Me Up & Down," "Dirty Water" and "Journey To Tyme" — very much in the U.S. 1966 tradition.

I'm unsure if any other product has seen release, but a live tape I've heard sounds like they fit right in with the Medway garage trash scene. One highlight was the cover of "Somebody To Love," done up like the **Great Society**'s original raga-esque version.

## THE SHERLOCKS
(Montreal, PQ Canada)

*Beat Not The Bones* 8 song 12" EP, 1991
    Primitive Records, Canada

Formed as teenagers, **The Sherlocks** were considered by some to be Canada's answer to **The Creeps** — or at least disciples of the same type of R&B inspired garage.

The inner sleeve notes contend, *"Just what is it that makes **The Sherlocks** one of the most exciting new groups in today's music scene? Elementary,*

*my dear rock-fan! It's got to be that unbridled energy and enthusiasm!*

*"From the soul inspired, kick-butt tempo of 'How Low' to the evil, low-down stompin' 'One Black Sheep,' from the harp wailin', dynamic 'Stephany' to the righteous ballad 'Comin' Over,' from the Bo Diddley R&B blast of 'Through The Bars' to the dark and moody 'Girl You Captivate Me,' **The Sherlocks** give you more bang for the buck than any new band I can think of!"*

There isn't much to add to that accurate assessment except to say that a cool cover and some nice inner sleeve photos make this a completely successful package.

It's sad to say that I don't think anything else appeared from this talented combo.

## THE SHIFTERS
(Toulouse, France)

Formed in December, 1985, with at least a 45, EP and LP to their credit, reportedly in a **Pretty Things**-like R&B vein.

## SHINDIGGERS
(Melbourne, Australia)

Described by James Peirce as "cool R&B garage sounds." Music fan Milly Muleskinner adds, *"I have their 1985 single called 'Go Wild.' It also has a rendition of 'Secret Agent Man.' To my knowledge they recorded two other 45s: 'Baby Let Go' and 'Beat Is Back.' They disbanded in the summer of 1990/91."*

## THE SHINY GNOMES
(Germany)

Untitled 3 song 7" EP, 1986
    Glitterhouse Records, Germany
*Wild Spells* 9 song LP, 1986
    Pastell Records, Germany

It's a difficult task to meld the power of garage and the trippiness of psych into a danceable stew, but **The Shiny Gnomes** found the recipe. Their debut EP is a perfect blend of garage muscle and psych stylings, with the cover of **The Countdowns**' pulsating "Sex Maniac" especially invigorating.

Their *Wild Spells* LP far exceeded all expectations, however, as the shimmering, majestic production and confident performance stuns the listener. Additional instrumentation such as violin, trumpet,

**182**

piano, and sitar make this an almost orchestral affair, as on the mesmerisingly psychedelic "Temple Balls." A whirlwind of percussion and buzzing sitar engulf the track, making it an unforgettable experience.

Likewise, "Daddy's Stroposcope" stands out in its powerful delivery. **The Shiny Gnomes** certainly proved that music could be psychedelic without sacrificing muscle or energy.

Then a musical tragedy happened: the band signed to the major Polydor label. Predictably, their major label debut was a weak, watered down "rock" record, with little of the subtle melody and style of their previous discs.

Collector and fan Ingo Schittko wrote this author and contended that the band gained up their lost momentum with subsequent releases, recommending the 1989 *Fivehead* and 1990 *Colliding* LPs, as well as the band's 1992 return to an indy label with the LP *Innocent Aval*.

I'd like to hear them for myself.

## THE SHIVERS
*(Australia)*

"Washaway" b/w "Dolphin Blues" 45, 1989
"Downtown Sister (Town Is Gone)" plus 2 others 7" EP, 1991
 Mushroom Records, Australia

**The Stems'** Julian Matthews and Dave Shaw were in **The Shivers,** at least for their debut "Washaway" b/w "Dolphin Blues" 45 on Mushroom in 1989. It has been described rightly as "soft pop," and is not highly recommended. "Washaway" is reportedly a previously un-recorded **Stems** song from their live set.

The follow-up 45 delivers another un-exceptional mid-tempo pop number with a couple of unmemorable tunes for the B-side. **The Shivers** hardly hold up to **The Stems'** mark of quality in any regard.

## THE SHOUTLESS
*(Sweden)*

"Insane" b/w "I Tell No Lies" 45, 1984
*Out Of Reach* 7 song 12" EP, 1985
"Buy The Eye" 7" flexi in *The Eye Magazine*, 1985
"Baby Come On" b/w "Stay By Me" 45, 1986
*Bowery At Midnight* 8 song 12" EP, 1986
 Rainbow Music, Sweden
*Hung Up* 7" flexi, 1987
 De Los Munster Magazine, Spain

**The Shoutless'** debut 45 shook with the same fury as their already-known

**185**

countrymen **The Nomads**. The comparison between the two bands is actually far-reaching, as they both mined the field of mega-distorted guitar and booming anthemic garage songs.

Their 12" was a bit of a sideways move, since it contained somewhat tame cover versions of '60s classics like "1-2-5" and "Pretty Big Mouth," though the band's version of **The Standells'** "Mr. Nobody" does come off better. Their momentum picked up again with the "Baby Come On" 45, which re-established their knack for crunchy guitars and anthemic melody.

Also like **The Nomads, The Shoutless** moved progressively out of the garage genre and into the netherlands of hard rock, with their *Bowery At Midnight* 12" a yardstick of their departure. There are a few worthy tracks, however, most notably the wonderfully titled "Eat Some Food," and the pounding "Do The Eye" (which had already been a magazine's flexi).

A few more discs would appear, but none would recapture the band's initial excitement. Here's a case where the two rarest examples of the band's work, their 45s, are also their most accomplished.

## GARY SHULZ
*(Phoenix, AZ USA)*

Shulz made a plethora of home-made cassettes in the late 1980s, most of them featuring whacked out '60s pop covers. He does a hilarious cover of **The Rutles**-cum-**Beatles** "Cheese And Onions" on one release, and pulls off a sweet version of **The Monkees'** "You Might Just Be The One" on another. I don't think any of this stuff was actually released to the public.

## THE SICK ROSE
*(Italy)*

*Get Along Girl!* 3 song 7" EP, 1986
*Faces* 12 song LP, 1986
*Double Shot* 2 x 45s, 1987
*The Hot Roses* 15 song cassette, 1988?
 Indie Records, Italy
*Shaking Street* 10 song LP, 1988
 Electric Eye Records, Italy
*Covers* 4 song 7" EP, 1989?
 Indie Records, Italy
*Renaissance* 10 song LP, 1989?
*Floating* 26 song CD, 1990
 Synergy Records, Italy
*Alive And Well* 12" EP, 1991
 Rubber Records, Australia
*Other Faces* 16 song CD, 1994
 Dionysus Records, USA

Also a *Lost Trails* magazine 45 ("Bad Day Blues"), plus appearances on an Italian compilations LP *Tracce '85*, and the French compilation *Yellow Purple Italian Explosion*. Their fan club also released a home video of their 1987 European tour.

Italy had never heard anything like **The Sick Rose**.

Even during the first anarchic wave of European garage-punk in the mid-1960s, nothing so raw, aggressive or plain nasty had ever surfaced. The northern industrial town of Torino was the unlikely nest for these mop-topped vipers, and in 1984 they began to spread their fuzz-and-Farfisa throughout the continent, and beyond.

**The Sick Rose** were arguably the first European garage band to have the impact globally in the same manner as **The Chesterfield Kings**. Their expertly realized fuzz'n Farfisa attack embraced U.S. '66 punk, and spit it out with a distinctly Italian flavor.

They contributed killer cuts to the Italian *Eighties Colours* and U.S. *Battle Of The Garages* compilations, then followed up with their own 7" EP in 1986. The sound was raw and direct, and much more aggressive and snarled than ever expected from a European outfit, and the response was predictably enthusiastic in their native country.

This mastering of the American garage sound was culminated with the *Faces* LP. Though recorded in the most basic fashion, this collection of a dozen tracks is a heavy-weight contender for most consistently meaty garage record ever. There's a bit of melodic garage-pop in "Everybody Wants To Know" and "I'm Not Trying To Hurt You," while the remainder of the LP blasts into orbit fueled by super-fuzzed guitars and Luca Re's snotty, yet engaging vocals.

Though he sings in English, a thick Italian accent flavors all of his vocal work, giving the band the European flavor that helped to set them apart from the pack. This LP would prove to be the band's high-mark, and a monument to their love of the garage genre.

It's easy to see why, since the vital ingredients of classic garage-rock are all present and accounted for throughout *Faces*: deeply resonant and snotty vocals courtesy of the dynamic and intense frontman Luca Re, shimmering and playful organ from Rinaldo Doro, and fuzzed, demented guitar tones from Maurizio Campisi and Diego Mese. We shouldn't forget Dante Garimanno and Maurizio Rubinetti — they supply the all-important primitive, pulsing, skin pounding drum beat.

Though these elements had all been smashed together for years before in other bands, no one quite got the mixture

right like **The Sick Rose**. With these Italians, equal doses of sweat, style, passion and guts all mixed into their instantly identifiable sound.

A deft touch of classic pop sensibility and musical prowess also helped this quintet rise far above their fellow cavemen — soon after the release of *Faces* they were quickly hailed as one of the premiere garage bands from any country, in any era.

Their sophomore LP, *Shakin' Street* was a fairly pedestrian hard-rock LP, without much of the verve or attraction of their earlier efforts. It was a shame, but **The Sick Rose** followed the path to more commercially acceptable and bland material.

Band Leader Luca Re had not turned his back on the garage sound, however. He joined the pure '66 sounding **99th Floor** to carry on in **The Sick Rose**'s early footsteps — while remaining until at least 1995 as the only original member of **The Sick Rose**.

They did release two more packages of 45s, though, that contained outtakes and purely garage material that didn't fit with their new direction. While the band probably sees these discs as footnotes to their development, they are really the last gasps of garage greatness from these Italian giants.

The *Double Shot* EP is really two separate 45s in one sleeve; a beautiful package highlighted by two Maurizio Campisi originals and a cover of the **Golden Dawn**'s "My Time To Leave." The *Covers* EP features renditions of four '60s classics, all done in the best **Sick Rose** tradition.

The fan-club issued *Hot Roses* cassette also contained rare and unreleased tracks from their pure '66 garage period, including covers of **The Doors**' "Take It As It Comes" and **The Shadows Of**

**184**

Knight's "Dark Side." This would effectively be the last glimpse of **The Sick Rose** as Italian garage kings.

Their place in the garage world is firmly entrenched, however, and will certainly gain in stature with the passing of time. Future Italian garage bands will be measured by the standards set by **The Sick Rose**.

The line-ups would shift, but Luca Re would keep **The Sick Rose** blooming for several more albums, and they still perform throughout Italy as of this writing. Their style is harder, leaner, and more commercial now, but Luca Re hasn't forgotten his roots; his other band, **The 99th Floor**, continues on in the garage tradition, and sounds every bit as inspired as the fuzz lords who grew strong and loud from fertile Italian soil ... **The Sick Rose**.

## THE SIDEWALKS
*(Los Angeles, CA USA)*

They formed in April 1981 and eventually became the nucleus of **The Rain Parade**, reportedly more Merseybeat-ish than the polished moody **Rain Parade** output. **The Sidewalks** didn't release any vinyl, though the **Rain Parade** track "Look Both Ways" has been said to reflect their sound. That track later showed up as a bonus **Rain Parade** track on their debut LP and CD re-issue.

## SIDE WALKERS
*(Rome, Italy)*

The Side Walkers reportedly had at least six privately pressed cassettes between 1987-1989. They then became the cooly-named **Silent Shapes**, also in the garage-punk mold.

## SILVER SURFERS
*(Milan, Italy)*

Featuring ex-**Pression X** members, this garage punk/surf band released the *If You Are Pression X* private cassette, and the song "She Said Yeah" on the *Lost Trails* 45 #10, 1989.

## SIR CHIME & THE LOVERS
*(Milan, Italy)*

"Old Blues Drunker" on a split 45, 1987
   Stampa Alternativa Records, Italy

Reportedly a garage rock combo.

## SIT 'N SPIN
*(Edison, NJ USA)*

"Invisible Man" b/w "Lupine Valentine" 45, 1993
"Santa Claws" b/w "Auld Lang Syne,"
"Nightmare After Christmas" 45, 1994,
   Worrybird Records, USA

Both of these pop-garage-punk slabs were recorded at **The Gripweeds'** home studio, which explains the clear bright production and upbeat atmosphere.

The twisted Christmas theme 45 is actually the more interesting of the two listed, with catchy melodies and punchy playing. (And the funny/creepy Darren Merinuk color cover art is a hoot!)

The band later developed into an all-female act, with several other slabs of vinyl forthcoming. I suspect that they also possess pleasing power pop garage — and will be worth a listen.

## 6 T's NIGHTMARE
*(Germany)*

Nothing known.

## THE SKEPTICS
*(Frederick, MD USA)*

*Worry Beads* 9 song cassette, 1985
   Funeral Snack Music, USA

There's a certain homey warmth to the band's self-released cassette because there isn't a "space" separating the band and the listener — no artificial walls of high-tech recording or delivery. This is direct communication, and also a fun sounding band. **The Skeptics** bounce between twangy instrumentals and surf-ish tunes, along with straight garage and jangley ballads.

This cassette includes both tracks this author eventually selected for the *Beasts From The East* compilation LP, along with some other uninhibited home made songs of fun.

An LP appeared in 1986 entitled *Snallygaster*, but by then the band had figured out what it was doing, and the charm had evaporated.

## THE SLEEPWALKERS
*(San Diego, California USA)*

A R&B and surf oriented band which included music enthusiast and zine maker Andy Rasmussen — with no known product, but a set list with standards like "Roadrunner" and some intriguing film influenced originals like "Lobo" (is Rasmussen an Ed Wood/Tor Johnson fan?) and "Spiderbaby" (also a Lon Chaney fan?).

## SLEEVES
*(Genova, Italy)*

*Five Days To Hell* LP, 1987
    Cobra Records, Italy

A rock band with reportedly '60s touches, also with another 12" on Cobra.

## THE SLICKEE BOYS
*(Washington, D.C. USA)*

*Hot and Cool* 5 song 7" EP, 1976
*Separated Vegetables* LP, 1977
    (reissued on Limp Records, 1980)
"The Brain That Refused To Die" b/w "Love In" 45, 1980
"Here To Stay" b/w "Porcelain Butter Kitten" 45, 1981
"When I Go to the Beach" b/w "Invisible People" 45, 1983
*10th Anniversary* 4 song EP, 1988
    Dacoit Records, USA
*Mersey, Mersey Me* 4 song 7" EP, 1978
*Third* 4 song 7" EP, 1979
    Limp Records, USA
*Here To Stay* LP, 1982
*Cybernetic Dreams of Pi* LP, 1983
    (also Twin Tone Records, USA)
    Line Records, Germany
"When I Go To the Beach" b/w "You Got What It Takes" 45, 1984
*Uh Oh ... No Breaks!* LP, 1985 (also Twin Tone, USA)
*Your Autumn Eyes* 3 song 7" EP, 1987
*Fashionably Late* LP, 1988
"This Party Sucks" b/w "Little Red Riding Hood" 45, 1988
    New Rose Records, France
"Eighteen" b/w "Misunderstood" 45, 1988
    Midnight Records, USA
*Live at Last* LP, 1989
    Giant Records, USA

One of the first and best of the late '70s U.S. punk bands, **The Slickee Boys** also helped to jump-start the appreciation of '60s punk. They released many '60s punk flavored tracks over their almost decade and a half career, often covering tunes by **The Hangmen, Chocolate Watchband** and **Yardbirds**. Though one of the most fabled "live" bands ever, they were never able to rise above cult status.

**198**

*THE SLICKEE BOYS, 1985*

Baltimore area writer Jim Maher has been a **Slickees** fan for many years. I asked him to contribute a more complete analysis:

*The Slickee Boys were one of the first of the garage/psych revival bands, and also one of the most fun — with legendary live shows complete with zany outfits in glitter, polka dots and psychedelic swirls.*

*Their sound didn't include just garage and psychedelic influences, but also elements of surf, punk, frat rock, country and rockabilly. There were a number of Slickee Boys (and even one girl) over the years, with guitarist Marshall Keith being the only constant.*

*Keith and guitarist Kim Kane assembled the band in early 1976, originally with Martha Hull as the singer. In 1977 Hull was replaced by Mark Noone, and the band's core of Keith, Kane and Noone was established (they went through three drummers and six bassists over the years).*

*Although The Slickee Boys released tons of singles and compilation cuts, they only released five full length albums in the 14 years they were together — and one of these was a live album while another was the compilation Here To Stay, collecting stuff from early EPs.*

*All of their records are worthwhile, but 1983's* Cybernetic Dreams of Pi *is the best. Many of the Slickees' records were only available as French or German imports, and most are now long out of print.*

*The Slickee Boys were always an enormously popular live act in the Baltimore/Washington area, packing clubs with many regulars (including myself) who wouldn't miss a show. Because of day jobs and such, the Slickees didn't tour as much as they no doubt would have liked. They earned a big reputation in Europe, although they didn't tour there until 1988. This tour is documented on* Live At Last, *the band's only live album.*

Not long after the European tour, Kim Kane left **The Slickees** to form **Date Bait,** and he was replaced by **Slickees** roadie John Hansen. This post-Kane version of the band played regularly in Baltimore/Washington clubs, but only got into the studio once (to record "Down the Line," a cut for a **Buddy Holly** "tribute").

In 1990 **The Slickee Boys** called it quits. The mid-'80s version of the band — Kane, Noone, Keith, plus bassist Bill Maxwell and drummer Dan Palenski — still gets together as of this writing every year around Christmas for a raucous pair of reunion shows — one in Baltimore and one in D.C.

— by Jim Maher

## THE SLINGBACKS
(U.K.)

Nothing known, but they were reportedly influenced by the *Pebbles* garage compilation LPs, and existed circa 1992.

## THE SLOW SLUSHY BOYS
(France)

*Get Crazy* LP, 1990
*Pretty Monster* 11 song CD, 1992
Untitled 3 song 7" EP, 1994
    Larsen Records, France
"G.U.R.L." 45, 1994
    Twang Records, Germany
"How Could You Lie" 45, 1994
    Face Records, Italy
Plus many compilations.

For some unknown reason, as I've discussed before, some French find it inherently difficult to really let loose in a rock band. Even the groups who portray themselves as frantic rockers turn out to be little more than hyped-up pop bands. That's somewhat true for the early sounds from **The Slow Slushy Boys**.

Their debut LP isn't exactly "wimpy," but it falls back on safe pop conventions which mask their garage roots. There are some inspired moments here, but they're hidden mostly by a cautious approach.

Many of these problems were solved with their *Pretty Monster* CD. It's much more raw, upbeat and garage-like, with a much less "safe" attitude. The recording is rather amazing as well, considering it's 8-track origin.

This band just keeps getting better, as evidenced by their 1994 7" EP. The lead off track, "The Girl She Always Smiles," is a hypnotizing pop-garage mood-ballad, with memorable guitar hook, pulsing rhythm section and tuneful vocals. In short, it's one of the best French A-sides I've heard in many years.

I haven't heard the other recent offerings, but I have an idea that **The Slow Slushy Boys** have come into their own.

## THE SMEARS
(Bloomington, IN USA)

*Smears In The Garage* 6 song 10" EP & 13 song CD, 1995
    Dionysus Records, USA

This trio of Hoosier gals weren't into the retro-garage scene at all — they were really a gritty and sloppy punk act. They did have a sense of humor, though, so on a visit to Los Angeles they donned matching black turtlenecks and recorded a half-dozen homages to the '60s girl-group sound for Dionysus. The cover art even parodies perfectly the popular *Girls In The Garage* compilation series, right down to the lettering and cheesy liner notes.

The garage-**Smears** deliver the goods, with great covers of "What A Way To Die," "The Hurtin' Kind" and a sleazy take on Billy Childish's "Cum Into My Mouth." The band original, "Don't Mess With Him," also makes the grade.

Punk rock girl group fans will find this a must.

## THE SMELL OF INCENSE
(Norway)

I stumbled upon this band in the excellent 1995 *Crohinga Well* fanzine. While I haven't heard any of their sounds, I'm confident that they belong in the book based on the descriptions of some of their recordings: covers of **The Jefferson Handkerchief's** "I'm Allergic To Flowers" and **HMS Bounty's** "A Visit To Ashiya" for starters.

They began in late 1991, and the album *All Mimsy Were The Borogroves* was released in September, 1994 on the Norwegian Colours label. There was also a limited edition 45 (of 500 copies) released in May, 1994 on Germany's September Gurls label.

This all "sounds" imminently interesting, though I suppose I actually should *hear* some of this before deciding!

**187**

## THE SMOOTY FILTH
(Rennes, France)

"Sur Une Note De Resto" b/w "Steppin' Stone" 45, 1994
*Greenstuff* 13 song CD, 1994
   Les Grignous Records, France

Vocalist Regis sent along their debut long-player — it's on CD only, I think. It features blistering harmonica, great back-up vocals, and some tasty organ — all in the best **Monks, Kinks, Shadows Of Knight, Pretty Things, Sonics** and **Seeds** tradition. Like many fine garage records (and like their 45), the session was recorded in England at Toe-Rag studios. Both releases are whole-heartedly recommended.

Regis says, *"The band was born in 1990, when five friends decided to play music they have loved for years. At that moment we were sixteen years old and nobody among us could play his own instrument. Then we played and played — after many weeks the band began to sound like what we had always wanted."*

He continues, *"We entered the haunted house of the '60s Garage Punk and we would never get out of it."*

The band also had eight original songs on the compilation CD *Gringnous Volume 6*.

**The Smooty Filth** sound like a band that could dominate the French garage scene for the second half of the 1990s — if they can manage to stay together and continue to release records that stand up to the quality of the early work.

## THE SMUGGLERS
(Vancouver, BC Canada)

A 45 on Nardwuar Records was released in 1990, and they also have at least another 45, a 10" and an LP. What I've heard is totally unexceptional suburban-white slightly R&B tinged garage — perhaps the product of hype, money and promotion — but without musical merit.

## SNAKEHANDLERS
(Richmond, VA USA)

Yet another group that mutated into **The Organ Grinders**.

## SNIPERS
(France)

They have an untitled seven song 12" EP on France's New Rose Records from 1983. I've only heard a party-styled version of the R&B standard "Tallahassee Lassie" and a jangley pop original sung in French called "La Meilleure Maniere," plus the harmonica-driven "Snipers Theme." This is yet another band which I'm certain would be a great deal of fun on stage in a smoky room after a couple of beers.

Make that a bunch of beers.

## SNOWDROPS
(Torino, Italy)

"Marylouise Blues" b/w "That's Why" 45, 199?
   Toast Records, Italy
*Get Pissed* LP, 1992
   Blubus Records, Italy

Reportedly a hard-psych act.

## SOFT BOYS
(U.K.)

This is a very influential late '70s group which helped in many ways to spawn the U.K. indy garage/psych movement. **The Soft Boys** featured, among others, **Robyn Hitchcock**, who would jump to major label prominence in the 1980s. Much of **The Soft Boys** output sounds like Hitchock's later patented quirky pop, with experimental edges intact.

Their complete story can be found in several mainstream publications, and has been documented extensively throughout the 1980s, so I'll end my comments here.

## SOMA HOLIDAY
(Los Angeles, CA USA)

Their only effort, "My Own Way," is on *The Obnoxious Rock & Roll Video Hour*. It's pretty snotty modern garage.

## SOMELOVES
(Perth, Australia)

"It's My Time" b/w "Don't Talk About Us" 45, 1986
   Citadel Records, Australia
"Know You Now" b/w "Don't Have To Try" 45, 1988
"Melt" b/w "Jack Robinson" 45, 1989

*Something Or Other* 11 song LP, 1989
"Sunshine's Glove" b/w "Girl Soul" 45, 1990
*Sunshine's Glove* 6 song 12" EP, 1990
    White Label, Australia

**The Someloves** began as a side project with Dom Mariani and Gary Chambers of **The Stems** and Daryl Mather of **The Lime Spiders**. This lineup recorded the first two brilliant singles. "It's My Time" sounds like a long lost jewel from **The Stems** song book, complete with jangle guitars, a punchy arrangement and soaring vocals.

The follow-up 45 is another gem of sunny melody and shining guitar. "Don't Have To Try" is especially engaging, and the anthemic "Know You Now" is instantly memorable.

"Melt" is another instant classic, with an infectious guitar hook, smooth vocals and expert playing from top to bottom. The solid B-side "Jack Robinson" makes it one of the best 45s of the decade.

In 1988, after the demise of **The Stems**, Mariani and Mather recorded further singles and the equally fine *Something Or Other* LP with studio musicians — including Mitch Easter. The title track is another stunner — more on the mark than anything **The Hoodoo Gurus** or any other Aussie pop band ever attempted. The remainder of the LP is a sparkling, shimmering fulfillment of **The Stems'** promise — and a monument to the wide talent of Dom Mariani.

Mariani played some 1990 shows in Perth with a full lineup (without Mather) billed for some reason as **The Snails**. He went on to form **The Dom Mariani 3**, but without the pure power pop magic of his earlier work.

## SOMETHING WEIRD
*(Wilhelmshaven, Germany)*

Untitled 3 song 7" EP, 1994
    Weird Music Production, Germany

I've stumbled upon some seriously authentic '66 aficionados here, complete with bowl haircuts, turtlenecks and **Beatle** boots. Their self-produced debut 7" bursts with teen excitement and energy — and the requisite whirling organ, frantic maracas and tasty fuzz guitar.

"Wherever I Am" features a catchy chorus vocal and bright production, while the pair of flip-tunes shows that the fivesome can fuzz-out with the best Euro garage-niks.

These Germans also do one other important thing — they smile both on the front picture sleeve and also in the rear

**189**

sleeve band cartoon.

This music still evokes that most slippery of commodities — fun — right down to the band's smiling record label logo.

There's nothing weird about that.

## SONIX
*(Torino, Italy)*

"Brand New Car" b/w "The Beat" 45, 1990
    Drachma Records, Italy

Reportedly a garage band.

## THE SONS OF HERCULES
*(Austin, TX USA)*

"Tight Fit," "Once I Was" b/w "Bad Timing"
    Unclean Records, USA

This one is a close call. There certainly is a '60s garage influence here, but in a heavier, punkier way. The fuzzed A-side teeters on the verge of coolness, while the almost folk-rockish B-side moves **The Sons Of Hercules** close enough to the garage genre for inclusion here. An LP also exists of unknown quality — this is one act that I'll reserve my final judgment until after hearing some more tracks.

## LES SOUCOUPES VIOLENTES
*(Paris, France)*

A 1982 EP is reportedly very good, and they have at least three LPs out as well — the first is reportedly the best, and it's been said that they are worth seeing in concert. I've heard a few songs on tape that are very energetic upbeat R&B based party rockers complete with warbling organ — and sung in French.

They also show up on the French *La Chair Humaine Ne Vaut Pas Cher* compilation cassette. Just for the record, their name means "the violent flying saucers."

## SOUL HUNTER
*(Firenze, Italy)*

*Cain's Sing* 12" EP, 1985
"Fishes Like Water" b/w "You're A Better Man Than I" 45, 1986
*Maelstrom* 12" EP, 1986
*Nic & Nic And The Psychotic Drivers* LP, 198?
*Just In The Nick Of Time* LP, 198?
    Contempo Records, Italy

A psych pop group that also has a track on the *'80s Colours* compilation LP's bonus 45.

## THE SOUND EXPLOSION
*(Athens, Greece)*

"Hangover Baby" b/w "Some Other Guy" 45, 1993
    Pegasus Records, Greece
*Teen Trash #14* 13 song LP & CD, 1994
    Music Maniac Records, Germany
"I'll Shake The Universe" b/w "Why Can't You See" 45, 1995
    Dionysus Records, USA

Plus a planned 1995 45 on Germany's Outer Limits label.

This author has met enough musicians to last several lifetimes. Many, perhaps even most, have been lame-brained, moronic, self-destructive bozos, with little self-respect and even less talent.

And then I met **The Sound Explosion**.

*THE SOUND EXPLOSION, 1993*

It seems that whenever my faith runs thin, I run into some garage true-believers, people who live and breath the values of simple honesty, effort and determination — and also don't forget the fuzz and Farfisa. **The Sound Explosion** are all this and much more; they are one of the most powerfully talented garage bands of the 1990s.

I met them for a few days in their native Athens, and was fortunate to play one fantastic show with them. On stage they're almost possessed by the garage spirit as they twist, grind and push their audience into a pulsating fury. Many bands purport to have a wild stage show — **The Sound Explosion** delivers one, just as their name would suggest.

Off stage they were some of the most interesting, intelligent and sincere musicians I've stumbled across. They make music for all the right reasons — to communicate, to celebrate, to share — and that positive nature extends to visitors from half-way around the globe like myself.

And then there are the records. Their debut 45 is like a garage sacrament — feast on the holy body of Farfisa organ and fuzz guitar, drink of the holy spirit of tambourine and fierce vocals. The shimmering B-side is just as

**19D**

precious, completing one of my most treasured slabs of vinyl from any era. This is no idle hyperbole — this record is one of those rare finds, figuratively and literally.

The 45 served as just a snack for the main course — their debut LP. There's no point in picking out individual tracks for praise — the entire collection is a masterpiece of the 1966 garage experience. In an almost genre defining sweep, **The Sound Explosion** encapsulate all the elements that make this music so endearing — and deliver it with a smile.

New recordings are in the works as of this writing, so the best is obviously yet to come.

Maybe musicians aren't all that bad.

## SOUTHERN CULTURE ON THE SKIDS
*(USA)*

There are at least five LPs of their lo-fi twangey instrumental-**Link Wray**-styled stuff. Their three song *Santo Sings* 7" EP popped up on Zontar Records in 1992, and was worth a giggle or two. This style is an acquired taste, more fitting in the "trash" genre than strictly garage.

Amazingly, **S.C.O.T.S.** signed with mega-major Geffen records in 1995 — after countless gigs and more than ten years of touring.

## SOUTHERN FRIED KIDNEYS
*(Australia)?*

Their expose on garage-psych posers, "Psychedelic Clothes," is a hilarious send-up of the pretensions of any identifiable "scene." Along with **The Leopards'** "Psychedelic Boy," it succeeds in poking fun at those who take themselves — and their fashion — just a bit too seriously.

"Graveyard" and "Tree Where He Hangs" continue the tongues-in-cheek treatment, with some good giggles along with the fuzzy garage fun. I don't know if these were vinyl releases.

## THE SPACE CAKES
*(Mestre, Italy)*

*Out Of My Mind* 4 song 7" EP, 1993
    Tortilla Records, Italy
*Taste The Flavour Of...* 11 song LP, 1995
    Misty Lane/Helter Skelter Records, Italy

The debut EP reminded me a bit of early **Sick Rose** — and that's quite a compliment to these fellow Italians. The organ is bright and warbly, the vocals snotty, and the fuzz expertly placed. I also like the simple but moody aural production and gutsy atmosphere of this disc.

I've heard two other songs as well: "Images Part 1" and "Images Part 2," which are two heavily echoed slabs of fuzz punkadelia, with some inspired guitar-work and a driving beat. I'm not sure if this is from another 45.

Their subsequent LP is an excellent slab of '66 punk tinged with colorful garagadelia. The 10 original songs are of high quality, and the band has matured significantly since their first recordings. The **Sick Rose** comparison holds as well — the LP's only cover is of the stomping "I Want Love," which the **Sick Rose** also performed in their day.

**The Space Cakes** are yet another bright spot for the resurgent mid-1990s Italian garage scene.

# THE SPACEMEN 3
*(U.K.)*

*Playing With Fire* 9 song LP, 1988
*Taking Drugs To Make Music To Take Drugs To*
    13 song CD, 1994
    Bomp Records, USA / Fire Records, U.K.

**The Spacemen 3** were undoubtedly one of England's most influential (underground) bands of the 1980s. They certainly took inspiration from '60s psychedelia, updating it with '80s political consciousness, drugs and publicity marketing. They have a plethora of releases, and Bomp was one of the first U.S. labels to license their product; by 1994 their entire U.K. output would be re-issued in the U.S.

This author edited and distributed the video for the mesmerizing track "Revolution," from the 1988 *Playing With Fire* LP. It's a representative summation of their sound — purposely repetitious, hypnotizing, aggressive and thoroughly laced with chemical imbalance. The focus throughout their work was on excruciatingly simple guitar grunge, alternating with spacey synth moodscapes — certainly an acquired taste.

The band broke up in 1990 while riding the cusp of international attention. Members would go on to bolster **The Darkside**, whose efforts were more focused and yet thoroughly garage-adelic.

# THE SPACE NEGROS
*(Massachusetts USA)*

*Do Generic Ethnic Muzak Versions Of All Your Favorite Underground Punk/Psychedelic Songs From The Sixties*
11 song LP, 1987
    Arf Arf Records, USA

The 1987 *Generic Ethnic Muzak Versions Of All Your Favorite Underground Punk/Psychedelic Songs From The Sixties* LP is just that — 11 cover versions of some of the most known '60s punk/psych classics, done in an "elevator-music" style. This is a pretty hilarious prank perpetrated primarily by Erik Lindgren, but it also could be considered a torture for garage fans after repeated listenings!

# THE SPANKS
*(Belgium)*

An EP on Stoker Records is available, I believe in a more '70s punk vein.

# THE SPECTORS
*(Minneapolis, MN USA)*

"Oh, How You Do Now" b/w "Her Best Friend" 45, 1993
    OXO Records, USA
"When The Girl Of Your Dreams..." b/w "In My Grave" 45, 1993
    Prospective Records, USA

**The Monks** created a sound that should have spread further. Their fuzz-banjo, noose wearing, shaved head antics remain legendary to a faithful few, and their 1966 LP and several 45s are collectors' prizes.

Three of the original **Monks** surfaced after 25 years of obscurity — and were then roped in to sing back-up vocals on the screamer "Oh How To Do Now" for **The Spectors'** debut 45. It's a blasting, rolling, stomping garage punk fireball, bludgeoning the listener into submission. In other words, it's a faithful update of one of the **Monks'** best songs. A nice Mersey-ish original ballad graces the flip.

Eddie Shaw of **The Monks** describes **The Spectors** in the sleeve notes, *"Now listen as Keith sneaks into Satan's bedroom to render the sordid sounds of hell's bass climax. Witness how lead guitarist Adam milks a 10,000 watt cow at midnight, how drummer Dan, after repeatedly twirling Keith over his head in his version of Gorgeous George's airplane-spin, pummels a monk beat that will cause anyone's tonsure to flush with pride ... It's just too much! Music should never be like this. Wait a minute! Yes it should!"*

The second 45 features an insanely catchy A-side. The vocal line "When The Girl Of Your Dreams" is ironically completed by "turns (into) the girl of your nightmares...," and is aided by an upbeat arrangement and cool back-up vocals, provided by Keith Patterson formerly of **The Funseekers**. The band knew it was onto something good, so after a guitar break they simply modulate up and continue to sing the melody.

The direct hit of the A-side is mitigated by a dreadful attempt at soul-funk on the flip. I'll consider it a misguided stab at "diversity," and forgive and forget — and I'll wait and hope for what would be a very interesting LP.

## SPEEDBREAK
*(Greece)*

A Mediterranean surf band — now *there's* an idea — of unknown proportions.

## SPIDER BABIES
*(West Linn, OR USA)*

"Hey Baby" b/w "Spider Baby" 45, 1994
    Rat City Records, USA
*The Arachnophobic Sounds Of...* 4 song 7" EP, 1994
    Screaming Apple Records, Germany

Presumably named for the 1960s Lon Chaney, Jr. cult horror flick (where Chaney even "sings" the title song!), **The Spider Babies** are an enjoyably trashy punk outfit that balances its garage sensibilities with a crude distorted delivery. Dual Vox Phantom guitars and a touch of warbly organ are the focus.

There's also a combination of '66 and '77 stylings present, with a fun-loving attitude that merits attention to further output — if any exists. Both discs listed above sport excellent B&W picture sleeves.

These Oregonians are not to be confused with a much more straight-punk band from Los Angeles named **Spiderbaby**.

## SPIKES
*(Australia)*

Not to be confused with an Italian hard rock band of the same name. These **Spikes** have the 1986 *Six Sharp Cuts* 12" EP on Hybrid Records and the 1986 *Colour In A Black Forest* 11 song LP — both on Australia's Greasy Pop Records.

I've heard "She's Melting" and pretty darn cool "Theme From Acid Beach" —

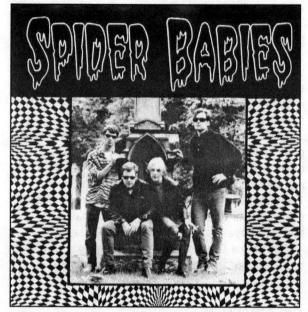

both credible heavy garage slices with plenty of echo, reverb and weirdness.

They also have a cover of "Ain't No Friend Of Mine" on the Hybrid compilation *Gyrations Across The Nations.*

## THE SPINNING WIGHATS
*(Los Angeles, CA USA)*

"Encore From Hell" & "10-5-60" flexi, 1987
    *Bucketfull of Brains Magazine*, U.K.

Also the "Christmas In New Zealand" flexi given away free at a U.K. gig, circa 1985.

Yeah, I know, this is really **The Long Ryders**, who gave a couple live tracks to a magazine but were compelled to use a different band name for contractual reasons. The *BFOB* flexi is very raw, indeed, documenting the very end of their fateful journey to Europe. I'm searching for the other flexi.

## SPIRAL
*(Canberra, Australia)*

Described to me as authentic '60s garage punk from the 1980s, with no known recordings.

## THE SPITTING LLAMAS
*(Sydney, Australia)*

Reportedly a raw '60s punk-styled band which formed in the mid-'80s. You won't find rappers with cool names like **The Spitting Llamas**.

## SPLAT CATS
*(Buffalo, NY USA)*

The *Sin 73* LP, among others, exist, though the band's sound is inconsistent at best. The LP's title, when turned upside down, spells out "Elvis." Why I remember this, I don't really know, but that fact is probably more interesting than the record itself.

## THE SPLIFFS
*(Australia)*

Untitled 3 song 7" EP, 1986
  Black And White Music, Australia

This odd release has no picture sleeve or any other information other than the song titles and authors. "You Know What They'll Say" has the A-side, and it's a surprisingly engaging power-pop number. It's easy to see how this band was popular with mods, thought the power-pop feel dominates any narrow mod stylings. The two songs on the flip are also enjoyable.

## THE SQUARES
*(Nancy, France)*

*Trapped In A Square* 11 song LP, 1991
*Curse Of The Squares* 14 song LP, 1992
  Hangman Records, U.K.
*Trapped In A Square & Curse Of...* 25 song CD, 1993
  Square Records, France
*Get Hip?!!* 4 song 7" EP, 1993
  Get Hip Records, USA
*Pure And Filthy Rhythm 'N' Punk* LP, 1994?
  Royal Records, France

A band must believe heart and soul in their music to release their own records. Multi-national conglomerate labels can spend more on "artist" lunches than record production, but the little-guy and gal band's largest expense can be the actual manufacturing of their product.

**The Squares** fronted the money for their debut vinyl LP, and then combined it with 13 new tracks for their second LP and combined-CD released on their own Square records.

This is bare-bones production from a primitive cave-bone band. The trio of Englishmen (living in France) pound out brittle basic R&B punk, with an emphasis on brisk beats and short, economic songs. Comparisons to Britain's idiot-garage-savant **Billy Childish** are accurate, (**The Squares'** drummer once played in **Thee Headcoats**), but **The Squares** exhibit enough of their own identity to avoid any copycat accusations.

Interestingly, though, **Childish**'s Hangman Records released the British vinyl versions of the first two LPs.

Their influences bridge the U.K. Medway sound to **Bo Diddley, The Seeds, Sonics** and **Kinks**, in a mixture they call "Rhythm & Punk."

The amps are turned up and more distorted than pop bands would dare. Their lyrics are too fun and un-self-conscious for intellectuals. Perhaps most importantly, **The Squares'** crude beat might make the superstitious run for their bibles.

They play their own instruments, they write their own songs, they release their own records. That's a pleasingly potent curse for any band.

## SS-20
*(Los Angeles, CA USA)*

Greg Shaw of Voxx had especially high hopes for this group to capture the imagination of the underground market, but once again he was wrong. Comparisons to **Siouxsie and The Banshees** were warranted, as the bombastic and dramatic vocals and guitar treaded similar territory.

Their 1986 debut LP, *Dream Life*, sounded very modern, indeed, and is listed here only because of the band's stunning rendition of The **Doors'** "My Eyes Have Seen You." Their follow-up promo EP, split with the crispy critter **Sky Saxon**, has a fine cover of **The Music Machine**'s "Trouble."

The Italian-only *Son Of Fantasy* LP was later issued, though it hasn't arrived mysteriously on my doorstep, so I can't write anything mysterious about it.

## THE STAIRS
*(Liverpool, U.K.)*

Their 1991 single "Weed Bus" b/w "Flying Machine" might be the band's most garage-like release. "Weed Bus" is a pretty obvious homage/rip-off of **The Who's** "Magic Bus," and a pretty fine song in its own right. The video for this track is reportedly excellent. "Flying Machine" is a combination jangle and guttural pop effort, with a catchy guitar riff and powerful arrangement — much more highly recommended than their subsequent LP.

At least two 7" EPs exist: *Mary Joanna* includes a cover of "I Can Only Give You Everything," and the other features a cover of the **Del-Vettes'** "Last Time Around." Two other 12" EPs also exist.

Their widely (major label) distributed early 1990s *Mexican R&B* album was a rather tame R&B-tinged outing, without much punch to distinguish it from

**193**

wilder groups.

I should mention, however, that several readers have mentioned to me that they rate **The Stairs** over similar groups (that I prefer) such as **The Tell Tale Hearts** and **Hoods**.

## STAMPEDERS
(Torino, Italy)

Untitled 4 song 7" EP, 1987
    Stardust Records, Italy

The EP includes a cover of "Mr. Tambourine Man."

## THE STAND
(Canada)

A mod-garage band with numerous demos, doing covers of **The Lyres, Untold Fables** and early **Stones**.

## THEE STASH
(Kent, U.K.)

"Should I Suck Or Should I Blow" b/w
    "Selling Jeans For The U.S." 45, 1993
    Get Hip Records, USA

This is another side-project for **Billy Childish**, and I believe that the Get Hip 45 is actually a re-release of the original British issue of a few years before. Hard to tell if this is a **Clash** homage or slag, but their version of "Should I Stay Or Should I Go" is pretty funny. As with all **Billy Childish** projects, there are other **Stash** records out there somewhere.

## STATUTO
(Pordenone, Italy)

Untitled 3 song 7" EP, 1986
"Ghetto" b/w "Non Speraci" 45, 1987
    DTK Records, Italy
"Ci Sie Tu" ("Substitute")
    b/w "Tu Non Sai" ("The Kids Are Alright") 45, 1990
    Face Records, Italy
*Senla Di Lei* 12" EP, 1990
*Vacanze* LP, 1988
    Toast Records, Italy
"Qui Non C'e Il Mare" 45, 1992
    RCA Records, Italy
*Zighida* LP, 1992
    EMI Records, Italy

A passable mod/ska/beat band, big on style, but not very muscular in the

**194**

rock department. I don't quite understand what attracted both the RCA and EMI conglomerates to these tame sounds. Maybe because they *are* tame.

## THE STAYRCASE
(Edinburgh, Scotland)

A 1988 LP on Mumblin Records exists. Says Glynnis Wilson, *"They had one completely over-the-top wild '60s punk LP. They also featured Lenny Helsing of* **The Thanes***, along with the regulars from the Scottish scene. This LP is a must have item!"*

## STEEPLE JACK
(Pisa, Italy)

"Levitation" b/w "Don't Fall Down" on split 45, 1987
    *Lost Trails* #5
"The Tin Soldier" on bonus 7" with *80s Colours Vol. 2*, 1987
*Serena Maboose* 12" EP, 1987
*Pow Wow* LP, 1988
    Electric Eye Records, Italy

The *Serena Maboose* 12" and *Pow Wow* LP are on the venerable Electric Eye Records, though for the life of me I can't remember a thing about them! I have found some **Steeplejack** tracks on a cassette, however, and they could very well make up the *Serena Maboose* EP. Intricate guitar work and moody production, along with some dynamic drumming make this a rather fanciful release.

## THE STEMS
(Perth, Australia)

"She's A Monster" b/w "Make You Mine" 45, 1985
"Tears Me In Two" b/w "She Can't Resist" 45, 1985
*Love Will Grow* 4 song 12" EP, 1986
"No Heart" 2 song flexi, 1986
    *Splendid Magazine*, Germany
*The Great Rosebud Hoax* LP (all the above on one 12"), 1987
    Citadel Records, Australia
*At First Sight, Violets Are Blue* 12 song LP, 1987
"At First Sight" b/w "Grooviest Girl In Town" 45, 1987
"For Always" b/w "Mr. Misery" 45, 1987
"Sad Girl" b/w "My Beach" 45, 1987
    White Label Records, Australia
"On And On" split 45, 198?
    Lost Trails Magazine, Italy
"Does It Turn You On?" split 7" EP, 1989
    Ex Nexu Magazine, Germany
*Let Your Head Rest* 3 song 7" EP, 1990
    Zero Hour Records, Australia

plus fan-club cassettes: *Live 1987*, *Dead Weed*, and *Flexis*, each limited to only 250 official copies each. The live concert tapes are of excellent quality, and show that **The Stems** were certainly at home on stage. There is also reportedly also a

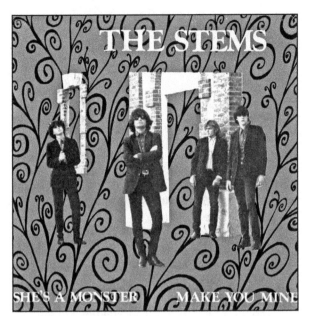

THE STEMS

SHE'S A MONSTER  MAKE YOU MINE

fold-out bootleg LP out in Italy — allegedly provided by a
well known indy label in Australia.

This book combines bands of many different
music proficiency levels, from the crudest one-off
efforts to professional outfits. **The Stems** were not
only a professional band, but one with the talent
to make a commercial stab at "the big time."

Luckily for us, their chosen style of music was
based on the mid-'60s garage pop format. Even at
their slickest, **The Stems** always recalled the
forgotten heroes of 1960s garagedom, updated and
improved for contemporary consumption.

The early 45s are rare and powerful '66 punk
statements, full of bluster and fuzz. The
performance on the 45s was notable, but the
band's songwriting and performance had
blossomed by the time of the *Love Will Grow* EP.
The melodically distorted guitar-songs recalled the
best work of **The Rain Parade** or **Dream Syndicate**,
but with their own distinctive vocal stamp. The
anthemic toe-tapper "Under Your Mushroom" also
kept their **Chocolate Watchband**-style intact. This EP
is simply one of the sweetest tastes of independent
garage rock for the decade, and is disappointing
only in its brevity.

Their debut LP was not disappointing in any
regard. **The Stems** masterfully blended imaginative
pop and garage into one of the most consistent
and meaty efforts in memory. Fuzz and jangle are
still up front, along with the wonderful Farfisa and
rattlin' tambourine. The sparkling production and
excellent performances rise above a mere garage
band, however, making this — *gasp!* — a
commercially viable product.

It is this fragile balance between
commerciality and garagemania that I

appreciate most from **The Stems**. They managed to
produce an incredibly energetic garage record that
could also be held up to the most stringent of
commercial standards.

The LP did gain some attention in their native
land, and charted highly there. Several music
videos also gained national airplay, and a song
from the LP landed in the major studio comedy film
*Young Einstein*.

Tensions centering around that enemy of
rock'n'roll — money — started to creep into the
band, and the future suddenly looked dim.

Richard Lane explained to George Matzkov in his
excellent **Stems** biography *Let Your Head Rest*,
*"Well, the money changed us because we had a
ten thousand dollar advance (for their LP). We
started thinking, 'Wow ten thousand bucks man,
let's be stars,' and we forgot that we were* **The
Stems**.*"*

Their friendships had eroded, and the breakup
was not friendly — this is always the saddest of
ways for any band to finish. They played their final
show on August 31, 1987.

Perhaps the greatest disappointment, however, is
that **The Stems** never managed to plant their seeds
outside of their native Australia (other than a few
records). Unlike **The Church** or **Hoodoo Gurus**, **The
Stems** didn't get that push to the next commercial
level.

Members of **The Stems** went on to many other
musical projects, however, including **The Someloves**
(with many wonderful power pop discs), **The
Stonefish, The Chevelles, The Shivers, The Summer
Suns, The Neptunes, The DM3**, and the studio
production of **The Marigolds**.

## THE STEPFORD HUSBANDS
*(New York, NY USA)*

"Why Aren't You There?" b/w "Yeah!" 45, 1984
"Seeing Is Believing" b/w "I'm Rowed Out" 45, 1985
"Seems Like Years" b/w "Kwik Way" 45, 1986?
   Cryptovision Records, USA
"We've Come A Long Way" b/w
   "Come And Take A Ride In My Boat" 45, 1993
   Get Hip Records, USA

"Why Aren't You There" is one of those classic
bits of garage psychedelia that seems timeless —
and also sums up the essence of a band in a
couple minutes of sound.

Crudely recorded and performed, it somehow
manages to encapsulate everything that's attractive
about people making their own music — it's direct,
moody, gritty and very human. The brooding organ
and plaintive vocals swirl in a stew of crashing
drums and twangy guitar, bashing away with brute

195

force. Also available on the seminal *Declaration Of Fuzz* compilation, this essential track is the "A" side of the band's first 45, and remains their signature tune.

The cool organ is back on the follow-up "Seeing Is Believing," which races in with under two minutes of garage angst. Their third 45 also keeps pace, with all of the elements that made **The Stepford Husbands** sure-shot garage-niks. "Seems Like Years" features a creepy guitar hook, murky vocals and that ever-present organ tone.

These records are so authentic sounding that you think that dust will fly out of the grooves. (I especially like the very end of one track, where the band lets the tape roll after the music finishes, and the members argue about doing another take!) These could have easily have passed for 1960s relics if not for the sub-standard '80s picture sleeves.

Something tragic happened after these three stellar 45s, however. The band changed membership and I believe also relocated to California. An LP followed of what can politely be described as "wimpy garbage." Gone was the moody organ, fuzzy guitar and general garage atmosphere, replaced by extremely lame, tame lightweight pop junk — clearly this was **The Stepford Husbands** in name only.

Their 1993 Get Hip 45 was somewhat a return to form, with the first cover version I've ever heard of "Come And Take A Ride In My Boat" — a sunny mid-'60s one-hit-wonder for the long forgotten **Every Mother's Son**.

Still, the best advice is to search-out the early 45s and avoid the 12" at all costs, ensuring **The Stepford Husbands** their deserved place in the "garage band hall of fame."

## STEPHEN'S RUIN
*(Germany)*

The 1985 "My Last Word" b/w "You Too" 45 and the 1986 *5497 Miles From L.A.* five song 12" EP are both on TM Records in Germany. I've only heard the 45's A-side, a heartfelt folk-popish ballad with some toe-tapping charm.

## THE STEPPES
*(Los Angeles, CA USA / Ireland)*

*The Steppes* 8 song 12" EP, 1984
Mystic Records, USA

This Irish-American combo subsequently released five more albums on Voxx Records, each exploring their amalgamation of folk, pop and hard rock. To these ears, very little of it is entirely successful, with only a few cuts per LP attaining any lasting worth. (I suppose that a "best of" collection might be pretty good then, with ten cuts representing five LPs!)

This first 12" EP, however, avoids the hard-rock pitfalls of the later work, and delivers a floating, moody and enjoyable Celtic folk affair. Against most prevailing opinion, it is still the disc I recommend most.

It should be noted that **The Steppes** did gather some significant underground attention in Europe as the 1980s came to a close, and were even slated to record some demos for **U2**'s Mother Records, although nothing apparently came of the deal.

Still, sometimes a band is best before they realize their formula, and for me this is the case with **The Steppes**.

## THE STEPPING STONES
*(U.K.)*

The *Mission Improbable* 4 song 7" EP was out on Youngblood Records in 1992, described to me by Darren Ross as having a "classic garage sound." I haven't heard them for myself.

## STEREO TYPES
*(New York, NY USA)*

*Bang The Conundrum* 3 song cassette, 1986
private pressing

This trio found a place in this book partly because of the photo included on the inner sleeve of their demo cassette. It features the triumvirate decked out in flowered coats, scarves and stove-pipe hats, looking into the camera with confident hopefulness.

I'm quite certain that this is a totally unknown band, and that I'm only one of several media-types who managed to hear their sounds. Yet there's something almost heroic about this unknown band and their little demo. Against all odds, and with no hope for "success" or "stardom," they recorded three of their songs and sent me a copy.

It's that dutiful eternal hopefulness of the garage band that is so endearing (and enduring.) The tracks themselves are loping, gentle **Beatle**sque ballads, with one, "Au Carroll," especially deserving of a wider audience. Indeed, there's a certain charm to these songs that fits the hopeful look of the band.

Perhaps they never made a record, or played their music to a packed house. I never heard from them again — but this simple demo cassette shows that they *were* a success.

They made me smile, and for that I'm grateful.

## THE STEWED
*(Kent, U.K.)*

*Heavenly Blues* 4 song 7" EP, 1993
*Black Mamba* 3 song 7" EP, 1994
 Twist Records, U.K. / Germany

While these dics were recorded at the venerable analog beat band heaven of Toe Rag studios, they fall into a much later '60s hard rock category. I dare say that with cleaner recordings this might be pedestrian stuff along the lines of early **Cult.**

The second disc is a bit more restrained, with a pretty faithful rendition of the oft-covered "Blues Theme." Still, I'll leave this to followers of a harder sound.

## THE STING RAYS
*(U.K.)*

*On Self Destruct* 4 song 12" EP, 1983
*Dinosaurs* 13 song LP, 1984
*Escalator* 3 song 7" EP, 1984
"Don't Break Down" b/w "Cover Version" 45, 1985
*The Essential Sting Rays* 16 song LP, 1987
 Big Beat Records
*June Rhyme* 3 song 12" EP, 198?
 ABC Records, U.K.
"Behind The Beyond" b/w "Perverted Justice" 45, 1986
 Kaleidoscope Sound Records, U.K.

Many LPs exist from this influential early '80s garage/trash combo, including appearances on the reportedly excellent Klub Foot live album series.

On a side note, a 45 by **The Bananamen** appeared in 1983 on Big Beat, purporting to be unreleased sessions from 1965. It was reportedly a dead-on take-off of **The Cramps**, and it puzzled the U.K. press as to its origin. The culprits were apparently none other than **The Sting Rays.**

*Note: These **Sting Rays** should not to be confused with a mid-1980s light-weight pop band from California of the same name.*

**197**

## STOLEN CARS
*(Novara, Italy)*

Untitled 4 song 7" EP, 1991
 Urlo Records, Italy

I remember the tracks "Walk On In" and "Wise Man" from their EP — which features very solid and spirited '66 garage punk at its best. Tight performances and powerful arrangements make **The Stolen Cars** one of the best Italian garage bands of which I've only heard a small taste — but I've no idea if they have anything else available.

## THE STOMACHMOUTHS
*(Sweden)*

"Don't Put me Down" b/w "Wild Trip" 45, 1985
 Sunlight Records, Sweden
Untitled 3 song 7" EP, 1986
*Something Weird* 14 song LP, 1986
*In Orbit* 6 song 12" EP, 1987
 Got To Hurry Records, Sweden
*Wild Trip* 18 song LP, 1987
 Voxx Records, USA

This author has ben searching for almost a decade for a copy of **The Stomachmouth**'s first 45, "Don't Put Me Down" b/w "Wild Trip." I thought I hit paydirt in 1992, when a friend in Paris showed me that she had *two* copies. Incredibly, they had two *different* picture sleeves, and she wouldn't part

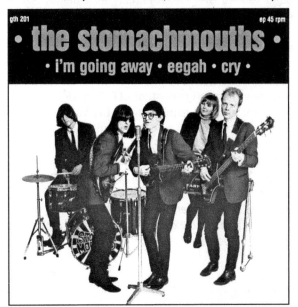

with either one! My search continues, and that should give a clue to the high esteem with which I hold **The Stomachmouths.**

For now, I'll just have to be happy with the fact that I have most of their other fine releases, starting with their second 7". It's a fuzz-drenched, groaning monster of a record, complete with enough blood-curdling screams to wake the dead.

This was soon followed-up by the super-cool *Something Weird* LP. This could very well be the garage album of a very fruitful 1986, with its combination of pure snot-garage, R&B madness and psych-surf overtones. It is simply as good a record as has ever come from the Swedish underground, and rates as highly as anything from the **Cornflake Zoo** and **Crimson Shadows**.

There's a bit of melody, as the masterful "Dr. Syn" proves, plus some humor in the playful interpretation of the traditional romp "The Cat Came Back." **The Stomachmouths,** despite the gruesome imagery connected with their name, were masters at combining a jubilant atmosphere with some gritty garage rock, style and fun.

Their *In Orbit* EP doesn't let us down either. It's a bit more raw and crude around the edges, but retains that swirling **Stomachmouths** sound, though two band members had changed. With the loss of these musicians it is even more clear the focus of the band was guitarist Stephan Kery, with his deceptively sly smile, mod clothing and screaming vocals.

A U.S. release on Voxx Records was to follow, but a dispute over money arose, and the tapes were never delivered to Los Angeles. Voxx released the *Wild Trip* LP instead, using rough mix versions of songs and concert tracks — material that the band sent to Greg Shaw initially as a demo, but released to their displeasure.

The record is of interest to fans, however, since some previously unreleased titles do appear, and the "live" side of the disc does show the band to a good advantage. Still, it would have been great to hear one more all-new studio LP from one of Sweden's greatest exports since the Volvo. (And just who is that "Randy Love" guy credited on the back cover of the *Wild Trip* LP?!?)

As Lindsay Hutton wrote on the LP's back cover, *"Since* **The Stomach Mouths** *slid ashore outta the dense cro-magnon rock'n'roll soup Teens of all ages the planet over, and probably beyond, have been smitten. Once kissed by these primordial fuzz drenched lips there's no turning back. No Cure. No How."*

## THE STONEFISH
*(Australia)*

Dom Mariani and Richard Lane of **The Stems** made the *From 20,000 Fathoms* 4 song 12" EP for Citadel in 1986. It contains surf-guitar fueled instrumentals, and is reportedly excellent.

## THE STORKS
*(Italy)*

I've been told that **The Storks'** late 1980s "Bad Girl" is a song worth of comparison to early **Wyld Mammoths** R&B garage, and that they also covered the entire **Tell Tale Hearts** debut LP in concert!

## STORM CLOUDS
*(U.K.)*

"Creature From Galaxy X" & "He's Trash" 7" flexi, 1988
    Unhinged Magazine, U.K.
*Psychotronic* 11 song cassette, 1990
*Lost In Space* 12 song cassette, 1990
    Acid Tapes, U.K.
Lost In Space 45, 1992
*2D Man* 4 song 7" EP, 1993
    Elefant Records, Spain

A duo originally consisting of Steve Lines (head of Acid Tapes) and Louise Allen. Home studios and the cassette sub-culture made it possible for offbeat projects such as these, where the creators are unhindered by budget and commercial concerns. The **Storm Clouds** usually employ heavy fuzz guitar, a primitive drum box, sound effects, tape manipulation and Allen's girl-ish vocals.

They released many cassettes, including the 12 track *Lost In Space*, a light-hearted 11 song tribute to all of our fave sci-fi movies titled *Psychotronic*, and an earlier effort, *It's Still Raining*. How can one not enjoy titles like "The Mushroom Men" or "Satellite Baby"?

Lousie Allen left in October 1993, replaced by Melanie Townsend. *"This has meant an end to the Sci-Fi/Fuzz pop and we're concentrating on the folk/psych side,"* said Steve Lines. Ken Flynn and Emily Drake round out the lineup.

The newer material with Townsend is indeed more pop-folk oriented, with gentle arrangements and some wonderful melodies — well worth continued listening.

Before releasing the newer efforts, Twang! was set to issue a 45 in December '94, and Elefant Records (Spain) was to release the *Not Of This Earth* CD in 1995, both featuring older tracks with Louise Allen on vocals.

Rainfall Records was also slated to release a 45 in late '94, and another 45 might pop up on Paul Ricketts' elusive Unhinged label.

This seems a good time to discuss Steve Lines' Acid Tapes:

This cassette-only label that has released more than 60 efforts by a variety of very obscure bands and solo artists, plus a few unreleased collections from the '60s. Very few of these artists have vinyl available, which makes Acid Tapes an interesting avenue for collectors of this genre. I've only heard a few of the releases, but they are very adventurous, and of high quality.

The label was originally formed in the early '80s by Alan Duffy, who would later start Imaginary Records. He handed the label over to fanzine publisher and musician Steve Lines in 1986, who dutifully carried on into the 1990s.

Lines is especially proud of the bands that have gone on from Acid Tapes to release vinyl, including **The Honey Smugglers, Ant Bee, Reefus Moon, The Rough Situation**, and **The Farewell Party**. He emphasizes that the label's mission is to promote new acts and music usually left unheard, and that it's not a profit-making concern. There certainly aren't many people out there releasing music for the correct reasons, and for this label's efforts alone we all owe a debt to Acid Tapes.

I'll refrain from printing their entire catalog, but as of 1995 the address for Acid Tapes was c/o Steve Lines, 28 Churchill Close, Calne, Wilts, SN11 8EN, UK.

## THE STRANGE
(U.K.?)

"Shake" b/w "Magic Spiral" 45, 1994
Twist Records, U.K./Germany

A very reverent version of the **Shadows Of Knight**'s pop groover "Shake" is the best thing here — the original on the flip is an unassuming little pop ditty. This isn't really all that bad, but there surely isn't anything strange at all about these lads. If anything, they could use a dose or two of strangeness to give their sound a little more taste.

## THE STRANGE FLOWERS
(Florence, Italy)

"Me And The Eggman" b/w "Janet's Faces" 45, 1989
Unique Records, Germany
*Teen Trash #11* 12 song LP & CD, 1994
Music Maniac Records, Germany

Forming in 1987 near Florence, Italy, this colorful group has toured Italy, Germany and Switzerland, depositing at least three demo tapes in its wake. The demo I heard bursts with energy and verve, as this decidedly trippy foursome weave lilting melodic guitar and vocals with a strong sense of beat and drive.

It is their debut 45, though, that merits the most praise. The double-sided gem shimmers with warm 12-string guitar and soaring vocal harmony. The "B" side, "Janet's Faces," might even be the stronger of the two tracks, with its spine-tingling chorus and beautiful arrangement. (All that's missing is a patented **Roger McGuinn** Rickenbacker solo.)

The long awaited LP (recorded in 1991) also features sparkling harmonies, expert guitar work and sensitive flowery arrangements. It veers a bit from their psych-pop sound into spacier areas, but always with discipline — there are no long rambling guitar jams, and even the longest track clocks in at only four minutes.

In the best tradition of the '80s **Moffs** and 1967-68 **Beatles, The Strange Flowers** are a blossom to cherish.

## STRAWBERRY ZOTS
(Albuquerque, NM USA)

Promoted as a bit more of a pop-oriented garage group, this Southwestern combo covered **The Electric Prunes'** "Get Me To The World On Time" on their first LP, *Cars, Flowers, Telephones*, 1989.

Though initially released on their own label, Acid Test, they were subsequently signed to RCA, and the LP was re-released by that conglomerate. The LP is pretty lightweight stuff, without any real "feel" for the genre, though they're certainly attempting to rip-off the elements of the sound. The last cut on the LP is one of the most moronic spoken-word attempts I've ever suffered through.

At least two other EPs subsequently appeared. I can't recommend any of their output. One witness reported to me that the band was very wimpy in concert.

## STUDIO 68
(London, U.K.)

This was a four piece mod band which has reportedly progressed over a few years into a rawer live garage sound, with several 45s and EPs to their credit. "Doubledecker Bus," from their debut 45, is a high-energy mod-pop effort slightly reminiscent of **The Prisoners** in mood. Energetic drumming propels the tune along, and a fine distorted guitar solo distinguish form the pack. That Hammomd B-3-sounding organ has to go, however. My advice: trade it in for a Vox or Farfisa post-haste.

## STUNDE X
(Dusseldorf, Germany)

Billed as "original paisley punk," I found this act in the excellent 1987 issue of Vienna's *Start Magazine*. A March 1986 concert in Dusseldorf is described, though I was unable to decipher much of the details. The two photos of the band look like they were a formidable and stylish garage act. The only aural sample I've heard is a well recorded live track on the 1987 *City Lights* compilation EP. It's very upbeat fuzz punk and makes me want to hear more — but I'm unsure if any studio tracks exist.

## SUBMARINE PROPHETS
(Sweden)

The late 1980s "Sir William Blake" 45 is reportedly pretty whigged-out, though not in a 1960s sense.

## SUBTERRANEAN DINING ROOMS
(Milan, Italy)

"European Son" on split 45, 1989
    Stampa Alternativa, Italy
*The Acoustic Side Of Spanish Knife* cassette
*There's No Rock 'N' Roll Sinner Without A Spanish Knife*
    12" EP, 198?
    Crazy Mannequin Records, Italy

Reportedly a psych act, and with a band name like that I wouldn't be surprised.

## THE SUBTERRANIANS
(Toronto, ON Canada)

Reportedly one of Toronto's first garage "revival" bands, forming in the early '80s and playing rather melodic styles. Their music reportedly influenced later locals **The Dundrells**.

## THE SUBTONES
(Germany)

*Popular Beat* 3 song 12" EP, 1985
    TNT Records, Germany
*Boys Want Fun* 12 song LP, 1986
    Teldec Records, Germany

The strange part about this German mod-garage-pop band was that they sounded distinctively British in their approach

**2ID**

and delivery. It's no surprise, then, that their version of **The Who's** "Circles" is their finest moment.

They released a few 45s, I believe, but I've only managed to hear their *Popular Beat* three-song 12" from 1985 and their *Boys Want Fun* 12 song LP from 1986. They both burst with revved-up excitement, but are perhaps a bit too clean or calculated to really be considered garage discs.

I'll give them an "A" for effort, though a little grit could have propelled them a bit further, I believe. An October 1985 single was announced, though I don't know if it was released.

**The Subtones** were obviously created for wider commercial consumption. Did this trio ever appear on the European pop charts?

## SUBURBAN NIGHTMARE
(Chicago, IL USA)

*A Hard Day's Nightmare* 7 song 12" EP, 1985
    Midnight Records, USA

As you've already read, this band mutated into **The Dwarves**, leaving any musical intentions in their wake. Before moving to San Francisco, though, these Chicagoans (Chicagoers? Chicagonians?) unleashed this very brief EP. The boys liked the '60s punk sound, they really did, but they just had to mess with it. That means that everything (including drums!) goes through a fuzz box at one time or another.

They credit themselves as performing "Hallucination, Perversion, Mastigation, Depression and Abstention" instead of musical instruments, so I think you get the idea of their mental states.

Can you imagine these guys when they're in their 40s or 50s? I'll bet their parents can't.

## CHRIS SUCH AND HIS SAVAGES
(New York, NY USA)

Self-titled 4 song 12" EP, 1989
    Chaos Records, USA

This EP is very much Hamburg-era **Beatles**-sounding, with **Chris Such** (formerly of **The Headless Horsemen**) looking every bit of **Stu Sutcliffe** on the B&W cover photo. "Leave My Kitten Alone" was of course one of those early **Beatles** set scorchers — and it's done here with reverence and snot. This is what The Fab Four could have sounded like in 1962 Hamburg if a good recording existed instead of those awful *Live At The Star-Club* tapes and albums.

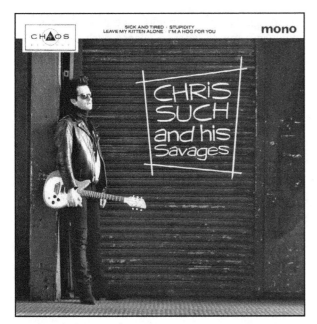

SICK AND TIRED · STUPIDITY
LEAVE MY KITTEN ALONE   I'M A HOG FOR YOU

CHAOS

mono

CHRiS SUCH and his Savages

This disc is also in glorious mono — just like everything else on the venerable Chaos Records.

## SUNDIAL
*(London, England)*

Glynnis Wilson notes, *"Early in their career, in the late '80s, Sundial was a wildly psychedelic unit. They are still together but have amalgamated their '60s influences with more current British indie pop styles. Their first two releases must be heard to be believed. There's a lot more information on this band in (the)* Freakbeat & Ptolemaic Terrascope *(magazines)."*

## SUNSET STRIP
*(Melbourne, Australia)*

The 1987 45 "Going Home" b/w "Yesterday's Gone" and the four song *Holocaust* 10" EP on Au-Go-Go Records are both reportedly worthwhile, though I seem to remember them having a harder-rock sound than true garagadelia. They do cover **The Standells'** "Riot On Sunset Strip," but in a strangely slow creep instead of the usual revved-up pace. It has a nice twisted fuzz solo, however.

**The Sunset Strip** remind me that there are countless other Australian bands — **The Bam Balams, Bamboos,** and **Eastern Dark** — for some — that are only somewhat associated with the garage mayhem described in this book, but which deserve a mention.

## THE SUPERKOOLS
*(Los Angeles, CA USA)*

Untitled 3 song 7" EP, 1993
 Screaming Apple Records, Germany

A band featuring former **Red Kross/Lovedolls** member Janet Housden — whom I remember as a rather funny young lady from our meetings in the late 1980s.

The 45 listed above is a raw punk experience, man, full of unpretentious howlings, rough guitar and head bobbing beats. There's some nice tremelo on "The Other Night," and good gutsy production throughout.

There's also at least one other 45 on Dionysus as well.

## SUPERFLUI
*(Ascoli Piceno, Italy)*

A garage punk band with the track "Fehi Meets Hele Hovey" on the bonus 45 with the *Tant Qu'il Y Aura Du Rock* compilation LP, 1988.

## SUPER K
*(Australia)*

"Recurring Nightmare" is a moody slow treatment in hypnosis, with low rumbling vocals, plucky guitar and enough tension to snap a rope. The only other track I've heard is the pounding "Go-Go," complete with Farfisa wheezing and simplistic female vocals. Two very different sides of a band — most likely comprising a 45 from the early 1980s.

**The Garden Path's** Vic Conrad told me he believes that Brad of **The Hoodoo Gurus** and the first keyboardist of **The Died Pretty** are the mainstays behind this side-band project.

## SURFIN' LUNGS
*(U.K.)*

*The Biggest Wave* LP on Beat International Records is the best known effort from this British surf group. (It must be awfully cold surfing off the British coast!) They made pretty traditional surf sounds, I seem to remember.

## SURFIN DEAD
(Germany)

This sounds like it could either be a surf cover band, or a **Grateful Dead** cover band, or both! Actually, they were a garage band with a three song 7" EP and untitled 12" EP — both on Glitterhouse Records in 1987. One fan has likened their sound to that of **Joy Division**!?!

## THE SURF TRIO
(Portland, OR USA)

*Shook Outta Shape* 18 song CD, 1994
    September Gurls Records, Germany
"Steamer" b/w "Another Girl, Another Planet" 45, 1994
    Pin Up Records, Germany

Surf music makes me proud to be American — at least for the two minutes it takes for it to explode through an AM radio. Eugene, Oregon's **Surf Trio** takes the 1960s surf myth, adds some **Ramones** bombast and buzz, then blasts it out like **Dick Dale** after a cocktail of motor oil and LSD.

Their 1994 LP is a nitro-fueled affair. "Ten Million Miles To Love" is a classic because of its title alone, and the tune is pretty good too! '60s purists will faint at the high volume and gritty appropriation·of the surf archetype, but that leaves epic artistic statements like "King Of The Surf" and "Lucky Surfer" for the rest of us.

The "Steamer" 45 adds a couple more solid tunes to their output; the A-side is a reverent surf number, while the flip a more punkish pop ditty. In a way this 45 is the band in microcosm — a cross between purism and raw rock expression. And has anyone noticed that this "trio" usually has four members?

These punk surf-niks also released several other records from the early to late '80s, including a couple EPs on Moxie and an LP on Voxx in 1986. Members later went on to or were shared with **The Wicked Ones** and **Marble Orchard**.

## THE SURREALISTS
(Seattle, WA USA)

*Where's Dada?* 6 song 12" EP, 1989
*Fish* 45 minute cassette, 1990
    Vagrant Records, USA

Many people think that it is a sign of weakness for a band to release its own material. That's an ignorant attitude, and one that thankfully didn't prevent **The Surrealists** from releasing their own recordings. Perhaps it would have been difficult to convince a record label to release such unique sounds, and these ears are glad that they did it themselves.

Vocalist/guitarist Erik "4-A" actually grabbed me as I was stepping onto a Seattle stage for a performance, and put his band's 12" into my hands. I probably would not have seen or heard it any other way, and I'm grateful for his effort.

**The Surrealists** combine an utterly individualistic sense of mood and structure for their psych nuggets, adding a bit of violin or noise at spots to set their songs apart.

Erik "4-A" has his own skewed view of the world, and it pokes through even on the band's excellent cover of **Lou Reed**'s "Pale Blue Eyes." His approach reminds me a bit of early **Zappa** or **Beefheart**, but within a more finely tuned structure.

Their subsequent cassette expounded on the band's sound, adding covers of **Robyn Hitchcock** songs as a good reference.

Bands like this fall between the cracks of attention, but I'm glad that I stumbled into the imaginative world of **The Surrealists**.

## THE SURRENDERS
(France)

Guitar oriented band reportedly in the **Byrds / Groovies / Barracudas** style, though I haven't heard a note of their stuff as of yet.

## THE SURROUNDS
(London, U.K.)

They've reportedly appeared in various incarnations from a harder punk sound to a more melodic psych sound, but always retaining their strong folk-rock roots. They only have one definite release, on the Target Records flexi sampler *Private Dream*, though collector Joss Hutton told me of a 45 with the track "California" was due out on Target as well.

Says Hutton, *"**The Surrounds** are one of the longest running London bands, they've been pushing their particular brand of folk-rock since around 1983. Mike writes excellent songs in the **Buffalo Springfield/Byrds/Big Star** vein, and plays an awesome 12-sting Ricky (Rickenbacker guitar)."*

## THE SWALLOWS
*(Switzerland)*

I've heard a cassette demo from March 1989 that is beautifully produced, featuring some great melodic '60s folk and **Beatles**-tinged pop.

"In My Heart" has a haunting melody and gentle atmosphere — adding up to one of the best '60s pop song efforts from the decade. "He's Only A Poor Court Jester" sounds like an outtake from *Rubber Soul* or a sequel to **Lennon**'s "I'm A Loser," while "I Can't Hear" ends their demo with a gentle and jangle ballad.

Quality garage-pop was a rare quantity for most of the '80s, making **The Swallows** an even more amazing find. Remarkably and unfortunately, I don't think anything by **The Swallows** has appeared on vinyl or CD as of this writing.

## SWINGING LONDON
*(Germany)*

At least one 45 exists, though I seem to remember it being pretty wimpy mod-pop.

## THE SWINGIN' FEZMEN
*(Los Angeles, CA USA)*

*We Are The Poohbahs Of Leisure* 4 song 7" EP, 1995
    Dionysus Records, USA

Now follow me — this is a one-off side project including former **Finks,** before going on to mine similar territory with the excellent **Huntington Cads**. The disc offers some meaty instrumental fun, with an emphasis on camp, a cheezy suburban atmosphere...and that wonderful headgear, the fez!

On a related note, I did manage to catch **The Huntington Cads** at a L.A. show in the summer of 1995. They were every bit as fun and exciting as **The Finks**, and vinyl was reportedly forthcoming.

## THE SWINGIN' GURUS
*(Hamilton, ON Canada)*

This is an apparently studio-only project featuring ex-**Chessman** vocalist Dan Beer and Gaven Dianda of **The Bards** and the (unknown to me) band **Creepin Chester**. Their psychedelically zany, sitar-filled track "Who Was The Last Guru?" is the highlight of the 1992 "alternative rock" sampler CD *More Hits, More Stars.* Glynnis Wilson reports that *"They wore East Indian costumes while performing."*

**203**

## THE SWINGIN' NECKBREAKERS
*(Hoboken, NJ USA)*

"You Better Dig It" b/w "Come On And Sing" 45, 1994
    Screaming Apple Records, Germany
"Workin' & Jerkin'" b/w "Good Good Lovin'" 45, 1994
    Estrus Records, USA
"I'm In Love With Me" b/w "Quit Your Belly Achin' Baby"
    45, 1994
    Telstar Records, USA

This trio has built quite an underground reputation in a short time, but all I've heard is the debut 45. It combines a punk sensibility, R&B grit, '60s frat-rock feel and grooving atmosphere to good effect — kind of like **Little Richard** playing with a roots rock band.

The flip "Come On And Sing" is a more straight punk-sludge affair with a good anthemic chorus.

There are also two LPs out — which I've yet to capture.

## SYD'S LAST PAINTING
*(Milan, Italy)*

"Scream Thy Last Scream" on split 45, 1986
    Crazy Mannequin Records, Italy

Obviously a **Syd Barrett** tribute of some sort, though no other information is known.

## TALISMEN
*(Portland, OR USA)*

A garage rock band with a focus on R&B. They played a reportedly wild show at the "Bad Musick Seminar" in 1988 in New York City — a spoof of the fakely independent "New Music Seminar" — and were said to be one of the best groups to perform there. They had one 7" release: "Fleetwood" b/w "Tiger In Your Tank" on Chaos Records in 1989.

## THE TALL BOYS
*(U.K.)*

"Another Half Hour Till Sunrise" b/w
   "Island Of Lost Souls" 45, 1983
*Wednesday Addams Boyfriend* 6 song 12" EP, 1984
*Final Kick* 4 song 12" EP, 1985
*Brand New Gun* 3 song 12" EP, 1986
   Big Beat Records, U.K.

Nigel Lewis, formerly of **The Meteors** and **Clapham South Escalators,** was also behind this slightly garage-influenced band which managed to land a song on the *Return Of The Living Dead* movie soundtrack album.

The debut 45 is a rockabilly affair, not far from **The Meteors'** sound. This type of American roots music with a heavy British vocal accent has always been odd to these Yankee ears.

The "Final Kick" title track is a stomping anthem, with heavily echoed vocals and a menacing atmosphere. The thick guitar dominated sound continues on "Interceptor" and the rockabilly-ish "Dragster." They also hand in a staccato version of "Action Woman" — was there any garage group of the 1980s that *didn't* cover this song?

*Brand New Gun* takes up where the previous EP left off, sounding very much like they were part of the same sessions. "Last House On The Left" is a fun roots-a-billy ditty, with the requisite twanged solo, while "Took A Long Time" is a bouncy acoustic based ballad.

Lewis also released a solo effort in 1986 on Media Burn Records. Music fan Dustine Walker says that "Nigel Lewis was one of the persons responsible for the garage/trash explosion in Britain during the 1980s — a very important figure this side of the pond."

## TANGLE EDGE
*(Norway)*

The 1989 *In Search of a New Dawn* LP on Mushroom Production Records is available; it's reportedly a mixture of psych and progressive sounds.

## TECHNICOLOUR DREAM
*(Italy)*

*Pretty Tomorrow* 9 song LP, 1985
   High Rise Records, Italy
*Beauty Is Truth* 12", 198?
   Voice Of Wonder Records, Norway

The *Pretty Tomorrow* LP was one of this author's most sought-after records of the 1980s. I finally tracked it down in its native Italy, thanks to some help from the band the **99th Floor.**

**Technicolour Dream** is really a two-man project; guitarist Fabio Porretti and bassist/vocalist Marco

***TECHNICOLOUR DREAM, 1985***

Conti, with several other musicians contributing at times. Conti looks eerily like American television star Jay Leno on the sleeve of their debut — I don't know if this is a good thing.

The sound here is early **Pink Floyd** strained through an Italian pop-psych filter — moody, melodic, spacey and wonderfully epic are fit descriptions. Backwards guitar, mesmerizing rhythms and colorful flourishes grace the entire production, making it one of the most intelligent, elegant records of the era.

I'm not sure if the *Beauty Is Truth* 12" is by this same band, though I saw it in a catalogue credited to "Technicolour Dream." This lack of information is most frustrating — I do know that this band developed into two separate outfits, one of which is Pale Dawn, contributing a grand track to the Italian *Eighties Colours Vol. 2* compilation.

Any further information would be greatly appreciated.

## TEENAGE CAVEMAN
*(Auburn, AL USA)*

Untitled 3 song 7" EP, 1993
    Homo Habilis Records, USA

I know of at least a couple other discs by this
Alabama combo, but this is the only one I could
uncover. It's a fuzzy punk slab combining a '77 feel
with a '66 garage atmosphere — not purist or
revivalist in any regard, but with enough of a
similar mood to call for inclusion here. The flip
features yet another credible cover of **The Sonics'**
"Boss Hoss," and there's nice white vinyl for this
release too.


## TEENY BOPPERS
*(Ragusa, Italy)*

The seven song "Head Out On The Highway"
private cassette saw release in 1992. It kicks off
appropriately with a garaged version of
**Steppenwolf**'s anthem "Born To Be Wild," then
settles down to more familiar garage territory with
a spirited "Route 66," **The Yardbirds'** "For Your
Love," then with live stabs at "Hey Joe" and "Mr.
Nobody." This stuff is crude and high-strung, just
like a teeny bopper should be.


## THE TELEPORT PARTY
*(Hamburg, Germany)*

Markus Steenbock headed up this garage &
groove oriented outfit in 1992. No known studio
tapes exist; I've heard a concert recording.


## THE TELL-TALE HEARTS
*(San Diego, CA USA)*

*The Tell-Tale Hearts* 12 song LP, 1984
*The Now Sound Of...* 6 song 12" EP, 1985
*High Tide (Big Noses And Pizza Faces)* 21 song CD, 1994
    Voxx Records, USA
"Too Many Lovers" b/w "Promise" 45, 1987
    Kavern 7 Records, Australia
"Take A Look Inside" b/w "I'm Ready" 45, 1991
"Circus Mind" b/w "Flying" 45, 1994
    Nevermore Records, USA

*"More than anything, this band is loved for their
ability to rave it up. On stage they are not to be
believed — dressed more authentically than many
bands were able to do even in 1966, moving
around like possessed dervishes,
playing music that pushes constantly*

**205**

*over the top, there is no better living example of
why R&B-based white garage punk was the most
powerful musical style of the last four decades."*
    — *Greg Shaw,* Voxx Teen Beat, Issue #4,
April/May 1986

That's strong praise from the Voxx head honcho,
and well deserved at that. **The Tell-Tale Hearts**
could be seen as the manic sound and style of **The
Crawdaddys** taken to its logical limit. A bit of teen-
punk-beat energy was infused with the more
traditional R&B influences, with the result being
one of California's best-ever garage combos.
    Formed from the remains of **The Mystery
Machine** and Mike Stax from a late **Crawdaddys**
lineup, **The Tell-Tale Hearts** had the look, the

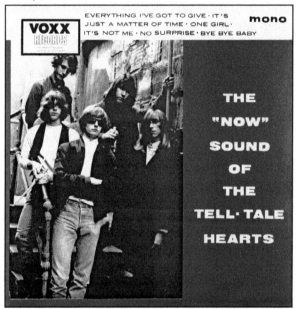

sound and the style to capture the growing
Southern California garage crowd — as well as
some broad-minded mods.
    Their debut LP jumps with excitement, as they
blend time-honored classics with their own worthy
compositions. "Crawling Back To Me" and "Come
And Gone" alone would seal their reputations as
the second coming of **The Pretty Things, Q65** or
**Downliners Sect,** and the remainder of the LP keeps
up to these high standards.
    Curiously, the band and its fans have lamented
the production of this LP, claiming that the unused
rough mixes were a much more accurate picture of
the band's sound. Detractors claim that producer
Greg Shaw re-mixed the album, (without the band's
knowledge or consent), creating a much tamer end
result. To these ears, however, I hear an expertly
actualized LP — one of the best in the genre.
    Mike Stax & Co. were able to rectify the situation
in 1994, when they re-mixed the tracks in question

for the Voxx *High Tide...* retrospective CD. It includes six re-mixes plus nine previously unreleased tracks — "I'm Gonna Make You Mine" and the "live" version of **The Seeds'** "Satisfy You" are especially welcome artifacts from the vaults.

To this author, ironically, the original 1984 LP mixes sound more powerful and complete than the later band-sanctioned efforts. Perhaps **The Hearts'** emotions from the mid-'80s still cloud their judgment and perception of those first mixes. The originals still sound better to me. The tracks — regardless of the mix in question — are still expert nuggets.

The lads made sure of the mixes on their follow-up, by recording in a vintage-equipped studio with only a three track tape recorder! The carefully arranged and performed *Now Sound* EP drips with reverb and a warm, moody sound — the type that digital equipment cannot reproduce. Four stellar originals and a couple logical cover tunes make this the definitive **Tell-Tale Hearts** disc, and sadly it is only an EP. Still, I'm sure that the band would choose this as the single collection they appreciate the most.

The band's anthology CD liner notes say of this period, *"In L.A. we got a not undeserved reputation for having a snotty, arrogant attitude towards our 'rivals.' One memorable quote came from Gwynne Kahn, then of* **The Pandoras,** *who dismissed us as thus: 'The Tell-Tale Hearts? Oh, they're just a bunch of ugly boys with big noses and pizza faces!'"*

The lineup would begin to fluctuate — with the original bunch calling it quits on Valentines Day, 1987 — and by the end of the decade only Stax remained as a **Tell-Tale Heart**. One last, great 45 was issued by Australia's ultra-cool Kavern 7 label, then the band fell silent.

Members of Springfield, Missouri's **Royal Nonesuch** migrated to California to join Stax in an attempt to revive **The Hearts**, but this attempt was apparently aborted as well by the early 1990s. More tracks were recorded, and a 1991 self-released 45 appeared.

By this time Stax was immersed in **The Hoods** — then word came that the **Hearts** had reformed in 1993 and started to play live shows again!

The 1994 Voxx CD helped spur interest again in **The Tell-Tale Hearts,** so as of this writing the saga of one of the world's finest beat & garage bands is still not yet finished.

## THE TEMPO TOPPERS
*(Norway)*

Untitled 4 song 7" EP, 1993
   That's Entertainment Records, Norway

From the cover photo this looks like a group of musicians in their late 30s or early 40s getting in on some garage pop action. The playing is predictably tight and professional — and the disc is produced by Arne Thelin of **The Lust-O-Rama** and **Kwyet Kings,** so all the right elements are in place.

"Lover's Lane" is a toe-tapping though unremarkable pop-stomper, and is overshadowed by the jangle ballad "There's Something Wrong On My Radio" on the flip.

## THE TEN COMMANDMENTS
*(Toronto, ON Canada)*

*Weird Out* 14 song LP, 1987
"Wherever I Go" b/w "Suddenly" 45, 1988
*Home Fires Burning* 10 song LP, 1989
"Revolution Man" b/w "Dark Angel" 45, 1991
*Miracle Mile* 16 song LP, 1993
   Sensible Records, Canada

Video: "Not True," & "City Of People," 1987

I love the bands that accept their crudeness — bands that unabashedly spew forth with enthusiasm, admitted limited musical ability and an urge to be heard. This describes the early sounds of Toronto's **Ten Commandments**.

Forming in late 1985, they took it upon themselves to bring the idea of '66-meets-**The Ramones** fun back to the Canadian scene — in contrast, a bit, to the more obviously '60s look and sound of Montreal's **The Gruesomes**.

Their first LP bursts with that crude excitement. Vocalist James Lord doesn't sing as much as vocalize (a quality I readily identify with), so his heartfelt punk blurtings are even more effective.

Every garage band should also be able to write their own "classic," and these lads contribute the blistering "Not True" to the genre's cosmos. It stands with the best.

A follow-up 45 showed the band in transition, growing as players, songwriters, and with Lord's vocals improving noticeably. This prepared listeners for the 1989 *Home Fires Burning* LP, which could be one of the most underrated underground rock records of the decade. Pure **Ramones**-mania drips through the punk-pop grooves, with clear production and an unrelenting sense of energy.

The fuzzed-out foursome never caught on in their native Canada, however, and this LP was especially

### THE TEN COMMANDMENTS, 1987

ignored. Lord then pressed up a 45 and LP in limited editions of 200 each. The LP was titled *Miracle Mile*, and featured fine unreleased and re-recorded material. By then the band had shattered.

The magic of recordings, however, is their ability to exist long after their creators have vanished. Find these records and discover a band in the finest tradition of the do-it-yourself garage punk ethos — **The Ten Commandments**.

### TEN TONS OF LIES
*(Los Angeles, CA USA)*

"Seeds Of The Next Season" b/w "You Lie" 45, 1985
    Voxx Records, USA

This part-time band contained regulars from the L.A. Cavern Club scene, so Greg Shaw at Voxx gave them a 45 specifically aimed at their peers. (The label even designated it as part of the "Cavern Club Series" of releases, though I don't think any others followed.)

The music is very innocent '66 pop-punk, with the right combination of Farfisa and fun. The participants are notable as much for their vintage clothing as their musical accomplishments! Drummer Paul Sakry was a full-time member of **The Untold Fables**, and also filled-in with **Yard Trauma** for a time, and he's the musical highlight here.

This is pretty fun stuff, not meant to be anything more than an homage to the sound dug by the kids in the scene.

**207**

### TEQUILA MOCKING BIRD
*(Melbourne, Australia)*

A **Byrds**-ish group which featured a few members of the **Bo-Weevils**.

### TEXACO LETHER MAN
*(Japan)*

Yes, that is the correct spelling of the band's name. They were reportedly the only completely American-sounding '60s punk group from the mid-'80s to early-'90s in Japan. On stage they reportedly performed as "juvenile delinquents," and their lead singer even wore vintage '50s gang gear. Their lead guitar player had a black Vox Phantom guitar — a very rare and expensive find in Japan!

### THE THANES
*(Edinburgh, Scotland, U.K.)*

*The Thanes Of Cawdor* 14 song LP, 1987
*Hey Girl + 3* 4 song 7" EP, 1987
*Hey Girl + 6* 7 song 12" EP, 1987
"Baby Come Back" 45, 1989
*Better Look Behind You* 10" EP, 1990
    DDT Records, U.K.
*Learning Greek Mythology With...* 4 song 12" EP, 1992
    Satyr Records, Greece
"Don't Let Her Dark Your Door Again" b/w
    "In God I Trust" 45, 1991
"Dozen Thoughts Buzzing" b/w "Antenna Surprise" 45, 1994
    Screaming Apple Records, Germany
"I've Seen Darker Nights" b/w
    "(Seems To Break Your) Happy Chain"
    45, 1995, Distortions Records, USA

The "No Need To Worry" & "Please Don't Cry" 7" 45 was in *Lost Trails Magazine* in Italy, 1989. "No Need To Worry" is a vintage **Golden Earring** song. The track "LSD (Got A Million $)" is on a free record (flexi or 7"?) in the U.K. zine *Sniffin Rock*, 1989.

They're also on the **Kinks** tribute, *Shangri-La*, on Imaginary Recs., U.K., 1989 with "You Shouldn't Be Sad," and with "Sun's Going Down" on *Misfit* the **Outsiders** tribute LP on Screaming Apple, 1992. "Honey I Need" was slated to be on the *Not So Pretty* **Pretty Things** Tribute LP on Corduroy Recs., Australia, late 1994. An EP on Weed Records in France and a compilation of **Thanes** material was also in the works.

Just as Americans embraced their heritage of 1960s garage, some groups from across the waters reinvented their own Euro-beat history. Lenny Helsing became the focus of many of these efforts in the U.K., beginning with the **Green Telescope**, and then blossoming with **The Thanes**. (He would also sit in with and inspire countless other combos — such as the **Beeville Hive V, Offhooks, The Stayrcase** and **The Television Personalities**.)

**The Thanes** debut LP is a masterpiece of beat style. Gritty yet structured, bluesy yet upbeat, the 14 tracks burst with a teen exuberance not heard in the U.K. since **The Pretty Things** or **Downliners Sect** some 25 years earlier. The beautiful color cover alone makes it one of the most attractive beat-packages ever.

Helsing also embarked on some odd marketing. Their *Hey Girl + 3* EP was a proud follow-up to their LP, but then mysteriously also appeared as a 12" with three additional tracks. A 10" EP also later reportedly saw release, though I haven't been able to confirm its actual existence.

The German-issued "Don't Let her Dark Your Door Again" does exist, however, and was even in the more traditional 7" format! It once again showed **The Thanes** to be the world's utmost practitioners of Euro-beat. Each and every **Thanes** disc builds on their reputation as one of the best beat bands the world will ever see and hear.

Their 1995 45 for the ever-cool Distortions label might be their best yet, with some pop-jangle added into the mix of solid beat grooves. Helsing shows no signs of running out of musical gas.

One would like to think that the faithful will one day be rewarded, and Lenny Helsing is one of those musical faithful. At least we can try to track down a few **Thanes** records and celebrate his dedication.

## THE THANGS
(Cincinnati, OH USA)

"Let Me Be" b/w "Lord Comes Knockin'" 45, 1986
   Day One Records, USA

This could be best described as "good time" garage music because of its infectious upbeat style and delivery. The anthemic choruses of "Let Me Be" drive home the point, along with the shimmering organ riffs. The B-side is a white R&B rave up, "Lord Comes Knockin'," with a good driving beat and frantic appeal.

Interestingly, this is the only other release I found on Cincinnati's Day One Records, the home of my faves **The Libertines**.

## THE THERAMEN
(Australia)

This wonderfully named seven-piece was made up of **The Puritans** and two **Cracked Jaffers**, reportedly playing R&B grunge for a series of five shows in 1990.

## THE THINGS
(Los Angeles, CA USA)

*Coloured Heaven* 11 song LP, 1984
*Outside My Window* 10 song LP, 1986
   Voxx Records, USA / Hitch Hyke Records, Greece

Perhaps no band from the 1980s re-captured the creative spirit of mid-period **Beatles** better than **The Things**. The soaring Rickenbacker guitars and angelic vocal harmonies, the looping **McCartney**-esque bass lines and imaginative arrangements were all in the same mold

as the best of the **Beatles**, and all expertly executed.

Their *Coloured Heaven* LP (note the "English" spelling) actually began life as a demo tape, but Greg Shaw jumped and thankfully released it. Though the recording is crude in spots, it displays a band bursting with energy and creativity. The Steve Crabtree originals are stunningly haunting, with his wistful vocals especially memorable and evocative.

"Eyes Of A Child," "She Came Out Of The Sky" and "It's Over" all bounce and move with a colorful skill. The trippy title track also shows that the band understood the merits of pure psych, as it shimmers side one to a close.

This debut was good, but the follow up *Outside My Window* is somehow better. Recorded in a "real" studio, this LP finally actualized the band's plethora of creative sounds. Backwards high-hat cymbals (reminiscent of some **Hendrix** tracks) and masterful production work bring the title track to life, and *Sgt. Pepper* effects highlight the mesmerizing "All Work And No Play."

The songwriting again is uniformly strong, as is the manic drumming of Roy McDonald. (I sat with McDonald after one mid-'80s gig, where he ate two ice cream sundaes and drank a couple Cokes. With that much sugar racing through his veins, I'm not surprised that he was known as the "Keith Moon" of the garage scene for his wild drumming. He went on to the major-label **Muffs**, with an ex-**Pandora**.)

*Outside My Window* is a stunning achievement, especially for an independent release produced on a limited budget. The LP did not fare well commercially, however, and lineup shuffles scattered the band (as it had throughout their history).

Crabtree could not muster the same energy for further efforts, as the surprisingly pedestrian self-titled 1989 LP showed. (The band was pictured on the back cover in bandannas and spikes — **The Things** a hard rock-metal act?!?)

Still, this is one band whose early recordings should be sought out with haste — they also contribute a standout track to the essential *Garage Sale* compilation.

Their sense of grace, style and melody was a welcome and glorious relief from the bland "pop" of the decade's mainstream.


## THE THIRD EYE
*(New York, NY USA)*

This was a late '80s, earl '90s foursome of guitarist Dino Sorbello (ex-**Blacklight Chameleons**), drummer Ken Anderson (ex-**Optic Nerve**), bassist Freddie Katz (ex-**The Gift**) and Abbey Lavine on vocals. They recorded at least four studio tracks that remain unreleased, and also contributed to the 1989 *Kaleidoscopic Vibrations* compilation LP.


## 1313 MOCKINGBIRD LANE
*(Albany, NY USA)*

"Hornet's Nest" b/w "My Hearse (Is Double Parked)" 45, 1989
*The Second Coming Of...* 4 song 7" EP, 1989
"Monkey Cage Girl" b/w "Pretty Boys" 45, 1991
"Psychedelic Monster" b/w "Dead Mary" 45, 1991
*The Proot Boots* 4 song "Live" 7" EP, 1993
"Slow Death" b/w "Dirty Bitch" 45, 1993
   Scarab Records, USA

*Have Hearse, Will Travel* 13 song LP, 1990
   Who's Driving My Plane Records, USA
   (Sundazed Records, USA)
*Triskaidekaphobia* 11+ song CD, 1993
   Midnight Records, USA
"Alice Dee" b/w "Spider and The Fly" 45, 1994
   Weed Records, France

*"Reviewers have used such adjectives as Raw, Primitive, Goulish, Deviant, Fiendish, (and a) fuzz explosion to describe the sound that emanates from 1313..."* — from a press kit

Named for the fictional address of *The Munsters'* 1960s television mansion, this upstate New York combo brought **The Chesterfield Kings'** spirit of '66 back into the late 1980s. Interestingly, this is a second or third generation garage band from the '80s — that is — they appeared after the first one or two initial waves of garage bands had come and gone. That certainly does not diminish their quality

or importance, it merely points out how enduring the genre has become.

Keeping to the basics, (fuzz, Farfisa and screaming), **1313 MBL** unleashed a string a must-have 45s leading up to their debut LP. The first two 45s feature the crudest of basement recordings, dripping with distortion and bombast. Extremely simple chord progressions are repeated by bass, guitar and keyboards, slamming home the garage point with a wonderful thud.

It is this simplicity that makes **1313 MBL** not only a stereotypical 1960s garage band, but a fun band as well. These guys and gal are totally unpretentious in their efforts; they play fuzzed-out garage music because they love it!

Their LP features a bit more polished production,

but doesn't have any less fuzz or grime. How can one not enjoy a band singing compositions like "Oooga Booga Baby" or "Dig Her Up"?

Several follow-up 45s displayed more ultra-distorted punk tendencies, though they weren't quite up to the band's early fuzz standards. They changed lineups frequently, as organist Kim noted, *"We go through more drummers than Spinal Tap!"*

Their *Triskaidekaphobia* CD continued with bubbling energy and smirking garage humor. (The title refers to the fear of the number 13.) Their anti-**Beatles** tirade "I Don't Wanna Hold Your Hand" is especially strong, along with the anthemic "Grab My Guitar." There's a good bit of "empty space" at the apparent end of the CD, followed by a few more surprises.

The subsequent Weed Records 45 is one of their best, showing that the combo has a wealth of worthy ideas and sounds.

**1313 Mockingbird Lane** made no bones about their standing as a pure 1960s punk band, keeping the flame alive decades after the first spark.

They can borrow my fuzz box any day!

## THE THOUGHT
*(Holland)*

Their 1982 debut has been described as insubstantial, but their self-titled 1985 LP for MCA has been heralded for its mixture of psychedelic pop and its version of **The Electric Prunes'** "I Had Too Much To Dream Last Night." Their follow-up 1986 Polydor LP, *The Dream Is Me,* was reportedly a disappointment, and the band split. Some members went on to form a band called **Shoot The Moon,** whose sound is unknown to me.

## 3-D INVISIBLES
*(Detroit, MI USA)*

Several LPs exist; one even has a 3-D cover and includes the viewing glasses! The band is often compared to **The Cramps,** and I guess that's a good starting point.

## THE THREE O'CLOCK
*(Los Angeles, CA USA)*

"Happen Happened" b/w "Mind Gardens" 45, 1981
(as **Salvation Army**)
New Alliance Records, USA
*Befour The...* 10 song LP, 1982, 1984
(re-issue of **The Salvation Army** LP)
*Baroque Hoedown* 8 song 12" EP, 1983

Lolita Records, France
*Sixteen Tambourines* 10 song LP, 1983
Frontier Records, USA

also a "fan club" 45, with unknown tracks

Video: "I Go Wild," 1982; "Jet Fighter," 1984

**Davy Jones** look-alike Michael Quercio, guitarist Gregg Gutierrez and drummer Troy Howell began as **The Salvation Army,** depositing one 45 and LP before evolving into their final form. Howell left to eventually join **The Eyes Of Mind,** then the "real" Salvation Army (a charity organization) made the band change their name — and **The Three O'Clock** was born.

The **Salvation Army** 45 and LP are frantic bits of addled energy, but with only a few tracks displaying the colorful pop skill **The Three O'Clock** would unleash. "She Turns To Flowers" and "While We Were In Your Room Talking To The Wall" both heap on the psych stylings, with backward guitars and pulsating guitar and vocals — in retrospect this disc is an interesting peek at the origins of what would become the growing Californian "'60s scene."

By this time the newly renamed band was in the middle of what Quercio reportedly had tagged the "Paisley Underground," a circle of friends and bands that unabashedly embraced the latest onslaught of garage-psych mania. **The Three O'Clock** would eventually gain critical attention and big money interest, and Quercio attempted to abandon the label, but it stuck with the band for years.

The first **Three O'Clock** release was the brilliant *Baroque Hoedown* EP. Recorded mainly at production wiz Earle Mankey's home studio, it bursts with wildly imaginative psych pop. Early **Pink Floyd,** *Sgt. Pepper* **Beatles** and a host of other classic psych sounds invade each groove of this debut, as Quercio's little-boy vocals entrance the listener.

(The band marveled at the fact that much of the studio equipment had originally been used by the **Beach Boys** on their *Pet Sounds* LP, and this helps to explain the band's warm vocals and lush reverb which soaks the entire production.)

The U.S. release had only five songs, but the French import has an extra three tracks, all of great interest. Especially of note is the reverent and powerful version of **The Byrds'** "Feel A Whole Lot Better," and the loopy version of **Pink Floyd's** "Lucifer Sam." Both of these songs were covered many times throughout the 1980s, but the **Three O'Clock** were among the first to rediscover these gems for a new generation.

While the band did deliver credible and creative cover tunes, "With A Cantaloupe Girlfriend" could be considered their definitive original composition. With surreal imagery and a catchy melody, it encapsulates the foursome's brand of charm and pop individuality.

This EP proved to be their creative high-mark, however, as they failed to grow musically with their popularity. The follow-up *16 Tambourines* is generally disappointing, with only the fanciful "Jet Fighter" capturing any of their initial magic.

It was around this time that I talked briefly with Quercio at Club Lingerie in Hollywood. His resemblance to **The Monkees' Davy Jones** really was remarkable, right down to his Melrose clothes and big belt buckle.

Guitarist Gutierrez left the band as they signed to **Prince's** Paisley Park Records, and the band's degeneration was soon complete. They released several utterly inept discs, each to critical jeers and plummeting sales.

Many times a band's first brilliant attempt is their finest hour. Such is the case with **The Three O'Clock** — and a fine hour it was indeed.

## THRU THE LOOKING GLASS
*(Los Angeles, CA USA)*

"Close Tonight" b/w
  "This One's For Me" & "She Smiles Her Cries"
  45, 1985
  Erika Records, USA

This was one of the flower fashion-conscious bands that became popular through The Cavern Club in the mid-'80s; a photo of one member even appeared in the 1985 *Rolling Stone* report on the L.A. psych-garage scene.

Their sound draws mainly on 1967-ish British/**Beatles** psych and progressive pop, with propulsive drumming and interesting, intricate arrangements. They have a very melodic and powerful sound, not unlike fellow Los Angelenos **The Things**.

Their lone known vinyl mines this sound, with "This One's For Me" the most traditionally pop. The other two tracks stretch the genre — this was one of the few of the paisley bands which sought to add its thoughts to the form rather than simply repeat past sounds.

They also appear on the *It's Happening* cable-TV show, and while the sound quality and mix are not the best, the group's style does shine.

## THE THYRD TWIN
*(France)*

A project of ex-**Vietnam Veterans**, with the *Churl* LP on Music Maniac in 1994.

## THE TIKIS
*(California USA)*

"Surfadelic" b/w "Junie" 45, 1981
  World Imitation Records, USA

The 1981 "Surfadelic" 45 was not meant to be part of any '60s revival movement, but was released as a side project of the art-noise band **Monitor**. It gives us two short psych-guitar instrumentals, each with a demented edge and mood. It's very cool, and pretty rare as well.

## THE TIKI TONES
*(Los Angeles, CA USA)*

untitled 4 song 7" EP, 1995
  Dionysus Records, USA

This is another side project involving several of the more eclectic **Swamp Zombies**. Here they dig deep into the instrumental surf, hot rod, outer-space instrumental sub-genres — with great success. Superb musicianship, songwriting and delivery separate **The Tiki Tones** from the latest crop of similar bands.

I was also lucky to catch the **Tiki Tones** at a 1995 Los Angles show, where they blasted through a cornucopia of instrumental sounds, always with a smile and sense of fun. They also looked quite spiffy in their matching **Tiki Tone** sweaters, washed in the light of their porch tiki lights.

Bands like **The Tiki Tones** (I just like writing their name) have injected new life into '60s genre music. I think I'll go right now and light my backyard tiki torches in their honor.

## TILT A WHIRL
*(U.K.)*

Nothing known, circa 1992.

## THE TIME BEINGS
*(Boston, MA USA)*

10 song demo cassette, 1985
5 song demo, 1986
   no label, USA (demos)

Now I remember why I liked **The Time Beings** enough for inclusion on the *Beasts From the East* compilation LP: they are *really* garagey. Imagine **The Seeds** after swallowing a couple cases of beer (instead of LSD), and you'll get the idea of this band's direct, simple appeal.

They had been bashing the tunes since at least the turn of the 1980s, and had accumulated these two power-packed demos by the time of the garage vinyl explosion. Oddly, they couldn't find a home for their stuff, as several labels passed on them. They boasted some great tracks, however, as their guttural garage approach was gritty, snotty — and as I said before — beer-soaked.

Songs like the anthemic "Freedom" and "Caveman" all documented the virtues of girls, cars, love, and ... beer. Their "Why Don't You Love Me" even topped the *Fuzbrains Magazine* 1987 staff poll as the best song of the year.

Even if there isn't any vinyl to spin, at least we'll have a bunch of great unreleased tracks for the "garage revival" that should hit sometime around the turn of the century.

## THE TIMELAPSE
*(Germany)*

A four song 7" EP, "It's Child's Play" on Sneaky Pete Records exists, as well as the eight song *Timelapse Now* LP on Germany's Smarten-Up Records. I believe their sound to be more mod-based, but with a garage twinge.

## TIME PILLS
*(Italy)*

Untitled 3 song 7" EP, 1989
   Face Records, Italy

Featuring Tony Face of **Not Moving**, **The Time Pills'** 1989 45 is a powerful guitar effort, which also features some fine emotional lyrics and vocals courtesy of Betty Blue. This isn't really '60s "garage" music, but it shares the genre's attitude and enthusiasm. Tony Face headed up Italy's Face Records, which released some fine indy records in the late '80s/early '90s.

## THE TIMES
*(U.K.)*

At least three early-'80s LPs of unknown qualities are available.

## THE TIMESHIFT
*(Vienna, Austria)*

*Paranoid Fears In A Concrete World* 6 song 12" EP, 1985
   Ton Un Ton Records, Austria

This mod-ish beat band released the "Dance The Beat" 45 in 1984, the *Paranoid Fears In A Concrete World* six song 12" EP in 1985, and I believe also the *On The Edge Of Society* LP. The *Paranoid Fears* EP has some interesting moments, as well as some more conventional pop efforts.

## THE TOMMYKNOCKERS
*(Los Angeles, CA USA)*

Untitled 3 song 7" EP, 1989
   S.F.T.R.I. Records, USA
*Caught Dead Inside* 7 song 12" EP, 1990
   Unique Records, Germany
"Noisy Beat" b/w "More To Come" 45, 1991
   Dionysus Records, USA
*Perception Is Reality* LP, 1992
   Skyclad Records, USA
"End Of My Mind" b/w "Haircut & Attitude" 45, 1993?
   Unique Records, Germany
"One Too Many" b/w "Have Faith" 45, 1993?
   Helter Skelter Records, Italy

Frustrated with the ultimate stalling of **Thee Fourgiven**, guitarist Rich Coffee formed a new power trio, **The Tommyknockers**. His back-up drummer and bassist personnel would revolve constantly throughout 1989 and 1990, even as a three song 7" EP appeared on the SFTRI label and

***THE TOMMYKNOCKERS, 1990***

a 12" EP on Germany's Unique Records.

**The Tommyknockers** have a "heavy" guitar based sound, but occasionally swerve into garageland, and that it why they are included here. The *Perception Is Reality* LP popped up in 1992, but was unfortunately on the inept Skyclad label. This reportedly meant a minimum of (positive) publicity, distribution, sales — or royalties! Despite Skyclad, **The Tommyknockers** continued to tour and record for other labels, with a plethora of releases by 1995.

Rich Coffee is a wonderful musician, person and a rock'n' roll true-believer who deserves great success. Let's hope **The Tommyknockers** will finally do the trick.

## THE TOWN CRYERS
*(Fresno, CA USA)*

"Girl With The Blue Sweater" b/w "What's Going On" 45, 1990
*In The Cool Part Of Town* LP, 1990
  Get Hip Records, USA

I've been to Fresno, and it is, how do you say politely ... "interesting." These cats proudly called the middle California city their home, where they certainly were the only band attempting **Yardbirds**-styled pop songs.

Their "Girl With The Blue Sweater" 45 on Get Hip also owes debts to **The Byrds,** but both songs seem to need editing and a bit of production help as well. Their subsequent LP, *In The Cool Part Of Town,* suffers from the same misjudgments, and really only partially fits into this genre because of its general blandness.

This certainly is not a poor band, but one which could have benefited from a little direction. They did have a funny line in their press kit: ***"The Town Cryers** have no intention other than to keep playing and pretending to their parents that they will finish college and amount to something."*

## THE TRAPMEN
*(Rennes, France)*

A four-piece including Denis Bigot, with a circa 1993 five song cassette demo full of thick warbly organ, driving beats, snarly vocals, and tight playing. "Cry In Vain" is a grooving original, with a catchy verse and cool atmosphere. This is obviously a talented garage-pop band — but I don't think any vinyl materialized as of 1995.

## THE TRASHWOMEN
*(San Francisco, CA USA)*

Untitled 4 song 7" EP, 1992
  Hillsdale Records, USA
*Spend The Night With...* 12 song LP, 1993
  Estrus Records, USA

This is perhaps the most appropriately named band in this book. "Trash" is a perfect description for this trio's combination of '50s sleaze clothing, minimalist garage-surf music and general kitschy atmosphere.

Their four song EP is a pretty cool little slice of distorted mood, with Elka "Kitten Kaboodle's" twangey reverbed guitar at the fore of the mono proceedings. All the tracks are instrumentals, with

the crude recording aiding the period-perfect aural reproduction. In a move of absolute low-brow taste, I recommend this disc fully to anyone who loves surf or hot rod music — as well as chicks in fishnet stockings.

Their debut LP adds some really screechy vocals to the instrumental mess. In a way I just gotta admire such awful crooning on a track like "Perversion" — God, maybe I'm getting *hip* or something. Naw, I probably just don't want to deal with three angry **Trashwomen.**

Says Shane "Pure Filth" White in the debut LP liner notes, *"I never saw a band argue as much as **The Trashwomen**. They can make a fuss about anything. Like what to wear on stage, what songs to play, who looks better than who, etc. Just like little brats. But that's half their charm. Same thing with their sloppy stage show. No matter how much they practiced, they were always fucking up. Kitten would be drunk and ready to vomit. Lead Pedal*

**213**

would be telling silly jokes to annoy the audience, and Boom would threaten them both if they didn't behave."

I really have a limited attention span for most of this no-fi recording stuff — like **The Mummies** — but for some unknown reason I really like **The Trashwomen**'s version of garbage-surf.

As White says, *"And as far as the dreadful quality recordings on this album, too bad."*

There's lots more of this **Trashwomen** garbage out there that I haven't heard yet — and I know that I'll get suckered into tracking it all down.

Ah, the price of being "hip."

## THE TREATMENT
*(U.K.)*

This is one of the first of the early '80s English bands delving into the psychedelic rubble. They have at least two 45s, "Stampout Mutants" b/w "Doncha Know" (1981), "Feeling Like A Ghost" b/w "Rowing Boat" (1987) — plus an LP entitled simply *Treatment,* released in 1989. I found their debut 45 to be only marginally interesting — though definitely strange with the song's title repeatedly menacingly by several disturbed vocalists. Their subsequent releases are supposedly very psychedelic, and very rare as well.

## THE TREBELS
*(San Diego, CA USA)*

"That's You" b/w "That Girl" 45, 1988
Whaaam Records, USA

Here's another fine San Diego roots R&B band, playing with a deliberate reverence for the genre and its stylings. In a way, they're like the infamous **Tell Tale Hearts** without the garage influence or Vox organ. That's certainly not a bad sound at all, as their 45 attests.

Former **Heart** Mike Stax joined the band in 1991 — which then evolved into the similar sounding **Hoods**.

## THE TRILOBITES
*(Australia)*

I admit a taste for well made power-punk-pop, and that's exactly what **The Trilobites** deliver. "Venus In Leather" is an infectious pop-rock nugget, and "American TV" is another power garage anthem that never lets up

**2I4**

— right down to the fake ending. These mojos know how to turn up the tempo without letting it slush into a hardcore blur, add in plenty of **Ramones** buzz, but retain a pop edge — just like the best of those original garage punks did in '66.

This couldn't be called '60s "revivalist" music, but it certainly takes all the best of that genre and squeezes in some modern energy as well.

I think there are several vinyl releases out there from the mid 1980s.

## THE TRIP
*(Queens, NY/San Francisco, CA USA)*

6 song unreleased cassette, 1985(?)
no label, USA (demo)

**The Trip** mesmerized listeners on the 1985 *Garage Sale* compilation cassette, and with the infectious "Stick Like Glue" on the second *Battle Of The Garages.* I thought that was it for recorded output, however, before stumbling on this half-dozen cassette demo. I'm not sure but I believe the bulk of these songs were recorded in San Francisco, the city where the entire band apparently moved to in 1983.

They pick up where "Stick Like Glue" left off, with plenty of reverbed vocals, jangley 12 string git ("I Wanna Make You Mine"), and mesmerizing garage-folk-psych ("Too Many Times"). The quality of these tracks is really stunning considering that I heard absolutely nothing from this band other than their two compilation appearances.

I remember in the late 1980s picking up an arty magazine in San Francisco, and *wham!,* there was **The Trip,** in their black leather, **Beatle** boots and Vox guitars. Someone must have picked up on this band's distinct flavor of garage-pop, and now I'm wondering about any other vinyl releases.

A band this good must have at least put something out themselves!

## TRISTAN AND THE ROSEWOOD
*(Nuremberg, Germany)*

A psychedelic-pop band with at least two LPs: 1989's *Drop The Job* on Herbe Scherbe Records and the 1990 *Jumble* LP on Musical Tragedies.

The two tracks I've heard were finely crafted organ and vocal dominated tunes with some nicely placed fuzz guitar. "Leaving All Behind" has a **Broken Jug** mood to it, while "I Got You" is an upbeat echo-laden rocker. Both lead me to believe that their two LPs are worth the search.

## THE TRODDS
(Boston, MA USA)

The first couple of 45s on Stanton Park Records were by this combo (1981 & 1982), producing what their label describes as *"weird psych reminiscent of **Hendrix**, early **Pink Floyd** and some more insane '60s bands."*

## TROUBLE
(Torino, Italy)

*In The Eye Of The Storm* private cass., 1990
*See Your City* CD-only, 1992
   Boom Records, Belgium

Reportedly a psych folk act.

## TRUE WEST
(Sacramento, CA USA)

*True West* 5 song 12" EP, 1983
   Bring Out Your Dead Records, USA

This highly-rated band would release several other discs, but none attained the energy or worth of their debut. The band released the 12" EP themselves, and caused quite a stir in the underground scene as it began to sell in good numbers. (This original issue, as well as a 45 containing two of its songs, are now very rare.)

It was a confident debut, as the mere five tracks displayed a powerful yet mysterious group of newcomers. The pulsating "Steps To The Door" opens up the disc, followed by the manic "I'm Not Here." Things settle a bit for the more melodic yet distorted "Hollywood Holiday," with the guitar-fueled sound of the band taking center stage.

Side Two contributes a steady version of **Pink Floyd**'s "Lucifer Sam," with **The Dream Syndicate**'s Steve Wynn adding some guitar — he also co-produced the EP. The moody guitar psych closes out with "It's About Time," achieving what any band would want, leaving the listener wanting more. The brevity of the disc is precisely the reason why the record is so appealing — it gives a taste, and makes one look forward to their next release. The band could not muster its original energy for subsequent releases, however, and degenerated into nothing more than a competent bar band.

I saw this first-hand in 1985, as **True West** played to a packed college-aged audience. The distorted duel-guitar stylings of the EP wore painfully thin in a club setting, with Gavin Blair's vocals also unimpressive. The entire band lacked the power of its early recordings; this show was an instructional illumination on the difference between the recording studio and concert stage!

Their less distinctive, more self-indulgent "rock" material also contributed to the band's general lack of spark, and the crowd reacted accordingly: they left or sat quietly as the band obliviously wanked on!

Still, their initial vinyl outing is a brilliant look at a band that had nothing further to create. Guitarist Russ Tolman would go onto to a solo career, but the fire was obviously out for **True West**.

## THE TRYFLES
(New York, NY USA)

"(Had Enough Of) Your Lies" b/w
   "When I See That Guy" 45, 1985
*The Tryfles* 11 song LP, 1986
   Midnight Records, USA

What a great name and look for a garage band, and these cats and kittens also had sounds equal to their style.

"(Had Enough Of) Your Lies" is the definitive "boyfriend/girlfriend cheatin'" song, with snotty exclamations, twangy lead git and enough garage atmosphere to fog anyone's glasses.

One of the best of N.Y.C.'s first wave of garage-niks, **The Tryfles** reportedly suffered from internal conflicts, though they did manage to stay together for more than two years. They apparently weren't talking to each other very much by the time that it came to finish their lone LP, but the results don't show the strain. (I seem to remember that this LP was also delayed because the first final mixes were accidentally destroyed.)

**The Tryfles** LP picks up where the 45 left off, with more failed relationships and girl/guy troubles a-plenty. Band originals dominate the disc in fine order, and the cover of "What A Way To Die" is also inspired fun.

Another plus for these folks is their great logo, gig posters and cartoon impressions of themselves, completing a fanciful picture of one of New York's best-ever garage outfits. Peter Stuart would move onto **The Headless Horsemen**, and the other members floated off to other projects as well.

## TUESDAY'S CHILDREN
(Los Angeles, CA USA)

Nothing known.

**215**

## THE TUMORS
*(Tucson, AZ USA)*

This mainly punk band evolved into **The Cryptics**, whose story you'll amazingly find in the "C" section. Their crude four song 1986 demo showed the band beginning to move in the general garage direction. They also had a video for their song "River Bottom."

## THE TURKEE NECKS
*(Limoge, France)*

13 song demo cassette, 1993
    private pressing, France

I won't soon forget my time with **The Turkee Necks**. It was Halloween night, 1992, and my band was headlining a show at the "John Lennon Auditorium" in Limoge, France. **The Turkee Necks** not only set up the show and put together the great surfing-Frankenstein decorations, they also performed a startlingly crude and exhilarating opening set.

The mix of English and French musicians attacked the stage with fervor, ripping through originals like "Goober Honey" and "Cold Turkee" with spittle and unbounded energy. Their keyboardist Olivier topped off the unlikely combo — his mussed hair and glasses perched precariously on his nose — while carrying his Farfisa Compact organ on his back as he played!

Olivier later appeared on stage during **The Overcoat**'s set, wearing a George Bush rubber mask and clutching a bottle of whiskey. He promptly stumbled into the guitar amplifier, toppling it in a heap.

Other members of **The Turkee Necks** later tackled me in a giant pile on stage, where one of them (temporarily) stole my watch! (Strangely, this was also the first of several shows where audience members would expose their private parts to us and the audience.)

If you have ever heard the '66 classic "Wildman," then you should understand the undeniably wonderful sound of **The Turkee Necks**. I believe that several slabs of vinyl were slated for release in 1994 and '95, but I'm unsure if they appeared.

I'd love to have another Halloween night with **The Turkee Necks**.

## THE TWEEDS
*(Massachusetts USA)*

"Part Of The Game" b/w "No More" 45, 1985
    Arf Arf Records, USA

"Part Of The Game" is a pleasant **Beatles**-cum-pop dance number from 1985, complete with smooth background vocals, a fake sitar solo (!) and timely organ splashes. The whole thing just doesn't jell completely, though, leaving an incomplete taste in my mouth. This was yet another Erik Lindgren production, and fits in with the eclectic slew of records he released on the always odd (and interesting) Arf Arf label. Lindgren even wrote the 45's flip, "No More," for The Tweeds.

## 28th DAY
*(San Francisco, CA USA)*

A fabulous jangley six song 12" EP appeared on Enigma in 1985, not really in the retro category except for the classic pop guitar mentality and fine vocals.

"25 Pills" leads off the disc, and is a good slice of **Plimsouls** meets **The Rain Parade** or **Dream Syndicate**. I believe that this EP was later re-released as a CD with extra tracks, and vocalist Barbara Manning went on to a solo career of some note.

## TWENTY FOUR HOURS
*(Pescara, Italy)*

"Switch For Madness" b/w "Foreign Lands"
    split 45 in *Urlo Magazine #2*, 1992
*The Smell Of The Rainy Air* LP, 1991
    private pressing, Italy

Reportedly a progressive psych band.

## THE 27 VARIOUS
*(Minneapolis, MN USA)*

*Hi!* 10 song LP, 1987
*Yes, Indeed* 12 song LP, 1989
"Granny Smith" b/w "E Too D" 45, 1990
    Susstones Records, USA
*Approximately* 11 song LP, 1990
*Fine* 12 song CD, 1992
    Clean Records, USA

Minneapolis was often called an alternative-music mecca for the 1980s, but few truly interesting sounds escaped from that cold Midwest burg. **The 27 Various** lived up to the city's reputation, however, slowly building a recorded output of finely crafted and intelligent records.

Starting as a recording-only duo of Ed Ackerson and Jed Mayer, the debut *Hi!* LP was a surprise in every regard. Touches of **Syd Barrett, The Beatles** and **Pink Floyd** buzzed through the disc, all highlighted by Ackerson's sly wit and charmed vocals.

Humor was a key element to the album's appeal, with "The Gormleys Will Miss Me" and "Furry Creatures From The Forest" the most obviously lovable examples. This 1987 indie release was

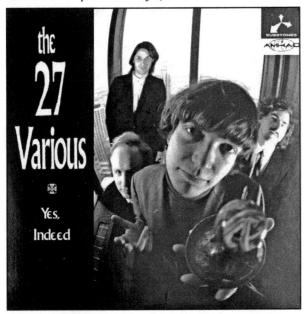

almost completely ignored, even by the underground, but was certainly one of the best records of that year.

The duo added Jay Orf on bass and Jerry Lefkowitz on drums, and proceeded to take their pop-psych vision to the stage. The subsequent LP, *Yes, Indeed* showed more of the first LP's charm, plus a tendency to add some pedestrian "rock" material to the mixture.

Purely psychedelic pop like "Shine That Smile" and the title track more than made up for the misses, yet a bit of editing would have made this a stunning follow-up. It's an illustration, perhaps, of an LP that would have served the listener best as an EP.

This author played one show with them during this period, and they came across much more forcefully on stage than on record. That's to be expected, I suppose, but it was gratifying to see that the band understood how to make pop music and also — on stage — rock music. They were also genuinely good people.

Orf was missing by the time that *Approximately* appeared, yet the band's

sound was intact as a trio. Once again the band strayed off into a few dead ends of hard rock, but their psych-pop efforts were better than ever. String arrangements and a variety of guitar sounds helped to flesh out the sound more than in the past, and the band's confidence in its material was obviously high.

I suppose I can even forgive them their stealing (and re-titling) of **The Byrds'** "Everyone's Been Burned," though I suppose they thought no one would notice. I did.

The *Fine* album found Ackerson searching for direction, and landing somewhere between attempted grunge and hard rock. There's little of the charm, precision, or songwriting skill that made the earlier efforts standouts.

The 1980s were not exactly bursting with imaginative, melodic and engaging psych-pop, but **The 27 Various** at times became masters at the genre. Throw out a few of the missed attempts, and the remainder is some of the most interesting pop music to fly out of Minneapolis — or anywhere else.

## THE TWISTED
*(New York, NY USA)*

"She's Wycked" b/w "The Thing" 45, 1984
    Midnight Records, USA

Orin Portnoy of **The Outta Place** and his brother Elan Portnoy of **The Fuzztones** recorded this one-off 45 on a home tape recorder. Very crude and moody, with the A-side a fuzzed-up **Fuzztones**-like rocker and the flip a slower, echo-filled instrumental of screams and horror movie imagery. Both tracks were included on **The Fuzztones** *Creatures That Time Forgot* compilation LP, so don't fret if you can't find the original 45.

## TYME ELIMENT
*(Huddersfield, Yorkshire, England)*

**The Tyme Eliment** began in March '87 after the apparent demise of the **Melaroonie Daddies** ( which reformed at the end of the '80s). They were a guitar, organ and three chord '60s punk band which featured Simon Harvey on lead guitar & vocals (who later joined the **Beatpack**). They had two cuts on the *Raw Cuts British Compilation* LP from their three song demo: the tracks "Tell Me" and "Strangelove."

**217**

## TYRNAROUND
*(Melbourne, Australia)*

*Colour Your Mind* 4 song 12" EP, 1987
    Cleopatra Records, Australia
"Want Of A Rhyme" b/w "Hello Or Goodbye" 45, 1987
*Succeeds Where Daylight Fails* 11 song LP & CD, 1990
"Uncle Sydney" b/w "Uncle Jack" 45, 1990
*Go Back* 19 song CD, 1992
    Polyester Records, Australia

**The Tyrnaround** could be considered one of Australia's best bands from any era. Their deft combination of flower-period **Beatles, Pink Floyd** and obscure underground '60s sounds is almost without equal.

They began playing in late 1985, though their vinyl debut wouldn't appear until a year and a half later. The *Colour Your Mind* title tracks is an

### *TYRNAROUND, 1986*

anthemic ode to psychedelic pop, full of powerful imagery and melodic turns. This track alone should preserve **The Tyrnaround**'s reputation for generations to come.

Their subsequent output found the band polishing their musical chops without losing sight of their psych-pop intentions. Their *Succeeds Where Daylight Fails* is full of innovative melodies and production touches, as well as catchy, memorable original songs.

*Go Back* showcases this Australian quintet's most notable moments in one coherent CD package. This retrospective might seem superfluous to the uninitiated, but even the most unsuspecting curiosity seeker should be pleasingly startled with

**The Tyrnaround**'s brand of expertly realized paisley-pop. This band also raises questions about the subjective concept of what exactly is "pop" amidst the disposable grunge of the '90s — and the band's compositions are well crafted musical conundrums.

These Australians define their pop as the by-products of melodic psychedelia, garage and folk, ingredients which all blend beautifully on *Go Back*. Soaring harmonies and beatific guitars chime throughout "Of Girl", "Want Of A Rhyme" and "Keys And Chains". Mind-warbling keyboards and warm engaging arrangements highlight the more trippy selections, including the masterful "Carroll By Candlelight" and "Hello Or Goodbye."

The appeal of the 19 track, 71 minute collection is perfectly balanced between the head and the feet. It never veers too far from the cerebral, while maintaining its toe-tapping quality, along with a melodic edge that some lads from Liverpool introduced quite a few summers ago.

In the final analysis it just doesn't matter how one defines the sounds here, because **The Tyrnaround** will succeed on whatever record store shelf they're shuffled onto.

### UG AND THE CAVEMEN
*(U.K.)*

A reportedly fine 1987 LP on Media Burn Records exists; yet another proud entry into the "Garage Band Name Hall of Fame."

## THE UGLY THINGS
*(Bologna, Italy)*

Untitled 4 song 7" EP, 1986
    Electric Eye Records, Italy

The track "Nobody's Son" is also on a split 45 in *Lost Trails #3*, 1986.

Someone in Italy told me that a member of **The Ugly Things** has taken some shots at this author and my band in some Italian music magazines. I won't take this opportunity to hit back — because this EP is a very good garage disc.

It very much reminds me of the **Unclaimed**'s type of garage rock — simple production based upon reverbed guitar and forceful vocals. "Every Cave Man" comes closest to this archetype, while "You Better Run" adds some organ, odd back-up vocals and tremolo guitar to the mix.

I'm unsure of any other releases, but it would have been interesting to see how this group would have developed from this promising beginning.

## THE ULTRA 5
*(New York, NY USA)*

"It's A Long Way Home" b/w "Sweet Love" 45, 1988
    Ultra 5 Records, USA
"The Bones Walk" b/w "She's The Girl" 45, 1991
    Screaming Apple Records, Germany
*Reincarnation* 12 song LP, 1991
*House Of Fun* 13 song LP & CD, 1992
    Who Stole The Summer Records LP, Greece
*Dead Or Alive* 12 song LP, 1992
    Moon King Records, USA/Mexico

Perhaps there is another 45 on the Greek label Who Stole The Summer.

Video: "Get Out Of My Life Woman," 1989

These creatures in black play slow, slow, moody, murky music; dark psychedelia with a sinister edge. **The Ultra 5** have an immediately identifiable gloomy sound, complete with brooding vocals, fuzzed guitar and a pulsating organ, reportedly owned originally by '60s groovesters **Vanilla Fudge**! They complete the effect with black leather, mini-skirts (on the women) and plenty 'o hair — this is pure garage psych mania, with fuzz to spare.

They began their pounding trip in the summer of 1986, and have been accurately called *"fuzzy garage punk and psychedelia with dark, swirling undertones and authentically trippy organ and droning guitar — a real weird mix that must be heard!,"* by Glynnis Wilson of *Feline Frenzy* magazine.

**THE ULTRA 5, 1988**

Both of their two 45s are essential slabs of slow psych, though most of these tracks also appear on their debut 12" LP. (They also contribute tracks to many cassette comps, and the 1989 **Rolling Stones** "tribute" with the song "Off The Hook" — which is also on the LP.)

The *House Of Fun* CD offered up a lucky 13 new tracks that show a cohesion that was lacking on the debut LP — these sessions were recorded purposely as an LP rather than a collection of singles, and that consistency shows. This is not say that the earlier tracks should be ignored — just that the group demonstrated growth and added proficiency as it went along. A standout track such as "City Of Fire" is the product of a band playing with confidence and experience.

A "live" LP recorded on a jaunt to Mexico is also an interesting artifact for the band, showing the mayhem possible with a responsive audience south of the border.

**The Ultra 5** take the gritty psych-garage of **The Fuzztones** and mix it with the grinding mood of **The Velvet Underground**, yet lose any sense of pretentiousness. This isn't really scary music, it just sounds that way.

Because of its individuality, the band's sound and look are very much an acquired taste. As I've said before, acquire their music and taste something good. It'll take a while to digest, but will make perfect sense as the mood hits you.

## THE UNCLAIMED
*(Los Angeles, CA USA)*

Untitled 4 song 7" EP, 1980
    Moxie Records, USA
*Primordial Ooze Flavored Unclaimed* 6 song 12" EP, 1982
    Hysteria Records, USA
*The Unclaimed/Thee Fourgiven/Lee Joseph —
Rock and Hard Rolls: Live in Europe 1987*
    16 song LP, Dionysus Records, USA, 1988
    (also includes 3 song 7" EP w/**Lee Joseph, Thee Fourgiven** and **Unclaimed**)

*"The Unclaimed was founded in my apartment in April of 1979. We were the first to really go all-out with the hardcore '60s sounds. Maybe at that time (there were also) The Chesterfield Kings or The Droogs, but The Unclaimed were the only ones really making a point of doing that kind of stuff. This was, of course, long before is was considered hip or O.K. ... well, you may not know this, but every city in this country has (now) got some kind band doing this stuff. I mean, you go to Nashville or Minneapolis or St. Louis — Athens, Georgia! — Memphis or Jackson, Mississippi — every town has got at least one '60s band."* — Sid Griffin, *Creem Magazine*, March 1986

**The Unclaimed** were certainly one of the very first and most influential groups of the garage resurgence. Eventual **Long Ryder** Sid Griffin was in the original lineup along with main-man Shelley Ganz, and a plethora of other notable musicians would also journey through the band's ranks.

Their first EP was a crude but spirited ode to the sound of '66, with Griffin's "Deposition Central" a particularly interesting lysergic moment.

The band — without Sid Griffin — would have its black-turtleneck **Music Machine** look together by their next vinyl outing, a six track 12" EP titled *Primordial Ooze Flavored*. Ganz is firmly at center stage — especially with the **Seeds**-ish "Walk On The Water" and the stand-out "Things in The Past."

The production on this second release is a bit clearer but no less authentic, with Ganz adhering strictly to the garage band formula of fuzz and Farfisa. (The original issue of this EP is very rare, but it was later re-issued in Europe with a completely different cover.) For this record the band was filled by Rich Coffee, Ray Flores and Matt Roberts — who all gave Ganz his strongest backing to date. Two other excellent tracks from this period also showed up on a *Lost Trails Magazine* 7" in Italy.

Ganz was apparently so single-minded about his '66 mission, however, that he eventually drove the rest of the band to quit and form the more eclectically influenced trio **Thee Fourgiven**. Undaunted, Ganz put together several other floating lineups of musicians (including **Yard Trauma**'s **Lee Joseph**), even managing to get the band to Europe on tour.

The tour was just under way, however, when Ganz quit and flew home after a few shows; **Lee Joseph** told me that Ganz thought that life on the road was "too tough." The remainder of the band continued on without him, and this is

documented on the *Rock And Hard Rolls* live LP, which ironically also includes **Lee Joseph** solo tracks as well as **Thee Fourgiven**.

The last **Unclaimed** vinyl was released several years later by Ganz under the band name **Atilla & The Huns**. It is a modestly interesting effort described elsewhere in this book.

**The Unclaimed**'s greatest legacy seems to be that they were one of the absolute earliest 1980s bands to rekindle interest in '60s garage sounds. For this their high place in garage history is assured and deserved.

Recalls Vicki Peterson of **The Bangles** in the March 1986 *Creem Magazine*, *"The first time I came across anyone who was remotely like me (in the '60s) sense was when Debi (Peterson) and I were playing pre-**Bangles** (on the same bill) with this band called **The Unclaimed** at some dive in Santa Monica. We didn't know what to expect; when they came on-stage with their black turtlenecks and started doing 'Hey Little Girl' we just melted."*

## THE UNCLAIMED WYLD TONES
(Belgium)

Nothing known.

## UNCLE SIDNEY
(Pittsburgh, PA USA)

Glynnis Wilson says, *"They were featured in Feline Frenzy #5. A psychedelic band with a very original, sophisticated sound which was at times routed as equally in the '60s as the '70s. They featured Greg who had been in **The Podz** plus three other members. They covered songs like 'Treacle People' by **U.F.O.**, 'Save My Soul' by **Wimple Winch**, and 'Gentle As It May Seem' by **Iron Butterfly**. A demo tape was made in 1989 but nothing ever became of it."*

## THE UNDERTAKERS
(Sweden)

*The Greatest Stories Ever Told*
8 song 12" EP, 1985
Midnight Records, USA

There was a slew of promising Swedish garage bands in the mid-'80s, but not much was really heard from **The Undertakers.** They did manage to put out this EP on Midnight, though it hardly shows off the band to its best advantage. The record owes as much to sloppy '70s Ramones-punk as to garage punk, but really doesn't do great justice to either genre. I do like their trashy version of "I Wanna Come Back From The World Of L.S.D," though — it's this disc's shining moment. Maybe I'll go throw this one on the stereo and give it another try.

## THE UNDERTAKERS
*(Eugene, OR USA)*

"Time Machine" b/w "Lookout" 45, 1992
  Tombstone Records, USA

The A-side here is one of those genre-defining moments, where the Vox guitars and organ are perfectly presented alongside spittle-dripping vocals and a thudding rhythm section. Delivered in beautiful mono, no less, "Time Machine" is a nouveau garage "classic" — a term that is always overused but no less accurate this time around.

The mayhem doesn't lift for the flip; a thumping screamer somewhat reminiscent of **The Ultra 5**. Organist Pat Yonally should especially be picked

out for commendations — his key tickling is the highlight of this all-around stellar garage outfit.

These **Undertakers** — not to be confused with several other groups from several eras with that name — also contribute two excellent tracks to the *Fieldburn* compilation CD of Oregon acts. Woefully, I don't think anything else has ever materialized.

No matter, this 45 has earned its place in the "Garage Hall Of Fame."

## THE UNHEARD
*(Wollongong, Australia)*

Untitled 3 song 7" EP, 1987
  Kavern 7 Records, Australia

Ahh, the virtues of the simple garage group: a few guitar riffs, some snarled vocals, a tambourine, and some sprouting hair to obscure one's vision. **The Unheard** utilize all of these time-proven tools on their sole vinyl outing, a three song slab 'o fuzz.

You have to love a band that puts a picture of a fuzz box on the front picture sleeve, and also makes sure that the negative "don't" appears in all three song titles — "Don't You Stand In My Sunshine," "I Don't Believe" and "I Don't Want Anything But You." Screams and fuzz dominate the disc's flip side, along with some expertly planted organ and snot.

They also planted four songs on a *Born Loser Magazine* compilation cassette, which include all the fuzz, echo, crazy guitar leads and primitive sound production that makes **The Unheard** an Australian benchmark for crude excellence. I believe a 15 song cassette-only release called *Fuzz Wild* also has made the rounds, though I haven't seen or heard it.

You can smash **Madonna, Springsteen, Phil Collins** and **Michael Jackson** all in a bucket — give me more from **The Unheard**.

And speaking of being unheard, here are a few more Australian combos that I've been told are in the '60s garage-psych tradition — but remain unknown and unheard by me: **The Feends, The Kryptonics, Sunnyboys, Girl Monstar, Spliffs, Swamp Monsters,** and the wonderfully named **Pineapples From The Dawn Of Time.**

## THE UNHEARD OF
*(Waukesha, WI USA)*

"Stranger" b/w "What About Me" 45, 1991
"I Will Always Love You" b/w "Erratic Love" 45, 1994
  Rocket Reducer Records, USA

I mistakenly put the debut 7" on the turntable at the expected 45 RPM — and maybe I should have left it there — the two murky tunes drag at the correct 33 1/3 speed.

The dingy Xeroxed sleeve tips off that this is a crude home made recording, and perhaps the photo of Vox amps and guitars prepared me for a different experience — the results are heavier, drearier, dirgier and less interesting than I prefer.

The A-side drags on for a numbing 6:30, while the more promising flip clocks in at half that time.

It uses the fuzz more effectively, and the odd recording ambiance reminds me of that classic '60s garager anthem "Blackout at Gretley" by **Gonn**. "What About Me" doesn't elevate up to that song's stature, but the *recording quality* is similar.

The second 45 has a bit more flavor, and I especially like the Vox keyboard wheezings on "I Will Always Love You."

The band says, *"The Unheard Of uses 'Vintage Vox' equipment (unlike modern reproduction) to achieve their unique sound. This is not a retro band nor some kind of attempt to bring back the past!"*

I know that this foursome played at least one gig — they included the record release flyer with their first 7".

## THE UNHINGED
(U.K.)

I believe this might be former members of **The Offhooks**.

## THE UNINVITED
(Caligari, Italy)

"I Turned Into A Snake" b/w "I Can't Bear With You" 45, 1994
For Monster Records, Italy

Here's some of my favorite stuff: knuckle-dragging punk garage, circa the *Back From The Grave* compilation series. The reverb on the guitar is turned up, the vocalist swallows his microphone and grunts and growls, and the crude aural production captures the proceedings beautifully.

I especially like the rattle sound at the end of "I Turned Into A Snake." Hey, this noise couldn't be any more unpretentious and fun.

## THE UNITED STATES OF EXISTENCE
(Baltimore, MD USA)

"Anything Goes" b/w "Makin' My Scene" 45, 1984
*The Collection* 16 song CD, 1994
  U.S. Fidelity Sounds Records, USA
*Introducing...* 11 song LP, 1986
  Bam Caruso Records, U.K.

Bam Caruso also released a promo 7" in 1986.

The garage/psychedelic revival was almost single-handedly signaled by the **U.S.E.**'s "Return To The Psychedelic," the lead-off track on the landmark 1981 *Battle Of The Garages* compilation album.

That brilliant slice of fuzzadelia sits comfortably on their *Collection* CD next to the band's entire 1986 *Introducing...* LP, plus various compilation and previously-unreleased tracks.

This really wasn't a performing outfit at all, but a recording project organized by organist Bob Tiefenwert and guitarist Paul Rieger. They added the boyish vocals of Dennis Davison and the solid drumming of Gary Schwartz, then sat in their basement studio layering with painstaking care their sole LP, *Introducing...*

Dripping with sitar, tambourine, echo and harpsichord, this colourful gem shines with the light once provided by groups like **The Electric Prunes** and **Strawberry Alarm Clock**. Rieger even managed to corral a few of the original **Association** to lend some angelic background vocals to the effort.

Drummer Schwartz once told me that he watched in amazement as these **Association** members added a sense of magic to the proceedings. Their contribution certainly adds a sheen to this expertly assembled production of flower-power fun.

This Baltimore amalgamation of paisley Nehru jackets somehow bridges the best of **The Blues Magoos** and **The Association**, then adds their own modern sensibility.

Davison and Schwartz would go onto **The Playground**, later relocated to Los Angeles and renamed **The Jigsaw Seen**. Elements of the **U.S.E.** magic could be found in this later group, though admittedly in smaller doses.

**The United States Of Existence** remain one of my favorite flower-pop groups of all time.

## THE UNKIND
(Germany)

Nothing known.

## UNKNOWN SOLDIERS
(Portland, OR USA)

At least one late 1980s 45 exists; an unsatisfying cross of some guitar jangle and **Doors** bombast. I believe an LP is out as well, though the only two tracks from the band that I remember are the unremarkable "Ambulance" and "You Fall Down."

The **Doors** comparison probably comes from the singer's incredibly low toned voice, but he sounds more like **T.S.O.L.**'s gothic-punk vocalist than the Lizard King. "Unremarkable" would be the best adjective I could apply.

**222**

## UNTAMED YOUTH
*(Columbia, MO USA)*

Several LPs exist: *Some Kinda Fun* and *More Gone Gassers* on Norton Records, plus some 45s in a frat-rock surf and trash style. **Untamed Youth** is highly recommended in some circles, though I haven't found any of their product yet.

## THE UNTOLD FABLES
*(Los Angeles, CA USA)*

*Every Mother's Nightmare* 13 song LP, 1985
Untitled 4 song 7" EP, 1987
*Aesop's Apocalypse* 11 song LP, 1989
   Dionysus Records, USA
Untitled 4 song 7" EP, 1987
   Mystery Scene Records, Germany

"When I finally got to see the fabled **Untold Fables**...I was amazed! Real sloppy, real loose, barely tuned (they had to use a pair of pliers to tune the bass), mildly competent, but with a swinging teenage energy and completely right attitude! Then on April 20, 1985, they became my

### *THE UNTOLD FABLES, 1986*

absolute #1 band. They were headlining the Cavern Club and something came together and jelled like never before. They were wailing, screaming, rockin' like unbridled motherfuckers! I was awestruck! I can't remember ever seeing a more high energy show, including hard core punk bands!"

   — Rich Coffee, from a press release, 1989.

That assessment sounds accurate, because I wrote in my 1986 journal, "It was a steamy summer night in Los Angeles, and The Cavern Club was packed. In one corner a wyld teenage combo was blowing out what sounded like **The Yardbirds** on speed — it was **The Untold Fables**! The crowd pulsated with sweat, and the band destroyed our ears with their mutant

Orange County sound."
   I also talked with vocalist Paul Carey in 1986:

TG: Are you "every mother's nightmare," like the title of your LP?
PC: *No, I get along well with my parents, but John our guitar player has trouble, because his father's a minister. John's probably the straightest guy in the band, but he has kinda long hair, and his older brother was an acid head in the '60s. So when John bought a pair of **Beatle** boots, his father said "You're wearing those 'acid shoes'! Oh no! What's wrong?!? Cut your hair!"*

   **The Untold Fables** are now rightfully remembered as one of the best L.A. 1980s garage bands. Their debut LP is their best moment, but all of their records stand the test of time. Their former members also remain involved in other various garage musical projects, proving that their love of the music was not merely a passing fad.

## THE UPPER CRUST
*(Vancouver, BC Canada)*

Alan Wright of the **14th Wray** hooked up with garage radio host The Amazing Larry and a couple other kindred cavemen for this 1992-93 studio project. A dozen song rough demo exists, and a half dozen crude fuzz and Farfisa tunes were recorded in a "real" studio, then sent to this author for a final mix.
   All seem gratified by the results, especially on the band's theme song, "We're The Upper Crust," the staccato "You Creep Me Out," and a fine rendition of that Northwest standard "Hang Up." This is true '66 fuzz punk at its best, with spittle, gritty determination and a lot of atmosphere and spirit.
   These tracks surprisingly haven't seen the light of day — yet.

## RONNI URINI & THE LAST POETS
*(Vienna, Austria)*

Several LPs and 45s from the 1980s and early '90s exist of this ex-**Vogue** member, all of which have been recommended highly to me — though the only trace of them that I've found has been a **Stooges** cover song from a 1986 10" EP.

## USELESS BOYS
*(Italy)*

A demo exists of this band, which later became the late 1980s' **The Birdmen Of Alkatraz**.

## VACANT STARE CASE
*(Richmond, VA USA)*

This was a very sloppy band in the **Chocolate Watchband** mode, with an EP rumored to be out in 1991, though I have no concrete proof of its existence. When I saw them in 1989 they prided themselves on their vintage equipment and clothing, but failed to accomplish much musically. File this band under "style but little substance."

## VAMPIRE LOVERS
*(Australia)*

The 45 "Sweethearts Blown Mindless" on Rubber Records is reportedly excellent. It's probably from the late 1980s.

## VEGETABLE MEN
*(Pescara, Italy)*

"Van Gogh's Blues Bus" b/w "It's A Reflex" 45, 1988
*It's Time To Change* LP, 1989
   Toast Records, Italy

Reportedly a psych band.

## THE VIBES
*(U.K.)*

*Inner Wardrobes Of Your Mind* 4 song 12" EP, 198?
*What's Inside* 11 song LP, 1984?
   Chainsaw Records, U.K.

I picked up a 45 by this band by mistake, thinking it was a new one by **The Vipers**! Very English trash rock is found on the 45 instead, with their other releases in a more garage vein.

The *Inner Wardrobes* EP begins with a cryptic voice saying *"This might be the answer you're looking for,"* which leads into the heavily reverbed and moody garage tune "I Hear Noises." The EP also contains a frantic cover of **The Outcasts**' "I'm In Pittsburgh And It's Rainin'," and the wackily titled "Hasil Adkins In My Head" — an homage to the eccentric rock-a-billy guitarist, I'm sure. This isn't essential stuff, but more engaging than that 45 I bought as a mistake.

The LP contains a cover of the garage anthem "Ain't No Friend Of Mine," but doesn't grab me overall as the "must hear" that some fans had suggested.

**The Vibes** would later become **The Purple Things**, with several other 12" releases.

## VIBRASONIC
*(East Sussex, UK)*

self-titled 9 song LP, 1995
   Yep! Records

**The Electric Prunes** found the keys to a time machine, and dialed up the exact time in 1985 when **The Dukes Of Stratosphear** were recording their *25 O'Clock* 12". **Syd Barrett** was there, of course, and together they then transported to a 1968 session at Abbey Road studios with **The Beatles**. George Martin handed the master tape to **Syd**, then he headed back through time to 1995 — and the **Vibrasonic** LP was the result.

None of the above actually happened, except for the LP itself. Any listener who enjoys the aforementioned influences will no doubt *need* this debut longplayer. It's mainly the effort of "Professor Vic Vibrato and "Dr. Tremelo Jones" — along with a number of guest musicians. "Tijuana Marijuana," "The Perpetual Motion Machine," and "The Unloved Insane" are all brilliant efforts.

The lysergic cover art is the topper for this freaked-out, sitar laced pop-psych explosion. I'm sure that there will be more to come from **Vibrasonic**. The time machine is warming up now.

## VICE BARONS
*(Belgium)*

untitled 4 song 7" EP, 1994
   Demolition Derby Records, Belgium

I think there are some other records from the **Vice Barons** floating around somewhere. If this one EP is any indication, then they're worth the effort to find.

**The Barons** mix surf and grit together into their own instrumental formula. Tracks such as "Suck-O-Rama" and "Thunderpussy" (along with the stripper on the picture sleeve) show the band's amorous intentions, and the twangy tunes live up to the promise of vice.

The instrumental form gained monumental steam by 1995, and bands such as **The Vice Barons** show why it can be such sinful fun.


## VIETNAM VETERANS
*(France)*

*On The Right Track Now* 12 song LP, 1983
*Green Peas* live double LP, 1985
*In Ancient Times* LP, 1986
*Catfish Eyes And Tales* LP, 1987
*The Days Of Pearly Spencer* LP, 1988
   Way Back/Music Maniac Records, Germany
*Crawfish For The Notary* LP, 1984
   Lolita Records, France

Many hard-to-find LPs exist with most of them re-issued by the ever vigilant Music Maniac Records, which also has three LPs out involving former **Vietnam Veteran** Mark Enbatta: *Hidden Passions* (1987), Lucas Trouble's *Temple Gates* (1987), and **The Vietnam Chain**'s *Susmola Beat* (1990). This last LP is a joint project of **Vietnam Veterans** personnel and the band **The Daisy Chain**.

**The Vietnam Veterans** is highly rated among many European fans. I found their debut LP to be of interest, but not of the earth-shattering stature that I had been led to believe. I haven't seen or heard any of their other considerable output.

So rather than leave you with what some would think is a lukewarm assessment, I'll let the band itself share their attitude from the liner notes of their debut *On The Right Track Now* LP:

*"This is what rock'n'roll is when it's played by the right people, not 'musicians' but human beings. The V.V.s are bored by most of the neo-garage bands. Psychedelia ain't a fuckin' dance craze, folks! It's a fuckin' way of life! Did you ever take a real fuckin' trip in your life? What do you believe in? You're just fuckin' squares, kids. ... The Vietnam Veterans just don't care about styles. They'd be psychedelic even if they'd*

**225**

*play tango."*
There's nothing I can add to that. As **The Veterans** would say, *"flash on!"*


## VIEWS
*(Brescia, Italy)*

*Namby Pamby* 12" EP, 1988
   Tramite Records, Italy
*Mummycat The World #2* LP, 1989
   Crazy Mannequin Records, Italy

Reportedly psych pop.


## VILE CHERUBS
*(Washington, D.C. USA)*

*Post Humorous* 9 song LP, 1988
   Dischord Records, USA

The *Post Humorous* LP is probably the strangest record on the mostly hardcore Dischord label. It was purposely released with a "stock" pre-printed LP cover — like the generic gospel or country LPs that hick bands have pressed up — but with some additional silk-screened additions. This helped give the LP a very weird ambiance — along with the music, of course, which is chaotic garage with a slight arty feel.

While the band lists an impressive array of original '60s gear on the LP's insert, this really shouldn't be considered a strict "revival" effort. It *is* an interesting find for the more adventurous listener.


## THE VINDICATORS
*(Calgary, AL Canada)*

*The Vindicators* 6 song 12" EP, 1989
   OG Records, Canada

Some people have heard enough of groups with Farfisa organ, snotty vocals, harmonica and sloppy enthusiasm. I am obviously not one of those people. Canada's **Vindicators** (not to be confused with several other groups of the same name) haven't tired of that formula either, as their lone 12" EP attests.

They crank up the Vox amps and give us more gasping slabs of teenage garagemania, sounding very much like **The Chesterfield Kings** at times. This is straight-ahead garage trash, which is actually a treasure from my viewpoint.

Regretfully, I don't think anything else materialized from these **Vindicators**.

## THE VINDICATORS
*(France)*

"What's A King Without A Crown" b/w "Crazee Head" 45, 1990
  Ugine, France

The "What's A King Without A Crown" 45 shows off a strong punk sound, destroying the image most French bands have of being light popsters. The 45 is on Banana Hoax Records, one of the best indie label names I've ever come across. I actually once saw it in a juke box in France!

## VIOLENTI LUNE ELETTRICHE
*(Cremona, Italy)*

self-titled LP, 1992
  private pressing

Reportedly a progressive hard psych act.

## THE VIPERS
*(New York, NY USA)*

"Never Alone" b/w "Left Your Hold On Me" 45, 1984
"You're Doin' It Well" b/w "You Don't Believe Me" 45, 1987
*Not So Pretty...Not So New* 20 song cassette, 1988
*How About Somemore* 13 song LP, 1988
  (includes the *Cover To Cover* 7" in the 1st pressing)
  Midnight Records, USA
*Outta The Nest* 12 song LP, 1984
  PVC Records, USA
*Nest In Peace* 16 song LP, 1989
"Got The Hurt" b/w "Hanger 18" 45, 1989
  Skyclad Records, USA

Video: "Never Alone/Tellin' Those Lies/We're Outta Here," 1984, "live" on the USA cable network's *Night Flight* TV show.

**The Vipers** accomplished what many bands have attempted for over 25 years: the melding of **Beatle**sque melody with the power of garage rock.

I remember clearly when I first heard their anthem "Nothing From Today," and how symbolic the song was for budding garage-niks. The vocal harmonies and **Byrds**y guitar tones were dominant, but with an aggressive vital presence. **The Vipers** displayed the long-lost idea that pop music could also have guts; pop music could have emotion and movement and vitality.

"Nothing From Today" was re-recorded for their debut LP, *Outta The Nest,* which became arguably the first major record of the 1980s New York garage

scene. Others had released their own product, but this LP was widely distributed through Jem worldwide.

(The 1989 re-release of *Outta The Nest,* titled *Nest In Peace,* contains four previously unreleased tracks, plus a limited 45 with two more un-released songs. Very cool, indeed, though the sax-drenched instrumentals on the 45 are not **The Vipers** at their best.)

**The Vipers'** combination of pop-psych with muscular arrangements brought back memories of the classic hours of pop-rock, when groups like **The Easybeats** could bring a smile to your face with one simple jangle of a guitar. They were also apparently good stage performers, at one time holding a six month residency at The Dive, hosting the "Thursday Night Cave Stomp."

The avoidance of wimpiness is perhaps **The Vipers'** greatest accomplishment. Countless others have tried to walk similar ground, only to water their "rock" sound down to impotent, lame pop. **The Vipers** always made sure that the correct quotient of "rock" remained.

Their subsequent 45s proved this point, as well as the commercial release of their early demos on cassette. Though rough and embryonic, these demos display a group with boundless creativity, energy and talent. While not meant to be a true follow-up to their debut LP, the *Not So Pretty...* cassette manages to be one of the best garage "albums" of the decade.

That initial vinyl LP did not stir commercial interest, however, and the band was delayed several years before finally releasing *How About Somemore,* an effort that didn't show off its '60s roots as much as the band's ability to write concise, professional pop. "That Ain't Fair," "Try Me" and "Talking To Stone" are the highlights from this somewhat unfocused album, which was issued with several different jacket designs. The free EP contained perfunctory versions of "Psycho" and "I'm Not Like Everybody Else," and is merely a footnote.

The band apparently made it to Europe in the late 1980s — this author found some very funny graffiti left from them in a bunker-like lair where bands stay when playing at one especially bizarre four-story music club in Germany.

The mark of a great song (and band) is an instant memory one can achieve from hearing it years later. "Nothing From Today" — and The Vipers — will remain pleasant fixtures in my memory for eons to come.


## VIV AKAULDREN
(USA)

Heavy weird experimental psychedelia is how I would best describe these cats. They have at least four LPs, including the 1986 *Old Bags & Party Rags*, 1987's *I'll Call You Something*, 1988's *Witness*, and 1990's *Vivian's Fountain*. They also have at least three 45s. I find this material to be a bit "heavy" for my tastes, but some fans rate them highly.


## VIVA SATURN
(San Francisco, CA USA)

Untitled 5 song 12" EP, 1989
*Soundmind* 11 song CD, 1992
  Spirit/Heyday Records, USA

The accepted idea that The Beatle's solo careers were 1/4 as creative as the band as a whole is worthy of debate. Is it fair to compare a solo effort to an earlier collaboration?

This same conundrum is applicable to Viva Saturn — a project of former Rain Parade guitarist/vocalist Steven Roback. Like a solo John Lennon record, for instance, Viva Saturn recalls at times the glories of a former band, but also misses the collaborate discipline which made that band identity so powerful.

The debut 12" collects tracks recorded from 1987-88, and shows Roback experimenting with different styles — while remaining somewhat in the hushed gentle aura made by The Rain Parade. "So Glad" is a microcosm of Roback's success and failure with this record, as it recalls the grandeur of mystery of the Rain Parade's best moments, while also

**227**

veering off inexplicably.

"Remember I'm Dead" is another near-hit, but this all is just missing ... something. The wistfully acoustic "Old World" is probably this disc's most surprisingly good moment, while "Wild Town" sounds remarkably like a late period Rain Parade outtake. It's interesting to note that fellow Parader Will Glenn contributes some violin to the proceedings.

The 1992 *Soundmind* CD is a more upbeat rock affair, described by *Melody Maker* as "*halcyon and euphoric psychedelia disappearing into a haze wash of chiming guitars and blissful singing.*" That's not exactly a misrepresentation, but perhaps on the high end of critical regard. Fellow Rain Parade alum Matt Piucci is along for the ride this time, and his added guitar muscle helps flesh out Roback's ideas and create more of a "band sound" than the solo-song writer ambiance of the debut disc.

The pulsing hypnotic title track is very much in the best Rain Parade tradition, with intertwined howling guitars, a simple shuffling rhythm and the aforementioned "blissful" vocals. The remainder of the disc is well produced, well written and performed — but still lacks some vital spark or part.

I know that with this entry I'm not performing my hype duties as a fan of The Rain Parade. Some writers rave and endorse any and all product — without reservation — from anyone associated with their favorite bands. I'll leave that to some trendy magazines.

I *do* recommend Viva Saturn to listeners, though, especially Rain Parade fans. It's up to them to decide if Roback's solo efforts are 1/4 as creative as his past band as a whole — or if Viva Saturn is better.


## THE VOGUE
(Vienna, Austria)

"Dancing In Trance" b/w "The Frozen Seas Of Io" 45, 1981
  Gig Records, Austria?
"Pill Girl" b/w "Step Inside" 45, 198?
  Paranoia Records, Austria?
*A Doll Spits Cubes* 14 song LP, 1985(?)
*Smoke Gets In Your Eyes* LP, 198?
  Ton Um Ton Records, Austria

This band was totally unknown to me until 1991, and featured Ronnie Urini, who also contributed to the *Trains To Disaster* compilation quite a few years earlier.

I'm unsure of the title of their debut LP, since the label calls it *Live - One of 300*, while the cover says *A Doll Spits Cubes*. Perhaps this is a limited edition of only 300 copies? Also, the inner label states that all but two songs were written by the band, although there are also songs originally written by **The Standells, Kinks** and **Zombies**, among others, credited to the band!

Further investigation finds that the band formed in 1979 — making them one of the first of the resurgent European garage bands. They also have two early 45s and two songs on a compilation somewhere out in the miasma of record land.

## THE VOID
*(U.K.)*

Appropriately, nothing known about **The Void**.

## VOODOO CHILD
*(U.K.)*

The *Acid Talks and Memories* LP on Aftermath Records apparently fits the genre, but with a harder rock guitar sound.

## VULCAN DEATH GRIP
*(New York, NY USA)*

One of Rudi Protrudi & Deb O'Nair's pre-**Fuzztone** bands of unknown makeup.

Another of his previous bands, **Tina Peel**, had at least two 45s out (and I believe a third as well). The photo sleeves on them are hilarious, with both Protrudi and O'Nair dressed in "New Wave" polka dots and skinny ties — definitely not the leather-clad **Fuzztones** we came to know!

## THE VULCANS
*(France)*

Nothing of a logical nature can be determined about this band at this time, Captain.

## THE VULTURES
*(Edinburgh, Scotland U.K.)*

This isn't the Italian group of the same name. This was another '60s punk outfit which was fairly short-lived in the later mid-'80s. There were no recordings released.

## THE WALKING SCREAMS
*(Athens, Greece)*

Self-titled 5 song demo cassette, 1994
 private pressing

A four member garage band which formed in early 1994, playing several gigs with Athens' finest combo, **The Sound Explosion**. Their demo showcases a snotty, organ driven crude sound — very much in the best *Pebbles*-compilation garage compilation tradition.

## WATCH CHILDREN
*(Ocean, NJ USA)*

*How Does It Feel To Be So White?* 10 song cassette, 1989
 no label, USA

"Demented" is the best capsule description for these wackos. Featuring two ex-members of **The Laughing Soup Dish**, this foursome carried on in the cacophonous, colorful netherworld. Mega-distorted guitar and reverb-crazed vocals drench their demo tape, with swirling keyboards and various other noises filling in the cracks.

**Syd Barrett** meets **The Seeds** on songs like "Go Go Action Girl," while pure pop surrealism takes over on "Salvador Dali's Still Dying" and "Coconut Lifesaver." The crude recording doesn't detract from the aural insanity, it magnifies it.

I once heard that *Kaleidoscope Magazine* was going to release this tape as an actual LP, but it never appeared. This is one effort that surely deserves a larger audience than the cassette-trading scene can afford.

## THE WATERMELON MEN
*(Sweden)*

*Four Stories By...* 4 song 7" EP, 1985
    Tracks On Wax Records, Sweden
*Past, Present, and Future* 12 song LP, 1985
"Seven Years" b/w "I've Been Told" 45, 1986
    What Goes On Records, U.K.
*15 Stories By...* 15 song LP, 1986?
    Bootleg, origin unknown
"I Can't Hide" split flexi (w/**Peter Case**), 1987
    *Bucketfull Of Brains* magazine, U.K.
*Wildflowers* 10 song LP, 1987
"True Confessions Of Love"
    b/w "Heading For The Woods" 45, 1987
"Empty Smile" b/w "Pictures Of Good Times" 45, 1987
    Yellow, Ltd., Germany

We all have had records that seemed to never leave the turntable. These records usually wore out our speakers, record needles and eventually our ears. **The Watermelon Men**'s *Past, Present, and Future* LP was one of those records for me. Its timeless combination of 12 string Rickenbacker guitar, sweet vocal harmony and solid danceable rhythms made it an addictive disc to the ultimate degree.

The *15 Stories By...* LP is a bootleg of their February 23, 1986 show in Stuttgart, Germany, and the sleeve is copied from their *Four Stories By... 7"*

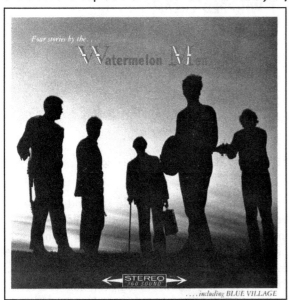

### THE WATERMELON MEN, 1985

EP. The sound is brittle but acceptable, and shows that the band was able to reproduce its delicate 12 string and melody filled sound on stage. This is more remarkable than one might think, since similar excellent studio bands through history — such as **The Byrds** and **Buffalo Springfield** — were notoriously poor in concert.

**229**

This Swedish combo also understood (like the aforementioned **Vipers**) that a dash of brash rock needs to be included in the mix, and they seemed to always know when to turn up the volume without drowning out the song.

Unlike **The Vipers**, however, this band was able to lure a larger label into its lair. The result was the demolition of the **"Watermelon Men** sound," with an incredibly average, tame pop band standing in its place. Ironically, the *Wildflowers* LP is as much a disappointment as their debut was a success.

Only two tracks, "Pouring Rain" and "Small Town Revolution," come close to recapturing their initial magic, and even these musical scraps are incredibly polite. (Did the record company burn the band's Rickenbacker guitars? Did they simply evaporate like liquid runoff in the Swedish spring?)

Both 1987 45s are also from the LP, and both are instantly forgettable — though it should be noted that Erik Illes is one of the most talented vocalists of the decade. He's simply wasted on inferior material, much of which is his own creation. Find their early records, and leave the rest behind.

One major theme throughout this book is the corruption of a musician's art by financial pressure or temptation. The downfall of **The Watermelon Men** is another example — it's amazing what some people will do presumably because of the lure of money.

Well, I guess it's not so amazing after all.

## THE WAY OUTS
*(San Francisco, CA USA)*

I don't believe that this is the same **Way-Outs** from Austin, Texas, which was a pop band from the late '80s. That said, I also don't know anything about this California group either.

## THE WAYWARD SOULS
*(Sweden)*

*Painted Dreams* 12 song LP, 1985
    Hybrid Records, U.K. / Tracks On Wax, Sweden
*Songs Of Rain And Trains* 10 song LP, 1986
    NMW Records, Sweden

**The Wayward Souls** followed in **The Watermelon Men**'s footsteps in mining melodious, **Byrds**y pop, though admittedly with a bit more of a straight rock sound at the fore. They were represented well on a few Swedish compilations, then made more positive marks with their debut 12".

Their second LP is much more tame, with generic "pop" and middle-of-the road compositions crowding out the more interesting material of the past.

I've also heard later 45s that display the group going in a "hard rock" direction, much in the same way that **The Watermelon Men** went in a straight "pop" direction.

It seems that the early recordings of many groups documented in the book are their best, and such is the case with this bunch of Swedes.

## WEDNESDAY WEEK
*(Los Angeles, CA USA)*

The mid-'80s *Betsy's House* EP is their first and perhaps best; full of fine female vocals and bright guitar. Several other LPs also appeared throughout the 1980s to some critical acclaim.

**Wednesday Week** are not really in the garage genre, but did share some of the enthusiasm and '60s pop flavor, so they get a nod here.

## WELLS FARGO
*(Rivalta, Italy)*

Self-titled 45, 1987
  Stardust Records, Italy?
"Bad Boy" b/w "The Wedding Day" 45, 1988
*Lost Highway* LP, 1989
  Toast Records, Italy
"Join My Gang" b/w "Flashback" 7" flexi, 1990
  Urlo Magazine, Italy
*The Hard Way* LP, 1992
  Ultima Musica, Italy

I believe that this band mixed garage and country influences in a way similar to **The Long Ryders**, though I haven't heard any of their output.

## THE WHANK MARVIN 3
*(origin unknown)*

I found this surf, fuzz and echo drenched instrumental group on an early 1990s demo cassette with no information other than the band name. It is very crudely recorded, sounding remarkably like some obscure California session from 1964 — though I suspect this group to be from England.

## THE WHAT...FOR!
*(Germany)*

Untitled 4 song 7" EP, 1988
*The What...For!* 14 song LP, 1989
Untitled 4 song 7" EP, 1991
  Twang-Tone Records, Germany

There is a timeless appeal for "white" teenage R&B music, especially in Europe, where beat music endures its countless revivals. The **What...For!** display all that's great about such stylings, as they bash out harmonica and fuzz-driven boozers on both of their discs.

They began in 1985 as **Batman & His Four Robins** (!), changed their moniker, then began to tour throughout Europe.

Their debut four song EP explodes with crude energy, which is refined (but not tamed!) on their long-player. The influence of **The Petty Things**, **Kinks** and **Downliners Sect** is powerful and well digested.

Bands that seem to passionately enjoy their music rate very highly with me, and **The What...For!** are certainly one of those groups.

Stroll on!

## THE WHIPPED CREAM
*(Sweden)*

Their 1991 *Other Delights* LP for Radium Records is supposedly a fine psychedelic effort.

## THE WICKED ONES
*(Portland, OR USA)*

*The Devil's In My Pants* 3 song 7" EP, 1989
  Get Hip Records, USA

Former members of **The Surf Trio** and **Miracle Workers** man this Northwest outfit, which went through many lineup changes before spewing forth their debut disc, the *Devil's In My Pants* 7" EP. The results are enthusiastic and snotty, but not yet polished to a high gloss. I played one show with them in Portland, and found them to be a rather tame act, large on attitude and small in personality. I believe another 7" is out on Moxie Records.

The title of their EP reminds me of comedian Jonathan Winters' quote, *"The Lord is in my mind, but the Devil is in my pants!"*

## THE WICKERSHAMS
(San Diego, CA USA)

Nothing known.


## THE WINDOWPAYNES
(Harrisburg, PA, USA)

"Green Slime" b/w "Planet Of The Apes" 45, 1994
    Get Hip Records, USA

This odd sounding 45 produces the weirdest version of the 1967 *Green Slime* movie theme I've ever encountered. The duo of Billy Synth and Dave Groninger dish up some compressed lo-fi goo, complete with hushed almost helium-induced vocals and super fuzzed guitar.

The flip is an homage to the *Planet Of The Apes* movie series, though the original version of this song *wasn't* ever actually used in one of those films. This is pretty bizarre garage stuff — and the first pressing was on slimy green vinyl, of course.


## THE WITCH DOCTORS
(Los Angeles, CA USA)

Untitled 4 song 7" EP, 1992
*Witchdoctors A Go-Go* 16 song CD, 1994
    Dionysus Records
Untitled 3 song 7" EP, 1994
    Screaming Apple Records, Germany

Four of **The Finks** (including a one-time **Fuzztone**) and Paul Carey of **The Untold Fables** formed this all-star super garage outfit in the fall of 1990. They would have most certainly ruled the much more active Los Angeles garage scene if they had appeared only five years earlier. I guess they'll simply have to settle for being one of the best '60s-inspired combos from 1980-1995.

All four tracks from their debut 7" are also included on their long-player, *Witchdoctors A Go Go*. It's surely one of those landmark garage efforts — full of reverb, expertly placed Vox organ, richly deep vocals and a playful atmosphere — all in glorious mono.

"Teenage Witchdoctor," "Don't You Think" and "Storm Clouds" are all meaty tracks worthy of forthcoming "best-of" compilations for the era — and there isn't a single dud among the 16 slabs of mayhem.

Rarely in the 1960s did a band have the musical sensibility, ability and performing acumen to deliver such a knock-out punch — it took until the mid 1990s for a band to perfect the formula first concocted nearly 30 years earlier. There simply aren't many bands — from any era — that could stand up to this quartet's dominating, daunting, daring sound. (Excuse my alliteration. I'm getting into the spirit of the band's cheezy mid-'60s album packaging, which included graphics for a half dozen "other" **Witchdoctors** LPs, which of course don't exist.)

Three more grimy tracks blast from the Screaming Apple EP, with a frantic cover of "Goin' To A Graveyard" leading the way.

I am sure the natives got very restless whenever **The Witchdoctors** took the stage.


## WOBBLE JAGGLE JIGGLE
(Brighton, U.K.)

Britain saw a plethora of heavy, late-'60s inspired psych outfits throughout the '80s and '90s — often called "festival bands" because of their dependable presence at open-air concerts. **Wobble Jaggle Jiggle** fits firmly into that acquired taste, full of long fuzzed jams, wah-wah guitar, spacey distorted vocals, and great song titles — "I've Got Gnomes", "Huge Great Psychic Spider" and "All Things Wobbley" should give one a look inside these cats twisted and substance-filled minds.

They have several cassettes from the 1990s, including the 12 song *Overflowing Bowl Of Jelly*, the 12 song *Rockadelic Reefer*, the nine song *Sockitome*, the *Surrealistic Clocktower* box-set and the 12 song *Spiralize Surprise* effort. At least one CD also exists.


## THE WOGGLES
(Athens, GA USA)

Untitled 4 song 7" EP, 1990
Untitled 4 song 7" EP, 1991
*Carnivore!* 4 song 7" EP, 1993
    Zontar Records, USA
Untitled 3 song 7" EP, 1992?
*Teendanceparty* 14 song LP, 1993
*The Zontar Sessions* 15 song LP, 1994
    Estrus Records, USA

A 3 song 7" EP was slated in 1995 for Japan's Wallabies Records, as well as a track on the *Beyond The Beach* instrumental compilation for Upstart Records, plus a slew of other compilation appearances.

A 1990 7" EP finds this Georgia band split between twangy and quirky originals, and straight-ahead garage cover tunes, with their version of **The Sonics'** "He's Waiting" winning out as the most enthusiastic of the bunch. The four

song 45 was a limited pressing of only 500 little vinyl buggers, on the wonderfully-named Zontar Records label.

Another limited edition EP appeared in 1991, followed by two more 7"s — all of which (minus "He's Waiting" but adding "Kudzu Creep") is collected onto the *Zontar Sessions* LP. The various session tracks add up to a very satisfying whole, with *Carnivore* an especially forceful track reminiscent of **The Kinks** meeting **Billy Childish** for a few dozen beers. A cover of **The Creeps'** "Hi Hi Pretty Girl" is another gritty highlight — but all 15 songs have something to offer.

Ironically, their true debut LP, *Teendanceparty*, fails to hold up the energy level and variety of the various EP tracks. Recorded in only two days in Seattle, Washington while the band was on tour, it lacks the punch and attention that makes the earlier work so interesting. "Count The Ways" is a worthy original, but a poor choice and faulty execution of covers sinks the platter; "Abba," "Wildman," "Hang Up" and especially "Get Yourself Together" are all misread by the band.

There was word of many other releases as of this writing, and I can only assume that the band has gotten back on track — and have taken the studio time to nail down (and edit) their developing sound.

I hope so, because **The Woggles** have the right spirit, guts and determination to make them one of the best bands ever from Athens.

What were the names of those other bands from down there?

## THE WOLFMEN
*(Los Angeles, CA USA)*

"Watusi Beat" b/w
   "She Loves Me, She Loves Me Not!" 45, 1991?
   Bobbette Records, USA

There's also a double 45 with **The Mummies**, as described in the chapter on compilations.

This is one release that attempted to look and sound exactly like a long lost 1966 gem — and succeeded. It was released without a picture sleeve and with a simple two color label that could pass for any thirty- year-old classic garage disc.

The sounds in the grooves also pass the exact reproduction test. "She Loves Me Not" features teen-angst blurted vocals and a cool guitar break, while "Watusi Beat" is another crude pounder with demented fuzz guitar and spastic spoken vocals — high compliments, indeed.

I believe that this "group" is really a record collector named Mark Lee Goodale, backed by the **Fly Rite Trio** of Big Sandy fame. Goodale reportedly played *all* of the instruments for a yet unreleased **Wolfmen** 45 for Dionysus Records.

## THE WOMBATS
*(Ohio, USA)*

"Utter Frustration" b/w "What Can I Do?" 45, 1980
"Bye Bye Baby" b/w "Give It A Number" 45, 1982
*Zontar Must Die* LP, 1983
   Voxx Records, USA

Some folks in late '70s/early '80s indie rock circles made a big fuss about these Midwest lads. I guess that they were one of the first in middle America to take punk rock back to its roots, and for this we do owe them a debt of gratitude.

In retrospect, however, much of their released product fails to hold up favorably to other, later practitioners of the same faith. "Bye Bye Baby" does a good job of uniting **Sex Pistols** energy with **Kinks**-ish garage, but most of the debut *Zontar Must Die* LP falls into an eclectic stew of "New Wave" mush. There's just not enough catchy straight-ahead songs to grab hold of for my tastes.

The later mid-'80s *Mud Puddles* EP on Homestead further amplified these problems, and confirms **The Wombats** as a sincere but missed try. In a way they remind me of **The Great Plains**, another Buckeye pop-punk combo which fell between the cracks of definition and attention.

## WONDERWALL

*(San Francisco, CA USA)*

**The Overcoat** played one bay-area show with **Wonderwall** in the fall of 1990. They were a surprisingly baroque-psych outfit, all in ruffled clothes and flowing hair. Their guitar-based psych/pop was almost free form, but without the long-winded pretensions of "progressive rock" — a rare bird in the '80s psych world. I'm uncertain if any recordings exist.

## THE WOODY PEAKERS

*(Trieste, Italy)*

*"Shake My Colours"* split 45, 1986
    Positivo Kids Records, Italy?
*Have You The Nerve To Face...* 12 song LP, 1988
    Vinyl Savage Records, Italy
*Going All The Way* 4 song 7" EP, 1990
    Peak Records, Austria

The band began in 1986, and a single may have appeared in 1986, though my information is in German, so my shaky translation may not be correct! Their organ player calls himself "Ugly," and previously played with the fabulous (and more psychedelic) **Running Stream**.

Their LP was recorded "live" in the studio, I believe, and this all should tell you that this band is yet another crude, loud, European garage outfit, destined to obscurity and a place in my eternally open heart. I especially like the plaintive reading of **Love**'s "Message To Pretty," in all of its staggering glory.

Their subsequent EP is also loud and fun, with the organ-fueled "I Need" and their version of **The Squires**' "Going All The Way" especially enjoyable. It sports a nice picture sleeve too.

A band couldn't sound this cool if they tried; it can only happen as a happy accident. And what kind of goofy guys would purposely give themselves such a weird name? I'd like to shake their hands.

Some members reportedly went on to a band called **The Grains**, with a 7" to appear in late 1995, though the group has already split.

## WOOFLES

*(New York, NY USA)*

One 12" exists; only partially in the genre. Some of it sounds like late '60s **Moody Blues**, and I'm not sure if that is really a good thing.

**233**

## WORLD OF DISTORTION

*(Boston, MA USA)*

This band owes as much to early '70s guitar antics as to a '60s punk mentality. They have a 1987 single on Stanton Park (the label with many bands seemingly sharing the same pool of musicians), and a 1988 LP on Voxx.

## THE WORST

*(Vancouver, BC Canada)*

*Live 'N' Dead* 6 song cassette, 1991
    no label
Untitled 4 song 7" EP, 1992
*Play Tunes From The Tomb* 4 song 7" EP, 1993
    Screaming Apple Records, Germany
Self-Titled 14 song LP, 1993
    Dig Records, France
*Teen Trash Volume #?* 18 songs, 1995
    Music Maniac Records, Germany

I wrote the liner notes for **The Worst**'s debut LP. Here they are:

I'll never forget my first glimpse of **The Worst**'s frontman Greg Johnson. He was on stage, but *his* band wasn't performing. Instead, he was up-front heckling some lame "industrial synth" band at a club in his native Vancouver.

A few minutes later, I watched helplessly from backstage as he was kicked unconscious and

*THE WORST, 1993*

dragged out of the place. I didn't even know him then, but I appreciated the fact that he put his body on the line that evening!

Soon after I was introduced to what was left of Johnson, and **The Worst** quickly became my favorite Canadian garage combo. They opened for my outfit, **The Overcoat**, a few times on our return trip to Vancouver, and then I was lucky enough to help place their first waxing, on a 7" compilation EP.

Two snot-filled EPs on the always-cool Screaming Apple label ensued, and then their first long-player.

The road to their international super-stardom hasn't been smooth, however. Past members of **The Worst** have wandered in and out of the band lineup like lost zombies, but Johnson's mission has remained clear and true. Nothing will make it through the Greg-o-meter unless it has fuzz, guts and fun.

The revolving door seems to have swung shut for now, thankfully, with some sympathetic cavemen in the clan. I was delighted to see two refugees from another of my fave underdog-garagers join up with Johnson: both guitarist/organist Rieuwert Buitenga and drum-hound Colin Raesler hail from the sadly gone **Night Stalkers**. While the **Stalkers** recorded some cool demos, nothing ever vinyl-ized, so it's great to hear their demented wailings within these grooves. Chris Williscroft adds the bass thumping, as well as some vocal screeching, along with Greg and Rieuwert (pronounced "Roo-ert," in case you were wondering).

(Compounding the mess is Colin Forsyth's guest organ on "The DT's," courtesy of another dead Canadian garage-gang, **The Vindicators**. **The Worst** are a haven, it seems, for lost Canadian garage-teens! Johnny "13 Fingers" from **Color Me Psycho**, James T. Massacre of **The Fiends** and **The Reptiles'** Eric Von Shlippen also jump onto the sonic junk-pile for these sessions.)

It all adds up to their big debut album, which reminds me why garage/psych music is so much fun: it's colorful, gritty, real, authentic, instant, honest and sounds great after a few beers. (No symphony can boast that!)

So take your lousy top-40, industrial-crap, fake grunge, metal and country music, and shove it down the pants of those guys from the "synth" band who tried in vain to eliminate Greg Johnson that one fateful night.

Move out of the way losers, 'cause here comes your **Worst** nightmare!

**The Worst**'s second and probably last LP was due out in 1995. Johnson's other band, **The Fiends**, has since taken over his attention.

## WOW WOW HIPPIES
(Japan)

Reports Glynnis Wilson, *"From the mid-'80s, the **Wow Wow Hippies** were a wild psychedelic band which featured amazing light shows and fabulous experience in the G.S. mode — "Group Sound" — a style to Japan, just* like '60s punk was to America. The focus was on vocal groups who imitated American and British sounds mixed with traditional Japanese pop music. They had their own typical uniforms which where period costumes: long jackets, ruffled shirts, tights, high boots and tasseled stockings along with a Colonel Sanders-type tie.

*"They sang in Japanese and made an appearance on the 'G.S. Carnival' video which featured various young Japanese garage & '60s-influenced groups performing 'live.' I have no idea if they released any CDs, but their freaked out 'Blue Mayonnaise' is the highlight of this video. They performed in Japanese."*

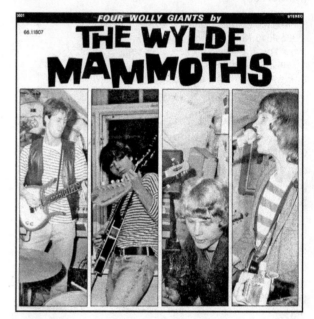

## THE WYLDE MAMMOTHS
(Sweden)

*Four Wolly Giants By...* 4 song 7" EP, 1986
   Mystery Scene Records, Germany
*Help That Girl* 4 song 7" EP, 1987
*Go Baby Go!!* 13 song LP, 1987
*Things That Matter* 14 song LP, 1988
   Crypt Records, USA
"Before It's Too Late" 45, 1990
   Unique Records, Germany
Untitled 4 song 7" EP, 1994
   Misty Lane Records, Italy

Ex-**Crimson Shadows** Johan and Peter Maniette formed the group in 1986, infusing more R&B into their basic garage formula. Their ultra-raw debut 12" bursts from the seams with the **Mammoths'** own brand of Swedish garage-blues. Recorded "live" onto a 2-track tape recorder in a basement, it races from start to finish, with only one song reaching the three-minute mark.

They went into a "real" studio for next year's

*Things That Matter,* and the improved facilities allowed the band to shine without losing their appealing gruffness. Especially engaging is their faithful rendition of the seldom-heard **Squires** classic "It's The Same All Over The World," though their originals more than hold their own.

Interestingly, these two LPs (and an additional EP) were released by Tim Warren's Crypt Records, best known for re-issues of original 1960s garage. Warren must have thought that **The Wylde Mammoths** were truly authentic, and worthy of his purist attention; the results are several great records.

Crypt even announced a brief American tour in 1987, though I can't recall details. I think, however, that one of **The Wylde Mammoths** met one of the (female) members of **The Brood** during this tour, and have since planned marriage!

I think I know what kind of music their offspring will grow up to like.

## THEE WYLDE THINGS
*(U.K.)*

One of several mid-'80s bands that evolved into **The Beatpack**.

## THE X-MEN
*(U.K.)*

"Spiral Girl" b/w "Bad Girl" 45, 1984
"Do The Ghost" 45, 1984
   Creation Records, U.K.

Associated with the "trash" movement of **The Sting Rays, Meteors, Tall Boys,** et. al., **The X-Men** clock-in with two suitably frantic and crude garage-abilly efforts. I dare anyone to turn the treble up all the way on their stereo and listen to the debut really loudly — over and over.

## YARD TRAUMA
*(Tucson, AZ/Los Angeles, CA USA)*

*Yard Trauma* 8 song 12" EP, 1984
   Bona Fide Records, USA
"Some People" b/w "No Conclusions" 45, 1983
"Try It" b/w "Christmas Tyme" 45, 1983
*Must've Been Something I Took Last Night* 12 song LP, 1985
*Face To Face* 10 song LP/CD, 1988
*Retro-Spex* 15 song LP, 1989
   Dionysus Records, USA
*Music* 13 song LP, 1986
   LSD Records, Germany
*No Conclusions* 12 song LP, 1986
   Lolita Records, France
"You Don't Tell Me" flexi, 1987
   Tant Qu'il Y Aura Du Rock Magazine, France

*The following are not strictly in the Garage genre, but are also of interest:*

*Takes Off* 5 song 12" EP, 1988
   Romilar-D Records, Spain
*Eyes* 3 song 7" EP, 1990
"Pressure" b/w "Alibi" 45, 1990
   Dionysus Records, USA
"Get Outta My Way" split 45 (with the band Ultra Violet Eye)
   1991, Cocktail Records, USA
*Lose Your Head* 12 song LP, 1991
   Gift Of Life Records, Germany
"Watching Monster Movies" b/w "Vicious Circle" 45, 1991
   Munster Records, Spain
*Oh My God!* 10 song LP & CD, 1993
   Helter Skelter Records, Italy /Hell Yeah Records, USA

Video: "I've Seen You Walking," 1985, plus "live" on the *Obnoxious Rock & Roll Video Hour,* 1987.

**Lee Joseph** deserves much of the credit for rekindling the '60s punk message. **Yard Trauma** released some of the best records of the early 1980s, he always served as a thoughtful, articulate spokesman for the genre, and his Dionysus Records label continues to document the rise (and fall) of the scene.

**Yard Trauma**'s debut 45 is a blistering punker, with snotty vocals and fuzz everywhere. It

has become one of the most sought-after

relics of the early '80s garage scene, and commands large sums on the collectors' market. It sports a home made Xerox sleeve.

Their follow-up 12" EP is no less fiery, with a dense, unrelenting guitar sound and splashes of Farfisa organ drenching the entire disc. **Joseph** would then leave the dust of Tucson for the smog

***YARD TRAUMA, 1985***

of Los Angeles, and **Yard Trauma**'s future became uncertain.

He and vocalist Tim Hupp (who goes by the stage name "Joe Dodge") would get together over the next year, putting together tracks that would eventually make up their *Must've Been Something I Took Last Night* LP. The collection of tracks from various sessions and studios is surprisingly cohesive, and a bonanza for '60s garage psych-heads.

The title track kicks off in pure **Electric Prunes** fashion, while feedback and a sly Hupp stand out in the eerie "I'm Invisible." **Joseph** takes the microphone for the snotty "Situations," while the group also shows their love for feedback and noise with the nightmarish "Black And White." All in all, the LP is a wonderfully colorful yet gritty psych gem — one of the genre's best. **236**

The quality of the band's music also led Hupp to L.A., and **Yard Trauma** was reformed for performances by 1986. For the next five years they would play all over the western U.S., and journey to Europe as well.

Their sound began to evolve out of the strict garage formula, as they explored all the types of rock they found interesting. Soon snatches of rockabilly, hard rock, industrial and pop all became part of the **Yard Trauma** sound, and they found a whole new set of fans.

Of the later releases, *Face To Face* is especially interesting. The classic '60s punk style is represented by "See Your Face," while the more dominant **Yard Trauma** stylings blast out of the powerful "I'm A Man" and "Fast Pace."

Another disc of note is *Retro-Spex*, which collects early demos and "live" performances. It's a fun look back at their garage days, and you can hear this author cheer wildly at the conclusion of one of the "live" tracks as well — a funny surprise for me when I played the disc!

**Yard Trauma** was thankfully one of the original garage bands not to sell out to commercial constraints, but instead followed their natural course and development. They eventually changed their sound because of musical interest, not the almighty dollar. Their 1991 *Lose Your Head* LP shows that maturation. All of their interests and influences are smashed into one pulsating ball of energy, blasting from the band at the speed of sound.

The *Oh My God!* LP is their epitaph, a fitting, gusty, unrelenting and unapologetic exposé on the hell of the little guy. **Bad Religion**'s Brett Gurewitz engineered this nitro-fueled nightmare, so you know that the guitars bite off your head and the drums pound your brain. Vocalist "Joe Dodge" is truly pissed of, about everything, and I can't blame him a bit.

These guys might *still* be the best band in LA, even though they weren't around to make it to their own final record release party.

## YELLOW SUNSHINE EXPLOSION
*(Germany)*

*Yellow Sunshine Explosion* 10 song LP, 1987
  Love's Simple Dreams Records, Germany

I must give credit to a band that makes its message so obviously clear: take one listen to the track "Take It Acid Is" and you'll understand what this band is talking about! Their debut LP is a literal explosion of sitars, reverbed chanting vocals, organ, flute and every other trippy device known to man and woman.

The results are brimming with energy, humor and melody, making this a psychedelic disc for all the ages. The lilting melody of "Isabelle" is appealing, along with the Eastern Indian instrumentation throughout.

I've been told that this band was capable of creating a stir in concert as well, so this was not merely a studio trip. Unfortunately, I don't think they released any other discs.

Eat a cap or swallow a cube, sit back and float down stream. **The Yellow Sunshine Explosion** has arrived to take you away ... they'd love to turn you on...

## YESTERDAY'S FOREVER
(Tucson, AZ USA)

This one-off included members of **The Marshmallow Overcoat** and **Thee Flypped Whigs**; they performed on one radio broadcast in 1989 — a strangely experimental psychedelic mess.

## YESTERDAY'S PAPERS
(France)

Nothing known.

## THE YUM YUMS
(Norway)

This was reportedly **Cosmic Dropouts** band leader Morten Henriksen's homage to three chord power-punk-rock-pop. I'm uncertain to how many releases they have, but at least one 45 exists on Germany's Screaming Apple.

## LES ZAZOUS
(Holland)

They have the *Wake Up* four song 7" EP, the "Chain Gang" b/w "Silver In A Winternight" 45 and an untitled 11 song LP from 1987 — all on Kelt Records in Holland. I note elsewhere erroneously that Kelt didn't have a 12" release — well here's one.

The only tracks I've heard are "Wake Up Wake Up," a pop effort with a slight country feel to it — the frat-rocking "Buzz Off" — and the pop-ish "Busdriver." It's not overwhelming stuff in my estimation.

## ZEBRA STRIPES
(Los Angeles, CA USA)

*Zebra Is Her Name* 10 song LP, 1989
Dionysus Records, USA

**Zebra Stripes** is really vocalist Zaida, plus back-up musicians including (then) husband **Lee Joseph**. She possesses a sweet and angelic vocal approach, mixing girlish charm and warm sensuality into an engaging whole.

She was first heard on a *Battle Of The Garages* compilation LP with her "Intro '66," then offered elsewhere both an English and Spanish version of **Kim Fowley**'s "The Trip."

Her sole LP is a combination of just about every rock and blues style, ranging from jumpin' rockabilly to straight garage and some moody-pop. **Zebra**'s rendition of "Hurtin' Kind" is the finest ever attempted, and her duo with **Lee Joseph** on **Lee Hazelwood**'s "Some Velvet Morning" is effectively creepy.

**Zebra** is a totally unique performer, and this LP is a lively record, unfortunately released at a very bland time. She would go on to join the trash-punk outfit **Hot Damn**.

# ALL TOGETHER NOW

## *Compilation Albums, Cassettes & Flexis*

*"The only thing left for the '60s sound is for the masses to hear it. For too long it's been the cult of a dedicated few, but now as the groups begin to tour and get more exposure for their records, students on college campuses and even high school hipsters are getting wise. This is quintessential youth music, a fact they recognize as soon as they get a chance to appreciate it."*

— Greg Shaw, *Voxx Teen Beat*, 1986

A plethora of various-artists compilation LPs, CDs, EPs, flexis and cassettes appeared throughout the 1980s and '90s, often giving a garage band its first and sometimes only exposure. Compilations have historically been an easy way to discover unknown bands, and this remained true for the garage-niks.

Many bands that you may have thought were "missing" from the "Echoes In Time" chapter listings make an appearance here. "Split" 45s, where two or more different bands share opposite sides of a release, are also included here.

Some of the compilations listed here are not strictly garage or psych collections, so I've attempted to list only the relevant bands.

## A-BILLY 7" COMPILATION EP
*4 songs, 1989 / What Wave Records, Canada*

**The Gruesomes**
**Deja Voodoo**

A must have for the "live" **Gruesomes** track "Three Men, One Coffin" — truly inspirational trash.

## ABUS DANGEREUX MAGAZINE

The French "alternative" magazine included 7" compilation EPs in its early issues. #6 included **MKB, The Slow Slushy Boys** and **Les Primitives**. #7 included **Les Ambulances, Mister Moonlight** and **The Cryptones.** Later they switched over to 3" mini-CD samplers. #14, for instance, featured **The Fleshtones, Cry Babies** and **Roadrunners**. #16 included **Swell, The Tommyknockers, Milk, The Overcoat** and **The Embryonics**. #25 also included a track by one of France's best new garage acts, **The Linkers.**

## ACID JAM
*LP, 1988 / Woronzow Records, U.K.*

A collection of **The Bevis Frond**'s Nick Saloman and friends, doing what the title suggests on a variety of tracks. A bit "heavy" for me, but suited to some tastes.

## THE ADVENTURE, ISSUE #4
*12 songs, LP, 1991 / Guiding Light Records, Denmark*

**The Stems**
**99th Floor**
**Dead Moon**
**Paul Roland**
**Bevis Frond**
**Green Pajamas**

This LP was given away "free" with *Adventures Magazine*. I'm uncertain if the tracks on the LP are previously unreleased.

## AMERICAN HEART & SOUL
*14 songs, LP, 1986 / Hi-Lo Records, U.K.*

**The Lost Patrol**
**The Mod Fun**
**Nashville Ramblers**
**The Key**
**Modest Proposal**
**Manual Scan**
**The Rumble**
**J-Walkers**

This British compilation of American acts is mainly mod-pop oriented. **The Lost Patrol** here is not the Canadian band, but instead a San Francisco act with smooth harmonies and a melodic flair, especially on "Jaguar Skies."

The undisputed highlight, however, is the vinyl appearance of "The Trains," a powerful track by **The Nashville Ramblers.** I had heard it for years as a cassette demo, and I waited not so patiently for it to pop up somewhere. It's a reverb-drenched moody ballad which combines a romantic and wistful quality, and was worth the wait to hear it in all its vinyl glory.

A special thanks to Bart Mendoza for tracking down this LP for me after a several year search. His band **Manual Scan** also contribute the bright and upbeat "New Song" to the collection.

## ANDY WARHOL
*12 song LP, 1988 / Crazy Mannequin, Italy*

**Captain Pepper & The Legendary Hearts**
**Inside Out**
**Super Lovers**
**Colour Moves**
**Francoise & The Bloomers**
**Comie Spoilers**
**Subterranean Dining Rooms**
**Twiggy & The Aliens**
**Falling Spikes**
**Acid Flowers**
**Pink Silence & The Mad Horses**
**Hitchcock's Scream**

An LP of unknown quality.

## ANSIA DE COLOR MAGAZINE 7"s

*4 song 7" EP, 1990 / Ansia De Color Magazine, Spain*

**Los Negativos**
**The Mystic Eyes**
**Los Impossibles**
**World Of Distortion**

Spain's **Los Negativos** and Buffalo, NY's **Mystic Eyes** deliver a couple non-LP gems, making this a worthy find.

*2 song 7" flexi, 1988?*

**Headless Horsemen**
**The Del Hoyo**

The Ray Charles R&B tune "What's I Say" gets the rave treatment by **The Headless Horsemen**, but isn't worth walking a million miles to find.

## ANTIPRIMA ROCK

*LP, 1990 / Citta Di Torino, Italy*

**Avvoltoi**

This might be a promo-only LP.

## APOCALISSE DI DIAMANTE

*LP, 1993 / Menhir - Toast, Italy*

**No Strange**
**Effervescent Elephants**
**Kryptastesie**
**Dasc**
**Steeple Jack**
**Pale Down**
**Mirror**

## AREZZO WAVE '88

*2 LPs, 1988 / Hiara, Italy*

**Five For Garage**
**Lokomotive Dragster**
**Vegetable Men**
**Chihuahua (France)**
**Les Satellites (France)**

A "live" recording.

## THE ARF ARF CONTEMPORARY MUSIC SAMPLER, Vol. 1

*14 songs, LP, 1984 / Arf Arf Records, USA*

**The Fugitives**

This Erik Lindgren studio project contains a gritty take of the Spencer Davis hit "Gimme Some Lovin'." Not spectacular, but nicely produced.

## ARRESTO CARDIACO #1

*Cassette, 198? / Arresto Cardiaco, Italy*

**Party Kidz (2 songs)**
**No Strange (2 songs)**

## BALONEY SANDWICH

*30 song cassette, 1990 / What Wave Magazine, Canada*

**10 Commandments**
**1313 Mockingbird Lane**
**Al Perry & The Cattle**
**Tommyknockers**
**14th Wray**
**The Cybermen**
**Marshmallow Overcoat**
**Yard Trauma**
**Evaporators**
**Janice K., "The Lady Elvis"**
**Frankenstein V**
**Watch Children**

As you'll see in this section, What Wave Magazine released a series of compilation cassettes, corresponding with issues of the zine. *Baloney Sandwich* might be their best, as it has a high "hit" percentage, weaving better known groups and newcomers together in a likable package.

My personal fave is Janice K, "The Lady Elvis," who gives us the weirdest version of an Elvis ditty that we've ever deserved. I don't think that it is meant to be psychedelic, but it most certainly achieves an other-worldliness!

## SYD BARRETT BOOK 7"

*4 song 7" EP, 1988 / Stampa Alternativa, Italy*

**Syd Barrett**
**Anthony Moore**
**Peter Sellers & The Hollywood Party**

This was rather odd: a book in Italian about Pink Floyd's founder **Syd Barrett,** with a 7" with several **Barrett** outtakes and two tracks from 1980s musicians as well. I'm not sure why the then-current bands are included.

## BATTLE OF THE BANDS

*18 song cassette, 1985 / Glitterhouse Records, Germany*

**Black Carnations**
**Swinging London**
**The Chud**
**The Dizzy Satellites**
**Lovecraft**
**The Blackberry Jug**
**The Chosen Monks**
**The Subtones**
**Die Sache**
**Exit Out**
**Fit And Limo**
**Broken Jug**
**The Hipsters**
**Land of Sex And Glory**
**The Surds**
**Acht Halbe**
**The Chocolate Factory**
**Trivial Heroes**

*Glitterhouse Magazine*, later becoming a prominent record label, released this cassette collection at the height of 1980s German garage mania. The point was to show that Germany was holding its own against the world's competition, and it worked.

This is one of the few cassette-only comps that deserved to be on disc, as it's chocked full of gems. Highlights include the pop-psych **Chud**, power-pop **Subtones** and the fuzzed **Broken Jug**.

## BATTLE OF THE GARAGES

*16 songs, LP, 1981 / Voxx Records, USA*

**The United States Of Existence**
**The Embarrassment**
**The Wombats**
**The Vertebrats**
**The Crawdaddys**
**The Stepmothers**
**The Unclaimed**
**Pete Holly & The Looks**
**The Chesterfield Kings**
**Eddy Best**
**The Slickee Boys**
**Brad Long**
**Billy Synth & the Turn-ups**
**Deniz Tek**
**The Darkside**
**Plasticland**

Here's the single disc that arguably rekindled the garage flame. Some of the tracks are admittedly only related to the garage sound, yet others by **The Chesterfield Kings, Plasticland** and **The Unclaimed** hinted at great things to come.

Champaign, Illinois' **Vertebrats** had already put out a 45 before landing a spot on this influential compilation.

They later recorded a session in Hollywood for Voxx — which remains unreleased. I know what that feeling is like — Greg Shaw managed not to release three separate records of mine over the years.

*The Battle Of The Garages* series was re-released in the early 1990s on CD.

## BATTLE OF THE GARAGES, VOLUME 2

*16 songs, LP, 1984 / Voxx Records, USA*

**The Vipers**
**Plasticland**
**The Miracle Workers**
**Mad Violets**
**The Fuzztones**
**The Impossible Years**
**The Prime Movers**
**True West**
**The Mystic Eyes**
**Yard Trauma**
**The Odds**
**The Seen**
**The Trip**
**The Fezmen**
**The Outnumbered**
**The Sharp Turn**

I consider this to be the best compilation record of the 1980s. Unlike most comps, it is solid from top to bottom, and like a good document it vividly relates the momentum of the garage scene in 1984.

If you could afford only one record from this entire book, buy this one.

## BATTLE OF THE GARAGES, VOLUME 3

*16 songs, LP, 1984 / Voxx Records, USA*

Zebra Stripes
The Tories
Thee Fourgiven
Hidden Peace
The Gravedigger V
The Eyes Of Mind
The Mutts
The Things
The Untold Fables
The Young Lords
The Mystery Machine
SS-20
The Tell Tale Hearts
Lee Joseph
The Pandoras
Electric Peace

Another solid entry, this time detailing specifically the mid 1980s Californian explosion. **The Mystery Machine, Hidden Peace, Eyes Of Mind** and **The Things** are the best highlights, but there are few, if any, real duds.

## BATTLE OF THE GARAGES, VOLUME 4

*15 songs, LP, 1986 / Voxx Records, USA*

The Cannibals
Les Thugs
The Other Side
The Surfadelics
The Klepstones
Sick Rose
Sex Museum
Los Negativos
Legendary Golden Vampires
Green Telescope
Birdmen Of Alkatraz
Bad Karma Reckons
Les Coronados
The Last Drive
Les Flamingos

The last of Voxx's *Battles* explored the European scene, where garage and psych music seemed to gain the most popularity. There are representatives from all of the garage-speaking countries, proving the "revival" to have worldwide connections.

## BEASTS FROM THE EAST

*13 song cassette, 1985 / Purple Cactus Productions, USA*

Great Plains
The Endorphins
Libertines
Danny & The Gentiles
Illegal Aliens
The Desposables
The Fugitives
The Impossible Years
Reptile House

This is the cassette-only version of the collection compiled by this author in 1985. The line-up would later be revised, and it would become an LP on Voxx.

This version, though, is a bit rawer, with the **Desposables, Impossible Years** and **Great Plains** supplying the Midwest grunge which was later eliminated on the LP. **Reptile House** would mutate into the **Marshmallow Overcoat,** and you can hear the development in these early tracks.

## BEASTS FROM THE EAST

*14 songs, LP, 1986 / Voxx Records, USA*

*BEASTS FROM THE EAST, 1986*

The Libertines
The Dwarves
The Skeptics
The Cynics
The Time Beings
Green
The Endorphins
The Cunts

As stated above, I compiled this LP along with Greg Shaw. We were attempting to produce a compilation that was a little different than the *Battle Of The Garages* series by stretching the narrow definition of the "garage" group.

The result is admittedly uneven, but my faves **The Libertines** and **Skeptics** both contribute some fine cuts. This comp is also different in that most of the bands were afforded two cuts rather than one, giving the listener a better feeling for the bands' sound.

## BEASTS OF THE BAJA
*24 song cassette, 1987 / Baja Arizona Music*

**Marshmallow Overcoat**
**Infinite Beauties**
**Al Perry & The Cattle**

Only of marginal interest to this discussion, this cassette does include a few "live" tracks of note, recorded in the Catalina Mountains at an Arizona music festival.

## THE BELGIAN GARAGEMANIA VOLUME 4
*14 song, LP, 1989 / Boom! Records, Belgium*
*(with bonus 45 by I Love Lucy)*

**The Spanks**
**The Midnight Men**
**The Pink Flowers**
**Van Rose Experience**
**The Excessives**
**The Mistreaters**
**King Koen**
**The Moonrakers**
**The Candy Dates**
**The Wankees**
**The Softies**

A continuation of the *Second Belgium 6T's Boom* series, with a new title. **The Pink Flowers** contribute two shimmering melodic tracks, with "She Was" as memorable as underground pop can be. **The Mistreaters** add a rare track on Side Two, the faithfully R&B "Bloodhound," while **King Koen** hits the mark once again with "What About You" and **The Candy Dates** deliver a sweet pop tune in "Simply Going Backwards."

This could be the strongest edition in the series, though admittedly I'm missing Volume #3.

## THE BELGIAN GARAGEMANIA VOLUME 5
*14 songs, LP, 1989 / Boom! Records, Belgium*
*(with bonus 45 by The Strikes)*

| | |
|---|---|
| **Shakin' Zorro & Bandelero's** | **D.S.E.** |
| **The Venus Juices** | **Family Foundation** |
| **The Pink Flowers** | **King Koen** |
| **The Beatlejuices** | **The Stoneage Romeos** |
| **The Candy Dates** | **The Killer T-Bag** |
| **Too Late For Jane** | **The Mudgang & Tom Wolf** |
| **Rick Tubbax & The Taxis** | |

Another solid entry from the Belgian scene, with a heavy emphasis on pop this time around. **The Pink Flowers, Beatlejuices** and **Candy Dates** all create jangley melodic moments, while the always dependable **King Koen**

brings the grit and grime with "I Guess You Ain't My Kind At All." **The Stoneage Romeos** also add a little garage spice with their theme song. A very satisfying conclusion (I think) to this series.

## BELGIAN MANIA GOES TO ITALY
*CD only, 1992 / Boom - Face Records, Italy*

**Trouble**
**Drunk Penguins**
**Lilith**
**Revolution Children**
**Daltonic**
**Groovers**
**Hermits**
**Nicotine Spyral Surfers**
**Baked Brains**
(plus nine bands from Belgium)

I can only assume that this is a sequel of some kind to the five-part Belgian scene compilations of the late 1980s. What in the world would **The Baked Brains** sound like?!?

## BEYOND THE BEACH
*19 song CD, 1994 / Upstart Records, USA*

**The Daytonas**
**Jon & The Nightriders**
**Huevos Rancheros**
**The Mermen**
**The Woggles**
**The Aqua Velvets**
**The Halibuts**
**Southern Culture On The Skids**
**The Goldentones**
**Laika & The Cosmonauts**
**Hillbilly Frankenstein**
**Insect Surfers**
**Paul Johnson**
**Teisco Del Rey**
**Man Or Astroman?**
**Spies Who Surf**
**Tin Machine**
**The Ultras**
**The Falcons**

Instrumental music fan Scott Moody calls this a solid modern surf/instrumental collection, with Finland's **Laika & The Cosmonauts** one of his personal favorites.

## BEYOND THE WILDWOOD: A TRIBUTE TO SYD BARRETT
*14 songs, LP, 1987 / Imaginary Records, U.K.*

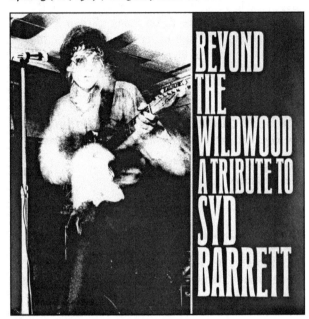

The Mock Turtles
The Ashes In The Morning
Plasticland
SS-20
The Lobster Quadrille
Paul Roland
The Paint Set
Fit And Limo
Tropicana Fishtank
The Shamen
The TV Personalities
Opal
The Soup Dragons
The Green Telescope

This was one of the first of an endless parade of "tribute" LPs, and it is also one of the best. Syd never sounded better than in the hands of these enthusiasts, as they flesh out his wacky compositions with their own arrangements. A true treat, and a fitting tribute to the Madcap.

Skyclad Records later issued the compilation CD in the U.S. with some forgettable bonus tracks: **The Chemistry Set** with a passable version of "See Emily Play," and a horrible hard-rock version of "Gigolo Aunt" by **Death Of Samantha**.

## BIZARRE BEAUTIES - A FAB COMPILATION #2
*13 songs, LP, 1989 / Fab Records, Germany*

Sharing Patrol
The Needles
Groove Farm
Shiny Gnomes
The Heartbeats
Birdy Num Num

Swinging London
The Risk
The Extremes
The Kliek
The Chemistry Set (U.K.)
The Babysnakes

An interesting blend of garage (**Shiny Gnomes, Heartbeats**) and mod (**The Risk, The Extremes**).

## BLOCKSCHOCK - LIVE
*11 songs, LP, 1987 / Wall City Records, Germany*

The Chud
Dizzy Satellites

## THE BOB MAGAZINE FLEXIS

This East Coast U.S. newspaper-sized zine included a 7" Flexi in each issue throughout the 1980s and '90s. They often featured well known garage or psych-oriented acts such as **The Long Ryders, Robyn Hitchcock, Bevis Frond, Lime Spiders, Fleshtones, Dentists, Headcoats,** etc.

## BONE IN ROCHESTER
*13 song LP, 1987 / Jargon Records, USA*

The Ferrets
The Projectiles

The rare **Projectiles** track is the highlight of this 13 band peek at the "underground" scene of Rochester, New York, circa 1987. Most of the other tracks are fairly tame and bland, and don't fit directly into the garage or psych category.

## BOOM SHANKAR LIVE
*Cassette, 1988(?) / Private Release, Italy*

Vegetable Men
No Strange

A promo-only release.

## BRIAN JONES DIED FOR YOUR SINS
*Cassette, 1987 / Tambourine Man Records, Italy*

Peter Sellers & The Hollywood Party
Bad Medicine
Acid Flowers
Human Jukebox
Screamin' M.M.
This Gun For Hire
Acid Flowers
Falling Spikes

## BUCKETFULL OF BRAINS COMPILATIONS

The English fanzine included 7" vinyl or 7" flexi samplers starting in each issue from at least the mid-1980s. They included excellent rare bits from the **Died Pretty, Plasticland, Long Ryders (AKA The Spinning Wighats), Robyn Hitchcock, The Soft Boys, Barracudas, Watermelon Men, The Church,** as well as less than necessary leftovers from more pedestrian acts.

## CAFE AU GO GO!

*15 songs, CD, 1991 / TKCA Records, Japan*

**Club Aces**
**Back Door Men**
**Fave Raves**
**The Hair**
**The Gear**
**The Planets**

An all-Japanese mod-garage compilation — complete with an all-color fold out sleeve displaying some fine '60s fashions. **The Back Door Men** included here should not be confused with the mid-1980s combo from Germany.

## CAT O' NINE TAILS

*30 songs, cassette, 1992 / What Wave Magazine, Canada*

**The Creatures**
**Scarlet Drops**
**10 Commandments**
**The Overcoat**
**Lost Patrol**
**The Cunts**
**The Mood**
**The Cryptics**
**The Cellar Dwellars**
**The Cybermen (U.S.)**
**The Cryptones**
**Fridge Magnets**
**New Avengers**
**The Worst**
**14th Wray**
**Evil Hoodoos**
**Slow Slushy Boys**
**The Gruesomes**
**Janice K., "The Lady Elvis"**

Yet another fine cassette-only entry from *What Wave;* this one was included with issue #21. **The**

**Cellar Dwellars** contribute "Something To Say," the only track other than their one Get Hip 45 that I know of, and **Janice K** delivers an unintentionally psychedelic version of "Viva Las Vegas." *What Wave* included **Janice K.** on many of their compilations, and she never failed to evoke the weirdest specter of **Elvis** imaginable.

## CICADAS:
## An Electric Guide To The Greek Underground

*12 songs, LP, 1987 / Pegasus/Hitchhyke Records, Greece*

**Blue Light**
**The Mushrooms**
**No Man's Land**
**Villa 21**
**Human Grape**
**Anti Troppau Council**

An interesting look into the mid-'80s Greek underground, featuring a wide scope of sounds and styles.

## CITY LIGHTS COMPILATION EP

*4 songs, 7", 1987 / Fab Records, Germany*

**Stephen's Run**
**Bo Hatzfeld & The Headhunters**
**Stunde X**
**Beathoovers**

A "beat" style consumes most of this disc, with also the only vinyl recording I know of by the more garagey **Stunde X** — they contribute a meaty "live" track.

## COOKING WITH GEORGE, MARK TOO

*33 songs, 2 LPs, 1985 / Australian Broadcasting Corporation, Australia*

**The Arctic Circles**
**The Dust Collection**
**The Garden Path**

This is a mostly pedestrian collection of 13 Australian underground acts, highlighted by the energetic punk-pop of the **Arctic Circles,** the ethereal **Garden Path** — and a stand-out track by **The Dust Collection,** "So Sad Here," that appears only on this album. The 12" vinyl version of this compilation was packaged in a plastic 16MM-type film canister; it was also released in a three *cassette* box-set. Very odd, indeed.

## COOL SOUNDZINE's MORE HITS-MORE STARS

*22 songs, CD, 1992 / Mission Control Records, Canada*

This CD adorned the only issue of the *Cool Soundzine*, a double-CD sized magazine featuring the acts on the disc. Most of the acts are "alternative" or mainstream edged rock, with only **The Dave Rave Conspiracy** and especially the **Swingin' Gurus** of interest.

## COWBOY TEASHOW VOLUME 3

*4 bands, 4 songs, 10" EP, 1992 / Rocket Sound Records, USA*

**27 Various**

"Say Anything You Want" by **The 27 Various** is included.

## CRAWLING FROM WITHIN

*77 Records, LP, USA / (put together by Bang! fanzine)*

**The Brood**

I really don't know much about this disc, except that it has a couple of early rare **Brood** cuts on it.

## DAGGER KILLER COMPILATION, VOLUME 2

*20 song cassette, 1988 / Dagger Tapes, USA*

**Marshmallow Overcoat**
**Sporting Bachelors**
**The Ultra 5**

Keith Grave put together several volumes of this cassette series, with bands ranging from gothic to hardcore to garage. This volume featured unreleased **Ultra 5** and an alternate **Marshmallow Overcoat** mix.

Volume 4 features only a couple garage cuts: two from **The Unknown Soldiers** and one from **The Double Naught Spys.**

## DAYDREAMS AND NIGHTMARES

*16 song cassette, 1990 / Acid Tapes, U.K.*

**Effervescent Elephants**
**Storm Clouds**
**Tropicana Fishtank**
**Ken Flynn**
**Bevis Frond**
**The Chemistry Set**

Yet another Acid Tapes sampler, with an array of psych moods represented. Italy's **Effervescent Elephants** are always pleasingly trippy, as they are here, and **The Chemistry Set** hand in a nice version of "Mr. Soul." The undisputed highlight, though, is a soaring pop track titled "Remember" by **Ken Flynn.** It's one of those classic mood pieces which evokes imagery and emotion. It's simply beautiful.

## THE DEADLY SPAWN

*14 songs, LP, 1986 / Bona Fide Records, USA*
*(includes 7" flexi with* **The Stump Wizards** *and* **Voodoo Love Gods***)*

**Velvet Monkeys**
**Liquid Generation**
**The Brood**
**The Skeptics**
**Thee Fourgiven**

Bona Fide's follow-up to their fine *Train To Disaster* comp, and like most collections it has its ups and downs. **Liquid Generation** are a big highlight, as well as the always dependable **Brood** and **Skeptics.**

## DECLARATION OF FUZZ

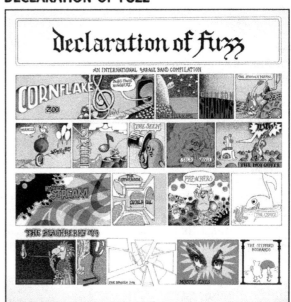

18 songs, LP, 1986 / Glitterhouse Records, Germany

The Not Quite
Miracle Workers
Blacklight Chameleons
Cornflake Zoo
Sick Rose
Stepford Husbands
The Seen
The Other Side
Blackberry Jug
Crimson Shadows
Mystic Eyes
Running Stream
Stomachmouths
Green Telescope
Cynics
Broken Jug

This incredible collection rivals the *Battle Of The Garages #2* as the best of the 1980s. Many "new" groups were given their vinyl debut, and there's also a good number of psych-inspired acts included as well. This is a must-have collection, by any standards.

## DESTINATION BOMP!

48 songs, 2 CDs / Bomp! Records, USA

Flamin' Groovies
Poppees
DMZ
Rodney & The Brunettes
The Last
Crawdaddys
Stiv Bators
Vertebrats
Plimsouls
Barracudas
Jon & The Nightriders
Zebra Stripes
Mystery Machine
Pandoras
Tell Tale Hearts
Gravedigger V
Miracle Workers
The Things
Eyes Of Mind
Steppes
SS-20
Green Pajamas
Hangman's Beautiful Daughters
Spacemen 3

Bomp! is arguably the first American independent record label to actively search out "new rock music." It boast that it's survived 20 years of industry trends and pitfalls by concentrating on the music first, without regard to commerciality and marketability. The results crowd this 48 song, two CD set. The closest thing to a hit is The Plimsouls' classic "Million Miles Away,"

**248**

but the quality is top-notch throughout — Bomp! realizes that chartability is not the measure of a song's worth. Garage, power pop, punk, psych and just plain weirdness — Bomp! has seen it all, and probably will for another 20 years.

## DIG THE MISTY SOUND OF...

19 song cassette, 1993 / Misty Lane Records, Italy

The Others
Hermits
Stoici
Headstones
99th Floor
Boot Hill V
Mole People
Croakers
Cellophane Flowers

The cream of the Italian garage crop of the early 1990s, especially handy for tracks from bands like **The Cellophane Flowers** and **Boot Hill V** which don't have readily available vinyl. **The Others** shine as usual, along with their side-projects **The Mole People** and the **Others Watch Band** (doing a cover of the **Chocolate Watchband's** "Loose Lip Sync Ship").

## DIMENSIONS OF SOUND

17 songs, LP, 1987 / Mystery Scene Records, Germany

Crimson Shadows
Thee Fourgiven
United States Of Existence
Blacklight Chameleons
Untold Fables
Thanes Of Cawdor
Stomachmouths
Not Quite
Zebra Stripes
Royal Nonesuch
Yellow Sunshine Explosion
Comedown
Otherside

From the beautiful front cover (of Jon from **The Royal Nonesuch**) down, this one is a real treat, with plenty of rare tracks and a great package. Definitely another one of the top garage compilations of the decade.

## DISGRACELAND

29 song cassette, 1988? / What Wave Magazine, Canada

Al Perry & The Cattle
10 Commandments
Purple Toads
The Gruesomes

Ultra 5
Cheepskates
Tyme Eliment
Green Pajamas
Mystic Eyes

My favorite name for a compilation, from my favorite Canadians, Dave and Rena O'Halloran at *What Wave*. This edition of their ever-expanding list of cassette releases (and now records) features standouts by the **Ultra 5, Gruesomes, Mystic Eyes** and **Green Pajamas.** It's pretty strong throughout.

## DON'T ADJUST YOUR TV SET... THERE'S NOTHING WRONG WITH YOUR NEEDLE
*11 songs, LP, 1986 / Cryptovision Records, USA*

**Stepford Husbands**
**Mod Fun**

These two groups are the only highlights in this otherwise ho-hum set of bands.

## THE EAST COAST '60s ROCK'N'ROLL EXPERIMENT
*15 songs, LP, 1986 / Performance Records, USA*

**The Smithereens**

This is an absolutely dreadful "tribute" to pop music of the 1960s, full of grimacing misfires and horrible cover versions of songs like "Secret Agent Man" and "I Want To Hold Your Hand." Only **The Smithereens'** very funny and cool surf version of the *Hang 'Em High* movie theme — titled "Hang Ten High" — is worthy of listening.

## EIGHTIES COLOURS, VOLUME 1
*10 songs, LP, 1986 / Electric Eye Records, Italy*

**Sick Rose**
**Technicolour Dream**
**Party Kidz**
**Birdmen of Alkatraz**
**Out Of Time**
**Four By Art**
**No Strange**
**Pression X**
**Double Deck Five**
**Paul Chain Violet Theatre**

Italy became a hotbed for garage-psych sounds, with proof hidden in these grooves. Rare and previously unreleased tracks make this a meaty peak into the Italian underground, which culminates in this series' second volume. This is a must-have, if it can be found.

## EIGHTIES COLOURS, VOLUME 2
*13 songs, LP, 1987 / Electric Eye Records, Italy*
(includes a 45 w/**Steeplejack** and **Soul Hunter**)

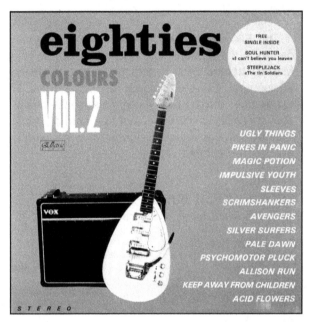

**Ugly Things**
**Pikes In Panic**
**Silver Surfers**
**Acid Flowers**
**Pale Dawn**
**Scrimshakers**
**Psychomotor Pluck**
**Keep Away From**
**Sleeves**
**Children**
**Allison Run**
**Impulsive Youth**
**Magic Potion**
**Avengers**

This is a rare occasion where the second LP in a compilation series is even better than the first. Plenty of psych included with the garage here as well. I'd love to find **Allison Run**'s *God Was Completely Deaf* LP and **Magic Potion**'s *Four Wizards In Your Tea* LP, since those two bands are stunning on this disc! This is undoubtedly the finest Italian sampler of the 1980s.

## ESTRUS HALF RACK

*3 x 7" EPs in a package, 1991 / Estrus Records, USA*

**#1:**
The Derelicts
The Fastbacks
Gorilla
Kings Of Rock

**#3:**
Marble Orchard
Mono Men
Mudhoney
The Mummies

**#2:**
Phantom Surfers
Prisonshake
Seaweed
Untamed Youth

This EP collection had less of a strict garage nature, but **The Mummies, Untamed Youth** and **Marble Orchard** don't disappoint — and **Mudhoney** is also cool with their "March To Fuzz" anthem. The Estrus beer coaster and stickers also make this a cool package, which is housed in a hard 7" audio tape box. It was a limited edition of 2000, with the first 500 on colored vinyl.

## ESTRUS LUNCH BUCKET

*3 x 7" EPs in a package, 1990 / Estrus Records, USA*

**#1:**
The Brood
Falling Spikes
Fallouts
Game For Vultures

**#3:**
Rocket Scientists
Shadowy Men On A Shadowy
    Planet
Seaweed
Young Fresh Fellows

**#2:**
Gas Huffer
Girl Trouble
Marble Orchard
Mono Men

What can you say about three 7" EPs full of garage mania? Estrus outdid themselves with their first box-set, with killer tracks from most involved (including several bands that don't quite fit in the genre, but are of interest nonetheless.)

A hard 7" audio tape box houses the discs plus "trading cards" for all of the bands. Only 1,500 of these babies made it out the door, though I think that all of the Estrus box-sets have since been re-issued on CD.

## EX-NEXU MAGAZINE COMPILATIONS

*4 song 7" EP, 1988? / Screaming Apple Records, Germany*

The Ultra 5
The Stems
The Projectiles
The Electric Shields
The Kliek

This short-lived German garage zine spawned the increasingly important Screaming Apple label, and this is their first release. I believe it is the only EP that appeared with the magazine — it's a much sought-after disc because of the previously unreleased **Stems** and **Projectiles** tracks.

## EXPLODING UNDERGROUND

*14 songs, LP, 1988 / Direct Hit Records, USA*

*EXPLODING UNDERGROUND, 1988*

Sick Rose
The Blue Up?
Birdmen Of Alkatraz
Marshmallow Overcoat
The Projectiles
The Mad Violets
The Headless Horsemen
The Cheepskates
Blacklight Chameleons
The Green Today

Another worthy collection, with rare **Sick Rose** and a previously un-released **Mad Violets** track, plus an alternate mix from **The Marshmallow Overcoat**. Direct Hit's Dennis Dalcin also published the excellent *Kaleidoscope Magazine*, which included a two song 7" flexi from **Green Today** in a 1986 issue.

## A FABULOUS COMPILATION
*12 songs, LP, 1987 / Fab Records, Germany*

**Living Stones**
**Chocolate Factory**
**The Otherside**
**The Candlestick**
**The Girls**
**Passengers**

There are some enjoyable cuts on this otherwise lightweight mod-ish compilation. **The Otherside**'s "Mrs. Jones" is the obvious high point.


## FACES VOLUME 1
*CD only, 1993 / Face Records, Italy*

**Kryptastesie**
**Shantish (ex Steeplejack)**
**Others**
**Mirrors**
**Dave Electric**


## FIELDBURN
*23 songs, CD (only), 1993 / Pro-Arts, USA*

**Marble Orchard**
**The Undertakers**
**The Electric Flies**

A Eugene, Oregon compilation of 10 bands, with the above three of relevance to this book. **The Undertakers** contribute previously unreleased tracks which are the highlight, and both tracks from an **Electric Flies** vinyl 45 also make their CD debut.


## 55 MILES FROM MEXICO
*18 songs, CD, 1993 / Houses In Motion Records, Germany*

**The Overcoat**

An edited re-mix of **The Overcoat**'s "Beverly Pepper" is the only psych-pop entry on this compilation of Tucson, Arizona groups.


## FERMIAMOLI!
*13 songs, CD, 1993 / Sottosopra Records, Italy*

**The Others**

Like above, the inclusion of **The Others'** "In My Time" is the only garage element on this "underground" compilation. The track also appears on **The Others'** debut LP on Music Maniac.


## FIFTEEN MINUTES:
## A TRIBUTE TO THE VELVET UNDERGROUND
*14 songs, CD, 1994 /Imaginary Records, U.K.*

**Echo & The Bunnymen**

This U.K. label gave us a brilliant **Syd Barrett** tribute a few years ago, then stumbled with a hapless **Byrds** blunder. There have been more than a couple other **Velvets** tribute LPs as well — no one has gotten it right yet. **Nirvana** sounds tentative on "Here She Comes Now," **Lee Ranaldo** (who?) butchers the delicate "Stephanie Says," and even **Echo & The Bunnymen** drags things out on "Foggy Notion." Lame packaging, without any information, also doesn't merit the more than $20 import price. Go find a beat up $3 vinyl copy of *V.U.* and hear the real McCoy.


## FOUR SONGS FOR A SULTRY SUMMER NIGHT
*4 song 7" EP, 1993 / Sundown Records, Australia*

**The Daytonas**
**The Moment Of Truth**
**The Breadmakers**
**The Puritans**

Sweden's **Daytonas** contribute the pleasingly surf-ish "Christmastime For Fun," which makes perfect sense for a Summer theme record, right? **The Moment Of Truth**'s "Penetration" takes out the vocals but keeps the surf guitar intact.

The flip shows **The Breadmakers** singing the praises of a "Brand New Souped Up Lovin' Machine" — that's a car. The venerable **Puritans** conclude the proceedings with "Rocky Road Blues," a hopping little organ and harmonica-filled R&B number.


## FOUR YOUR LOVE
*4 song 7" EP, 1993? / Twist Records, U.K./Germany*

**Sacred Hearts**
**Soon**
**The Strange**
**Mild Mannered Janitors**

**The Strange**'s organ-fueled garage tune "Perfect Dream" is the highlight of this mod and pop-tinged sampler, though **The Sacred Heart**'s melodic number "Shine" is pretty catchy as well.

## FREAKBEAT MAGAZINE 7" COMPILATIONS

**1987:**
The Steppes
The Bevis Frond

**1988:**
Kenne Highland Clan
Billy Syndrome
The Ectomorph
The Green Pajamas

**1989: #1**
Dementia 13
The Inn

**1989: #2**
The Chemistry Set
The Colored Plank
Bargepole
Twink

**1990:**
Viv Akauldren
Tyrnaround
Treatment
Watch Children

**1993:**
Submarine Prophets
Nick Riff
Nova Express

The incredibly colorful *Freakbeat* magazine regularly included EPs of related bands, usually of unreleased tracks. A great variety in style and quality marks the series, but there is usually at least one track of interest on each EP.

## FROM THE VAULT FLEXI

This Australian collector's magazine included the 7" flexi of **The Church**'s "Musk," circa 1990.

## FROZEN LAUGHTER: A TRIBUTE TO THE RISING STORM

*4 songs, 2 x 45s, 1994 / Distortions Records, USA*

Head & The Hares
Sandoz Lime
Rising Storm

Two current bands pay homage to the 1960s garage/psych punkers **The Rising Storm** with excellent covers versions on one disc, and **The Rising Storm** itself adds two "new" re-union tunes on the second disc.

## FUN WITH MUSHROOMS

*15 song LP / 20 song CD, 1992 / Delerium Records, U.K.*

Boris & Bolshie Balalakia
Saddar Bazaar
Praise Space Electric
14th Wray
Harold Juana
Dead Flowers
Tangle Edge
Watch Children
Dean Carter & The High Commission
Omnia Opera
The Inn
Wobble Jangle Jiggle
Mooseheart Faith Stellar Groove Band
Terrence McKenna

*CD bonus tracks:*
Cosmic Kangaroos
Reefus Moons
Marshmallow Overcoat
Dr. Brown
Jasmine Love Bomb

The follow-up to the successful *Psychedelic Psauna* compilation
finds the Delerium boys straying even further into spacey and twisted arenas. **The 14th Wray**'s "Yuppie Deadhead Party" is pretty hilarious, and indicative of the sense of mischief that is pervasive throughout.

**The Watch Children** also contribute one of their few tracks ever to see the light of day — and it's therefore an essential slice of dementia. The more cosmic "festival" bands dominate the collection, but as always with Delerium, there's a bit of inspired lunacy for every taste.

## GARAGE GOODIES
*16 songs, LP, 1986 / Melt Down On Media Burn Records, U.K.*

| | |
|---|---|
| The Surfadelics | Change Lings |
| Vertex | Codeine Cowboys |
| X-Men | Legendary Vegetarians |
| Milkshakes | Bad Karma Reckons |
| Jailbirds | Killed In Action |
| Nips | The Creepshow |
| Commuters | Sting Rays |
| Spots | The Cannibals |

This LP is a good introduction to the U.K. "trash-rock" scene of the mid-'80s.

## GARAGE SALE
*19 song cassette, 1985 / ROIR, USA*

The Mosquitos
Thee Fourgiven
The Vipers
The Shoutless
Gravedigger V
The Cheepskates
The Trip
The Aromatics
Boys From Nowhere
The Not Quite
Mystic Eyes
The Things
The Addition
The Fuzztones
Tell Tale Hearts
The Unclaimed
The Crickle
Wildfang
The Pandoras

*Garage Sale* is arguably one of the two or three finest '80s garage/psych compilations, and certainly the best cassette-only effort. The exposure given to it by *Goldmine Magazine*, which sponsored the release, helped inspire yet another wave of garage bands. The line-up is certainly an inspiration, with duds no where to be found. Highlights include previously unreleased tracks from **The Things, The Mosquitos** (their best tune ever released), **The Trip, Thee Fourgiven** and **The Not Quite**. Most of the best bands from the early-'80s scene are represented, making this a fertile hunting ground for enthusiasts — I wish it was out on vinyl or CD. The cover is a great "garage caveman" cartoon by **The Fuzztones'** Rudi Protrudi.

## GARUNGE
*24 song cassette, 1987? / What Wave Magazine, Canada*

Projectiles
Purple Toads
Royal Nonesuch
Janice K., "The Lady Elvis"
The Cheshyres
Deja Voodoo

**The Royal Nonesuch** were going to release "She's So Satisfyin'" as a 45, but when that fell through, they gladly handed it over to the *What Wave* folks for inclusion here — this tape is worthy for that track alone. Added bonuses are the always dependable **Gruesomes, Projectiles,** and of course, **Janice K., "The Lady Elvis."**

## GOAR MAGAZINE COMPILATIONS
*4 song 7" EP, 1993 / Goar Records, Germany*

Al Perry & The Cattle
Flyte Reaction
The Green Pajamas

This German underground zine covered a variety of genres, often veering into garage land. The EP listed above featured more unreleased magic from **The Green Pajamas.**

## HANGIN OUT AT MIDNIGHT
*12 songs, LP, 1986 / Midnight Records, USA*

**The Cavemen**
**The Cheepskates**
**Absolute Grey**
**The Fuzztones**
**The Tryfles**

This was a collection of outtakes, demos and odd tracks, with an early **Fuzztones** demo for "The Witch" the most attractive.

## A HANGMAN SAMPLER
*12 songs, LP, 1988 / Hangman Records, U.K.*

**Mighty Ceasars**
**Prisoners**
**Timmy Tremelo**
**The Kravin' "A's"**
**The Aunty Vegetables**
**Rockin' Richard & Whistlin' Vic**
**The Black Hands**
**Milkshakes**
**Del Monas**
**Billy Childish**
**Mindreaders**

Billy Childish's label unleashed another taste of the Medway scene. **The Prisoners'** "There's A Time" is a wonderful previously unknown bit — one of their finest pop songs actually, and how could I not enjoy "The Man With The Golden Gonads" from **Timmy Tremelo**? Solid lo-fi entertainment from beginning to end.

## HARTBEAT MAGAZINE FLEXIS

The German zine included 7" flexis in each issue, including tracks from **The Infidels, Twink, The Beatitudes** and **Jasmine Love Bomb** in 1988-1989.

## HERE AIN'T THE SONICS
*15 songs, LP/CD, 1989 / Popllama - Estrus Records, USA*

**Nomads**
**Thee Headcoats**
**Girl Trouble**
**The Cynics**
**Mono Men**
**Young Fresh Fellows**

**Original Sins**
**Fallouts**
**Screaming Trees**
**Marshmallow Overcoat**
**Game For Vultures**
**Kings Of Rock**
**Surf Trio**

**The Sonics** were one of the most influential of the original punk garage bands, and this LP paid tribute to their importance. I think it's several cuts above most of the other tribute LPs, and it sold well for several years at least.

## HIPNOSIS
*12 songs, LP, 1991 / Aishna Records, Spain*

**Los Mescaleros**
**Los Bisontes**
**The Philisteins**
**Los Fossiles**
**The Beatpack**
**The Blue Bus**
**The Nomads**
**The Ultra Five**
**The Sick Rose**
**The Sex Museum**
**The Cryptones**
**Los Negativos**

A solid effort put together by *Ansia De Color* fanzine, with a mix of Spanish and world garage acts. A rare early **Cryptones** cut is the real find here.

## IN THE CROWD MAGAZINE FLEXI

This modzine included a 7" flexi with picture sleeve, featuring **Manual Scan** and **The Rick** in issue #18.

## THE INVASION OF THE TAMBOURINE MEN
*LP, 1987 / Tambourine Records, Italy*

**Bad Medicine**
**Peter Sellers & The Hollywood Party**
**Mixed Confusion**
**Silver Surfers**
**Screamin Men Club**
**Acid Flowers**

## IT CAME FROM CANADA LPs, VOLUMES 1 - 5

*OG Records, Canada*

VOLUME 1:
14 songs, 1985
**Deja Voodoo**
**Enigmas**
**Gruesomes**

VOLUME 2:
15 songs, 1986
**Deja Voodoo**
**The Gruesomes**
**Ten Commandments**

VOLUME 3:
15 songs, 1987
**Deja Voodoo**

**The Gruesomes**
**The Ten Commandments**

VOLUME 4:
16 songs, 1988
**Deja Voodoo**
**Gruesomes**

VOLUME 5:
16 songs, 1989
**Vindicators**
**Deja Voodoo**
**Gruesomes**

Each of these five LPs featured the best alternative Canadian music around, with at least a couple garage bands of note on each.

## KALEIDOSCOPE MAGAZINE

*8" flexi, 1987*

**The Shamen**
**The Boys From Nowhere**
**The Woodies**

Like many other zines, *Kaliedoscope* included a flexi with its issues.

## KALEIDOSCOPIC VIBRATIONS

*13 songs, LP, 1989 / Direct Hit Records, USA*

**Nicotine Spiral Surfers**
**The Grovellers**
**Sex Museum**
**Los Negativos**
**The Third Half**
**AED**
**Electric Shields**
**Dimentia 13**
**Viv Akauldren**
**Peter Sellers & The Hollywood Party**
**Sandoz Lime**

*Kaleidoscope*'s follow-up to the *Exploding Underground*, with a few new gems to discover, though more eclectic in nature than its first LP.

## KELT RECORDS 7" COMPILATION EP

*4 songs, 1986? / Kelt Records, Holland*

**The Other Side**
**The Comedown**
**The Happy Tombs**

This EP is worth tracking down for another brilliant **Other Side** track.

## KINETIC VIBES MAGAZINE COMPILATIONS

**The Overcoat**
**Lust-O-Rama**
**Cryptones**
**Ultra 5**

The French fanzine included a 7" in its first issue, 1992. It included previously unreleased cuts and a cut-out picture sleeve.

## LARSEN FANZINE COMPILATIONS

**#1, 1991**
Mescaleros
Vindicators (France)
Flan System
Klames

**#2, 1992**
The Slow Slushy Boys
Teen Appeal
Bookmakers
Cry Babies
Universal Vagrants

**#3, 1992**
The Juanitos
The Overcoat
The Wait
King Size

**#4, 1993**
The Squares
The Jekylls
The Gorgons
The Greenfish
Last Drive

**#5, 1993**
Groggy Holly
Shadowland
Lust-O-Rama
Ultra 5
Greedy Guts
Pyramidiacs

**#6, 1994**
Milkshakes
Lyres
Blue Devils
Crusaders
Turkee Necks
Maki's Bright Experience

**#7, 1995**
The Kliek
Bogeymen
Pray Rien
Dirteez
Preachers
Maybes
Linkers

This French publication includes a 3" mini-CD in each edition, featuring a mix of new and established garage and psych groups from around the globe. These CDs are some of the best mini-comps any magazine has attempted.

## LET'S TALK ABOUT BOYS
## 7" COMPILATION EP
*4 songs, 1988 / Soon To Be Rare Records, Germany*

The Brood
The Wet Ones
The Blue Up?

The name of the record company is appropriate, because this is a rare record, with more great cuts by **The Brood** and two more all-girl groups.

## LIVE IN EUROPE '87
*3 song 7" EP, 1988 / Dionysus Records, USA*

Lee Joseph
Thee Fourgiven
The Unclaimed

This 45 was given away with the first pressing of the *Live In Europe* LP featuring the same acts.

## LIVE IN LONDON
*20 song cassette, 1987 / What Wave Magazine, Canada*

Purple Toads
Vipers
Gruesomes
Link Protrudi & The Jaymen
Headless Horsemen
Cheepskates

An edition of only 500 copies, this collection of bands who blew through London, Ontario at one time or another has some choice cuts for collectors. Sound quality is pretty raw, but is made up for with spirited performances and interesting song selection. Again, plenty of lesser known Canadian bands are also given space here, but it's the U.S. entries that hold the most interest.

## LOSE YOUR MIND
*10 song cassette, circa 1989 / label unknown, Italy*

Sick Rose
Effervescent Elephants
Pikes In Panic
Peter Sellers & the Hollywood Party
Double Deck Five
Birdmen Of Alkatraz
Liars
No Strange
Out Of Time

A good look into the Italian garage underground.

## LOST TRAILS MAGAZINE COMPILATIONS

**#1:**
Technicolour Dream

**#2:**
Sick Rose (alternate version of "Bad Day Blues")
Out Of Time

**#3:**
Ugly Things
The Fuzztones ("live")
The Gravedigger V
The Tell Tale Hearts

#4:
**Backdoor Men** (two "live" songs)
**Effervescent Elephants**

#5:
**Miracle Workers**

#6:
**Stems**

#7:
**The Unclaimed** (two unreleased studio tracks)
**The Vipers**

#8:
**The Thanes** (2 songs)
**The Steppes**

#10:
**Electric Shields**
**Flies**
**Silver Surfers**

This Italian zine was a slick exponent of the garage sound, and included 7" EPs of the top Italian and world garage acts. These 45s are now much sought-after collectibles because of their high quality and band selection.

Several of these feature tracks are available only on these discs — and all of these releases would add up to make a fine compilation album.

## LUCIFER'S FRIENDS
*LP, 1987 / Crazy Mannequin Records, Italy*

**Acid Flower**
**Jazz Butcher** (U.K.)
**Kin Squad & Dinah Shore Headbangers**
**Falling Spikes**
**King Holiday & The Shadowmen**
**Diggers Maze**
**Hitchcock's Scream**
**Degenerazione Musicale**
**Sir Chimes & The Lovers**
**Membranes** (U.K.)
**Pink Silence & Mad Horses**
**Bad Medicine**
**Jacobites** (U.K.)
**Last Train From Drug Hill** (U.K.?)
**Subterranean Dining Rooms**

## MAN OR ASTROMAN / HUEVOS RANCHEROS
*split 7", 1994 / Get Hip Records, USA*

A beautiful full-color cover houses two songs each from Alabama's **Man Or Astroman?** and Canada's **Huevos Rancheros.** (I should note here that not surprisingly the worst Mexican food I ever had was on tour in Canada.)

**Man Or Astroman?** deliver their usual instrumental attack — nothing spectacular but pleasing. **Huevos Rancheros** sound about the same — one would think all of these tracks were by the same band if they hadn't looked on the label.

That doesn't mean that the tracks are not good, just similar — and that's why they were combined for this "split" 45.

## A MIDNIGHT CHRISTMAS MESS
*15 songs, LP, 1984 / Midnight Records, USA*

**Wednesday Week**
**Yard Trauma**
**The Point**
**Suburban Nightmare**
**Cheepskates**
**Tryfles**
**Plan 9**

Midnight released several volumes of its Christmas concept: rock bands doing their own Christmas songs. This was the first of those LPs, and some of it's pretty cool, especially **Wednesday Week, The Point** and **Yard Trauma.**

## A MIDNIGHT CHRISTMAS MESS AGAIN!
*13 songs, LP, 1986 / Midnight Records, USA*

**The Slickee Boys**
**The Vipers**
**The Cheepskates**
**Das Furlines**
**Dimentia 13**

**Das Furlines** are the high point here, with their version of **The Monks** song "Oh How To Do Now" done up as "O Tannenbaum Now." **Dimentia 13** is also as trippy as ever.

## A MIDNIGHT CHRISTMESS PART III

*13 songs, LP, 1987 / Midnight Records, USA*

The Gorehounds
The Brood
Dimentia 13
John Frankovic

**The Brood** are the stars on this third and final installment of Midnight's Christmas collection. A tape of all three playing in the background on Christmas morning is my idea of a good time.

## MINDEXPANDING, Volume 1

*14 songs, LP, 1995 / Destination X Records, Italy*

The 99th Floor
Gips
Head & The Hares
Kartoons
Sciacalli
The Hairy Fairies
La Macchina Del Tempo
I Pirati
The Hermits
Vandali

This is a solid all-Italian collection, with four tracks from **The 99th Floor** as the most obvious highlight. **Head & The Hares** also offer a beautiful folk-rock treat, and **La Macchina Del Tempo** (The Time Machine) gives a spirited version of the **Max Frost** tune "Shape Of Things To Come" — not to be confused with **The Gips**' cover of **The Yardbirds**' "Shapes Of Things."

Future volumes look promising, reflecting what appeared to be in 1995 a resurgent Italian '60s punk/garage scene.

## MISFIT - A TRIBUTE TO THE OUTSIDERS

*14 songs, LP, 1992? / Screaming Apple Records, Germany*

The Morlocks
The Thanes
The Quatloos
The Dukes
The Birminghams
The Ultra 5
The Mono Men
The Lust-O-Rama
The What...For!
The Beatpack
The Kliek
The Gretsch
The Tell Tale Hearts
The Eastern Green

**The Outsiders** are one of the most influential beat bands of all time, so it's

fitting that many of the 1980s best beat-inspired acts get a crack at paying homage. **The Thanes, Dukes, What...For!, Beatpack, Kliek** and **Tell Tale Hearts** have carried on in the best **Outsiders** tradition for years, so it's no surprise that they also shine here.

This isn't a crack on the following bands, but what are **The Mono Men** and the **Ultra 5** doing on this album? They don't show any Nederbeat influences in their own material, so it's odd to hear them included in this tribute. Their tracks aren't bad — and **The Ultra 5** is actually very good — I just wonder how they ended up here.

No matter — this is an excellent tip of the hat to **The Outsiders**, and that's what it set out to be, regardless of the acts involved.

## MOVIMENTI ITALIANI '91

*LP, 1991 / Autoprodotto Records, Italy*

Twenty Four Hours
Thee Trouble
Groovers
The Stolen Cars

## MR. GARAGERS NEIGHBOURHOOD

*17 songs, LP, 1989 / What Wave Records, Canada*

10 Commandments
The Vindicators
The Chessmen
Thee Fourgiven
Sporting Bachelors
The Cynics
Mystic Eyes
The Gruesomes
Ultra 5

The tireless workers at *What Wave* magazine put this out, giving equal time to Canadian and world garage bands alike. Rock'n'roll would be cool and thriving throughout the world if these folks had their way. As it is, we'll just have to settle for some cool **Cynics**, **Mystic Eyes**, **Vindicators** and **Gruesomes**.

## THE MUMMIES VS. THE WOLFMEN

*4 songs, 2 x 7" 45s, 1991 / S.F.T.R.I. Records, USA*

**The Mummies**
**The Wolfmen**

The packaging is the best park of this two-45s set. A 10 page 7" comic book detailing the battle between **Wolfmen** and **Mummies** is included as the sleeve.

As for the music, **The Wolfmen** tracks are serious let-downs after their solid debut 45. The "Insane In An Insane World" is a pedestrian slow dirge, while the flip is a very common rockabilly track, which makes sense since **The Fly Rite Trio** is the backing act for vocalist Mark Lee Goodale.

**The Mummies'** "Victim Of Circumstances" is actually (and surprisingly) one of their better efforts, though the recording is minimal at best. Yet another lame version of "Land Of 1000 Dances" (a song I really don't like) fills out the disc.

And the winner is ... **The Mummies,** by default.

## THE MUNSTER DANCE HALL FAVORITES

*4 songs, 7", 1987 / Teenager From Outer Space Records, Spain*

**Surfin' Lungs**
**Sex Museum**
**Spacemen 3**
**Enemigos**

Yet another magazine releasing a comp, with some obscure and cool tunes. The parent *La Herencia De Los Munster Magazine* included a 7" flexi with **The Landlords** and **The Shoutless** in its 1987 issue #7.

## THE MUSIC MANIAC GIMMICK COMPILATION

*11 songs, 2 LPs, 1989 / Music Maniac Records, Germany*

Record #1, side A:
**Shane Faubert** "Yesterday's Leaves"
**Dizzy Satellites** "Time Has Come"
**Last Drive** "Hell To Pay"

Record #1, side B:
**Droogs** "San Quentin"
**Mark Embatta** "Winter"
**Daisy Chain** "Rebellion"

Record #2, side A:
**Fuzztones** "Ward 81"
**Vietnam Veterans** "Wolf"

Record #2, side B:
**Link Protrudi & The Raymen** "Black Widow"
**Miners Of Muzo** "Night Of The Miner"
**Cheepskates** "Bite The Bullet"

I list the tracks specifically for this "gimmick" compilation with good reason: There are intentionally no labels printed on the records, and the records are pressed on clear vinyl — which makes it impossible to find the grooves for individual songs.

The groups and songs are listed on an insert, and to make sense of it all you must do what I did — listen carefully to all four sides and play detective to recognize each artist and song. I've done that work, so if you find this rare record all you have to do is figure out which record is #1 and which is #2!

Oh, the tracks are pretty cool, but probably not worth the big bucks this item is commanding on the collectors' market.

## NEOLITHIC SOUNDS FROM SOUTH EUROPE

*LP, 198? / Electric Eye Records, Italy*

**Silver Surfers**
**Avvoltoi**
**Monks**
**Superflui**
**Electric Shields**
**Storks**
**Five For Garage**
**Primeteens**

This looks to be a fine collection of Italian garage acts, though I haven't been able to track down a copy.

## A NIGHT WITH A CRAZY MANNEQUIN

*Cassette, 1990 / Crazy Mannequin Records, Italy*

Peter Sellers & The Hollywood Party
Subterranean Dining Rooms
Mr. Jones
Views
Backwards
Crazy Blues
Red Roses In The Sand

A promo-only cassette.

## 99TH FLOOR MAGAZINE FLEXIS

| #1: 1983 (7") | #2: 1985 (10") |
|---|---|
| The Fuzztones | The Brood |
| The Vipers | Boys From Nowhere |
| Plasticland | Tell Tale Hearts |
| | The Podz |

These are amazing (and rare) documents of the early-'80s U.S. garage scene, with some essential and rare songs. Grab these if you ever see them — they are indispensable relics from the early 1980s garage explosion.

## NOW PUT ON YOUR FACE AND JOIN THE RACE

*4 song 7" EP, 1994? / Demolition Derby Records, Belgium*

The Squares
The Perverts
Percolators
Sin Alley

I thought I had heard too many covers of **The Seeds'** "Pushin Too Hard," but **The Squares** make it all new somehow — maybe it's their total trash treatment, complete with added "stronger than dirt" chord progression. My faves **The Perverts** add "Ik Ben Zo Wild, Man!," which is a clever re-working of **The Tamron's** "Wildman" sung in Dutch.

The flip has **The Percolators**, a band I'm not familiar with at all, with a frantic track called "Save It." They apparently have many releases out on various labels, but that's all I know about this German act. **Sin Alley** is another band that I haven't heard before, this time from Belgium. Their "Zack" is an unremarkable rockabilly tinged tune with female vocals.

## OH MY GOD, MY MOTHER'S ON CHANNEL 10

*16 songs, LP, 1989 / Nardwuar Records, Canada*

The Mighty Squirrels
Enigmas
Gruesomes
Vindicators
Headless Horsemen
The Smugglers
The Event
Double Naught Spys
The Chessmen
Tell Tale Hearts
The Evaporators

A worthy Canadian comp with some fine examples of zit-teen-angst — and some good songs too. This was the **Double Naught Spys** vinyl debut, with the wonderfully titled "One More Beer."

## ON THE ROCKS

*4 song, 7" EP, 1990 / Gift Of Life Records, Germany*

Mono Men
Marble Orchard
Game For Vultures
Roofdogs

More rare tracks from the Washington state Estrus label of noise.

## ORACOLO

*2 LPs, 1988 / Toast Records, Italy*

Side A
Italian Beat Bands 1966-1967

Side B
**No Strange** "Bom Shankar Suite"

Side C
**Lestelle Di M. Sehifano** (Psych 1967)
**Ezzu & Richiero**
**Vegetable Men**
**Peter Sellers & The Hollywood Party**

Side D
**Massimiliano Casacci**
**Afterhours**
**Act**
**Difference**
**Double X**

Apparently a mixture of original 1960s garage and their 1980s counterparts.

## THE OTHERS / THE HEADSTONES

*4 song 7" EP, 1993 / Misty Lane Records, Italy*

**The Others**
**The Headstones**

**The Others'** brilliant originals "It's Eerie" and "Fallin' Off My World" are also on their debut *Teen Trash* LP, joined here with two other cool tunes from Massimo Del Pozzo's side-band **The Headstones.** They're a couple more fine fuzz and Farfisa '66-styled punkers.

## THE OTHERS / THE MOLE PEOPLE

*4 song 7" EP, 1992? / Primitive Records, Canada*

**The Others**
**The Mole People**

Three more essential **Others** garage punkers, with a cut from yet another **Massimo Del Pozzo** side-project, **The Mole People.** A demo exists of several more crude demo recordings of **The Mole People** — all in a very cool '66 mode.

## THE OTHERS / STOICI / CROAKERS / FOSSILS

*4 song 7" EP, 1994? / Misty Lane Records, Italy*

**The Others**
**Stoici**
**Croakers**
**Fossils**

A collection of four Italian garage combos: **The Others'** offering here is a very crude and authentic-sounding punk ballad titled "Poor Man's Thing." The Croakers contribute "I'm In Love With Her," a toe-tapping caveman special with cool organ and a great crash cymbal sound. **Stoici** deliver a faithfully moody reading of "Sun's Going Down," while **The Fossils** blast out "We're The Fossils," with a twisted addled energy. Dig that lo-fi mono sound!

## PENGUINS AND BONDAGE

*19 songs, LP, 1992 / That's Entertainment Records, Norway*

| | |
|---|---|
| Anal Babes | The Willy B. Review |
| Peau De Peche | Cavebones |
| Monsters Of Doom | The Lust-O-Rama |
| Consumers | Trbngr |
| Der Schnell Orkester | The Cutbacks |
| Thee Baloonatics | The Tempo Toppers |
| The Time Lodgers | Graceland |
| Kare & The Cavemen | Astroburger |
| Kung Fu Girls | T-zers |
| The Bogeymen | |

A very mixed bag of Norwegian underground styles, with the **Monsters Of Doom**'s "Tabletop Surfer" a twangey little treat, **The Time Lodgers'** "Okay!" a sweet **Beatles**que power pop snack, **Kare & The Cavemen**'s frantic "Monster A-Go-Go" and the **Kung Fu Girls'** punk-pop "Girls" the highlights of side one.

The flip includes the always-fun **Bogeymen** and **The Lust-O-Rama,** whose track also appears on one of their EPs. **The Cavebones** deliver a very distorted and funny "I'm The Wolfman," while **Astroburger** adds a very mellow ballad. And what the hell is that weird woman singing at the end of side two?

## PEOPLE ARE STRANGE #1

*Cassette, 198? / People Are Strange Magazine, Italy*

**Mr. Jones**
**Peter Sellers & The Hollywood Party**
**POW**
**Backwards**
**Subterranean Dining Rooms**
**Degenerazione Musicale**
**Funhouse**
**Live At Backdoors**

## PSYCHEDELIC PSAUNA

*23 songs, 2 x LPs, 1991 / Delerium Records, U.K.*

Sundial
Magic Mushroom Band
Nick Riff
The Petals
The Porcupine Tree
Poisoned Electrick Head
The Bevis Frond
Alice's Orb
John Fallon
The Gothics
Tyrnaround

The Coloured Plank
Cosmic Kangaroos
Reefus Moons
Marshmallow Overcoat
Mandragora
Dr. Brown
Orzic Tentacles
The Jasmine Love Bomb
Dimentia 13
The Trodds
Treatment

This also appeared as a CD, I believe, with a few less tracks than the vinyl. This was *Freakbeat Magazine*'s first long-playing compilation, which was seemingly in the works for several years — and was well worth the wait.

The best samplers are both engaging and demanding, and *Psychedelic Psuana* scores highly — so to speak — on both points. Old familiar favorites like **Bevis Frond** and **Dimentia 13** are present, along with some welcome tastes of excellent newcomers such as **The Petals** and **Reefus Moons** — who would both go on to produce some stellar tracks well into the mid 1990s.

The balance between the garagey, poppy and trippy selections is well thought out, and the colorfully bizarre cover artwork is a perfect compliment to the sounds.

The folks at Delerium and *Freakbeat* pour their love and enthusiasm into each of their projects — and *Psychedelic Psauna* stands as a monument to their musical devotion.

## PTOLEMAIC TERRESCOPE MAGAZINE 7" COMPILATION EPs

*#5:*
Dead Moon
Napalm Beach

*#6:*
Randy California
Current 93

*#7:*
Sundial
Dave Jackson
The Overcoat
T.S. McPhee

*#8:*
Richard Sinclair's Caravan Of Dreams
Nurse With Wound
The Underworlde

*#9:*
The Green Pajamas
Mandragora
Mick Hutchinson

*#10:*
Mooseheart Faith
Grooveyard
Dr. Brown

*#11*
The Jim McCarty Band
The Magic Mushroom Band
Ian Matthews

*#12:*
Kaleidoscope
White Heaven

*#14:*
Wall Of Sleep
The Sidekicks
Medicine Ball
Jane Pow

*#15:*
Mike Gunn
S.F.H.
Pearls Before Swine

The U.K. zine included EPs in each and every issue, with the odd distinction of not having labels on the records, with the song titles etched into the vinyl! Not all of these tracks apply to the garage/psych genre — some are noise, experimental atmosphere sounds, or jams — but most are of keen interest to garage fans.

## PUGET POWER 7" COMPILATION EP

*4 songs, 1989 / Regal Select Records, USA*

Mono Men
Fallouts
Nights And Days
Sugar Sugar

More Washington garage blasts, with **The Mono Men** in the lead.

## PUNTO ZERO LPs & FANZINES, VOLUMES 1-4, 7-8

*Toast Records, Italy*

Volume 1
**Statuto**
**Barbieri**
**Hey Joe**
**Wells Fargo**
**Peter Sellers & The Hollywood Party**

Volume 2
**Vegetable Men**
**AfterHours**
**Dreamachine**
**Liars**

Volume 3
**No Strange**
**The Trouble**

Volume 4
**Snowdrops**

Volume 7
**Starfuckers**
**Moonshiner**

Volume 8
**Joe Perrino & The Mellowtones**
**Cellophane Flowers**

## RAW CUTS LPs, VOLUMES 1 - 7

*Satellite Records, U.K.*

*VOLUME 1: FRANCE, 1985*
**Les Thugs**
**Les Coronados**
**Les Scurs**
**Flamingos**

*VOLUME 2: SWEDISH BEAT*
*16 songs, 1986*
**Hidden Charms**
**Dr. Yogami**
**Backdoor Men**
**The Bottle Ups**
**Slobster**
**The Sinners**
**Problem**
**The Slammers**

*VOLUME 3: GERMAN UNDERGROUND*
*16 songs, 1987*
**Legendary Golden Vampires**
**Dizzy Satellites**
**Nirvana Devils**
**The Chud**
**The Broken Jug**
**The Beatitudes**
**Les Black Carnations**
**Shiny Gnomes**

*VOLUME 4: AUSTRALIAN NITRO*
*15 songs, 1987*
**Mad Turks From Istanbul**
**The Assassins**
**Liz Dealey & The Twenty Second Sect**
**The Spikes**
**Bloodless**

**The Coneheads**
**Fear And Loathing**
**King Snake Roost**
**Primevils**

*VOLUME 5: SWEDISH BEAT #2*
*16 songs, 1987*
**The Hijackers**
**The Preachers**
**Highspeed V**
**Cornflake Zoo**
**The Undertakers**
**Bangsters**
**Subterraneans**
**Crimson Shadows**

*VOLUME 6: AMERICAN PSYCH WARS*
*16 songs, 1987*
**The Dwarves**
**Marshmallow Overcoat**
**Thee Fourgiven**
**The Time Beings**
**Royal Nonesuch**
**The Marsupials**
**Yard Trauma**
**The Cattle**

*VOLUME 7: U.K. GARAGE DISEASE*
*21 songs, 1988*
**The Thanes**
**The Aardvarks**
**Purple People Eaters**
**The Offhooks**
**Melaroony Daddies**
**Tyme Eliment**
**The Stayrcase**
**The Morticians**
**The Beatpack**
**Beeville Hive V**
**The Beat Poets**

These was a generally excellent comp series, with each volume covering a different country's scene. Especially noteworthy are the Swedish, U.S. and U.K. editions, with a plethora of cool rare and unreleased tunes each.

The man behind Satellite/Beat International, Chris Green, mysteriously disappeared one day, along with all the bands' master tapes! I'd like to hear from him some day...

## A REAL COOL TIME:
## DISTORTED SOUNDS FROM THE NORTH
*14 songs, LP, 1985 / Amigo Records, Sweden*

The Nomads
The Bottle Ups
Wilmer X
Watermelon Men
Dr. Yogami
Slobster
The Creeps
Problem
Hidden Charms
The Shoutless
Wayward Souls
The Preachers
Occasional Dead Flys
The Pyromaniacs

This is probably the best Swedish sampler of the time, and a good place to see what all the fuss (and fuzz) was about. An alternative mix of **The Watermelon Men**'s "Back In My Dreams" is especially worth the search.

## THE REBEL KIND
*14 songs, LP, 1983 / Sounds Interesting Records, USA*

The Sickidz
The Unclaimed
The Slickee Boys
The Point
The Viceroys
Plasticland
The Shout
Miracle Workers
The Nomads
The Long Ryders
United States Of Existence
The Last
True West
Fuzztones

This LP has become one of the landmark 1980s compilations — a signpost of sorts — similar to the Voxx *Battle Of The Garages* series. **The United States Of Existence** offer a great cut, as do **The Slickee Boys** and **The Miracle Workers**. Many of the tracks are previously released from then-current LPs, but they are also some of the strongest songs ever from **The Point**, **True West** and **Long Ryders**.

I've worn out the term "essential," but it applies here as well. The LP has since been re-issued in Europe with a different cover design.

## ROCKABILLY PSYCHOSIS AND THE GARAGE DISEASE

This 1984 Big Beat Records release was described to me by fan David Kerekes as *"an uneasy mix of original (1960s) numbers (such as 'Psycho' by **The Sonics**) and (1980s psychobilly) stuff such as **The Meteors**, **The Sting-Rays** and **Guana Bats**."*

## ROCK AGAINST PROHIBITIONISM
*LP, 1990 / Wide Records - Stampa Alternativa, Italy*

Funhouse
A-10
Celibate Rifles (Australia)
Unlimited
Afterhours
What Tyler (U.K.?)
Magic Potion
Ravings
Electric Manchakou (U.K.)
Not Moving

## ROCKBEEF
*LP, 1988 / Tramite Records, Italy*

Views
Settore Out
Kim Squadand (2 songs)
Liars (2 songs)
Not Moving (2 songs)

A "live" recording.

## ROMANTISCHE STRASSE
*Cassette, 198? / label?, Italy*

Steeplejack
Keep Away From Children
Nightdriving Gossip
Birdmen Of Alkatraz
Effervescent Elephants
Magic Potion
Kryptastesie
Harley Davidson Philosophist
Joe & The Family Stoned
Grey Coffeepot
Subterranean Dining Rooms

## THE RUTA 66 ALBUM
*18 songs, LP & CD, 1991 / Capote Records, Spain*

**The Overcoat**
**Chris Wilson**
**Paul Roland**
**The Raunch Hands**

This fine Spanish magazine released their own compilation LP late in 1991, featuring many of the bands that regularly graced their pages — several of them fit nicely into the garage/psych/trash category. Chris Wilson's acoustic version of his **Flamin' Groovies** classic "You Tore Me Down" is undoubtedly the highlight, and worth the price of admission alone.

## SEARCHING FOR COOL
*4 songs, 1994 / Corduroy Records, Australia*

**The Daytonas**
**The Saucermen**
**Teengenerate**
**The Breadmakers**

Only 500 of these little buggers were pressed, and include some suitable crude garage, R&B and punk from Sweden, Australia and Japan. The run-out groove states, *"The Last indie 7" made in Australia — Nov. 1994.* Are all the vinyl pressing plants in Australia now defunct!?!

## THE SECOND BELGIUM 6T's BOOM
## VOLUME 1
*16 songs, LP, 1987 / Waterloo Sunset Records, U.K.*

**The Sandmen**
**The Some Kinda Weird**
**The Marsians**
**The Office**
**Eliot Ness**
**The Clan**
**A Beatboy**
**The Voners**
**Rockfort**
**The Spanks**
**The Leftovers**
**The Faling Fellows**

This is the first in the very artistically successful compilation series of Belgian garage, mod and pop acts from the mid to late 1980s. **The Office**'s "Your Loving" is a

beautifully melodic pop ballad, catchy without being sickly sweet, while **The Clan**'s "Bring On The Booze" is just the opposite — a leering, fuzzy bit of harmless and smirking fun.

## THE SECOND BELGIUM 6T's BOOM
## VOLUME 2
*14 songs, LP, 1988 / Waterloo Sunset Records, U.K.*

**The Midnight Men**
**The Strikes**
**The Moonrakers**
**I Love Lucy**
**Hysterical Young Insects**
**The Garbage Gang**
**The Some Kinda Weird**
**The Uncalled Wyld-Tones**
**Rebble Pebble**
**The Magic Minstrels**
**The Paranoid Polaroids**

Another solid collection of many bands that I've only heard here. This is one of those cases where a compilation serves its purpose, by making a variety of bands available that the casual music buyer — or dedicated researcher — would ordinarily miss.
Especially cool here **The Garbage Gang**'s garage punk "Wanna Get Away" and **The Some Kind Weird**'s chimingly snotty "Walked My Body Home."

## SNAP! CRACKLE! POP!
*15 songs, LP, 1992 / Twist Records, U.K./Germany*

**The Miracle Birds**
**The Cutbacks**
**The Lust-O-Rama**
**The Breadmakers**
**The Mild Mannered Janitors**
**The Studio 68!**
**Jane Pow**
**The Nerve**
**The Sacred Hearts**
**The Shadowland**
**E.J. Quit**
**Soon**
**Peau De Peche**
**The Cosmic Dropouts**
**The Cybermen**
**The Lust-O-Rama**

An international collection, with Norway's **Cutbacks** delivering a very energetic punk-pop ditty, Australia's **Breadmakers** doing a somewhat uncharacteristic (and cool) surf instrumental and **The Lust-O-Rama** slicing through "Soapy" — a song I know something about myself.
**The Cosmic Dropouts**' "Gone Gone Gone" and **The Cybermen**'s instrumental "Way Out" highlight

the flip side, which is marred somewhat by several lightweight mod pop acts.

## SOME KINDA WEIRDOS IN THAT CAVE THERE!

*35 songs, cassette, 1992 / Cryptic Tymes Magazine, Canada*

**1313 Mockingbird Lane**
**Slow Slushy Boys**
**Tommyknockers**
**Prehistoric Cave Strokers**
**Thee Flypped Whigs**
**The Evil Hoodoos**
**The Cryptones**
**The Graverobbers**
**The Backwards**
**The Orange Alabaster Mushroom**
**The Overcoat**
**The Stormclouds**
**The Watch Children**
**The M-80s**
**Marble Orchard**
**14th Wray**

Alan Wright put together one of the most colorful collections for this cassette-only release. **The Flypped Whigs** debut with a couple crude practice session cuts, including a suitably crude version of **The Marshmallow Overcoat**'s "She's So Satisfyin.'" Other bands like **The Evil Hoodoos** and **Prehistoric Cave Strokers** seemingly appear only on Canadian compilation cassettes, and throw in some crude efforts here as well.

Italy's **The Backwards** delivers a sizzling version of "Tomorrow Never Knows," while **The Watch Children, 14th Wray**, and **The Orange Alabaster Mushroom** bring the totally whigged-out garage-psych to the party. A winner from start to finish.

## SOMETHING ABOUT JOY DIVISION (A TRIBUTE TO JOY DIVISION)

*LP, 1991 / Vox Pop Records, Italy*

**Allison Run**
**Silver Surfers**
**Comie Spoilers**
**Afterhours**
**Subterranean Dining Rooms**

## SOUNDS FROM THE LOWER SONORAN DESERT (L.S.D.)

*11 song cassette 1992 / Acid Tapes, U.K.*

**Marshmallow Overcoat**
**River Roses**
**Deadbolts**
**Black Sun Ensemble**

**Cryptics**
**Johnies**
**Sidewinders**
**The Cattle**

Here's another compilation produced by this author. The idea was to get all of these Tucson groups to record at the same studio, with the same producer, resulting in a more consistent product.

The tapes were completed, then Voxx lost the cover art and band photos, then eventually dropped the LP from its production schedule! I have the last laugh, however, as these tracks have now seen the day as a cassette release on Acid Tapes in England.

(Two of the songs have also appeared as a 45 for **The Cattle, The Marshmallow Overcoat** track was on their *All You Need Is Fuzz* CD, and the **Black Sun** track showed up on one of their LPs.)

## SOUNDS OF NOW

*16 songs, LP, 1987 / Dionysus Records, USA*

| | |
|---|---|
| **Zebra Stripes** | **The Last Drive** |
| **The Legendary Golden** | **Yard Trauma** |
| **Vampires** | **The Special Ones** |
| **The Beguiled** | **The Brood** |
| **Al Perry** | **The Cynics** |
| **Thee Fourgiven** | **The Untold Fables** |
| **Jonny Sevin** | **The Lazy Cowgirls** |
| **The Chud** | |

Dionysus flew into the compilation race with this fine disc. Especially interesting is the vinyl appearance of an early **Jonny Sevin** track, as well as **Al Perry**'s "Glue Sniffin' Revival."

## A SPLASH OF COLOUR
*12 song LP, 1982 / Warner Bros. Records, U.K.*

**Mood Six**
**The Times**
**Miles Over Matter**
**The Silence**
**The High Tide**
**The Earwigs**
**The Doctor**
**The Barracudas**
**The Marble Staircase**

One of the first so-called "psychedelic revival" compilation LPs to be released in England, and by a major label no less. It proved to be more noteworthy as a signal of things to come, since much of the LP is weak and more identifiable with the mod revival of the day.

## SPLENDID MAGAZINE FLEXI

This German zine included the rare **Stems** tracks "No Heart" and "Lon Chaney Junior's Daughter" on a 7" flexi in their second issue. These 1984 sessions were released circa 1990.

## STOMPING AT THE KLUBFOOT

*Volume 1: 16 songs, LP, 198? / ABC Records, U.K.*

A live compilation LP featuring four bands with four songs each. **The Stingrays** deliver a cover of a **Seeds** song and **The Bad Roads'** "Blue Girl."

*Volume 2: 14 songs, LP, 198? / ABC Records, U.K.*

Seven bands with two songs each this time, with **The Tall Boys** giving us yet another version of "Action Woman," and the original "Ride This Torpedo."

## STONEAGE CASSETTE
*12 song cassette, 1987 / Stoneage Magazine, Italy*

**Creeps**
**Stomachmouths**
**Sick Rose**
**Running Stream**
**Liars**
**Ribelli Cromati**
**Avvoltoi**
**The Mystery Kings**

Another do-it-yourself cassette comp by a magazine.

## STONEAGE CASSETTE
*Cassette, 198? / Stoneage Magazine, Italy*

**Fleshtones**
**Lyres**
**Vipers**
**Thee Fourgiven**
**Statuto**
**Subterranean Dining Rooms**
**Degenerazione Musicale**
**Peter Sellers & The Hollywood Party**

The magazine's follow-up compilation, sporting another stellar lineup.

## TALES FROM ESTRUS
*4 songs, 7" EP, 1991 / Estrus Records, USA*

**Night Kings**
**Ultra 5**
**Marble Orchard**
**The Mummies**

Another super-creepy psych track from **The Ultra 5** is the highlight here, along with the ever-crude **Mummies**. (Have I mentioned before that they *dress like mummies?*)

## TANT QU'IL Y AURA DU ROCK, VOL. 1
*16 songs, LP, 1988 / Stop It Baby Records, France*

**The Trembles**
**Les Maniacs**
**The Cannibals**
**Lombego Surfers**
**The Miners Of Muzo**
**The Dukes**
**Drastic Gastric**
**Lost Patrol**
**The Vipers**
**Yard Trauma**
**The Sporting Bachelors**

**The Trembles'** cuts are worth the price of admission alone, plus the inclusion of some obscure Euro-garage bands with their only vinyl available. The *Tant Qu'il Y Aura Du Rock Magazine* #10/11 also included a 7" flexi with **Yard Trauma, Freewheelin' Trio** and **The Tamrons**.

## THESE DOGS LIVE IN THE GARAGE
*15 songs, LP, 1987 / Arf Arf Records, USA*

**The Tweeds**
**The Demons Of Negativity**
**The Fugitives**

This is noteworthy for the studio in-joke track by **The Demons Of Negativity**, which is in the finest '60s-psych-novelty tradition. Its similarity to "The Diamond Mine" off of the first *Pebbles* '60s garage compilation is unmistakable.

## THIS AIN'T THE PLIMSOULS
*21 tracks CD, 1992 / Zero Hour Records, Australia*

**The Chevelles**
**The Kryptonics**
**The Barbellas**
**The Plunderers**
**The Slaters**
**Fear Of Falling**
**The Pyramidiacs**
**The Diehards**
**The Lonelyhearts**
**The Crusaders**
**The Clockwatchers**

**Chopper**
**27 Various**
**The Dangtrippers**
**The Droogs**
**The Wishniaks**
**Head Candy**
**The Mandrakes**
**Sick Rose**
**Los Valendas**
**Slep & The Redhouse**

Obviously a power-pop **Plimsouls** tribute, but of unknown quality.

## TIME BOMB: THE BIG BAND THEORY
*12 songs, LP, 1987 / Skyclad Records, USA*

**Mad Violets**
**Love Delegation**
**Fleshtones**

Here's an LP of **Fleshtones** odds and ends, plus efforts by their friends. Once again we are treated to a previously unreleased **Mad Violets** track, which makes this a valuable find.

## TOKYO FLASHBACK #2
*11 song CD, 1992 / P.S.F. Records, Japan*

**White Heaven**
**High Rise**
**Marble Sheep**
**Overhang Party**
**Ghost**

The second in a series of compilation CDs highlighting the heavy late 1960s inspired Tokyo psychedelic underground. For fans of more "progressive," less pop-oriented psych.

## TOTAL DEEP
*14 song Cassette, 198? / private release, Italy*

**Night Driving Gossip**
**Blue Tempo**
**Vodka Kafka**
**Standard Deviation**
**Anarchic Pine-Apple**

## A TOWN WITHOUT PITY
*29 song cassette, 1983 / Iconoclast International, USA*

**The Hecklers**
**Yard Trauma**
**Rotte Kapelle**

This is a very rare release, with only a couple hundred making it out the door. The quality throughout is top-notch, however, and displays some fine cuts of garage and psych. The totally unknown (inside and outside of Tucson) **Rotte Kapelle** contribute some acid-drenched tunes, and **Yard Trauma** adds some unreleased early tracks as well. **The Hecklers** (pre-**Cattle**) deliver the fuzz as well, but this a sadly unrecognized collection of local Tucson, Arizona talent, circa 1983. When I read in magazines about the "1980s Tucson Sound," it's bands like these that one should think of, not pretenders like **Giant Sand** or **Green On Red**!

## TRACCE 85 - BATTLE OF THE BANDS
*LP, 1985 / Radio Records, Italy*

**Sick Rose**
**Hidden Charm**
**Psycho Farm**
**Double Deck Five**
**Party Kids**
**Prostitutes**

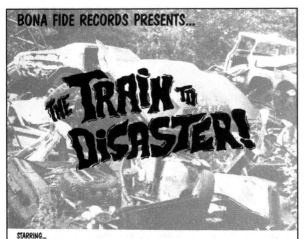

BONA FIDE RECORDS PRESENTS...

**THE TRAIN TO DISASTER!**

STARRING...

BILLY SYNTH & THE TURNUPS · YARD TRAUMA · THE VELVET MONKEYS
THE LONE KETAMINE MILLIPEDE · THE SLICKEE BOYS · THE MAD VIOLETS
GEORGE BRIGMAN & SPLIT · THE LEFT · THE DOOTZ · THE BEATNIK FLIES
BEN WAH and special guests from Austria RONNIE URINI & THE LAST POETS

## TRAIN TO DISASTER

*13 songs, LP, 1983 / Bona Fide Records, USA*

The Beatnik Flies
The Dootz
The Slickee Boys
Yard Trauma
The Velvet Monkeys
The Mad Violets

Notable for yet another early **Mad Violets** track, plus a great **Yard Trauma** song, and an incredibly dumb and enjoyably funny track by **The Dootz**.

## TRY ONE OF THESE...

*4 song 7" EP, 1992 / Moxie Records, USA*

The Overcoat
Falling Spikes
The Worst
14th Wray

This author compiled these fave acts, giving the **14th Wray** and **The Worst** their vinyl debut. Both deliver finely crude slabs of garage-adelia.

## TUNES FROM THE CRYPT

*21 song cassette, 1990 / Cryptic Tymes Magazine, Canada*

Marshmallow Overcoat
The Mourning After
Smugglers
Jigsaw Seen
14th Wray
Sanity Assassins
Beatpack
Night Stalkers
The Cattle

Deja Voodoo
Al Perry
The Hurtin Kind
Prehistoric Cave Strokers

This is the first cassette comp from the first issue of this Canadian zine. Sound quality is uneven, but **The Cattle** deliver a moody version of "Little Black Egg," **The Cave Strokers** add a hilarious "Cave Bangin'," and the **Night Stalkers** give us a cool cut from their demo. Add an unreleased **Overcoat** track and some **Beatpack**, and you have a comp worth searching out.

## TUNES FROM TUCSON

*24 song cassette, 1987 / Sitting Duck Studios, USA*

Deadbolts
Marshmallow Overcoat
The Cattle

By 1987 many music insiders were looking at Tucson to be the next big "underground" music center, similar to Athens (GA) or Austin or Seattle. There was enough interest to put together some comp tapes for consumption outside of Arizona, and this was one successful example. (Lee Joseph of **Yard Trauma** had started the series of local comps in 1981!) While a wide range of styles were represented, the garage flag was carried by the folky-pop of **The Deadbolts**, early fuzz of **The Overcoat** and distorted wailings of **The Cattle**.

## UNHINGED MAGAZINE FLEXIS

This U.K. fanzine published sporadically throughout the '80s, including 7" flexis with picture sleeves in each issue. They included **The Stormclouds** in 1988, **Wednesday Week** in 1989, **The Chemistry Set** in 1990 and **The Green Pajamas** in 1992. This author also had a flexi slated for a 1992 release, and I'm still waiting for it to appear — and I'm told periodically that it will.

## UNICORN VOLUME ONE & TWO LPs
*Unicorn Records, U.K.*

ONE: 12 songs, LP, 1987
**The Leopards**

TWO: 12 songs, LP, 1987
**High Style**
**Sex Museum**

This mainly mod label put out a few surprises, including tracks from these cool acts.

## UNLOVED: A TRIBUTE TO ARTHUR LEE & LOVE
*4 songs, two 45s, 1994 / Chunk Records, USA*

**The Lyres**
**The Veronica Cartwrights**

**The Lyres'** "live" version of "Signed D.C." is passable, but that tune has simply seen far too many cover versions for it to have much of an impact. **The Veronica Cartwrights** clock in with an interesting take on "Message To Pretty" — faithful enough to the original but with a different flair. Two other dreadful bands destroy "My Little Red Book" and "Can't Explain" in a truly head scratching manner.

There was also a full-length **Love** tribute in 1994 by another U.S. label that is reportedly very poor.

## VALLEY FEVER
*28 song cassette, 1982 / Iconoclast International, USA*

**Stainless Steel Kimono**
**Green On Red**

The aptly titled *Valley Fever* was Lee Joseph's first venture into compilations, and an ambitious undertaking at that. 28 tracks of mostly "New Wave" exuberance is documented with great success. There's an energetic charm in most of the material, though most of it does land outside the garage/psych genre.

Two notable exceptions are a **Jefferson Airplane**-ish track from the oddly named **Stainless Steel Kimono,** and a raw live psych recording of **Green On Red**'s "Apartment Six". Remember, **Green On Red** were *not* based in Tucson, but this track was recorded at a bar there.

## THE WAKING DREAM
*13 songs, LP, 1985 / Psycho Records, U.K.*

**Green Telescope**
**The Mood Six**
**Magic Mushroom Band**

This U.K. sampler misses the mark in most cases, but is absolutely essential (there's that word again) for the early **Green Telescope** tracks, especially the creepy version of "I'm A Living Sickness."

## WARFRAT TALES
*14 songs, LP, 1983 / WarfRat Records, USA*

**Rain Parade**
**The Last**
**Wednesday Week**
**The Question?**
**The Point**

Here's a great look at the L.A. "Paisley Underground" before anyone was really paying attention. The recordings are rough and honest, and evoke a great sense of energy. The **Rain Parade** tracks are alternate mixes of songs that eventually ended up on their landmark debut LP.

## WAVE FROM THE GRAVE #2
*24 song cassette, 1986? / What Wave Magazine, Canada*

**The Gruesomes**
**10 Commandments**
**Purple Toads**
**Projectiles**
**Merik Trout Pact**
**Klepstones**
**Psych Out**
**Janice K., "The Lady Elvis"**
**The Cheshyres**
**Royal Nonesuch**

Lots of Canadians represented here, of course, but I especially liked France's **Psych Out**, Missouri's **Royal Nonesuch**, and Rochester's **Projectiles**. Of course, there's also outer space's **Janice K., "The Lady Elvis"**. Come to think about it, perhaps Janice *is* **Elvis**. Have you ever seen them both in the same room at the same time?!? If I haven't already mentioned it, *What Wave* should get a special award for helping make so many bands available to interested listeners. Their series of cassette compilations is unrivaled in this world.

## A WEB OF MYSTERY
*4 song 7" EP, 1993 / Misty Lane, Italy*

**The Overcoat**
**The Others**
**The Lears**
**Lust-O-Rama**

Another fine effort from Brian '66 at Misty Lane, with **The Others** and **The Lears** especially engaging. This release also has a beautiful op-art cover as well.

## WEIRD OUT! THE SWEDISH GARAGE SCENE 1986-1992
*16 songs, LP, 1994 / Misty Lane Records, Italy (included bonus **Wylde Mammoths** 4 song 7" EP)*

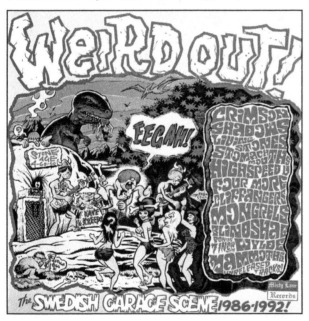

**Livingstones**
**Blindshag**
**Mongrels**
**Stomach Mouths**
**Highspeed V**
**Crimson Shadows**
**Four Sure**
**Cliffhangers**

I was slightly disappointed at this retrospective LP of unreleased Swedish garage. There really isn't any first-class studio material here — the noteworthy bands deliver passable "live" concert tracks — but the overall presentation and attitude is still worth a look and listen.
**The Wyld Mammoths'** 7" EP is also priceless, as is Darren Merinuk's full-color cartoon artwork.

## WHAT EXACTLY IS A DREAM
*Cassette, 198? / Crazy Mannequin Records, Italy*

**Dinky Silence**
**Allison Run**
**Uncle Tybya**
**Flavio & Peter Funny Joke**
**Impulsive Youths**
**Falling Spikes**
**Shadowmen**
**Mythical Jungle Junkies**
**King Holiday**
**Simone Searsellini**
**No Strange**
**Bad Medicine**
**Pit**
**Reptile Chime**
**Marco Vox**
**Chetro & Co**
**Mad Horses**

It should be noted the **Falling Spikes** listed in these various Italian compilations is not the U.S. band.

## WHAT'S ALL THE FUZZ ABOUT?
*29 song cassette, 1990 / What Wave Magazine, Canada*

**Thee Fourgiven**
**The Chessmen**
**Sporting Bachelors**
**The Beatpack**
**Mystic Eyes**
**The Cynics**
**Marshmallow Overcoat**
**The Ultra 5**
**Yard Trauma**
**Al Perry & The Cattle**
**The Cheepskates**

There's plenty to pick from with 29 tracks crammed onto this tape. *What Wave* always loads up on the Canadian talent, but those bands seem to be the weaker link here. Highlights, though, include a **Mystic Eyes** track, an early **Marshmallow Overcoat** demo, **The Ultra 5** and **The Cheepskates**.

## WHO ARE THEM?

*12 song LP, 1991 / Face Records, Italy*

**The Marshmallow Overcoat**
**Sancho Panza**
**Statuto**
**Magic Potion**
**Pow**
**Lilith**
**Fasten Belt**
**Tony Face Big Roll Band**
**Not Moving**
**No Strange**
**Double Deck Five**
**Excessives**

*WHO ARE THEM?, 1991*

Yes, it's yet another "tribute" LP, this time for **The Who,** with the cover material ranging from their earliest days to their last gasps in the '80s. Several other **Who** tribute LPs also appeared in the 1990s.

## WORONZOID

*double LP, 1989 / Woronzow Records, U.K.*

A sampler of Woronzow Records artists, but I haven't heard it as of yet.

## YELLOW PURPLE & ITALIAN SUNSHINES

*11 songs, LP, 1987 / Venus In Furs Records, France*

**Joe Perrino & The Mellowtones**
**Sick Rose**
**Miners Of Muzo**
**Four By Art**
**Effervescent Elephants**
**Ramblers**
**Liars**
**Birdmen Of Alkatraz**

A beautiful package — including a very trippy cover featuring **Brian Jones** (when he was still alive) — highlight this European hit parade. Almost all of the tracks have since been released elsewhere, but this is still a fine sampler for those who don't already have substantial Italian product.

## *Some Other "Tribute" LPs*

A slew of "Tribute" compilation albums also flooded the market in the late '80s up to the mid 1990s, with some targets being **The Kinks, Beatles, Brian Wilson (Beach Boys), The Monkees, Love, Rolling Stones, The Byrds, Jimi Hendrix, The Rutles** (!), and on and on, with varied success. It is safe to say that the public is mostly sick of seeing tribute projects, especially when few come close to capturing the magic of the original band.

Some of the other better efforts are described in the text above.

# MY BACK PAGES

## The Underground Fanzine Movement

*The popular movement of the fanzine came to life in the middle 1960s, as science-fiction buffs began to express their own grass roots beliefs and desires through handmade newsletters and journals. The explosion of popular culture surrounding rock music helped to create an offshoot of that movement: the rock & roll fanzine.*

The rock fanzine movement exploded again with the onset of the 1970s punk generation, as a whole new sub-culture sought to express itself outside of the mainstream commercial media. It could be suggested that the amount of 'zine activity reflects the vibrancy of any pop culture movement; an excited rock sub-culture expresses itself not only through its music, but through its printed pages.

The garage and psychedelic sub-community was no different. Inspired by such seminal do-it-yourself punk 'zines as *Bomp!, Maximum Rock 'N Roll* and *Slash*, 1980s caveteens created their own network of scattered publications.

The range in mood, style and content varied greatly; some of these, such as the slick *Bucketfull Of Brains*, published regularly to a larger audience, while others like *Living Sickness* copied-off a few pages when they got around to it and mailed it to friends. The common link between all of these efforts was the throbbing need to communicate the depth of appreciation and devotion to garage & psych music.

What follows is a listing of (primarily) garage and psychedelic fanzines from around the world. Most of these published several issues and amazingly survived for a number of years. Many lasted for only as long as the publishers' initial inspiration.

Again, I'm sure there have been and continue to be many more "garage" 'zines than I have listed here. They are extremely difficult to find — much more difficult than records — because of their small print runs and limited circulation.

I am always searching for more.

## ABUS DANGEREUX (France)

A slick later-'80s 'zine in French, covering much of the alternative scene, with occasional features on the garage world. Issues included hard 45s and later 3" CDs, including cool cuts from **The Cryptones, Les Primitives, The Fleshtones** and **The Embryonics** amongst others.

## ALL OR NOTHING (Italy)

A glossy slick 'zine beginning in 1993, with good graphics — covering garage and mod sounds from the 1960s to today.

## ANSIA DE COLOR (Spain)

A 1/2 sized photocopied 'zine covering the worldwide psych and garage scene. Later issues contain flexis. Written in Spanish.

## ARIO - DALLA PSYCHEDELIA ALLA TELEMATICA (Milano, Italy)

Nothing is known except issues #1 and #2 are from 1991.

## ASYLUM (Scotland, U.K.)

A small 4-5 page Xeroxed effort starting in the late 1980s and given away free, covering the local garage scene.

## BAD TRIP (Atlanta, GA USA)

Edited by Bruce and Paige Ciero, it began publication circa 1991 and featured the best of the garage and pop-punk world from the 1960s to present. Wacky graphics and a fun conversational style made this one of the most fun reads of the 1990s.

## BAM BALAM (U.K.)

Nothing known.

## BANG! (Medford, MA USA)

Nothing known.

## THE BEAT GOES ON (Torino, Italy)

At least six issues exist, circa 1986-1987.

## BIFF BANG POW (France)

A mid-1980s photocopied 'zine with many cool photos and a very '60s look.

## BIG SUR (Italy)

I'm unsure how many issues of this excellent full-sized publication appeared — their second edition is from 1989. It included many articles, reviews, photos and information about the global garage scene, written in Italian.

## BLITZ (Los Angeles, CA USA)

A long-running professional tome covering all sorts of interesting underground music, with an emphasis on '60s sounds.

## BLOW UP MAGAZINE (Germany)

This Xerox 'zine covered **The Sick Rose, Fuzztones** and **Stomachmouths** in its one year (1987) of operation.

## THE BOB (New York, NY USA)

While this magazine did not cover the garage scene only, it did offer continual strong support for garage/psych bands, and their flexis often included pertinent acts.

## BORN LOSER (Australia)

I think that two Aussie women put this out in the late '80s to early '90s, featuring a variety the international garage scene, plus a look at Australian bands of note. I hear that this zine is rather good, and I believe the editors promoted some garage shows locally as well.

## BORN LOSER (Rome, Italy)

At least five issues of this Xeroxed, full sized 'zine exist from 1992-1993, with a multitude of photos and cheesy graphics. Garage, trash and '60s culture is the focus — written in Italian.

## BOSS (France)

At least nine issues from the late '80s into the '90s, more recently focusing on the grungier garage sound.

## BREAKTHROUGH (origin unknown)

Todd Abramson edited this 1984 effort which featured original '60s punk as well as **The Lyres** and **Chesterfield Kings**.

## BUCKETFULL OF BRAINS (U.K.)

As I mentioned before, this was a very professional looking and reading 'zine, which kept up publication from the early 1980s through at least the mid 1990s. It featured the best garage

BUCKETFULL of BRAINS
ISSUE 12

with free Plasticland flexi disc

Robyn Hitchcock    Playn Jayn
Long Ryders    Gene Clark
Band Of Outsiders    Moberlys

and psych bands on a regular basis, but also veered off into more pedestrian guitar and commercial rock bands. The early years edited by Nigel Cross with significant contributions from Phil McMullen were arguably the best.

Unlike the commercial U.K. press, *B.F.O.B.* was unafraid to herald American groups. Strangely, though, in later years they often hyped bands that Americans themselves would not touch. The 'zine also helped to perpetrate the myth of the Arizona "desert rock" sound — which seemed rather funny to those of us who actually live here.

## CAFE BLEU (Napoli, Italy)

Issues zero through #2 are circa 1986-1987 — including apparently at least one cassette as well.

## CAN'T BE BEAT (U.K.)

Nothing known.

## COMME UN BOOMERANG (Montreal, PQ Canada)

Nothing known.

## COOL SOUNDZINE (Hamilton, ON Canada)

I think this was a 1992 one-off, designed really to house the compilation CD *More Hits — More Stars*. **The Swingin Gurus** is the only garage band of note on the comp and in the 'zine.

## CROHINGA WELL (Asse, Belgium)

Andre Van Bosbeke edited this thick, good looking Belgian effort — written thankfully in English. Fashioned in style (and layout) much like the U.K. *Ptolemaic Terrascope,* is centers more around psych and freak bands, with a plethora of reviews, interviews and features. I'd say it's excellent all around. There were 10 issues published as of mid-1995.

## CRYPTIC TYMES (Canada)

Allan Wright and Charlene Coleman of *What Now?* magazine started this publication in late 1990. Unlike the former 'zine, this one detailed solely the garage/psych scene. Lots of spirit,

graphics and love for the genre highlight the first issue, while subsequent issues boasted improved writing, a wider scope of interest, and massive review sections. Wright would move to Seattle and continue the publication until 1994 with his wife Lisa. They later started a power pop/'70s punk 'zine.

The compilation cassette included in the debut issue of *Cryptic Tymes* is detailed in the "All Together Now" section.

## THE DAVY MAGAZINE (Messina, Italy)

Editor Bob Costa gives wide coverage to the underground sound in this clean-looking full sized 'zine. Appearing in the mid 1980s, it survived into 1995, and gave ample space to garage and psych acts. It is written in English, but Costa's grasp of the language is sometimes tenuous, leading to some interesting interpretations.

**DEJA VOODOO TRAIN (Montreal, PQ Canada)**
The OG Records newsletter.

**DOLCE VITA (Vallese (VR), Italy)**
Mainly a mod 'zine, with some garage coverage. Issues #1-3 were from 1991-1992.

**EL ATAQUE DE LOS TOMATES ASESINOS (Spain)**
Nothing known.

**EL TELEFONO ROJO (Spain)**
Translation: The Red Telephone.

**ERA OF SOUND (Brisbane, Australia)**
Edited in the early 1990s by James Peirce, also the bassist for the excellent R&B garage band **The Apaches**.

**EVERLASTING TRIBUTES (France)**
This early 1980s 'zine was written in French and combined '60s articles with current information on bands such as **The Chesterfield Kings.**

**EX-NEXU (Germany)**
Jurgen Richardt's production later spawned the essential Screaming Apple Records. I believe there was only one excellent issue, written in German, that included a 7" EP as well.

**FACES (Piacenza, Italy)**
At least 17 issues exist, from 1980-1989.

**FAR OUT AND FISHY (U.K.)**
Nothing known.

**FEEDBACK (Victoria, Australia)**
Milly Muleskinner edited this mid 1990s publication that she describes as a "hell-bent hipzine."

**FELINE FRENZY (Toronto, ON Canada)**
One of the most "'60s-ish" looking 'zines of the era, fashioned after teen 'zines like *Tiger Beat*. Though Xeroxed, it was chocked full of '60s  graphics, teen magazine reprints, and (fully clothed) pin-up photos of fave '80s garage groups. This was also one of the larger zines, with issues reaching up to 100 pages. Local radio host, concert promoter, and all around good egg Glynnis Wilson was the editor.

**54321 (Spain)**
Nothing known.

**FREAKBEAT (U.K.)**

 This was the most graphically sophisticated psychedelic 'zine of the 1980s. Each issue had a full color cover, and each page was printed in two other colors; 3-D glasses were included with each issue!
Ivor Trueman and Richard Allen made sure that every psych and garage group worthy of mention was included somewhere in these pages. Flexis of the best bands also were included, making this one of the most sought-after publications in any genre. A true feast for the eyes, and one of the finest fanzines of any era! It published at least through the mid 1990s.

**FREAK OUT MAGAZINE (Scafati, Italy)**
A companion to the "Radioluna One" garage radio show, it began publishing in 1989, and has had at least five editions to date.

**FUCK YEAH! (San Diego, CA USA)**
A very fun and crude early 1990s half-sized Xerox effort, full of garage punk energy and irreverent attitudes. They reproduced liberally from the first edition of this book — with my permission.

**FUNBEAT (France)**
Nothing known.

**FUZBRAINS (Worcester, MA USA)**
Edited by Deb Beadry with at least 15 issues through 1987, covering garage and all rock in general in a very enthusiastic manner.

**FUZZ BUZZ (New York, NY USA)**
The Fuzztones Fan Club Newsletter, including gossip and inside news. A "Fuzztones Songbook" was also printed circa 1988, with lyrics from a dozen songs and band photos.

**FUZZ (Spain)**
Nothing known.

**FUZZ SCREAM (Patras, Greece)**
Spyros Kaskavelis edited this Greek-language effort from 1993. The Xeroxing is crude, but the subject matter and graphics are lovingly presented.

**GARAGE LAND (Spain)**
Nothing known.

**GEW GAW (Athens, Greece)**
George Markov edited this excellent Greek-language 'zine, which started publication in January, 1995. Fashioned in style after the *Ptolemaic Terrascope*, it covered the best of the world garage scene.

**GLITTERHOUSE (Germany)**
A very slick magazine, unfortunately (for English readers) in German. It did cover the best new groups of the mid -'8os, though, and was widely distributed and read. Glitterhouse Records later replaced the 'zine.

**GO (Waco, TX  USA)**
I believe that this was actually a newsprint 'zine that covered 1960s Texas punk, but with some limited coverage of the new garage sounds.

**GOAR (Germany)**
A slick semi-pro 'zine from the early 1990s covering the "alternative" scene, with an open eye for the garage and psych sounds. Issue #8, for instance, featured **The Green Pajamas** and **Al Perry & The Cattle**. Written in German.

**GOSH (Bologna, Italy)**
At least five issues of this were distributed from 1991-1993, covering original '6os sounds. One issue reportedly included a 7".

**GRAVEDIGGER (Wiltshire, U.K.)**
Mojo Mills of fine garage outfit **The Nuthins** edited this full-size 60-page effort that debuted in 1995. Seemingly countless features on the best new garage bands jam its pages, with many photos and record cover reproductions as well. *Gravedigger* reflected the strength of the garage rebirth in the mid-1990s, and is excellent all around.

**GROOVY EYES (France)**
Stephane Robert of Dig Records published this diehard garage 'zine in the early 1990s, with good graphics and an enthusiastic attitude. Robert later started a record label and distribution company — which later disbanded after reportedly owing many labels and bands large

sums of money. He also reportedly sold copies of the first edition of this book without paying the publisher for them.

**HAIRY HI-FI (U.K.)**
Nothing is known, but what a great name!

**HARTBEAT (Germany)**
Another very interesting 'zine graphically. While from Germany, this is thankfully (for me) printed in English, and often contains lengthy interviews and articles on obscure groups from the '6os to '8os. Many reviews and photos made this a must.

**HEY LITTLE BIRD (Los Angeles, CA  USA)**
Published briefly in the mid-'8os by L.A. fashion-head Audrey Moorehead.

**HIPPY HIPPY SHAKE (Alameda, CA  USA)**
Nothing known.

**IN YER EAR (Canada)**
A regional Canadian zine that did feature a "Live" 45 by **The Cynics** in a later issue.

**INCOGNITO (Englishtown, NJ  USA)**
Nothing is known, but I think this is a mod 'zine.

**INNER MYSTIQUE (Stillwater, OK  USA)**
One can only imagine what it was like to publish a garage/psych 'zine in the middle of Oklahoma in the 1980s!

**INSIDE MIND (France)**
Nothing known.

**277**

## KALEIDOSCOPE (St. Petersburg, FL USA)

**KALEIDOSCOPE**

THE NEW ITALIAN GARAGE & PSYCHEDELIC UNDERGROUND

— Also —

THE MIND'S EYE, THE CHEEPSKATES, THE 27 VARIOUS, THE HEADLESS HORSEMEN, ALWAYS AUGUST, THE PROJECTILES, THE MARSHMALLOW OVERCOAT

This 'zine was fashioned in layout style after the British *Bucketfull Of Brains*, but featured only cool garage acts from the '60s and '80s. It gave wide support to many bands through its several issues from the late 1980s, and each issue was eagerly awaited. Editor Dennis Dalcin expanded the 'zine into a record label, Direct Hit, releasing compilation LPs of current and '60s groups.

## KICK OUT THE JAMS (Spain)

Oscar Garcia is an active punk and garage fan, beginning this handmade 'zine in the late '80s — written in Spanish.

## KICKS (New York, NY USA)

Like the excellent *Ugly Things*, this very professional, well written and passionately presented magazine was omitted from the first edition of this book because it primarily features music from the 1950s and 1960s, and rarely features new acts. Still, it is one of the finest fanzines in any genre, and anyone interested in the history of trash, rockabilly and/or garage would find it a great treat.

## KINETIC VIBES (Marseille, France)

At least a couple issues of this nicely printed effort exist, beginning in 1992. Editor Phil Petit does something useful — he provides the text in both French and English, making the information accessible to a worldwide readership. Many of the best European 'zines are in their native language — which of course makes sense, but prevents a wider audience from getting the information. A 7" EP was included in the debut issue.

## KING BEE QUARTERLY (Missouri, USA)

"Mad" Jon McKinney of **The Royal Nonesuch** edited this blues and garage 'zine in the mid 1980s.

## LA HERNCIA DE LOS MUNSTER (Spain)

A very influential Spanish 'zine that published from the mid 1980s and often included a flexi. Written in Spanish.

## LIVELY ARTS (San Diego, CA USA)

Nothing known.

## LIVING SICKNESS (Hayward, CA USA)

A crude late 1980s Xerox 'zine, put out by fans for fans in true grass roots fashion. It also featured reprints of articles from the '60s, plus local (Northern California) band news.

## THE LONG WRYTER (Holland)

A fanzine for the band **The Long Ryders**.

## LOS 20 LACTEOS (Spain)

Nothing known.

## LOST TRAILS (Italy)

An important garage 'zine for Italy, it often included a "hard vinyl 45," (not a flexi), and these has become very collectable. Very professional in style and content, though written in Italian, which limited its readership outside its native country. That's a shame for English readers, because *Lost Trails* covered some of the most notable acts featured in this book.

## LOST MYNDS (Montreal, PQ Canada)

Great graphics and printing make this a worthy read from the mid 1980s, though issues in the '90s were reported as well. Edited by Mr. Ed and Flipped Out Phil (of the infamous Primitive record label), it focused on original 1960s Quebec garage, but also 1980s garage as well.

## MAKING TYME (Maywood, NJ USA)

Edited by **Mod Fun**'s Mick London, one can assume this is a mod 'zine.

## MERLIN'S MUSIC BOX (Greece)

Another late 1980s entry into the genre, but it quickly became a slick 'zine with a color cover and expert graphics by the end of the decade. It covered (in Greek) the "alternative" scene, but gave liberal space to international garage bands. It looks good enough to be the *Rolling Stone* magazine of Greece — but *R.S.* could never be this cool. Editor Yiannis Kastanaras is one of the funniest, kindest, most dedicated music fans I've ever had the pleasure to meet. I cannot begin to explain his patience and good humor.

**MISTY LANE (Rome/Ostuni, Italy)**

Brian '66's Xerox 'zine of original garage and new sounds, lovingly put together with great graphics and a very positive attitude. One of the best ever, with about a dozen issues, continuing into 1995. Brian also runs the Misty Lane record label, with many sampler cassettes and vinyl releases.

**THE MOLE (Hamilton, ON Canada)**

Bruce Mowatt edited this circa 1984-88 'zine with an emphasis on garage sounds.

**MORALS OF THE UNTOLD FABLES (Los Angeles, CA USA)**

Newsletter for the band **The Untold Fables**, published by Rich Coffee.

**MY MIND'S EYE (Germany)**

Nothing known.

**MYSTERY SCENE MAGAZINE (Germany)**

Only one issue was printed in 1986. Written in English, with **Plasticland** on the cover and featuring **The Not Quite, Tell Tale Hearts, Otherside, Sick Rose, Green Telescope, Miracle Workers** and **Cornflake Zoo.** Excellent all around.

**NEW SCENE (France)**

A 'zine that mainly featured **The Fleshtones**, written in French and English.

**NEXT BIG THING (Scotland, U.K.)**

Lindsay Hutton edited this, one of the most widely read and distributed 'zines in the genre, with more than 20 issues out in the 1980s. It resurfaced in 1994, with a 7" EP included, and coverage of a wide variety of garage and punk-pop sounds. Hutton also reportedly ran the fan clubs for **The Fuzztones, Cramps** and **Fleshtones** in the 1980s, besides publishing N.B.T.

**THE NEW EXPLOSION (Germany)**

Good grass roots support for international garage bands made this English-language effort a welcome addition.

**99th FLOOR (New York, NY USA)**

Ron Rimsite kept us all up-to-date on the garage happenings on both U.S. coasts with this 'zine, which had a flexi in two of its issues. This 'zine also displayed the biases and cliques that formed as the '80s garage scene grew stronger; much name calling and finger-pointing went on here. Nevertheless, it was a fine publication, and the flexis are essential.

**NOISE FOR HEROES (San Diego, CA USA)**

Editor Steve Gardner has been a tireless supported of independent music for many years. His thick, info-jammed *N.F.H.* 'zine survived about 25 issues before he switched his focus to his NKVD record label in 1994. He regularly championed the underdog and little known groups, and often made sure to include the new garage and psych acts along side hardcore or punk-pop groups.

**OUTASITE (Rochester, NY USA)**

Published by **Chesterfield King** vocalist Greg Prevost, this late '70s/early 1980s effort was one of the earliest neo-'60s fanzines. It included a cool interview with members of **The Chocolate Watchband** in one issue, which was later used as the liner notes for a French re-issue LP.

## THE OUTER LIMITS (U.K.)

Members of **The Tyme Eliment** published this Xeroxed, 1/2 sized garage zine from 1987-1989. It is reportedly excellent.

## PEOPLE ARE STRANGE (Toscana, Italy)

Issues #1-2 are circa 1989.

## PROJECT BLUE (Rimini, Italy)

Issue #1 is from 1993.

## PSYCHAGOGOS (Greece)

Published by Nick Kontogouris, a '60s record collector, and reportedly very good. I believe I met Nick in Greece, but I can't find a copy of his 'zine anywhere in my files.

## THE PSYCHEDELICATESSEN (Tucson, AZ USA)

This is the magazine which preceded this book; it featured interviews, plenty of photos, and many, many reviews in its five full-length issues, 1986-1990. It then served as a newsletter for another five years — featuring the activities of **The Marshmallow Overcoat** and **Purple Merkins**.

## PSYCHEDELIC MUSHROOMS (Scotland, U.K.)

James Waldie edited this half-sized Xerox publication in the early 1990s. Despite its name, it centered on the mods, though it was also apt to throw in garage and psych pop info as well in its 15 or so pages.

## PSYCHO-BABBLE (Los Angeles, CA USA)

The Voxx Records newsletter, it supplied a wealth of international garage-psych information throughout the 1980s and '90s, with many issues.

## THE PTOLEMAIC TERRASCOPE (U.K.)

Put together by folks working with the **Bevis Frond** family, and featuring mainly psych bands from around the globe, always including an EP of eclectic music. Editor Phil McMullen is one of those rare music-fans-turned-writer: he knows what he's talking about, still cares about music, and sincerely works to help other talented people.

The range of interest for the magazine is wide and passionate, with finely detailed features surrounded by seemingly endless reviews of the wildly (and mildly) interesting and divergent acts.

McMullen's contributions to the early years of *Bucketfull Of Brains* also can't be underestimated. When he and Nigel Cross left in the late 1980s, so did the heart of *B.F.O.B.* That heart resurfaces at the *Ptolemaic Terrascope* (say it five times fast) — making this a fine U.K. counterpoint to *Freakbeat* — meaning it continues to be one of the best music magazines in the world.

## PURPLE FLASHES (Burke, VA USA)

Nothing known.

## RATBEAT INTERNATIONAL (Finland)

I seem to remember this a primarily a punk publication, with space given to the Euro-garage movement in the late 1980s.

## RAVE UP (San Francisco, CA USA)

Nothing known.

## RAVE-ON (Germany)

Another English-language 'zine giving support to cool garage-heads everywhere. Very grass roots, with enthusiastic and positive coverage given to many underdog bands.

## RAW AND ALIVE (France)

Laurent Bigot edited this photocopied full-size 'zine which featured many lesser known garage groups from the '60s to '80s. Reportedly very cool.

## REACCIONES (Spain)

Written in Spanish and English, this smaller format 'zine gave equal coverage to mod and garage.

## REACTION IN G (Milano, Italy)

This **Syd Barrett**-era **Pink Floyd** 'zine published at least one issue in 1992.

## ROADRUNNER (Rho-Milano, Italy)

Two issues exist from 1992-1993.

## ROLLER COASTER (Torino, Italy)

The first edition in 1983 includes a cassette with the band **No Strange**; there are at least four issue out from the mid 1980s.

## ROLLER COASTER (Athens, Greece)

A cool underground 'zine with a full color **Fuzztones** cover on their 1992 debut. They had at least two issues, both written in Greek.

## ROMILAR-D (Spain)

This 1980s 'zine later turned into a prominent independent record label.

## RUTA 66 (Spain)

A very slick magazine, looking very much like a "Spanish *Rolling Stone*." Unlike the bloated *Rolling Stone*, however, it covered only "cool" garage and punk acts from the '60s, '70s and '80s. Written in Spanish, and professional in every regard.

## SHAPE OF THINGS MAGAZINE (Pavia, Italy)

Published from 1986-1988 by Sandro Cesarini, whom I was lucky enough to meet in 1992 in Verona. Issue #2 included a **Doc & The Medics** "live" cassette; #3 had a **Fuzztones** "live" cassette, #4 had a **Creeps** "live" cassette; #5 had a **Chesterfield Kings** "live" cassette; and #6/7 had a **Miracle Workers** "live" cassette.

## SHAKE! (Athens, Greece)

Another fine Greek-language 'zine, with at least two issues from 1992 and 1993. Great graphics and a wide array of articles and reviews makes this one of the best new garage 'zines around. And it would be even better if I could read it!

## THE SICK ROSE NEWS BULLETIN (Torino, Italy)

At least two issues of this magazine for the **Sick Rose** fan club exists circa 1988.

## THE SIDEWALKERS MAGAZINE (Rome, Italy)

One issue exists from sometime in the '80s.

## SMASHED BLOCKED (USA)

Mainly a 1980s mod zine (with many Vespa scooter photos), but with some garage input.

## SOMETHING HAS HIT ME (Middlesex, U.K.)

While editor Mark Raison says in his circa 1992 debut issue that he's interested in presenting just about any '60s influenced sound, it's mod music which gets the most ink here. He seems to have an open mind about garage and psych, however, and perhaps later issues were more balanced.

## SOUND AFFEX (San Diego, CA USA)

Tireless music lover Bart Mendoza edited this Xeroxed, typewritten 'zine, with at least nine issues out in the late 1980s and early '90s. Mod to garage and psych are all given enthusiastic coverage. True to the term "fanzine," in all the best ways.

## SOUNDS OF PURPLE (Corvina, CA USA)

Nothing known.

## SPLENDID (Germany)

Another slick German 'zine written in English, with great coverage of the best 1980s groups, plus a flexi.

## START (Vienna, Austria)

Manfred Breiner AKA "The Elk" was the mastermind behind this mammoth 'zine, with at least a dozen issues from the early "80s through 1987. Issue #11/12 is 130 pages of the best new garage and psych groups, with comprehensive coverage of parties, major shows, records, with many great photos. It isn't written in English, however, so the text will keep its secrets from me.

## THE STEMS: Let Your Head Rest, An Illustrated Biography (Australia)

George Matzkov of the Zero Hour label compiled this fervent fan look at one of the best garage-pop bands ever. The emphasis of the magazine-sized book is on "what should have been," that is, the accepted opinion that **The Stems** should have gained much greater success, especially outside their native Australia. Plenty of photos, gig poster reproductions, newspaper articles and commentary make this a loving tribute. It originally also contained an essential three song EP of previously unreleased **Stems** gems. Excellent.

## STONEAGE (Pordenone, Italy)

At least three issues of this existed in the 1980s, including a cassette.

**STONE AGE NEWS (Los Angeles, CA USA)**
A weekly one-page newsletter given away at the door of L.A.'s Cavern Club in the mid 1980s, keeping the scenesters up on the latest news.

**STRAIGHT (Germany)**
Nothing known.

**STRAIGHT FROM THE GROOVEYARD (Sweden)**
Edited by garage-nik Jorgen Westman in the early to mid 1980s, featuring **The Creeps, Fuzztones, Maryland Cookies,** etc.

**STRANGE THINGS (ARE HAPPENING) (U.K.)**
Published by the folks at Bam-Caruso Records, it featured slick graphics and fabulous stories on '60s & '80s acts, but was short-lived in the late 1980s due to its very expensive printing cost.

**STRYCHNINE (Napoli, Italy)**
Issue #1, 1988, included a 7" flexi of **Birdhouse** and (the 1980s) **Monks**; #2, 1989, had a 7" flexi with the **Celibate Rifles.**

**SUB ZINE (Delft, Holland)**
A half-sized effort with at least seven issues out through 1994, covering a wide spectrum of underground and especially trash rock and garage. Written in Dutch.

**SWEETEST FEELING (Piacenza, Italy)**
At least four issues existed from 1985-1988.

**TANT QU'IL Y AURA DU ROCK (France)**
This 'zine later became Stop It Baby Records. Written in French.

**TEENAGE KICKS (France)**
Nothing known.

**THRILLS (France)**
Nothing known.

**TOM THUM (Australia)**
Jackie Vidot introduced the debut of this nicely presented 'zine in December, 1992, with a new name promised for the proposed 1993 follow-up. It balances both '60s and '80s-'90s coverage nicely, with a conversational style and well thought-out graphics. No word if that second re-named edition ever appeared.

**TOMMY (Fagagna, Italy)**
A smaller sporadic effort which reportedly expanded into a "video-

zine," sampling a variety of international underground music video. At least 105 issues appeared from the 1980s into the 1990s!

**TOP GEAR (Fairfax, VA USA)**
Mainly a mod zine, but also featured "cool" garage acts as well.

**TOUCH OF TRASH (U.K.)**
A mid 1980s full sized 'zine reportedly covering garage.

**TRASH BEAT (Hoboken, NJ USA)**
Mike Stark edited this 1980s garage 'zine.

**UGLY THINGS (San Diego, CA USA)**

Mike Stax edits this incredibly professional, thorough, well-written journal originally built around his appreciation of **The Pretty Things,** and then branching out to include any and all worthy beat/ punk groups of the 1960s (as well as 1970s). *Ugly Things* has given almost no coverage of any kind to the garage groups of the 1980s and 1990s — that's why his 'zine was omitted from the first edition of this book — but Stax argued convincingly that *Ugly Things* should be included in this second edition. It's one of the best fanzines in any genre I've ever seen, so here it is.

**UNHINGED (U.K.)**
Another U.K. publication which heralded American groups, along with those from the rest of the world. The content of this 'zine was very eclectic, ranging from avant garde to jangle-pop. Many garage and psych bands were featured, however, and an uninhibited spirit made this 'zine a worthwhile read. Many fine 7" flexis were also issued in its mid to late 1980s heyday.

**UNTAMED WHIRL (USA)**
A promotional newsletter published by the band **Untamed Youth.**

**UP! (San Francisco, CA USA)**
Another short lived publication circa 1988 edited by Beverly Patterson, mixing 1960s features and 1980s garage news and reviews.

**URLO (Taranto, Italy)**

A reportedly very professional 'zine which covered only the Italian underground, including punk, hard rock, dark music, wave, noise, and garage, beat, psych, etc. There are at least 34 issues dating from 1983.

**VOXX TEEN BEAT (Los Angeles, CA  USA)**

An early '80s Voxx Records newsletter, which was replaced by *Psycho Babble* — it gave some mid-1980s garage followers the only news they could find of the exploding L.A scene.

**WAKE UP IT'S '66 (Thessaloniki, Greece)**

This 45 page full-size 'zine made its debut in 1995. It featured a color comic cover and features on **The Others, 99th Floor, Sound Explosion, Brood** — and a plethora of reviews and commentary. Lovingly done by Apostolos Kanakaris and friends Alex and Chris, it is one of the most enthusiastic and fun 'zines in garagedom. They also stand firmly against CDs: "Save The Vinyl" is their battle cry!

**WATCH THIS (Scotland, U.K.)**

Lindsay Hutton's **Fleshtones** Fan Club newsletter.

**WHAT NOW? (Kingston, ON  Canada)**

A late 1980s 'zine that mixed political consciousness with a gritty garage mentality. A real fan effort that deserved greater attention. It evolved into the more garage-music oriented **Cryptic Tymes**.

**WHAT WAVE (Canada)**

The premier Canadian 'zine of the 1980s, it covered all the best of the garage/ psych groups — with much encouragement for Canadian groups. In true fan-fashion, much praise and encouragement is heaped on the well-deserving bands, and the reader is treated to great photos as well. The 'zine often included a compilation cassette and sometimes a "hard vinyl 45." A true labor of love edited by Dave and Rena O'Halloran, who also formed the What Wave record label.

**WHO PUT THE BOMP (Los Angeles, CA  USA)**

This slick, professional looking and written magazine followed the '70s punk explosion and paved the way for the '80s garage revival; edited by Greg Shaw, of course.

**WIG OUT! (Tacoma, WA  USA)**

A 'zine put out by the group **Girl Trouble** throughout the '80s into the '90s, combining band hype, goofy movie reviews and kitsch culture.

**WIPE OUT (Memphis, TN  USA)**

Begun in the late '80s with some garage coverage.

**WILD THING (Verona, Italy)**

Issues #1-#3 were circa 1986-1987.

**YEAH!!! (Los Angeles, CA  USA)**

The Dionysus Records newsletter, with pertinent updates and information on upcoming releases of many of the best garage groups from the '80s and '90s.

# VIDEO KILLED THE RADIO STAR

## *Garage Television & The Global Village*

*While the advent of amateur video equipment made it possible for virtually any band to document itself, a relatively few garage and psych bands spent the money necessary for a professional music video production. Even the term "music video" is misleading — while video tape was certainly the quickest and cheapest material to capture images, it should be noted that the professional standard for music video production in the 1980s and 1990s remained motion picture film. The prohibitive cost of film production cut the number of professional independent garage videos even further.*

The obstacles were greater than mere money: even the best independent garage band videos then had to compete with much larger budget "commercial" clips for broadcast space. It is amazing that a few did manage to sneak onto the commercial airwaves and cable systems.

There was a substantial network of regional and local "alternative" video programs in place across the U.S. and Canada by 1990, but the "above-ground" music video revolution was, for the most part, a missed opportunity for the '80s garage and psychedelic bands.

Most struggling garage bands could not compete with the major labels for music video image quality, distribution and promotion, but several major label bands did explore the "garage" and "psychedelic" look on film.

Australians **The Church** wandered throughout the entire decade without a U.S. hit, then watched in 1988 as their very serene and trippy clip for "Under The Milky Way" sent them to the top internationally. They also released a home-video collection in 1990 which featured all of their best psych-tinged videos from the past decade.

The U.K.'s **Echo And The Bunnymen** had always produced provocative music video (their hour long home-video *Pictures On The Wall* is a stunning effort), and countrymen **The Soup Dragons** offered us a colorful tribute to Syd Barrett with 1988's "Majestic Head."

**The Fleshtones** appeared heading for commercial success after their inclusion in the film *Urgh, A Music War* with "Shadowline," and their 1982 in-the-studio rendition of "Want" was an exercise in strict 1960s TV-show fun.

**Robyn Hitchcock** did nothing to hide his obvious love of psychedelia in the simplistic and dreamy clips "I Often Dream Of Trains" and "Raymond Chandler Evening," while becoming even more obviously freaked out with his "Madonna Of The Wasps" and "Balloon Man" promos.

**The Hoodoo Gurus** seemed perfectly at ease in front of the camera, and very garagey indeed in the mid '80s "I Want You Back" and "Like Wow." The **Gurus** seemed to be making a bid for the big-time by the time **The Bangles** were singing background in their video for "Goodtimes," but the playful "What's My Scene" showed that their garage hearts were true. Even their ultra-commercial (for them) "Come Anytime," 1989, has that garage spark. Their sci-fi themed "Another World" video is one of the funniest in the genre.

**The Smithereens, The Pogues, The Died Pretty, The Bangles, The Dream Academy, Sam Phillips, XTC, Julian Cope, Lime Spiders,**

**House Of Freaks, B-52s, Young Fresh Fellows** and even **Prince** (!) all displayed within their videos a playful love and admiration for the genre, even if their music did not directly reflect it.

**Tom Petty**'s mid '80s "Don't Come 'Round Here" clip openly embraced the psilocybic Alice In Wonderland op-art atmosphere of '66; he would also feature "Psychotic Reaction" as an encore for his early 1990s stage shows.

One can only imagine what a big budget music video would have looked like in the hands of true believers like **Plasticland** or **The Rain Parade** — and how it would have affected the fashion-conscious MTV (zombie) audience. (**Opal** and **Mazzy Star** *did* benefit from some appropriately low-budget clips, however.)

While countless deserving bands were kept from the major media spotlight, many pounced on the opportunities available locally. The original 1960s garage combos could perhaps hope for a one-time shot on a local talk show or kid's dance party show. They never imagined their garage-descendants would have the luxury of a new wrinkle in the medium: cable TV.

When cable television became commercially viable in the early 1980s, cable TV companies began to bid against each other for the rights to major U.S. cities' markets. Each city council entertained offers, then picked the company or companies which they thought would serve the community best.

One bargaining chip the cable companies used in these high-stake proceedings was "public access" television. Cable companies would promise the availability of facilities and funds for the public to use in the production of local programming. The plethora of cable channels would then offer the space for local producers to air their views to the community at large through the electronic soap-box of television.

Well, that's how it is supposed to work. The reality of the process is another story, meant for another book. The point of all this is that some local producers did manage to create programming based upon the 1980s garage revival.

Perhaps the most circulated was a show produced sporadically in San Diego, Los Angeles and Berkeley, CA, called *It's Happening*. The format of the half-hour program followed the well-worn formula established in the '60s on *Ready Steady Go, Hullabaloo* and *Shindig*: bands would perform "live" in the studio, teenagers would dance to their favorite garage records, and the hosts would attempt to look as "hip" as possible.

The cable-TV show turned the clock back to

1965, and recreated the teen rock/dance show phenomenon. About the only difference from the original '60s shows — besides the sometimes shoddy technical quality and awkward host segments — was the use of color TV cameras.

Starting in 1984, *It's Happening* featured many important new garage bands, though the producers admitted they were usually from the same small pool of their California "friends." This narrow-cast and clique-ish mentality prevented some relevant bands from making appearances.

Perhaps more important than the sound, though, was a prospective band's look. A group might sound cool, but they had little chance of appearing on the show if they weren't decked out in the correct 1960s vintage uniform. (There were a few exceptions to this rule, most notably the one-time appearance of a more traditional soul group.)

Despite these tight constraints, several impressive performances were documented on *It's Happening* up through the mid-1990s. **The Fuzztones, The Unclaimed, Tell Tale Hearts, Nashville Ramblers, The Event, The Leopards, Things** and several others were preserved on video, giving many of us the only glimpse possible of these neglected acts. The show was only seen in a handful of U.S. markets — through cable TV — but the public access production had completed as least 25 episodes as of this writing, featuring over 30 bands.

While public access television was designed to be not-for-profit, home video was another blossoming commercial venture of the 1980s. No one ever thought that amateur video machines and tapes would become common household appliances when they were designed in the 1970s.

Suddenly the market boomed, and with it the also unanticipated industry of renting and selling pre-recorded video cassettes. Rentals and sales of movies and music videos on cassette became commonplace, and with it, another chance for the garage/psych scene to gain a foothold in the

developing new technologies.

Several home video cassette compilations were released during this period, including the 19 song *The Obnoxious Rock & Roll Video Hour* in 1987, which featured many of the bands on the Los Angeles Dionysus label, plus some other related acts. Live footage and concept clips are mixed effectively, and the raw edge of the production is tempered with the high quality of the performances.

Another worthy effort is the one hour 1990 release, *Slipping Through The Cracks: An Uprising Of Young Pacifics*. Released by Skyclad Records' Iceworld video division, it is also a mix of live and concept footage, with a lower-quality "public access" look dominating the 19 clips of West Coast independents. Still, it is of some interest.

PHOTO BY T. GASSEN

*THE FUZZTONES, ON THE SET OF THEIR 1989 "NINE MONTHS LATER" MUSIC VIDEO*

Skyclad also released in 1991 a compilation of U.S. East Coast bands called *Frozen Ghosts.* I haven't heard any word on the quality of the production, but it could likely feature more "public access-quality" footage. The phrase "buyer beware" should come to mind when considering Skyclad video releases — ironically, that's the phrase they include on some of their reportedly bootleg CD releases of **The Sex Pistols**.

There certainly exists more than enough top-quality clips to fill several more hours for home release, and it remains to be seen if the best of the 1980s (garage) music video output is ever compiled for commercial consumption. For now the electronic jewels will rest in various collectors' files, as dozens of bands did produce their own clips.

I've seen quality videos for the **Not Quite, Miracle Workers, Chesterfield Kings, Mad Violets** and **Gruesomes**, among many others.

Perhaps garage fans in years to come will finally get to see them as well.

# A NOTE ABOUT COMMERCIAL GROUPS

## *The Underthrow Of The Overground*

*The new psychedelic and garage sound rarely managed to dent the major commercial market in the 1980s and '90s, though a wide variety of established bands did borrow some aspects of the sound and use it in a more commercial application. Sometimes the use of these sounds (and fashions) was subtle, sometimes obvious and blatant.*

The Cramps were hailed by the art/punk underground in the late 1970s, though their appeal would ultimately spread across many marketing genres. Amazingly, their commercial appeal would build to enormous proportions by the early 1990s. Their influence is incalculable, and is described in detail in several other biographical books.

Proto-punkers The Ramones also cannot be forgotten as a lasting symbol of '60s garage, even after their long string of major label LPs. For some they remain the enduring image of kids with bowl haircuts and guitars. They even deposited an LP of '60s garage covers in the 1990s.

The Smithereens would pop into the "Top-40" limelight with their update of classic Beatles melodies and crunchy garage rock. Their string of melodic hook-filled albums since the

*ECHO & THE BUNNYMEN, 1983*

early 1980s is probably the closest that commercial radio got to promoting the pure '60s pop sound.

Athens, Georgia (USA) became a hotbed for what would eventually be called "college radio" bands, with The B-52s and REM scoring most notably in the charts — both with obvious bows to the 1960s. The B-52s' use of Moserite Ventures style surf guitars, cheesy organs and '60s fashions was seen by some as instrumental in rekindling early 1980s underground interest in crude garage rock.

Seattle became the other main U.S. underground youth center of the 1980s, with a seemingly endless stream of loud (and most often lame) guitar bands, but with The Screaming Trees and Mudhoney serving notice of their '60s lessons.

Newly accepted commercial groups from overseas also began to embrace the garage sound, as Australia boasted fuzz-popsters The Hoodoo Gurus and moody jangle guitar kings The Church. Each skirted on the edge of massive international commercial appeal.

England was especially active in all the burgeoning musical trends of the "New Wave," and sprang forth with a slew of garage/psych associated groups. Echo

And The Bunnymen became one of the world's most successful (artistically and commercially) alternative groups for the '80s. Their imaginative, progressive pop sound was universally hailed as fresh and original.

The Bunnymen made no secret, however, for their love of psychedelics, and concert tapes circulated of them performing sets of *Pebbles* compilation songs and Chocolate Watchband covers; it was becoming obvious that the commercial influence of the '66 punk sound was stretching throughout the globe.

The quirky Soft Boys had gained some U.K. attention in the late 1970s, and Robyn Hitchcock graduated from that combo to engage listeners through the '80s and into the '90s with his not-so-disguised extensions of eccentric Syd Barrett mania.

(It should also be noted that the much-publicized mid-'80s "Acid House" disco movement in the U.K. (and then beyond) had no relevance or connection to the garage/psych scene — it was merely an attempt at co-opting the un-manageable garage/psych fashion into the commercially accepted disco drone.

Suddenly tie-dye shirts and psychedelic drugs were marketed along with the usual drum machine ramblings, with many un-enlightened kids believing that this was indeed the "spirit" of the 1960s!?! In a way, it was the most readily accepted attempt at "reviving" the trappings of the '60s, though the approach was pale, vapid, empty — and eventually forgotten. Disco — or electronic dance music — is rightfully the sworn enemy of garage-heads.)

A listing of some other commercially oriented groups from the 1980s and '90s who wore the smirk of the '60s sound on their sleeves could include: House Of Freaks, Thee Hypnotics, Mighty Lemon Drops, Doc And The Medics, Siouxsie and the Banshees, Del Fuegos, BauHaus, Game Theory, Guadalcanal Diary, Television, Miracle Legion, Eleventh Dream Day, Flaming Lips, Red Kross,

Julian Cope & Teardrop Explodes, The Jesus & Mary Chain, Television Personalities, The Violent Femmes, The Scientists, Loop, Flying Color, Candy Flip, Screaming Blue Messiahs — amongst many others.

Each displayed varying degrees of appreciation for with the genre. These groups — and many other similar bands — are of only partial interest to the subject of this book, so I won't use much more ink on them now.

Nevertheless, what follows is a short list of a few major label records of note from the 1980s and '90s that could be associated *in some small manner* with the garage & psychedelic phenomenon. This is not meant to be a "best of" list for these groups, but instead a sampling of what I feel to be their most representative garage or psychedelic-related releases.

All are worth a listen, and ironically they will be the easiest to find of any of the records listed in this book.

*THE B-52's, 1982*

**The B-52's**
self titled (1st LP), 1979
**The Church**
*Hindsight* double compilation LP, 1987
*A Quick Smoke At Spot's* LP, 1991
**The Cramps**
*Psychedelic Jungle* LP, 1981
**The Damned**
*Alone Again Or* 45, 1987
**Dream Academy**
*Life In A Northern Town* 45, 1985
**Echo & The Bunnymen**
*Ocean Rain* LP, 1984
*Reverberation* LP, 1990
**Robyn Hitchcock & The Egyptians**
*Globe Of Frogs* LP, 1988
*Queen Elvis* LP, 1989
*Perspex Island* LP, 1991
**The Hoodoo Gurus**
*Mars Need Guitars* LP, 1985
**Roger McGuinn**
*Back To Rio* LP, 1991
**The Pretenders**
self-titled (1st LP), 1980

**Radiohead**
*Pablo Honey* LP, 1994
**The Ramones**
*Acid Eaters* LP, 1994
**R.E.M.**
*Life's Rich Pageant* LP, 1986
**Smashing Pumpkins**
*Siamese Dream* LP, 1993
**The Smithereens**
*Beauty and Sadness* EP, 1983
*Green Thoughts* LP, 1988
*11* LP, 1989
*A Date With...* LP, 1994
**Soup Dragons**
*The Majestic Head* 45, 1988
**XTC**
*Mayor Of Simpleton* 45, 1989

*Information in the mainstream press is readily available for commercially marketed groups, so documentation of their importance to the 1980s/90s garage and psychedelic explosion will end here.*

# THE 1995 GARAGE & PSYCHEDELIC "HOT 100"

I've described in the previous pages thousands of groups and records from the 1980s and 1990s, and they're included because I believe each of them to be of interest and worth. We all seem to be intrigued in the western world by "who is the best," however, so here's my personal list of what I believe to be the top 100 groups included in this study. (Remember that for the most part I disregard the more commercial groups on major labels.) Groups from 11 different countries are represented. The groups are listed alphabetically — there is no numerical rating putting any band "in front of" or "behind" another — they are simply part of what I call my "Hot 100." The purpose of this list is to assist interested readers in searching for new sounds — with this as a starting guide based upon my knowledge and personal taste. Refer to the "Echoes In Time" chapter text for specific releases of interest from these groups — at least one of their releases was exceptional for the group to be included on this list. Remember, these are simply my selections. Use them as a gauge for your own assessments.

THE BACKDOOR MEN (Sweden)
THE BACKWARDS (Italy)
THE BARRACUDAS (U.K.)
THE BLACKLIGHT CHAMELEONS (USA)
THE BO-WEEVILS (Australia)
THE BROOD (USA)
BROKEN JUG (Germany)
THE CHEEPSKATES (USA)
THE CHESTERFIELD KINGS (USA)
BILLY CHILDISH & assorted groups (U.K.)
CORNFLAKE ZOO (Sweden)
COSMIC DROPOUTS (Norway)
THE CRAWDADDYS (USA)
THE CREATURES OF THE GOLDEN DAWN (USA)
THE CREEPS (Sweden)
THE CRIMSON SHADOWS (Sweden)
THE CRYPTONES (France)
THE CYNICS (USA)
THE DENTISTS (U.K.)
DIMENTIA 13 (USA)
DOUBLE NAUGHT SPYS (USA)
DREAM SYNDICATE (USA)
DUKES OF STRATOSPHEAR (U.K.)
THE EYES OF MIND (USA)
THE FLAMIN' GROOVIES (USA)
THE FLESHTONES (USA)
THEE FOURGIVEN (USA)
THE FUNSEEKERS (USA)
THE FUZZTONES (USA)
THE GARDEN PATH (Australia)
THE GRAVEDIGGER V (USA)
THE GREEN PAJAMAS (USA)
GREEN TELESCOPE (U.K.)
THE GRUESOMES (Canada)
HEAD & THE HARES (Italy)
HEADLESS HORSEMEN (USA)
HIDDEN PEACE (USA)
THE KLIEK (Holland)
THE LAST (USA)
THE LAUGHING SOUP DISH (USA)
THE LEARS (USA)
THE LEOPARDS (USA)
THE LONG RYDERS (USA)
THE LUST-O-RAMA (Norway)
THE LYRES (USA)
MAD VIOLETS (USA)
MARSHMALLOW OVERCOAT (USA)
THE MIRACLE WORKERS (USA)
THE MOFFS (Australia)
THE MYSTIC EYES (USA)

THE MYSTREATED (U.K.)
LOS NEGATIVOS (Spain)
THE 99th FLOOR (Italy)
THE NOMADS (Sweden)
THE NOT QUITE (USA)
OPAL (USA)
THE OPTIC NERVE (USA)
THE OTHERS (Italy)
THE OTHER SIDE (Holland)
THE OUTTA PLACE (USA)
THE PANDORAS (USA)
THE PETALS (USA)
PLAN 9 (USA)
PLASTICLAND (USA)
THE PRIME MOVERS (Boston, USA)
THE PRISONERS (U.K.)
THE PROJECTILES (USA)
THE RAIN PARADE (USA)
REEFUS MOONS (U.K.)
THE ROYAL NONESUCH (USA)
THE RUNNING STREAM (Italy)
SEX MUSEUM (Spain)
SHINY GNOMES (Germany)
THE SHOUTLESS (Sweden)
THE SICK ROSE (Italy)
SOMELOVES (Australia)
THE SOUND EXPLOSION (Greece)
THE STEMS (Australia)
THE STEPFORD HUSBANDS (USA)
THE STOMACHMOUTHS (Sweden)
TECHNICOLOUR DREAM (Italy)
THE TELL-TALE HEARTS (USA)
THE TEN COMMANDMENTS (Canada)
THE THANES (U.K.)
THE THINGS (USA)
1313 MOCKINGBIRD LANE (USA)
THE THREE O'CLOCK (USA)
THE TRYFLES (USA)
THE 27 VARIOUS (USA)
THE TYRNAROUND (Australia)
THE ULTRA 5 (USA)
THE UNCLAIMED (USA)
THE UNITED STATES OF EXISTENCE (USA)
THE UNTOLD FABLES (USA)
THE VIPERS (USA)
THE WATERMELON MEN (Sweden)
THE WITCHDOCTORS (USA)
THE WORST (Canada)
THE WYLDE MAMMOTHS (Sweden)
YARD TRAUMA (USA)

# 1995
# Photo Pages

*The original paper book contained eight photo pages in its middle. They are recreated here, with a few additions.*

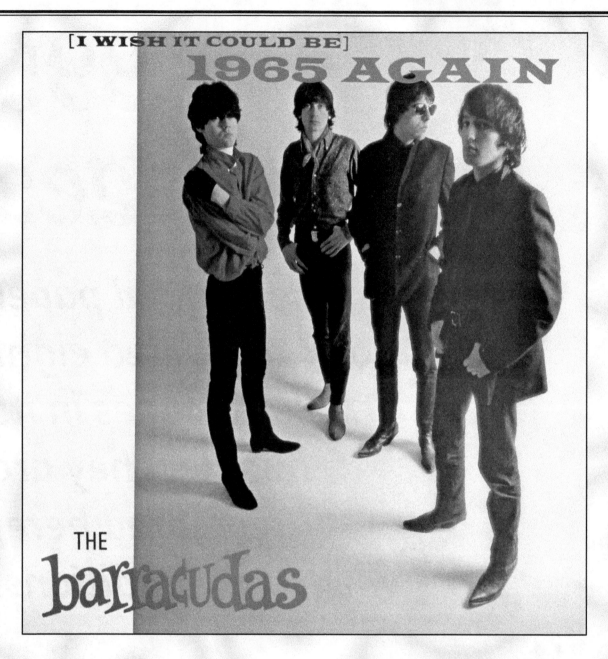

**[I WISH IT COULD BE] 1965 AGAIN**

**THE barracudas**

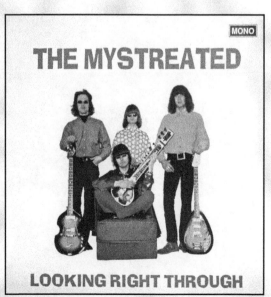

**THE MYSTREATED**

MONO

**LOOKING RIGHT THROUGH**

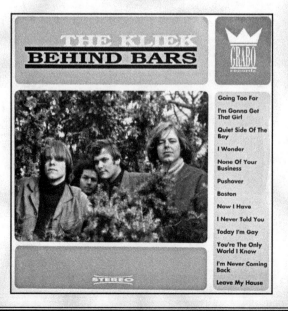

**THE KLIEK**
**BEHIND BARS**

GRABO records

Going Too Far

I'm Gonna Get That Girl

Quiet Side Of The Bay

I Wonder

None Of Your Business

Pushover

Boston

Now I Have

I Never Told You

Today I'm Gay

You're The Only World I Know

I'm Never Coming Back

Leave My House

STEREO

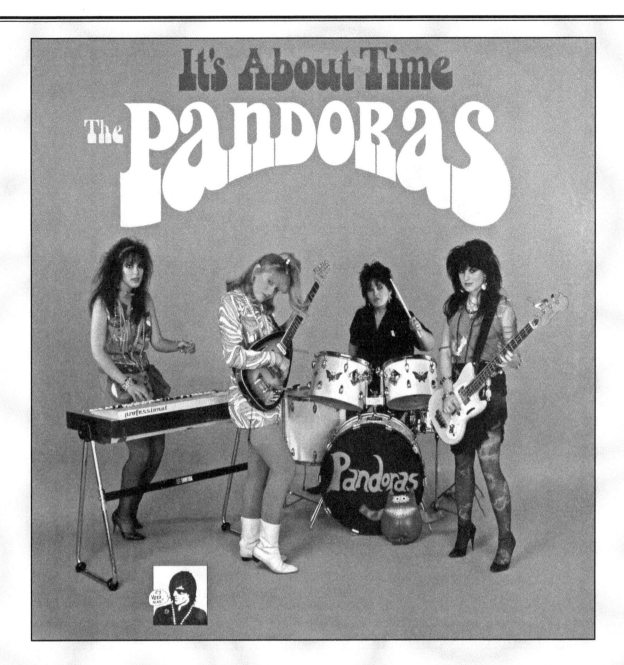

Here are the

# The Chesterfield Kings

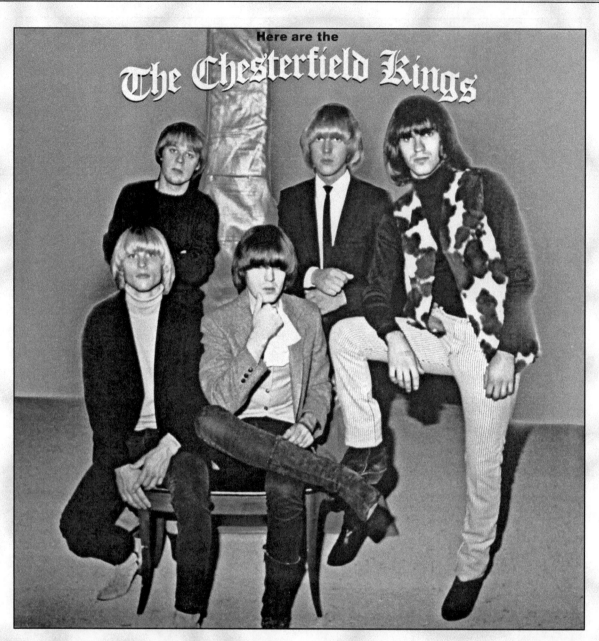

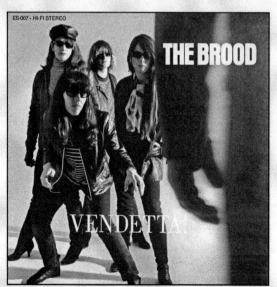

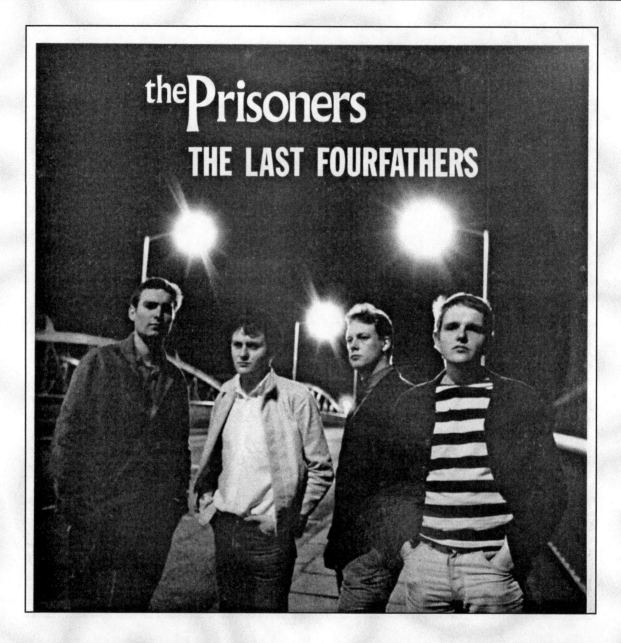

# the Prisoners
## THE LAST FOURFATHERS

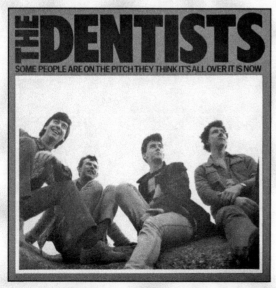

# THE DENTISTS
SOME PEOPLE ARE ON THE PITCH THEY THINK IT'S ALL OVER IT IS NOW

STEREO

the thanes

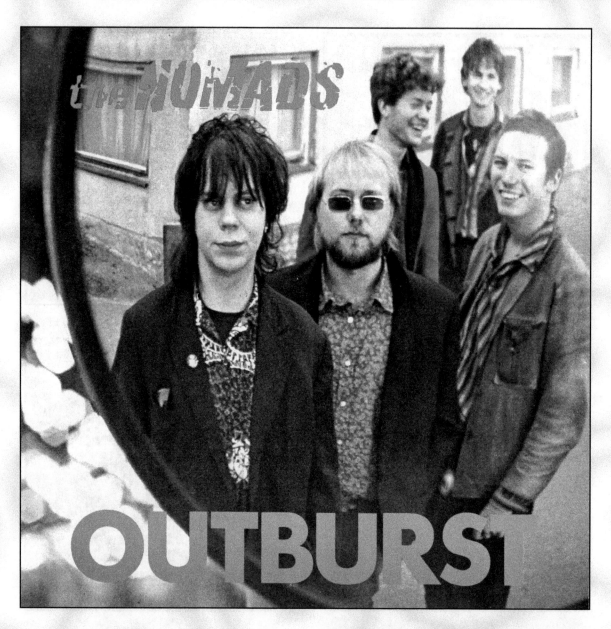

the NOMADS

OUTBURST

THE STOMACH MOUTHS
SOMETHING WEIRD

WATERMELON MEN

SEVEN YEARS B/W I'VE BEEN TOLD

# 1995-2014
# Global
# Updates

## by
## Timothy
## Gassen

# THE AUTHOR'S UPDATES
## 1995-2014

We begin the additions to the 1995 "Knights of Fuzz" book with the author's own extensive scene and band updates. Remember to also read the additional **Guest Authors** chapter, **Garage Feature Articles** chapter, **Fan Submitted Updates**, and other update chapters for many *hundreds* of other bands and record releases that may not be included in this update below.

---

## A NEW CENTURY FOR THE KNIGHTS

The very definition of what constitutes "garage" and "psychedelic" music has evolved since the 1995 edition of "The Knights of Fuzz" saw publication. New sub-genres of the sound have laid claim to the garage moniker, while trippy sounds far-removed from their 1960s grandfathers' label themselves psychedelic. I enjoy many of the bands in the "somewhat-related-to-garage" category, but this book remains focused on those who take the 1960s definition of garage and psych-pop to heart.

And a curious battle it is for today's young bands that see 1985 as a distance in the far past much as the 1980s revivalists saw 1965. The fact that new 1960s-styled bands keep appearing – now with musicians born in the 1980s and later – baffles many observers. Luca Re, vocalist with Italy's long-running garage kings The Sick Rose, explained to me, "The 1960s sound now has become a musical standard, like folk music. It is a form that can continue as its own, like classical music, in its own way."

And I think Luca is correct – even as kids redefine garage to be heard as "lo-fi" or "psycho-billy" or "shoegazer trance," the original 1960s-style will also somehow survive.

But how new garage and psych bands approach their sound is much different in 2014 than, say, in 1984. Freddy Fortune, of the essential Fortune & Maltese band, told me, "Back in the 1980s and 1990s most if not all of the obscure garage bands from the '60s were so mysterious, you really had to search out fanzines or actually track down the bands yourself if you wanted to know more. So it was almost some kind of new frontier of a forgotten time.

"Today, all one has to do for research is use the Internet and many of those mysteries unravel in front of your eyes immediately," he continued. "I also think that, because another 20 years has passed by, that new bands that really 'get it' and try to do that authentic sound are getting to be fewer and fewer. It's also harder to find songs to cover that nobody has heard. In the 1980s you could get away with playing the Sonics – now it would be an utter cliché to do that."

Nick Salomon, the force behind the long-running U.K. hard psych Bevis Frond, agrees. "In the 1980s the garage bands had

probably been directly influenced by the classic '60s bands, while now it's a couple of degrees of separation. I'm guessing The Chesterfield Kings (and others) actually bought records by The Electric Prunes or The Standells and saw them on TV while it was actually happening. Now, you'd be checking them out online as a kind of historical artifact. (Today) it's less to do with the feel of the times, and more to do with the look and an approximation of the sound."

So garage bands are still forming, but in what form their released music will survive is also up in the air. The neo-garage movement began when vinyl records were still king, then by the early 1990s even indie labels could release affordable CDs – and in the 2000s the CD gave way to Internet digital downloads as a dominant format. Then, completely unexpectedly, vinyl records began a slow and steady revival of their own.

This acceptance of vinyl record releases in the second decade of the 2000s is especially advantageous for current garage-psych bands, since that is the way many fans believe this music is meant to be heard. Garage fans already understand the tactile enjoyment of holding an actual physical release, with a cool cover graphic, and an actual disc to play.

Digital files on a portable device are fine for listening on an airplane, but can you imagine the stunted impact that The Beatles' "Sgt. Pepper" album would have had in 1967 (or if released now) without its colorful gatefold sleeve and carefully arranged two-sided song line-up? A list of file names on a computer hard drive can never duplicate the immersion into a band's style and sound like an actual vinyl record and its sleeve. As Get Hip Records honcho Gregg Kostelich told me, "Downloading bores me to tears."

The irony is delicious – as the digital media world engulfs us globally, garage fans can find even more new vinyl releases to share and spread their gospel. And remember that vinyl can survive the decades. The U.S. Library of Congress still accepts the vinyl record as the preferred long-term archive medium for music. No one knows the long-range survivability of digital files or CDs, but the good old vinyl record can last for hundreds of years.

But while the vinyl record remains the ultimate goal for garage fans, the digital download is still the current king in the commercial music industry – with serious ramifications for the garage scene.

We've certainly witnessed a profound change in how most listeners consume music with the acceptance of the Internet as the global default communication medium – a form that was just getting a foothold when my original 1995 book was published. The positive ability to instantly hear and see a band from anywhere in the world is certainly welcome, but it also has severe ramifications on how fans are found and cultivated. It is difficult for kids today to comprehend that 1980s neo-garage lovers, like me, had to find a street address somewhere and write an actual paper letter to a band in Sweden or beyond, ask a few questions, and then hope that in a month's time perhaps they would answer. By definition fans who took this time and effort over years were dedicated – "**True Believers**" – as I will call them throughout this book.

Today a kid can zip through a whole nation's musical scene in a day, chew on some of it and spit it out – and move on to more new *free* meat in a different genre. A person's attachment to a band, as a "fan," is today very tenuous.

"Yes, the Internet has made everything easy to find or hear, but that hasn't generally led to bigger audiences, more sales, or more knowledgeable fans," Bart Mendoza of Manual Scan and The Shambles told me. "When everything is available all the time, nothing is special."

And "free" is also a vital term, since now people who call themselves "fans" can steal a band's entire discography – years of hard work and investment – with a few keyboard clicks and a few minutes of download time. While this kind of electronic bootlegging and stealing affects major label profit margins, it is absolutely devastating to the indie record market – and especially threatening in smaller sub-scenes such as garage-psych.

Prominent garage labels have told me that their sales of actual physical releases – vinyl and CDs mainly – have dropped dramatically since the ease of illegal Internet downloading has become the norm. Within a day of an indie label releasing a vinyl record or CD for sale its entire contents are invariably online and shared illegally through underground Web pages and networks. This simply means that garage labels and bands are making less and less profit and therefore are releasing fewer and fewer records. A band could once turn a profit with sales as low as 1,000 copies of an album – but now the results of a release can be 200 sales or less.

Illegal downloading, simply, is crippling – and could kill – a fragile, small scene such as garage-psych.

Perhaps the most disturbing trend is that "fans" who upload and download bootlegged music – especially those under 30 years of age – do not even admit or understand they are thieves. They equate the technological ability to share digital files as the right to take other people's intellectual property. These are not music fans. They are simply thieves. Even editions of this book (and our "Knights of Fuzz" DVD) have been shamelessly copied illegally and distributed online. If you actually are a fan of music (and this book), just don't do it!

Another un-welcome consequence of the ubiquitous social-media web sites is the immediate negative opinions "fans" can post for the world to see. A band can need years to write, record and save the money to finally release a record – but an anonymous online social-media user can spend just five seconds to deem it "Trash, garbage...worthless." I see this kind of cowardice in the online world everyday, and it is often spewed by someone who has never created anything themselves. This kind of selfish, idiotic communication only further depresses the garage-psych scene that instead needs nurturing and intelligent, positive, factual feedback.

How a record label does its public business also has shifted since 1995, in great part because of the Internet and digital download world. Never an easy business to maintain in any era, independent record labels have struggled to survive – especially in the garage-psych genre. Many of the 1980s and '90s main U.S. garage labels (such as Get Hip, Bomp!, Dionysus, and Estrus) diversified their range of styles, distancing themselves from the perception of being merely a "garage revival" label. Many other labels simply stopped operation.

Other long-time garage-related labels soldiered on, amazingly releasing a slew of new material to its niche market. Important labels such as Detour, Dirty Water, and Twist (all in the UK), Screaming Apple, and Soundflat (in Germany) all survived the new century, all the way to this 2014 writing. A few new labels, such as Portugal's fine Groovie Records, Greece's Action, Lost in Tyme, and Sound Effect, and the USA's 13 O'Clock Records also joined the economically-tough record-releasing fray. (There are *many* other relevant record labels, as noted throughout this book.)

It is also more obvious in 2014 that many in the small garage music world very consciously want others to simply fail. While this kind of selfish competiveness has always been part of any music scene, the Internet gives the instant ability to lash out at competing labels, or bands, or even other fans. (Or a label or popular band can simply ignore garage comrades and not allow them even to step into the fringes of their own online network of contacts.) This selfish behavior makes me so sad, and repels me from wanting to delve even deeper into the neo-garage scene – an effect I'm guessing is also felt by other potentially-interested Web users just discovering garage music.

The use by bands of Internet "crowd-funding" sites such as Kickstarter and Indiegogo also has revealed the overly self-interested nature of some garage record labels. The mere idea that fans could directly fund a band's release – with no record label as the middle man – is an ultimate threat to an indie label. After all, if a band can appeal directly to their fans and then make their own record, why is an actual record label even necessary? The answer: in many ways, today, record labels are not necessary. This has resulted in some label owners voicing privately to me (and publicly) their wish that bands fail when using crowd-funding campaigns, and voicing their disdain for bands that attempt (and succeed) when using that method to release music.

This attitude of "there's only room for me to succeed" – so common in all levels of the business world – makes the global garage music scene shrink. Cooperation and goodwill between bands, fans, and record labels, in comparison, can grow and spread an underground sound such as garage-psych. That spirit was much more in evidence (in my view at least) in the original 1980-1995 garage revival era.

"There was also a dedication that doesn't happen today, and there was a sense of unity between all the different little scenes," longtime garage-scene musician Bart Mendoza told me. "In the old days it was, and for many of us, remains, a way of life."

I still consider The Chesterfield Kings the most significant band of the neo-garage era, and vocalist Greg Prevost told me, "I remember playing the Peppermint Lounge (in NYC) around 1981 to 1984 in particular – and it was like this family – everyone was friends, guys and gals with 'the look' or not, just people turned onto this sound, including guys from other bands, guys from the coolest record stores – it was actually a great vibe.

"It was great while it lasted – but that feeling and camaraderie is not present these days," he continued. "There is still the movement and the spark among guys who are in bands, but the universal following is sort of lost."

And make no mistake – the financial feasibility of operating a '60s-styled garage band has changed since the 1980s, and not for the better. "In the 1980s and early '90s most of the people in my bands did music for a living," Bruce Joyner of the seminal early 1980s The Unknowns told me. "There was a circuit to play in each large town or city. I fed myself and paid the rent. Today that is not the case – musicians usually work full time jobs or live at home with their parents. Paying jobs, playing clubs locally or state-to-state, are rare. More musicians do it as a hobby on the garage band level, not as a paying thing."

And the commercial struggle in the garage world meant that the significant financial investment beginning in the 2000s from Little Steven Van Zandt (longtime guitarist with Bruce Springsteen) was especially impactful. His Wicked Cool label signed and promoted new garage bands – even placing The Chesterfield Kings and other label-mates on national TV for performances and on TV show soundtracks.

Little Steven's very public and expensive promotional splash in the garage world of the 2000s rubbed some garage purists the wrong way – "Who does this rich guy think he is, coming in and taking over the scene we built" was a sentiment I heard from some – but his innate understanding and dedication to the authentic sound and style of garage music cannot be disputed. He also continues to play many neo-garage bands on his "Little Steven's Underground Garage" radio shows, giving acts exposure not available elsewhere. Little Steven should be remembered as one of the greatest modern mainstream supporters of the garage-psych sound we love.

And while commercial bands which feature some element of the garage-psych sound are not the focus of this book, their influence can't be ignored. The White Stripes' early 2000s success is among the most financially lucrative in indie rock music history, and while they don't fit the 1966 definition of "garage," they certainly exposed similarly raw sounds to millions of unknowing kids. Unfortunately, this also meant that other, lesser-inspired bands adopted the affectation of some similar "garage" elements in a careerist stab at financial gain – and those bands won't be found in this book.

Some notable commercial groups that do merit praise include The Raveonettes, with many fine releases – dig their superb 2014 cover of the Doors' "The End" as one example. Both The Hives and The Vines have also deposited blistering garage-fueled major label records, too. Yes, we could start to discuss Oasis and other mega-acts somewhat associated with the garage-psych "sound," but again, they are not the focus of this book, which is centered on what is most certainly best when still in the underground.

In these difficult financial times some of the most important garage-psych bands from the original 1980s revival era somehow continued to tour and make records. As of this 2014 writing, genre greats such as The Fleshtones, Fuzztones, and Cynics are still going strong, and The Chesterfield Kings only recently called it quits after three decades of mastering the garage world. (This makes my own 25-year Marshmallow Overcoat garage band journey seem brief!)

And there were some notable reunion shows, too. In December 2013 the "Paisley Underground" series of concerts in L.A. and San Francisco featured The Bangles, Three O'Clock, Dream Syndicate and Rain Parade – the same impressive lineup that graced a landmark 1982 show at the Music Machine club in Los Angeles.

Guitarist Matt Piucci, of The Rain Parade, told me, "It seems like even more fun now – and I do feel we have a legacy of which we can be proud, and this can only come with time. Now that we are thirty plus years past our inception, history really does include us as an influential and important band. We have a lot of respect from our peers and from younger bands." Not stuck in the past, though, Piucci adds, "It's great to have this thing, Rain Parade, that we can celebrate, and to have that thing engender interest from really cool musicians so that new, other things can flow from it."

A series of popular garage music festivals also continue to take place annually, most successfully in Europe each spring and summer. The tribes shall gather and the fuzz shall be shared!

Even more amazingly, some of the most important original **1960s** garage-psych acts managed to play well-received and powerful shows in the 2000s. Question Mark & The Mysterians, The Chocolate Watchband, Standells, Sonics and even the glorious Monks showed they still had the garage fire decades after their debut. I even saw Peter Noone (of the 1960s Herman's Hermits) perform in the 2000s with Vance Brescia on guitar (of the 1980s neo-garage-pop Mosquitos) in an authentic 1960s-styled show that would have made any Beat fan proud.

The Electric Prunes also re-formed and was still successfully recording and touring the globe as of this writing. Vocalist James Lowe considered the evolution of the garage eras and told me, "Probably the most glaring difference from the 1960s and now is the fact that we had no legitimacy back then. Music was not as open to new ideas as it might have appeared.

"The material available today is amazing," he continued. "With a computer you can go anywhere, hear anything – back then we would only 'hear' about songs and scratch for weeks to find a recorded copy. So we just made it fuzz a lot."

And there are still notable 1980s garagers still making some of the most vibrant sounds today. Swedish garage maven Jens Lindberg played in seminal 1980s bands such as The Crimson Shadows and Highspeed V – and continues the tradition today in The Majarajas. He told me, "In the 1980s I was like a child learning to walk – everything was new, you 'discovered' new songs every day, and it was like entering a big treasure chamber and you just found bigger, greater things the more you dwelled in that cave. In other words, we were innocent.

"Nowadays I feel like a connoisseur – I've heard so much so I can pick and choose what I want to create from a 60 year historic span of rock-n-roll," he said.

And with that span of time we also lost some of the neo-garage era's most dedicated musicians. Paula Pierce of The Pandoras left us in 1991 and Wendy Wild of The Mad Violets passed in 1996 – and we should not forget Lux Interior of the still wildly influential Cramps, gone in 2009.

In 2004 the garage scene was dealt one of its most devastating blows: Greg Shaw died of hear failure. The legendary record collector and music historian brought us Bomp! Records in 1974 and later Voxx Records, which specialized in the neo-garage revival. His good taste in underground rock is well known: DEVO, The Romantics, The Shoes, Plimsouls and Flamin' Groovies were all championed by him, and later he opened doors for The Miracle Workers, Pandoras and many other garage revivalists, too.

It should be emphasized that Greg Shaw's "Pebbles" compilation album series (and the later "Highs In The Mid-Sixties" series) was instrumental in the garage revival. Without these collections of original 1966-styled garage sounds, many bands (like mine) wouldn't have had a roadmap to create their own garage sound.

His influence could also be much more direct. Garage fans probably have never heard before that Greg Shaw made a line of credit available at a pressing plant so Lee Joseph could start Dionysus Records in the mid-1980s. Dionysus became one of the leaders in the global garage movement – thanks in great part to Greg Shaw. He was one of those rare music guys who was not threatened by other talented people – he wanted others to succeed.

He became a good friend and mentor to me in the 1980s and 1990s, and my time in Los Angeles was centered at the Bomp! offices, their record warehouse and his Cavern Club. The first time I saw a huge chunk of his personal record collection I almost fainted – it was almost an entire house filled with records – he guessed more than a million of them. "Even if they were spinning 24 hours a day, I know I'll never hear them all before I die," he said to me circa 1985.

Upon seeing the first edition of this book Greg Shaw gave me a grand title – he dubbed me "The Guru Of Garage." His intentions were two-fold: to help establish me further as a garage music authority, especially for the revival era, and then also to perhaps take some of that responsibility off his own shoulders.

By the 1990s Greg wanted to escape the perception that he was only interested in the 1960s and its revival sounds. In reality Greg Shaw was interested and involved in a wide range of sounds and styles and was a very forward-looking person. So he called me "The Guru Of Garage" – always with that sly little smile of his – and helped my work to promote and preserve the revival garage era, all the way to his death.

I hold this title proudly, Greg, thanks to you. I miss you greatly.

Losing other personal friends such as Alan Wright (of The 14th Wray and others) in 2004, Greg Johnson (of The Worst, and The Fiends) in 2009, and Mark Smith (Creatures of the Golden Dawn) in 2011 emphasized to me that soon all that will be left of our garage scene will be the records we've made.

So it is with that adult understanding, far away from the first blush of fervor and dedication I felt to underground rock as a teenager, that we begin the updates to the original 1995 "Knights of Fuzz" book.

And with goodwill to all garage bands everywhere...

## DOWNLOADS AND WEB SITES

Note that we generally do not include the recent trend of digital-only-download releases in the following updates or discographies. We are not prejudiced against legitimate (legal) band or record label download-only releases – we simply understand that they can change or disappear online without notice, making them difficult to collect later. A vinyl record or CD, even in micro-batches of only 100 or so, can still exist in their original form and be collected years later, and that is one main goal of this book: to inspire the reader to go out and collect garage-psych music!

We don't list Internet Web site addresses for the same reason. Almost all of the sites we listed in previous versions of this book have disappeared or changed Internet locations. We want this reference book to be usable years from now, so we focus on what will not change with time – the vinyl and CD releases of the garage-psych bands we love. (A plethora of current garage-psych-oriented Web sites can be found quickly using a web search engine. Those search results will, of course, constantly change.)

## WHAT IS HERE AND WHAT IS NOT

Also keep in mind, as explained in the 1995 book listings introduction, that the amount written about a band here is not indicative of their importance. Whether we include a long feature piece or just a one line mention, almost every one of these bands deserves to be found and heard.

And, in many cases, what some fans might see as the omission of a band or record release can be due to several important facts: 1) we only can write about the releases we have heard; 2) the emphasis of this book is on the bands and records we are especially inspired by; and 3) not every release by a band might be relevant for the focus of this book – for example, some bands start in the garage and later move on to other genres.

So, if you believe a 1960s-styled band or exceptional recording is "missing" in this book, we suggest sending more information and sounds to us to consider including in future editions. **Contact information is at the front of this book.**

---

## UPDATES AND NEW LISTINGS

For bands already in the 1995 book, in the entries below you'll see the term "**(UPDATE)**" next to their band name. You can read more about them in the text of the original 1995 book. For bands *new* to this book, we'll add the band's hometown (if known) and country of origin, such as "**(TUCSON, AZ, USA)**," next to their name.

*Remember again that every release and every '6os-styled garage-psych band may not be listed or reviewed here.*

---

## THE ACETONES (UPDATE)

Holland's beat kings The Acetones hit the bullseye with their self-produced 1996 "Sixteen" CD (on Henk's Crazy Diamond Records). Expertly-played gritty garage punk at its finest, "Sixteen" features really well-recorded live tracks showcasing true rock muscle, with the Q-65's "Cry In The Night" a special highlight among their killer originals. They followed up with the 1997 "In Your Eyes" album. There is also a 300-copy 1995 EP on Lada Records featuring four fine 1960s covers. The Acetones remain one of the most under-rated garage groups of the revival era – and I recommend them as highly as anything in this book.

## THE ACID LEMON (TORINO, ITALY)

The eight-song "Introducing" CD (2003 on Teen Sound) is classic '66 fuzz n' Farfisa garage in the U.S.A. style, but with the distinctive Italian tinge that makes so much of that country's bands top-notch. A special tip 'o my hat for their tremolo-laden cover of the Electric Prunes' "Get Me To The

World On Time" – always reassuring to see the new bands pay rightful homage to the original masters. The band lineup features former members of Italian favorites The 99th Floor Paolo Messina on guitar and Simona Ghigo on the Farfisa – so you know the sound here is tops. The CD was reportedly issued only as a 300 copy limited edition.

## AGENTEMUSIK (GERMANY)

The glued-on front and back covers of this 1998 10" EP certainly signal a crude release, and the grooves prove this correct. It's strictly lo-fi for the vaguely spy-garage sounding EP (limited to 400 copies) on Avalanche Records (distributed by Swamp Room in Germany).

## DAVIE ALLAN AND THE ARROWS
### (LOS ANGELES, CA, U.S.A.)

The re-formed Davie Allan combo wowed crowds again in the late 1990s with his patented fuzz guitar attack (with Dionysus records guru Lee Joseph lured out of retirement for the new Arrows lineup). Allan re-recorded two of his classics, "The Born Losers Theme" and "The Glory Stompers," for a Get Hip 45. Coupled with the 1998 Total Energy reissue of his "Fuzz Fest" LP, Allan captured a new generation of fans.

Somebody should check the birth certificate for Davie Allan. His 2000 "Dynamic Sounds Of" CD on Total Energy doesn't sound like the effort of a 1960s veteran, it sounds like he's still back there and never turned off his fuzz box. Damn, it's embarrassing (to today's kids) when guys who are in their sixties (at the least) are cooler than today's hottest new booty shakers.

## THE ALLOY SIX (STOCKHOLM, SWEDEN)

Yet another cool Swedish garage group – my lord, is it in the genes up there or something? The 2014 "Eye To Eye" rehearsal-room demo is a moody slow number, with a mesmerizing guitar lick and then some nasty fuzz on the chorus. Worthy of release, I'd say! I heard a few more of these demos, and it shows a band ready to go into a studio and create their own sound. I can't wait to hear the results.

## GERRY ALVAREZ ODYSSEY
### (TORONTO, CANADA)

Longtime Gruesome Gerry Alvarez embraces more of a '66-styled psych-pop style for his 2006 solo debut, "Candy Prankster" (on Ricochet). This is supreme hook-laden garage-power-pop, with the title track a fitting overture for the entire album. There is a serene, hypnotic quality at work here, aided by excellent arrangements and a modern-yet-period production style. Purists need not apply here – this is a modern interpretation of the Beatles-esque pop-psych we love so well. And it's one of my favorite releases of the early 2000s. As Gerry sings, "Open Up Your Mind."

A second CD album, "Omega Tea Time" (2010 on Ricochet) also exists.

## THE ANGRY DRAGONS (See the "Fan Submitted Updates" chapter for more information.)

## THE AQUAVELVETS (UPDATE)

The Springfield, Illinois quintet has collected their various vinyl treats together with some new tracks for their 1997 "The Then...The Now" CD. The timeless Vox organ sound is everywhere, rounded out by a tongue-in-cheek friendliness and an utter lack of pretension.

This here's some good, corn-fed punk-pop from the heartland, topped off by the smirking "Brian Jones Haircut." How could you not bow to the lyrics, "If I can't have a Brian Jones haircut, then I don't want any hair at all," or "He died when he was 27, now he's in haircut heaven." Nothing sacred with these cows. Oh, don't confuse these boys with an instrumental act from San Francisco that answers to the same moniker.

## THE AR-KAICS (RICHMOND, VA, U.S.A.)

There are at least four 7"s from 2013 and 2014, and a 2014 album in the works. What I've heard is crudely-recorded basic garage rock, with distorted vocals and a general DIY raw approach. It's pretty darn cool, though I haven't found any of their actual releases yet to hold and love for myself.

## ARTHUR'S DREAM (PEINE, GERMANY)

German psychedelia always strikes me as having a bit more of a direct approach than the U.K. or U.S. style – perhaps less introspective and more rocking – and the 1999 "Lost Inside The Grannary" album (1999 on Rays) is a good example. There's plenty of trippiness here, they just also make sure to remind the listener that they are a rock band as well. "Stumbling" reminds me a bit of elegant 1967-ish Stones, even. At almost 12 minutes long, "Heads For The Crowd" will surely satisfy the acidhead music fan (like me).

2003's "Echo! Echo! Echo!" (on Rays) adds some prime covers, including Electric Prunes and Love, along with their distinctly German originals. Arthur's Dream is more difficult to categorize than many of the bands in this book – which means their music is also pretty darn interesting.

## THE ASTRAL WEEKS (ITALY)

The 1999 500-copy "A Yellow Dream" LP on the venerable Psych-Out Records is much more of a hippy-ish affair than most in the book, with a loose Grateful Dead feel for most of it. "A Flower With Your Name" has more energy, but this disc is designed more for fans of laid-back, meandering psychedelia.

## THE ASTRONAUTS (GERMANY)

Obviously not the U.S.A. band from the 1960s, the 1994 four-song 7" EP (on Pin Up Records) does feature some cool instrumental surf sounds, complete with vintage pinging-and-poinging guitar ambience. And dig that crazy cover photo – man, these cats look like they came direct from Uranus!

## THE ATOMIC BUDDHA (CT, U.S.A.)

Atomic Buddha formed in 2006 with Keith Grave and Adam Schwartz (formerly of the Sanity Assassins). "Blottered" is a limited edition album of 100 CDs, and it's a raw, lo-fi affair, with guitar amps turned to 11.. As the sleeve writes, "Recorded in the basement by Dave."

## THE ATTENTION (VIENNA, AUSTRIA)

The self-titled album (2009 on Screaming Apple) is included on the 2012 "Getting All" CD, making a double album. It's Euro-beat mania with a touch of Mod here, with some pulsing production on "Have A Drink" and a Cavern Club feel on "Dandy Groove." The dance groove is unavoidable on "Kaiser's Dance," one of the most infectious tracks to have invaded my brain in many moons. If you have even a drop of soul in your body it be impossible not to dance to that song. I dare you! The Attention is first class.

A 2012 follow-up album is also on Screaming Apple and two other 45s are out there, somewhere.

# B

## BABY WOODROSE (COPENHAGEN, DENMARK)

This Danish band captured more mainstream attention in their home country and Europe in the 2000s, but I've only heard their 2001 "Blows Your Mind" album (on Pan). There are as many as eight more albums, plus many singles (including a 2002 wildly colorful 45 sleeve on Bad Afro Records) and other releases through at least 2012.

The debut shows a vibrant, energetic garage-psych stew (with an accent on the psych), with some nasty fuzz and distinctive vocals. Plenty of reverb and a general lysergic feel make this a colorful, original outing. Baby Woodrose has the ability to sound both period and modern at the same time – a difficult quality that can explain why they were able to attract fans outside the garage underground.

## THE BALD GUYS (BOSTON, MA, U.S.A.)

Let's also give a nod to The Bald Guys, whose 1997 surf-and-destroy "Secret Mission to Spy Land" 45 on Stanton Park goes down smooth after a dose of Bomboras, for instance. Here's yet another case where I actually prefer the B-side, in this case the stomping "Teleport." This is my first appetizer from the Bald Guys' trash compactor, but I'm hungry for more.

## BANG! (PARIS, FRANCE)

Garage music has its iconic imagery, of course – if you see a bowl hair cut, Vox organ and screaming vocalist on a cover of a record you know it must be '60s garage. The same goes for Mod bands – if you see a cover with the red-white-blue bullseye on a shirt, button-down long sleeve shirts and white jackets with pins on it, you can be sure it is a Mod record.

And so you will instantly understand the Mod-pop sound on the 2002 three song EP on Teen Sound. I enjoy a lot of Mod music, and Misty Lane has enough of an open mind to include Bang! on their mostly garage label. Good for them and us!

## THE BARRACUDAS (UPDATE)

The vintage output of The Barracudas only sounds better with time, and I still wonder why the media gatekeepers didn't allow them into the mainstream at the dawn of the 1980s. Much of their material has been re-released, and the 1994 Voxx "Drop Acid With The Barracudas" is a colorful (though somewhat mistitled) artifact especially worth finding. There are several other re-packages of Barracudas material, and I recommend you get busy finding them.

## THE BARBWIRES (SWEDEN)

A unique production style highlights the three-song 1997 "Rattlehead" 7" EP on Kook Records – it sounds **BIG**, with an in-your-face result that still retains its vintage surf-instrumental roots. Surf guitar can tend to sound very "tinny" after even a few minutes, but here it is good and fat.

## THE BARON FOUR (U.K.)

The "Yes I Do" b/w " Girl" 45 was issued by State Records in 2013, and it is a slice of picture-perfect 1965 teenbeat angst. The B-side reminds me a lot of the classic '60s teen lament "Hurtin' Kind," and "Yes I Do" continues the garage beat, complete with slightly atonal vocals, perfect for the mood. There is also the limited "5 to 4" b/w "She Said" 45 (on Groovie in 2013). I gotta find it!

## THE BASEMENT BRATS (UPDATE)

The "Curse Of The Brats" album (1996, on 1+2 Records, Japan) compiles tracks from 1991-1995 in the pop-punk style. This isn't '60s garage rock, but the Basement Brats would do fine on a bill of garagers – the fun attitude and toe-tapping Sonics-meets-The Ramones feel is there.

## THE BASEMENTS (GREECE)

The 2011 "I'm Dead" album (on Lost in Tyme) is anything but dead, as the boys furiously blast the garage and R&B-fueled

fuzz throughout. The highlights are many, capped by the majestic stately jangle of "Stray Mood," which holds its own with any 1966 Euro-Beat classic. Another Pick Hit: the swaggering gritty, beautiful "What's Going On."

The Basements' '66 sound is so authentic that I can see in my mind's eye exactly what they look and sound like at midnight, on stage, as they pulse and fuzz through their set. The walls of the tiny club are sweating, and everyone leaves exhausted and happy. Yep, good garage rock is a blessing, and The Basements are a sacrament to consume again and again. In case you can't figure out what I am saying: this is a must-have!

The 2010 "Heart Of Stone" EP (on Lost In Tyme) is moody, dark and mysterious. The title track is a real stand out blacklight garage-psych piece, and the mesmerizing "I Wanna Leave You" another moody gem.

## STIV BATORS (YOUNGSTOWN, OH, U.S.A.)

The frontman vocalist is best known for his punk bands The Dead Boys and Lords of The New Church, but I really dig his more power-pop efforts on Bomp! Records. The Disconnected album (1980 and 1994 as a 10"; on CD in 2004) adds a New Wave edge to his punkish delivery, and "The Last Year" (also a Bomp! 45) is a standout pop-garage-punk anthem for the era.

I also appreciate his take on the Electric Prunes' classic "Too Much To Dream." As a kid I heard his version more than the original!

## THE BEATPACK (UPDATE)

"The Time And The Pleasure" album (2013 on Screaming Apple) collects 1989-1991 tracks, and all benefit from a kind CD re-mastering, especially for the earlier crude tracks. The swinging "Not Tonight" still sounds great, no matter what the format. This is a worthy collection, and long overdue!

Hugh Dellar and the boys reunited for live shows in 2014, 22 years after the band first broke up. They also reconvened in the studio, and the "I'm Walkin" b/w "Hey Senorita" mono 45 (2014 on State Records) are their first recordings since 1991.

"I'm Walkin" is a first-class rave-up, worthy of original '65 Euro-Beat comparisons. Stellar vintage production highlights both sides, and "Hey Senorita" is a fine, toe-tapping flip. This is primo! One very unusual detail about the State Records 45s is the super-thick vinyl and vintage-style brown paper sleeve. These heavy 45s are unique and just plain cool.

## THE BEFORE & AFTER (U.K.)

Years ago this two-song CD in a cardboard sleeve arrived on my doorstep, and for the life of me I'm not sure much more than that – even my U.K. band origin is a guess. I do know it

was recorded at the infamous Toe-Rag Studios in the U.K. and was released on the Boom label in Belgium in late 1996. There's some fine electric sitar and other super-psych effects on "More Ice Cream," an instrumental that would fit as a theme song for a Strawberry Alarm Clock party. The vocal "Necessary Changes" features heavy fuzz and a distinct U.K.-1968 feel, almost like a Dukes Of Stratosphear outtake. Yes, this is cool. Very cool.

## PETER BERRY & THE SHAKE SET (NORWAY)

Recorded at the analog mecca Toe Rag Studios in the U.K., the "Berry Express" EP was issued by Larsen Records in 2008.

## BEG BORROW STEAL (RENNES, FRANCE)

Forming in 2010, the quartet released a 4-song 10" EP (in 2012 on BBS Records). Their track "Monkey" is a fuzz-laden winner.

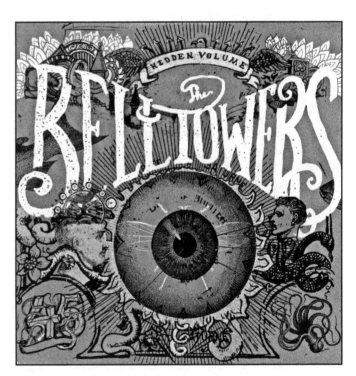

## THE BELLTOWERS (ORLANDO, FL, U.S.A.)

With former members from The Lears and Green Today (two of my favorite U.S.A. jangle bands of yesteryear) The Belltowers issued a 2014 "No Matter" b/w "She's Gone" 45 on Hidden Volume Records. It has a royal dose of Byrds (and some Love as well), and certainly conjures up all that I loved about the previous Lears: supreme Rickenbacker 12-string heaven and expert arrangements that take all the best 1966 folk rock touches and compiles them into three minute pop-garage jewels.

I've also heard an album's worth of demos, courtesy of vocalist and guitarist Paul Mutchler, and they contain the kind of Rickenbacker magic that I dream of nightly, including a shimmering cover of the Flamin' Groovies classic "I Can't Hide" and The Byrds' contemplative "Thoughts And Words." Oh, I think there's a lot more to come from the Belltowers' treasure chest!

Seriously, I could listen to this all day, so I think I'll go get started.

## NIK BENSEN (SAN FRANCISCO, CA, U.S.A.)

You better bring the heavyweight lysergia with a title such as "Psychedelic Juggernaut" (2000, on Free City Media) and soloist Nick Bensen does his best. This is modern psychedelia in mood, recording and approach, with lots of digital accompaniment – so purists beware! If you dig some Bevis Frond or Dimentia 13, then you probably have the framework to appreciate this very unique style. The 2001 follow-up, "No Resistance" (on Free City Media) continues this eclectic trip, with tracks that are more "soundscapes" than traditional songs, though the title song has more of a trad psych feel. This is highly recommended to those who can look beyond stylistic trappings and can focus on the highly creative sounds within.

## THE BERRIES (NEWBERRY, SC, U.S.A.)

These boys describe themselves best: "A little surf, a little fuzz, a little psych, a little Merseybeat... and a whole lot of garage. It's the Berries, and they want to install the spirit of 1966 in your head." Though more gentile than a really nasty fuzz-garage combo, "Candy Apple Sky," from their 2013 self-titled CD (on their own Zombie! Records) is a fine manifesto of their garage love. Welcome to the fuzz, lads!

(This band is not to be confused with the 1966 garage combo of the same name from Chicago.)

## THE BETA RAYS (DETROIT, MI, U.S.A.)

The 2002 four-song 7" EP on Pure Vinyl is really lo-fi garage, and I know fans of that late 1990s/early 2000s sub-genre would especially enjoy this. The band shared some members with the instrumental Silencers, featured elsewhere here.

## THE BEVIS FROND (UPDATE)

There has been an avalanche of Bevis Frond releases since the 1995 paper book, continuing the heavy guitar attack of Nick Saloman and guests. Even if I have not found them, you should.

## BEYOND FROM WITHIN
(PITTSBURGH, PA, U.S.A.)

A mainly one-man operation of Steve Andrews, this is eccentric modern folk-psych, with a 2009 self-released CD. There are '60s elements incorporated in this sound, to be sure, but in a much more modern context that I think could be more fully realized with a fuller organic (real person) lineup.

## BLACKLIGHT CHAMELEONS (UPDATE)

The 2003 "A Field Guide To The Blacklight Chameleons" (on Tripwave) combines the band's previous 1986 vinyl EP and 1988 LP onto one 21-song CD. The Blacklight Chameleons – I have always loved that band name – remain sinfully under-rated by genre fans, and to my ears are one of the best garage-psych bands of the 1980s. There are so many fine songs and performances throughout this release, highlighted by Dino Sorbello's soaring guitar. If you can't find the original vinyl, then find this CD and hear for yourself why this band needs to be remembered.

## THE BLACK SUN ENSEMBLE (UPDATE)

I am so sad to report that Jesus Acedo, the guitarist and force behind BSE, died in my Tucson, Arizona hometown in 2013. He had played sporadically throughout the years in acts with similar names to BSE, and in similar styles, but never caught again the magic of the first 1985 album. I produced a few tracks for BSE in 1987, by the way, and I still have an unreleased mix of the band's finest song, "Dove of The Desert," which is available in other recordings elsewhere.

## THE BLOW UPS (BERLIN, GERMANY)

There's a European-flavored R&B-based garage feel on the 2014 "Turn on, Tune In, Blow Up!" album on Teen Sound. It's nothing fancy to my ears.

## THE BOGEYMEN (UPDATE)

There is also the 1993 "You've Got No Scruples" b/w "Let Me Give You My Love" 45 and "Gimme A Little Sign" EP on Detour Records.

## THE BOHEMIAN BEDROCKS
(NEW YORK, NY, U.S.A.)

Now this is one cool find: the fine Optic Nerve, in 1984, when they called themselves The Bohemian Bedrocks. Made up of drummer Ira Elliot and guitarist Elan Portnoy of The Fuzztones, Orin Portnoy of The Outta Place on bass and Bobby Belfiore on vocals and guitar, the Bedrocks is like one-band-compilation of the NYC neo-garage scene in the middle of its first blush.

They recorded some rehearsal-room demo tracks, and they have the feel of the garage Fuzztones mixed with the later folk-rock feel of the Optic Nerve. Belfiore's wonderful vocals are there, as is an early version of one of his best Optic Nerve songs, "Ain't That A Man." The recording is basic and slightly crude, but better than almost all of the bands since then that purposely recorded on a cassette 4-track in an attempt at sounding "garage."

The self-titled 2012 album on Screaming Apple includes 10 of these tracks, and is a essential peak back into that seminal NYC scene of the mid-1980s, when bands could mingle and make garage music that stands the test of time. Kudos to Screaming Apple for making the album cover look like it came out of a moldy basement from 30 years ago and was just found to share with garage nuts like me.

## THE BOMBORAS (UPDATE)

They are one of the planet's most accomplished instrumental-trashers, and they regularly packed underground clubs across our fair garage nation. Their 1997 "It Came From Pier 13," on Dionysus, continued their tradition of expertly crafted cheese. This time there's a teen-movie soundtrack feel; witness the cover art – a combination of images from classic '50s sci-fi flicks such as "It Came From Outer Space" and "It Came From Beneath The Sea." The Bomboras' vortex features plenty of hot-rods, chicks, cheap booze and rubber monsters, and a '63 Fender reverb amp never sounded so good.

Rolling Stone, People and even Psychology Today (magazines) all reported in the mid-1980s that the garage music revival would sweep the country. Change trends. Shape fashions. They were off by a decade or so, but the major-label release of The Bomboras' 1998 "Head Shrinkin' Fun" tried to finally prove them right.

The Bomboras symbolize the evolution of mainstream thinking toward garage sounds. The "retro" tag was once the commercial kiss-of-death for fine 1980s paisley punk groups

like Yard Trauma and The Miracle Workers – but now you can find tiki-shirts at K-Mart and Mod lamps at Target. "Retro" is happening, man, and the sounds that never went away, but haven't been heard, are finally stealing the edge of a spotlight.

Matching hot-rod outfits, go-go dancers and twanged reverb suddenly (after 15 years) led to what I'll call "The Bomboras' experiment" – a Geffen-released album for Rob Zombie's Zombie A Go-Go Records.

I scratched my head the first time I heard promos for the new album on MTV, sandwiched between Smashing Pumpkins and Madonna blurbs. I had a flashback to 1990, when a video for one of my own garage bands popped up in between a $500,000 Peter Murphy clip and the latest from REM.

Such mainstream attention then for garage/psych was considered a fluke – but in the 2000s it can be treated as a legitimate trend.

And with good reason. "Head Shrinkin' Fun" is a fabulous garage/trash/instrumental introduction for the masses. The lads didn't "clean up" for their shot at the big time; they remain the gnarled, fuzzy, completely out-of-control nutbars that cranked out four previous indie label gems.

"Head Shrinkin' Fun" would have fit perfectly at their former label, Dionysus, and that's the best sign of all. The only thing different for The Bomboras this time out is some marketing muscle and therefore a chance to infect more listeners. Unfortunately, the album didn't open the door just a crack wider for the pile of other garage devotees that press up 500 albums and hope to land a local gig. They deserve to be heard, too.

Also recommended: "The Organ Grinder" and "Swingin' Singles" albums, both on Dionysus.

## THE BOOZE (ATLANTA, GA, U.S.A.)

The meat of the "Our Favorite" album (2010 on Screaming Apple) is '60s-styled R&B, full of rave-ups and finely honking harmonica. The Booze also throw in some more Mod-tinged pop tunes, and those I think shine the brightest for them. "Cut My Heart Out" and "There Goes My Girl" boast expert song construction and a confident, toe-tapping delivery. They must sound great on a dance floor.

A lot of music trends have passed since the original '60s sound, of course, and there also is the slightest U.K. New Wave pop tinge to their sound, circa 1980 or so. Their track "Can't Stand Losing You" has that feel, and I'm not sure if it is a conscious addition or not to the band's sensibility. Regardless, I like it!

Two more albums exist; a self-released 2007 effort and a 2011 release on Lonestar Records.

## THE BOSS MARTIANS (UPDATE)

One of the planet's finest reverb-and-twang combos returned in 1997 with "13 Evil Tales," their second album for Dionysus. These Seattle instrumental freaks use a hot-rod theme as a backdrop for their twangy onslaught, but there's also plenty of their surf mood to satisfy the wave-crashers. The vocal selections are also killer, with "Gonna Have Fun Tonight" sounding a bit like a long-lost Bobby Fuller track, full of jumpy melody and tapping pep. "She's Creepy" made me break into the mashed potato, and I'm not even sure exactly how that dance really goes. And is that sound effect at the beginning of "Evil Martian" from my fave crummy movie, "Frankenstein Meets The Space Monster?"

The Boss Martians also earn bonus points for a flawless recording and a slate of all-original material. These boys make mince-meat of a whole flock of other surf-instro-trash pretenders, and do it with a smile on their face and their foot slammed on the gas pedal.

The 2002 four-song 7" EP on Pure Vinyl is another meaty rarity, complete with beautiful starburst blue vinyl and full-color sleeve by the always-perfect Darren Merinuk.

Many other fine Boss Martians releases are available; among them I recommend "Move" (on Dionysus), "Invasion of the Live Boss Martians" (on Vagrant) and "Making The Rounds" (on MuSick), a 3-song EP on Teen Sound, and a fab 1995 7" picture disc on Dionysus.

## LES BREASTFEEDERS (MONTREAL, CANADA)

This long-running sextet formed in 1999, and the excellent music video for their 2004 garage-pop anthem "Mini Jupe Et Watusi" was included on our own "Knights of Fuzz" DVD. Equal parts wild garage energy and pop hooks, the 2004

debut album "Dejeuner Sur L'Hebre" (2004, on Blow The Fuse) – sung in their native Canadian French – is both original and also classic garage.

The 2006 follow-up "Les Matins De Grande Soirs" album continues the fun, with a ferocious attitude and more and more pop hooks. Yes, I have no idea what they are singing about in French, but it sure is darn cool. They've toured extensively in North America and Europe, and reportedly lead singer Luc Brien was injured by flying debris at a 2010 show in Vancouver at the Winter Olympics. There is also a 2011 album titled "Dans La Gueule Des Jours."

This is a much more "modern" approach to garage than countrymen The Gruesomes, but Les Breastfeeders are also right there at the top of the heap for Canada's garage sound.

## BRIAN JONESTOWN MASSACRE
(SAN FRANCISCO, CA, U.S.A.)

San Francisco's Brian Jonestown Massacre, which created much attention with their first two 45s, gained additional press for their 72 minute debut long player "Methodrone" (1995).

The CD title says it all, as distinctively British-sounding drone pop is the formula here, with purposely repetitive bass and drums layered with moaning guitar and mumbled vocals. The drugged and numbed ambiance of Spacemen 3 is an obvious reference point, and any fan of U.K. trance pop will certainly pick up and groove on this dreamy vibe.

They continued to gain press – mostly for the tiresome behavior of band members (as shown in the 2004 film "Dig!") – and released a slew of other material which alternated between interesting and not. Not my cup of fuzz, but many indie fans outside the traditional garage-psych scene still rate them highly. As of this writing they are going strong – and continue to sustain a fan base.

## THE BROKEN HEARTS (CT & NY, U.S.A.)

The 2003 "Want One" CD (on Paisley Pop) is a compilation of the band's mid-1980s album and other demos. This is infectious Beatles-esque jangle pop – just give one listen to "When I See You Looking My Way" and I dare you not to bob your head and smile. One of the demos, "That Kind of a Girl" has that special McCartney pop charm, and there are plenty of other hooks throughout. This is lovingly re-issued and a real winner.

## BRONCO BULLDOG (LEICESTER & LONDON, U.K.)

Twist Records in the U.K. has a knack for finding and championing really worthy bands that other labels seem to miss (at least at the beginning of a band's career), and Bronco

Bullfrog is a great example. They wrote me a note saying, "I'll bet this is right up your alley," and boy, are they right. Twist knows that I fall for power-pop with guts, sweet harmonies and catchy lyrics, great sound production, and a record that boasts a variety of arrangements. Bronco Bullfrog knows that original songwriting – and lots of it – can separate their band from a zillion others.

Their 1998 debut self-titled CD is a confident and powerful mix mid'60s sunshine paisley and modern power-pop – with soaring vocals and tight, catchy arrangements – not the stuff of a lazy garage combo in any way. The songwriting is so universally excellent that it makes a veteran songwriter like me envious at the seemingly easy manner the songs develop and unfold.

The 2000 "seventhirteight" album (also on Twist) continues the band's brilliant vocals, arrangements and general atmosphere of pop joy. There's muscle in there, too – "Blow Yourself Up" has the punch of Big Star along with all the sweetness. Simply brilliant stuff.

There several other releases – including "The Sidelong Glances Of A Pigeon Kicker" in 2002, "Oak Apple Day" in 2004, and the 2013 "Clarifoil" b/w "Never Been To California" 45 on State in the U.K. That last 45 is one of the most glorious sunshine-pop records I've heard in years, all in sparkling mono on a super-thick slab of vinyl. "Never Been To California" is simply stunning '60s pop on a high level rarely achieved in any era.

## THE BROOD: (UPDATE)

Dionysus continued to document the evergreen garage scene, with The Brood one of their longest surviving acts. Their fourth LP, "Beyond the Valley of the Brood," shows the four women from Portland, Maine adding to their decade-and-a-half legend. That formidable reputation is based on the combo's musical guts, not their gender. These kittens can chew up and spit out just about any other band, male or female, so stand back and absorb the fuzz, moody keyboards and sneer-infested vocals. I'll add that the Brood might be the best all-woman garage band of all time. Just saying.

---

*NOTE: Remember to read the original 1995 book and the other book update chapters for thousands of other bands and records not featured in this update section.*

---

## CARDBOARD VILLAINS
(STOCKHOLM, SWEDEN)

Forming in 2010, their self-titled album hit the racks in 2014, and the lead track "Right Behind" is a bouncy '65-ish pop-garage number, with a great guitar hook and sparkling production. That is the only track I could find from the album, and I want to hear more. PS: The vinyl LP is limited to only 200 copies.

There is also a 2012 45 "Gotta Let You Go" b/w "Ballad Of A Broken Man" (on Ghost Highway) – reportedly a 100-copy release. The number of first-rate garage groups from Sweden is really staggering – count the Cardboard Villains as one of the latest that I must track down.

## THE CARDINALS (GREECE)

The self-titled LP on Action Records from 1997 is impressive for several reasons, the most important being that it contains all original songs. The style is authentic 1965-Eurobeat, so if you are a fan of Nederbeat then The Cardinals are a bulls-eye hit. The fold-over style album sleeve is also picture perfect. The only let down is the rather shrill production style – I would have loved to been able to mix or master this release to tame the high end and deliver a more full-rounded recording. But the songs are top-notch. I shouldn't be surprised – Greek bands are consistently among the top of the neo-garage era. There is also a 1996 7" EP on Goblin Records.

## LE CAROGNE (ITALY)

These Italians incorporate some electronica and more modern elements into their sound, but the core inspiration can still be found somewhere in the garage. There's a self-titled album from 2009 and some compilation tracks for the more adventurous out there.

## THE CAVE 4 (UPDATE)

Netherlands is, of course, a hotbed for neo-surf sounds, so The Cave 4 is a natural for a U.S. debut album. What, that makes no sense? Well, tough. Their 1999 "Bikini Crash" CD (on MuSick) is a fine addition to your Tiki Tones and Bomboras playlist. I'm sure glad that recording studios can't charge extra for spring reverb; these cats would be bankrupt.

## THE CAVEGIRLS (GERMANY)

Lo-fi is the order of the day for the 1997 "Attack Of The 50 Ft. Cavegirls" six-song 10" on Avalanche Records. I like crudely-recorded garage music, but the band would have been better served with a just a bit more production here – the drums, for instance, are so weak sounding that is seems like someone is tapping a microphone with a finger. It's a limited 400-copy release in the same style of label mates Agentemusik, described previously.

## THE CAVEMEN (ITALY)

Misty Lane releases so many fabulous records from bands that might not ever get a chance elsewhere, especially from their home country of Italy. And The Cavemen are very Italian, to be sure. While they mine timeless U.S.-styled '66 garage, their Italian flavor is unmistakable, even when singing "All Is Wrong" in English on their eight-song 2006 "Il Buio E Tra Do Noi" CD.

The full-length "Fiore Nero" (2008) continues the guitar-oriented garage affection, with a more refined recording and sure playing. If you dig early Gruesomes-type garage fun, then The Cavemen are for you, like they are for me.

## THE CAVESTOMPERS (MOSCOW, RUSSIA)

One fascinating mini-trend that I've noticed in the latest round of neo-garage-ism is the appearance of Russian garage bands. I doubt there was even one in my 1995 book, but I am delighted they are starting to appear. The Cavetompers' self-titled CD on NO13ER Records is pretty standard guitar and organ garage music, but when it is sung in Russian it takes on an other-worldly feel for me.

The production is basic and the band tight – I bet these comrades really rock a small club in person. A limited 500-copy vinyl edition is also on Groovie Records. Pick Hits: "Go Go Go On" and the Animals-meets-Them-like "Night And Day."

## THE CHAINS (MONTREAL, CANADA)

Sloppy garage has its joys; I know this personally, since I've been mining it myself for decades. But when a band as accomplished, tight and powerful as The Chains comes along I can't help but smile in admiration. Their 2002 "On Top Of Things" CD (on Get Hip) has a long list of superlatives: a great recording, expert arrangements and confident talented vocals. It's that vocal prowess that perhaps separates The Chains from many neo-garage bands the most – these are polished but still right for a garage-pop record. "Nothing Left Behind" is a wonderful showcase, highlighting both the vocal sheen and well-crafted fuzz and Raiders-meets-the-Shadows Of Knight joy that is The Chains. I'll keep my Chains CD handy when I hear the tired complaint that "all garage bands sound the same." One spin of this and those arguments crumble at the feet of this simply beautiful music.

## JONNY CHAN AND THE NEW DYNASTY 6 (NEW YORK, NY, U.S.A.)

Oh yes I've been a fan of the New Dynasty Six since their 1998 debut "So You Want" album on Dionysus. Their infectious "Hey!" kicks off the disc, and for me it is one of the best neo-garage anthems of all time. I loved the track so much that we included the fab black-and-white video for it on our "Knights of Fuzz" DVD. There are plenty more hits here, including the chiming folk-rock love of "Time Has Gone" (co-written in part by Freddy Fortune).

Fortune is such a fan that years later he put out the band's unreleased second album, "I Hate You Baby!" on his own Sound Camera Records as a deluxe 2-CD set. It's more tongue-in-cheek garage fun/mayhem throughout, with "I Hate You Baby" a real barn-burner (not to be confused with the Marshmallow Overcoat's "Hate You Baby" – same sentiment, different songs). Only listen to this stuff if you want to have fun. There, I warned you serious music types in advance.

## CHEEPSKATES (UPDATE)

Shane Faubert has been cranking out haunting pop since the early 1980s, and his New York band, The Cheepskates, were one of the cornerstones for the 1984 "Summer of Fuzz." Their "Run Better Run" LP stands up as one of the most polished garage-pop efforts of that era, and it finally saw a 1990s CD release on Germany's Music Maniac Records. The title track remains a classic, and the bonus tracks are a special gift.

Faubert didn't disappear after more Cheepskates records; another stack of solo LPs continued to be championed by Music Maniac. "Squirrelboy Blue" (1997) proves that Faubert's supply of hooks and sweet melody is endless. "Don't Cry" is one of those rare delicious pop songs that brings tears to my eyes, and I'll sob until the more LPs appear.

## THE CHESTERFIELD KINGS (UPDATE)

When royalty, forgotten or banished, returns to take their rightful place on the throne, it's a loyal subject's duty to stand up and cheer.

When The Chesterfield Kings – the finest garage band of the entire garage revival – returns to glory with a new double-album, then it's time to scream like a maniac and thank heaven you exist. Yes, The Kings' 32-track "Surfin' Rampage" comeback album of 1997 is really that impressive – and surprising.

The Chesterfield Kings first owned the garage underground in the late 1970s, almost single-handedly re-inventing the worth of '66-styled fuzz rock. The original lineup dissolved by the end of the '80s, and the band drifted through a head-scratching hard-rock period before coming back to the altar of garage.

Well, sort of – "Surfin' Rampage" isn't a garage album. It puts away the fuzz, and is instead an ultimate homage to surf rock, California style. The details of surf production – including glorious harmony vocals – are placed perhaps more perfectly than they could have been in '64, and Gary Usher's legendary songbook never sounded so good.

The Chesterfield Kings once again toured the globe as fuzz ambassadors, and they returned to their patented paisley sound with the "Mind Bending Sounds of..." LP. Use "Surfin' Rampage" as a mere appetizer for that return of garage royalty.

The Chesterfield Kings scored another knockout punch against boredom with their 1997 "Trippin' Out" 10" six-songer. Released in conjunction with a Spanish tour, these half-dozen '60s covers served as a tantalizing appetizer for the Rochester, NY combo's long, long, long awaited "Mindbending Sounds of..." LP.

Inclusion of the garage standard "I'm Five Years Ahead of My Time" is especially ironic for The Chesterfield Kings, who celebrated their 20th anniversary of garage punkdom with

this 1998 release, while The Standells' "Sometimes Good Guys Don't Wear White" could just be their most fitting anthem. My personal fave, though, is their version of the rarely heard "Don't Blow Your Mind," a remnant of Vince Furnier's pre-Alice Cooper days with the forgotten, savage Spiders. (The original song was recorded down the street from me, here in Tucson, Arizona, in 1966.) Ahh, the joys of a fuzz box and a Rickenbacker guitar.

The Chesterfield Kings revived their own Living Eye label, and their 1998 "Wrong From Right" b/w "So What" 45 proved again that the Kings may never be equaled as garage royalty. They also roped The Lyres into a split 45, where The Kings play a Lyres tune, and the Lyres play a Kings tune. Pure genius.

"Where The Action Is" (1999 on Sundazed) was the second of their three-part resurrection plan, following up on their triumphant 1997 "Surfin' Rampage" double LP. This entry finally returned the band full circle to the tone of their genre shaping "Here Are The Chesterfield Kings" debut LP of 1982. That means it's snotty-nosed, fuzz-laden, 12-string Rickenbacker heaven. (Part three of the master plan was the long-awaited "Mindbending Sounds" LP, which had been cooking in the Kings' laboratory for several years.)

The Kings' original material is always top-notch, but their early records were almost completely choice covers. "Where The Action Is" heads back to that approach, with only four originals among the 17 cuts. It's fun to finally hear an official Kings version of the Chocolate Watchband classic "Misty Lane," especially since the Chesterfield Kings first recorded an unreleased demo of that song a full 20 years earlier!

The title of the LP is of course a nod to seminal pop-garagers Paul Revere & The Raiders, and trumpets the fact that Raiders frontman Mark Lindsay guests on a track. Lindsay, in an interview with me the year before, was sincerely enthusiastic about working with new garage bands, and his appreciation for the new sound rings true on "Where Do We Go From Here?" (also a 45). Another original, the cheekily titled "A Lovely Sort Of Death," is an instant classic. Period.

"The Mindbending Sounds of" album (2003 on Sundazed; reissued on Wicked Cool in 2006 with slightly different cover art) is another must-have for the band. The Kings also deposited a live album and scored more mainstream media appearances with their 2008 "Psychedelic Sunrise" LP. The production here is very slick – almost too good for a garage-psych album – but with all the flourishes that make the Kings supreme. I enjoyed perhaps even more the bonus "From Dusk To Dawn" CD that was included in a reissue vinyl edition of the album. It includes more essential lysergia and is a fine topper to the band's career.

Two later other vinyl 7"s worth finding are "Yes I Understand" on Sundazed and "Misty Lane" on Misty Lane.

The Chesterfield Kings finally called it quits in 2009 with reported animosity between long-time members Andy Babiuk and Greg Prevost. Perhaps, with time, bad feelings will subside – but the essential contributions that the band gave to the garage music genre will never fade.

Revival is a word often associated with modern garage sounds, but resurrection is the more accurate term for the work by The Chesterfield Kings. They will remain the Kings of the scene.

## SUZI CHUNK (CARDIFF, U.K.)

Her debut 45 (on State Records in 2012) features "Look Back And Laugh" b/w "Tripwire" – two songs written by Glenn Prangnell for a 1991 Kravin A's album. (Prangnell also plays in the backing band here, Groovy Uncle.) Oh, and check out the nice laminated '60s-ish U.K. flip-back 45 sleeve – beautiful!

The 1963 U.K. R&B style is perfectly done here, and Suzi's vocals are fine, indeed – but I have to wonder about the wisdom of a debut with no original material and re-recordings of 1991 songs (which were also done in good fashion originally). I understand the fun of replicating the whole 1960s "songs-written-for-singers" era, but it's still a bit odd of an approach.

There are also 2012 and 2013 Suzi Chunk albums, both backed by Groovy Uncle.

## THE CIRCUS MIND (ISRAEL)

This demo marks one of the first times I received modern psych music from Israel. They were hoping to attract a U.S. label to spread their floating, lysergic, progressive psych sounds beyond their borders. Fans of a heavier psych sound

will want to take the time search them out, since this 1998 demo makes me hope that there is more Israeli psych to hear.

## THE CLIENTELE (U.K.)

The "(I Want You) More Than Ever" b/w "6 A.M. Morningside" (on Elefant Records) is from 1999. Their "Suburban Light" album was issued in 2000 and reissued in 2014. Their sound is dreamy, melodic, echoed guitar pop, obviously influenced by '60s pop but also in line with 1990s U.K. indie-guitar pop.

## THE CLIQUE (UPDATE)

The "Reggie" b/w "She Doesn't Need You Anymore" 45 did appear, on the U.K. Detour label in 1994. There is also the "Early Days" EP on Detour, recorded in 1989 (featuring U.K. Mod-maven James Taylor on Hammond). After more digging I see there are at least five more 7" releases and a couple albums, reaching from 1991 to 2003! I should know by now, after all these years, that as soon as I believe I have a handle on all these releases that there actually are a bunch more for me to chase...

## THE CONGO EELS (U.S.A.)

There are so many picture-perfect 1966-styled combos out and about that it is easy to forget that in the early 1980s a band with the garage spirit was still a rarity. It is in that context – after punk and New Wave, and before the tide of neo-garage – that the Congo Eels deposited their five-song 12" (on Jim's Records, 1984). The crude garage feel is there, but not in an obvious 1960s fashion. This is also one of the few records that I've seen that presses the same five songs on each side of the vinyl!

## THE CONTRARIANS (NEW YORK, NY, U.S.A.)

The 2002 three-song 7" EP (on Pure Vinyl) is pretty standard U.S. R&B-based garage, with an especially bluesy rendition of the classic "Bad Little Woman." It's also on beautiful white and orange starburst vinyl.

## COOL GHOULS (SAN FRANCISCO, CA, U.S.A.)

There is a 2012 album, I believe reissued on cassette by the (currently) ultra-hip Burger Records. It seems to fit in perfect with Burger's wide definition of psych, mixing several eras of California folk-psych and ultimately finding its own sound. That's a big compliment!

I have this gut feeling that there are a whole bunch of U.S. West Coast bands like this that I have not heard yet, that are worth hearing, and belong in this book. Send those sounds my way, kids. I an still hungry.

## THE COVINGTONS (DETROIT, MI, U.S.A.)

Before Freddy Fortune went on to Fortune & Maltese and before Johnny Chan went on to the New Dynasty Six, they were together in The Covingtons. The four song 7" EP (on Freddy Fortune's own Sound Camera Records) was recorded in 1988 and 1989, but issued in the 2000s. It shows a band coming to grips with creating their own garage sound, and the lo-fi recordings reflect that. There are studio and "live" versions of "I Hate You Baby" (also later recorded by Chan, and also not the later Marshmallow Overcoat song.) If you are a fan of either main guy here then you will dig this.

## THE CREATURES OF THE GOLDEN DAWN
(UPDATE)

I've gushed over their brand of garage genius for decades, and their 1997 "Keys To The Kingdom" CD hits an almost impossible garage nirvana. How many bands taste better with age – especially after many years – let alone deposit one of the most inspirational garage discs of all time? No joke, this album puts The Creatures Of The Golden Dawn into lofty territory, rubbing shoulders with a handful of acts that deserve time capsule treatment.

Singer Mark Smith died in 2011, and Dionysus issued a "best of" for the band: "Dark Was The Night...Cold Was The Ground" in 2012. Seek out the many fine releases by The Creatures of the Golden Dawn. You will then be a "True Believer" listening to other true believers making music.

Also recommended: the 1991 Dionysus 45 "The Clown With The Broken Crown" and the "Blood From A Stone" four-song EP on Butterfly Records.

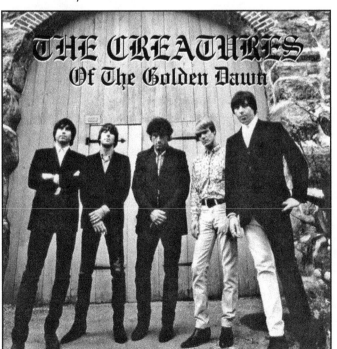

## CREEPLE PEEPLE: *(See the "Fan Submitted Updates" chapter for more information.)*

## CREEPZOTICA (SAN DIEGO, CA, U.S.A.)

This is actually the band Creepy Creeps' alter-ego, and their 2014 debut "Haunted Bossa Nova" album (vinyl on Dionysus) is a wonderful blend of surf-ish guitar and exotica – a neo-garage sub-genre explored throughout this book update.

The album kicks off with the deeply evocative "Head Huntin," with all the deep reverb and vibes you want in your surf-exotica party. More Pick Hits: "Enchanted Lagoon" (which sounds exactly as you'd think) and the moody and dramatic "Incident At The Luau." By the way, this sounds great played really loud!

There also is a 7" EP out on Dionysus.

## CRIMSON SHADOWS (UPDATE)

There have been several re-issues of classic 1980s Crimson Shadows material, including the "Out Of Our Minds" CD (2000, Inbetween Records, Holland). Yes, I love this band – I even wrote the liner notes for this release, and it was part of "The Knights of Fuzz" series done in cooperation with Inbetween Records. Groovie Records released a similar compilation in 2011 titled "One Step Beyond Sanity."

Amazingly, in 2010 new recordings saw the light of day with the "Nightmares" b/w "It's Too Late" 45 on Screaming Apple. "Nightmares" is a different recording than on the previous CD, and hits over 110% on the fuzz-o-meter. The flip is a marching stomping monster, too.

If you love garage music, and perhaps are just discovering the 1980s era, then find some Crimson Shadows (or other garage releases with Mans Mansson or Jens Lindberg) ASAP. They are essential.

## THE CRUSADERS (UPDATE)

The lime-green mystery liquid shouts volumes about The Crusaders and their approach to fun. Yeah, they're sporting purple medieval "crusaders" outfits in their band photo, but it's their maniacal grins and twisted faces – brought on obviously by the green fluid in the bottles they're clutching – that says it all: Australia's The Crusaders knew how to have a good time.

That feeling seeps through every crack of their 1997 "Addicted to Fuzz" vinyl 10" on Dionysus. The six-song slab gurgles and sputters and falls all over itself in the absolute best of ways, and is the perfect follow-up to their previous Australian-only CD and subsequent Dionysus 45.

All six songs, plus a full seven more, are also out as the "Keep It Up" CD. This French-only issue (on the always hep Larsen label) adds even more spittle to the stew, and the digital domain doesn't retract from the raw fun. Mix up some of that punch for me, boys, and pass the bottle.

Few bands capture the thrill of lo-fi spontaneity like The Crusaders. Their 1998 "Fat Drunk and Stupid" LP is the perfect follow-up to their Dionysus 10" EP – proving that the pursuit of booze and chicks is, indeed, a life worth living. Also on Dionysus: the six-song "Middle Age Rampage," from 1999, including a snot-laden cover of The Stem's classic "Under Your Mushroom."

## THE CRYBABIES (WORCESTER, MA, U.S.A.)

"This combo shows what can still happen when friends play music for the love of the sounds," writes the liner notes for the 2002 "How The Other Half Live" album. And boy do I love bands with this attitude. The album kicks off with a soaring version of "Man With Money," but the band originals hold their own, too. It's classic garage-pop, with plenty of folk-rock jangle and garage combo mood. Bands like The Crybabies are easy to overlook by hipsters, because they might not look like this week's fashion – but they make honest, heartfelt garage-n-roll. Real bonus points for the primo cover version of "I Wonder."

## THE CRYPTONES (UPDATE)

The French garage greats re-formed (but were thankfully not socially *reformed*) in 2007 for the "Shake Shake With..." CD (on Brutal Beach). You can feel the joy oozing out of the speakers, as The Cryptones have fun making garage music for all the right reasons. So much atmosphere and a grinning Cramps-vibe permeates "Purple Vibes," while fuzz madness drips out of the album's title track.

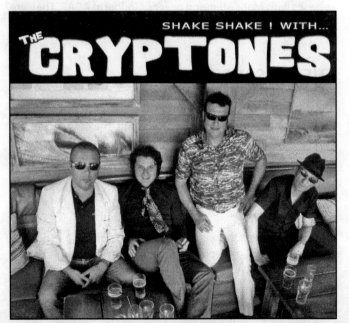

I couldn't figure out which to do first while hearing this again – dance or get a beer – so I did both. And only the best bands and records can do that to me. Merci, Cryptones.

There is also a song on a split 45 for the Abus Dangereux Magazine

## LOS CUCHILLOS (COSTA RICA)

I believe the only entry in this book from Costa Rica, Los Cuchillos ("The Knives") mine the ever-fertile realm of surf and garage. Starting in 2005, they've released an eight-song LP in 2008 titled "Monstronautas De La Era Atómica" – which might translate into "Monster-astronauts of the Atomic Era." Complete with handclaps, twang guitar, sci-fi sound effects (and an awesome monster comic art cover), it is the definition of garage fun. Imagine The Cramps sitting in with the Syndicate Of Sound, listening to the Ventures, and singing in Spanish, and you'll understand their winning formula.

The 2006 debut EP is more crudely recorded, and sticks mostly to more usual surf sounds. A third album is set for release in 2014. Count me in!

## THE CUNTS (UPDATE)

From the "Completely Other End of the Musical Spectrum Department" ... The Cunts celebrated 20 years of garage-punk mischief in 1998 with their self-released "A Secret History of..." CD (on Disturbing Records, natch), and to the uninitiated it will be a jaw-dropper. (Warning: for the duration of this entry I'll attempt to mention their band name as many times as possible, just to annoy the easily annoyed.) I've reveled in The Cunts' ridiculous antics for since the early 1980s, but fear most underground music fans still haven't heard of this Chicago non-institution.

This stuff is home-spun, absolutely original, obnoxious, sincere and refreshingly honest punk – make that with a capital "P." Imagine Zappa locked in a room with The Dead Boys, listening to a Shadows Of Knight album, and you might get a glimpse in at the sound of The Cunts.

That's probably why you haven't heard of The Cunts (there's mention #3, if you're counting) – along with the fact that their band's moniker has offended music reviewers for the band's entire existence. When they have managed to get reviews published, a nice big asterisk (*) usually replaces the "u" in Cunts, but that ain't gonna happen here, boys. Civilization crumbled long ago, we're in the good old US of A, and I'm in charge here, so go ahead and spell your name any way you want. At least for this one review.

"There Are Electrical Filaments on My Hamburger" has always been one of my fave Cunts tunes (mention #5), but "There's a Monster Head on My Baby," "I Hate Reggae," "Every Crease In Donna's Brain" and "Abstract Salamander Dilemma" ain't no slouches either, bubby.

Main Cunts (ha, ha, that's band-name mention #6) prankster Mike Pocius also scores big points with the band's slogan: "Have Fun Always." Throw back all that phony poser punk crap and scoop up this best-of. Just don't bug them about changing their name – after all these years they earned the right to keep it.

Also recommended: their 1995 "Why Baby?" CD, which adds 17 more aural bricks to their twisted wall. No "serious" band could go wrong with titles such as "Dog With A Human Head" and "Man Hanging Off Cliff With Pants Leg On Fire," and The Cunts don't drop the ball either.

## CURLEE WURLEE (FRANCE / GERMANY / U.K.)

I only have a beautiful 2003 picture disc 7" on Butterfly Records, which features well-produced 60s-Beat-Mod-pop. They also have at least three albums and at least a half-dozen 45s out as well, though I've never seen them on these American shores.

## THE CYNICS (UPDATE)

OK, so The Cynics have many, many, many fine releases out since 1995, and they continue to blast across the U.S. and Europe (especially Spain) as of this writing. This makes The Cynics one of the longest-running garage-oriented bands of all time, and I tip my hat to them for keeping this flame lit over the decades. Kids, try to keep a band going for just one month, and then you might understand how much work has gone into 30 years for The Cynics. A few album highlights include the 1994 "Get Our Way" album and 2002 "Living Is The Best Revenge," along with "No Siesta Tonight – Live In Madrid."

It has been many years since even The Cynics themselves would consider themselves a 1966-styled garage band – they have more of a hard rock sound in recent years, but are still one of the planet's best live bands. You have not really heard fuzz guitar until you have heard it "live" with The Cynics, and that ain't no joke, brutha!

Long Live the mighty Cynics. All hail rock and roll!

# D

## THE DARK MARBLES (LONG LAKE, NY, U.S.A.)
also known as **YOD CREWSY and the DARK MARBLES**

Yod Crewsey (formerly of the SplatCats) first formed The Dark Marbles in 1987, but it took until 2005 – after many bands in-between – for him to issue the three song "Let's Go" CD.

"The "Variety Pack" album (2011) collects tracks recorded since 1997, and is a wonderfully vibrant guitar-garage effort,. The jubilant power-pop of "Turn Me Around" is the first hook, and it's a real winner. It takes guts to cover Love's "She Comes In Colors," and the Marbles pull if off in fine form, minus the flute of the original and with a more muscular delivery – very groovy, indeed. Self-released and not well known, this CD album is certainly worth the search.

## DATE BAIT (UPDATE)

The 1995 "We Are Going To Eat You" b/w "I Want To Hold Your Hand" 45 (on Pure Vinyl) is another of Kim Kane's whacky releases. Kudos for the chewing sounds on "We Are Going To Eat You," a hypnotic Cramps-like number. Yes, that's the Beatles song deconstructed and shredded up on the flip side. There is also a 1998 album.

## RAY DAYTONA & GOOGOOBOMBOS
(SIENA, ITALY)

The 1998 three-song 7" EP on Pure Vinyl is fun space-age surfish instrumentals, and sports cool clear vinyl. There are at least five more 45s and a full five albums out there, too!

## THE DAYTONAS (UPDATE)

The 1994 "Don't Look Now It's The Daytonas" vinyl album appeared on the Australian Corduroy Records, with two songs not on the 1993 "Ready Set Go" CD. There's a 2-LP "Parabolica" set from 1996 also on Corduroy and 1997 single on Solamenta.

## DEAD MOON: (See the "Guest Authors" chapter for more information.)

## DEE-RANGERS (STOCKHOLM, SWEDEN)

"Five Spanish Minutes" (2005) continues Screaming Apple's everlasting commitment to garage music that makes you move, and also moves you. A nice power-pop touch – just a touch – compliments the confident garage-pop, and "You Gotta Understand" is as catchy and meaty an album-opener that you could ever ask for. Excellent organ and fuzz continue throughout, and "Hey Girl" is another scorcher that seems like a classic of yore, yet also of "now" and fresh.

At least four more albums and a half-dozen 45s also exist. I'd love to see some video of the Dee Rangers in concert – I bet it's a riot garage-rock party, to be sure.

## THE DEFECTORS (ARHUS, DENMARK)

A 1998 seven-song demo CD shows this Danish band loves classic 1966-fuzz garage – or perhaps I should say 1980s garage, since the band credits bands such as Miracle Workers and Creeps as their main influences. "Hey Hey Hey" and "Allright Girl" certainly sound like early 1980s Miracle Worker's out-take, and that is a great compliment. Not sure if these demos were issued, but the band did release a series of recordings from 2002 through at least 2009, proving this was no short-term garage love.

## THE DELMONAS
(UPDATE; also see Billy Childish in the 1995 book)

In the 1990s, especially, Get Hip did a fine job of rereleasing many worthy neo-garage records not readily available in the U.S.A., and their 2003 issue of "Do The Uncle Willy" helped spread the U.K. all-girl lo-fi fun of The Delmonas. (The LP was also released on vinyl in the U.S. in 1989 by Skyclad.) The sound of 1963 – I mean 1993 – never was so much fun! This collection also includes a couple unreleased demos and an alternate mix of the title track. I get the idea that kids just now discovering the 1980s Delmonas recordings will go ape over their party atmosphere and attitude.

## DEL NOAH & THE MT. ARARAT FINKS
(UPDATE)

Their track from the "Hot Rods to Hell" compilation whetted my appetite for their own 1998 "Blower Explosion" debut long-player on Skunk Records. Seventeen Del Noah surf and drag blasts might not be enough for me, so I snatched up their 1995 Dionysus EP as well. Pick Hit: "Sasquatch on a Snowmobile." It makes me wonder if these cats ever saw the "classic" 1974 bigfoot horror flick "Shriek of the Mutilated." I sure hope so.

## THE DELTARS (DES MOINES, IOWA, U.S.A.)

Back in the world of cruder elegance, the corn fields of Iowa shake with The Delstars' 1998 "Sound of Power." Pure surf 'n drag and trash compacted in 13 self-penned tracks, with plenty of twang for good measure. How can any human with a sense of humor not smile at "Ho Dads Rule" or "400 Hawaiian Shirts?" Besides, they've played downstairs at Bernies' Bagels in Columbus, Ohio – the site of this writer's many nights of college intoxication. (Go Ohio State Buckeyes!)

## THE DENTISTS (UPDATE)

My admiration for the unique Dentists has only grown with time. Their landmark debut vinyl LP was reissued on a much-better sounding CD issue in 2005 by RevOla in the U.K. – itself now long gone and sought after. A vinyl reissue followed in 2013 (on Trouble In Mind), and a new generation of fans are discovering their pop-garage joy. The 2010 "If All Flies Were One Fly" CD – furthering the band's reputation for whacky album titles – collects two dozen demos, outtakes and more for the dedicated fan like me. As noted in the band's original entry in this book, there are many find records to go out and discover, but go first to the debut LP, "Some People Are On The Pitch..." – you will remember the first time you hear it, as I still do 30 years later.

## THE DIABOLIKS (U.K.)

The Diaboliks' 1996 "Danger!" CD (and vinyl LP) on Dionysus shakes the rafters with trashy, sexy fun. Another Toe Rag studios analog production, this has all the fun of a DelMonas-styled effort, with a cleaner sound. Plenty of other releases abound, including a 10" on Dionysus (1998) and the wonderfully-titled "Three Fur Burgers...And A Hot Chilli Dog To Go!" album in 2000, the "Slaveboy," "Yes I Do" and "I Love Johnny Bravo" 45s, plus compilation appearances.

The "I Can't Sleep At Night" b/w "Never Thought You'd Leave" Me 45 on Mademoiselle Records is also great fun, and is mastered (to my ears) to sound exactly like it was coming from a 1960s AM radio!

## DING DONG DEVILS (LOS ANGELES, CA, U.S.A.)

The Ding Dong Devils are the exact opposite of mainstream America, and that is one reason why I love them. Sometimes they wear a Fez (onstage or off), most of the time Hawaiian shirts, all the time they smile, and don't care that you see that they are having fun.

Oh no, they are having fun! That is a big no-no in any era's hipster universe, where pretension and a mean snarl are always preferred. Piffle! I'll take The Ding Dong Devils' joyous concoction of Exotica, Tiki culture, '60s garage, rockabilly, and silliness any day. Imagine if the B-52s only did Martin Denny covers, and you start to get a little taste of The Ding Dong Devil's own mixed Polynesian cocktail.

Unknown to me until years later, the person I had worked alongside in the 1980s at an Ohio State University media department was none other than the Ding Dong Devil's bassist Julia Devine. Then I was just a snotty New Waver using O.S.U. equipment to Xerox cassette covers for my latest band demo, and Julia was only dreaming of her eventual delivery to California and the land of Tiki fun.

Now, with partner Brent Walker on guitar and a cast of other colorful loonies, they sound like they are having the times of their lives – and they want you to join the party. Can you think of any better reason to make music?

There's the 2010 "Tassels, Mai-Tais & Mischief" and 2012 "Hello Little Olives" albums, plus another slated for 2014. Crush some ice, get out the pineapple juice and some rum, locate your Fez, stir, and enjoy.

## THE DIRTY ROBBERS (U.K.)

"I Told You So" is very pleasant light garage pop, and the flipside of the Butterfly Records 45, a cover of the '60s classic "Dirty Robber" (and the origin of the band's name) is an almost bubblegum approach to that R&B raver. There are reportedly two albums out as well.

## THE DISTURBED (U.K.)

I absolutely love debuts like the 1997 "Eye Spy" b/w "Don't Stop" 45 (on Detour). Not only does it sport a truly fab op-art cover sleeve, but the six or so minutes of music on the vinyl gives us a little peak into a band's unique musical world. For a few moments you are transformed into a realm where only the band calls the shots, and you dig it or not. Oh, and I dig it! It's a fine combination of U.S. and U.K. '66 garage sounds, captured beautifully at the analog Toe Rag Studios in London, of course. And dig the homage to a classic Electric Prunes band shot on the back cover (pictured here). Ah, wonderful.

At least one more 45 was released in Australia on the Wild Eagle label in 2003 – I've heard the distinctly weird "Are You Alien"? from it – and I gotta find it, somewhere, somehow!

## DM3 (UPDATE)

Dom Mariani pens accomplished pop songs from the other side of the globe (to me) in Australia. I'll have his Stems records buried with me if I ever die, and if there's room, 45s from his later band, The Someloves, will cram their way in there too.

The songmaster has been cranking out gems with The Dom Mariani Three (DM3) since the 1990s, and Bomp's 1997 "Dig It The Most" collects 20 various Australian and European-only tracks for a long overdue U.S. release. Also check out the 1994 "Makin Time" 7" EP on Get Hip.

The short recommendation: Mariani and his two-man gang play power-pop at its best, complete with deliciously hummable melodies and a love for pretty girls. Hey, don't shut that coffin lid yet – there's room for a few DM3 discs, isn't there?

The 1999 "Rippled Soul" LP (and a 45, on Munster) is one to toss in my coffin, too. Mariani's arrow has hit the bullseye once again. He mines the power-pop side of the garage world, reminding me of a Mathew Sweet who listens to better records for inspiration. There's plenty of '70s pop influences here, too, from the Raspberries to Big Star, all wrapped up with Mariani's distinctive use of hooks, melody and wordplay. A singer from a fab Italian band once sat with me and marveled at this new LP. His sincere and puzzled question: "Why isn't The DM3 big in America?"

I see that a new "best of" collection is due in 2014 in his native Australia.

## THE DOCTOR EXPLOSION (UPDATE)

"The Subnormal Revolution" CD (on Get Hip, 1998) continues the garage mayhem, sung in Spanish, of course. There are lots and lots of other single and album releases, at least through 2011. Doctor Explosion capture the essence of garage music at its most joyful, and are one of the most fun European groups of the revival era.

## THE DOLL SQUAD (MELBOURNE, AUSTRALIA)

Some music fans just plain love girls in bands because they like girls and garage bands. Others simply hate girls in bands because they think only guys can rock. Not often is a garage band – made up of all women – heralded because they are a great band that deserves to be heard. Ah, but Doll Squad is different to my ears! Yes, they are nice to look at – no complaints there – but as a power-pop-garage band they bring the goods.

So it's that sweaty, sometimes gritty, meaty and fun kick-ass sound on "The Rock 'n' Doll Sound Of..." CD, (2006 on Teen Sound) that gets me. There is enough of the retro spirit to make me smile, and plenty of Ramones dirt to keep them barreling down a true rock highway. Kudos for "Don't Push Me Around" and "In The Mean Time," especially. With lesser-sounding bands in the same style making it bigger, I really scratch my head that Doll Squad didn't also get parachuted out of the underground. Maybe they are just plain too good as a rock band.

The 2006 four-song "Fast Girl" 7" EP (on Cherry Bomb Records) features three tracks from the LP plus the fine "Claudette Jones." Awesome stuff, girls.

## DONOVAN'S BRAIN (U.S.A.)

There are at least six more albums of this Zappa-Mothers-ish, psychedelic space jam, art rock, guitar nuttiness, but I've only heard their third album, "Tiny Crustacean Light Show" CD (2000 on Get Hip.) This isn't cute 1966 garage psych kids, it's wildly adventurous and defies simple genre tags, and owes as much to 1970s space rock as psych. You have to actually listen to these tracks actively, which will make Donovan's Brain "difficult music" for the less adventurous. As I like to say – or was it Zappa himself? – "Blessed be the weirdos."

## THE DOWN-N-OUTS (DENVER, CO, U.S.A..)

The "Introducing..." three-song 7" EP (1998, on Hipsville) gets the band barreling down the garage road at breakneck speed. The Denver trio boasts the guitar blast and vocal pipes of Michael Daboll, late of much-missed Element 79, and his new bandmates rise to his challenge.

Dig the 12 string buzz on "How Many Times?" – complete with gargled vocals and atonal back-up moans. Do I hear beer bottles opening in the background? Nah, these cats can only afford cans – of Schlitz. This slab is in mono and the band uses Radio Shack guitar cables exclusively. Don't ever, ever deny that America is a great place.

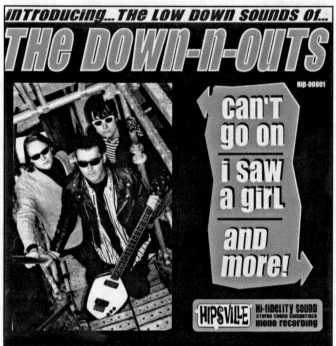

## THE DUKES OF HAMBURG
(SAN FRANCISCO, CA, U.S.A. / GERMANY)

Russell Quan of Mummies is involved, so you would guess correctly that this is more crudely-recorded, high-energy, R&B-fueled, fun garage noise. And you are correct, sir! The cover art of the 1998 self-titled LP on Dionysus is a parody of the 1960s "Star Club" albums (though the band looks a bit like The Rutles). There are two more albums on Dionysus, a slew of 7"s, plus a 2002 LP on Gearhead, and The "Little Lover" b/w "It's My Fault" 45 was issued by Screaming Apple in 1998.

Ah, but The Dukes came back with the 2014 "Liverpool Beat" album (on Dionysus), and now comes the confusing part, which still makes me scratch my head. According to Dionysus Records, "There are two DUKES OF HAMBURG just to let you know, both are a mix up from each-other, the DUKES OF HAMBURG from Bielefeld, Germany and the DUKES OF HAMBURG from San Francisco, U.S.A.

The story so far: In the early 90s, Thilo Pieper went to San Francisco and formed the American DUKES with members of THE MUMMIES, THE ASTRONAUTS, THE PHANTOM SURFERS and bassist Shannon Smith. The American DUKES toured up and down the West Coast and did two very successful European tours, then moved back to Germany and continued The DUKES in Bielfeld while the American DUKES were still doing shows.

Both bands play '60s beat and garage with wild abandon and are inspired by THE LORDS, RAINBOWS, CASEY JONES, and many of the '60s German Beat favorites as well as early PRETTY THINGS and other groups from the pre-psychedelic 1960s rock 'n' roll scene.

'Liverpool Beat' is the first album by the German DUKES OF HAMBURG on Dionysus Records, following the release of three American DUKES OF HAMBURG LPs on the label in the '90s."

OK, glad to clear that up!

## DUKES OF STRATOSPHEAR (UPDATE)

The now-classic "25 O'Clock" was re-issued on CD (on Ape Records, 2009) with several bonus tracks and demos, in an attractive hard cover mini-book format. It all sounds fab, and is one of the most essential collections for lovers of this book's focus. Only one complaint: the band released this CD themselves, and added "XTC as The Dukes Of Stratosphear" to the band's title. Of course it was an open secret in 1985 that XTC was actually "The Dukes of Stratosphear," but marketing this so clearly as a XTC album ruins the fun of the original costume party. And I'm sure it is with consternation that fans like me continue to believe that the first Dukes 12" was more interesting than the bulk of XTC's actual output.

## DUPONT CIRCLES (WASHINGTON, DC, U.S.A.)

There's something so engaging about a band's debut. There's so much hope, enthusiasm and just plain giddiness in getting out that first release, and that proud moment often produces some of the best garage/psych sounds. Washington D.C.'s Dupont Circles are a prime example, with the 1997 "Sarah The Weather Girl" and "Everywhere Girl" serving as happy, bouncy snapshots of a band just getting up to take its first walk. The prevalent pop feel doesn't overwhelm the band's obvious garage appreciation.

---

*NOTE: Remember to read the original 1995 book and the other book update chapters for thousands of other bands and records not featured in this update section.*

---

## THE EARLY HOURS (PERTH, AUSTRALIA)

The three-song "I'm Drained," "Hard Feelings," and "The Girl I Haven't Met" EP was released by Screaming Apple in 1996.

## THE EDDIES (LOS ANGELES, CA, U.S.A.)

The "In The Sunshine" (2004 on Twist) is rather bland modern pop to my ears, but I can see how more progressive Mods might find a hook there to reel them in (and which might explain their appearance on the Mod-friendly Twist Records). The "Gonna Sing About This" three-song CD (2013, all on Twist Records) is more modern pop, with a slightly New Wave feel, recorded with pop-whiz Earl Mankey.

The "Twice Around The World" album (2007 on Twist Records) displays a bit more flavor, with the vibrating "Don't Know Where To Start" a clear stand-out – and with Earl Mankey on drums, too. There is also a fine track on the Shambles tribute album, described elsewhere.

## THE EFFERVESCENT ELEPHANTS (UPDATE)

This wonderfully-named psych outfit knocked around Italy for more than a decade, since the 1980s, and their "16 Pages" LP (1997) was their loosest and trippiest release yet. The album is dedicated to Jerry Garcia, but there's also a wicked cover of the Doors' "When The Music's Over" balancing out the gentle mood. This stuff is only for those who want to stretch their brain – so if you are already reading this book then you are doing just fine.

## THE EL CAMINOS (KOBE, JAPAN)

That is not a typo in the band name, folks – yes this Japanese instrumental band added "The" to their adopted Spanish band name. So, literally, they are "The The Caminos." This is a completely authentic reverb-laden 1960s fuzz 'n surf instrumental world on the "Reverb Explosion" CD (on Del-Fi, 1997), and keeping company on the classic 1960s surf label Del-Fi only adds to their package. I love that a tinge of garage power creeps into their methods – this isn't laid-back snoring surf music – this rocks! They also sport one of the most authentic yet good-sounding recordings for the era. Yep, if the twang of a Fender spring reverb unit makes you want to dance, then The El Caminos are for you. Love their cover of the movie theme from "Exodus," too!

## THE ELECTRIC FLASHBACKS (ITALY)

You'd expect a much more psilocybic sound, based on the band name and cover art, but "The Lovely Art Of Electronics" (2012 on Teen Sound) is instead nicely produced, meaty modern garage. It relies heavily on cover songs, though, so the lads don't differentiate themselves from other garage acts. Interestingly, they cover two songs also from the earliest 1980s Marshmallow Overcoat career, the always cool "Have Love Will Travel" and "Stop It Baby."

## THE ELECTRIC SHIELDS (ARCHVILLE, ITALY)

Label honcho Massimo Del Pozzo produced the "Save Our Souls" album (2013 on Teen Sound), and it's a heavier garage sound this time out for his label. So it's Hammond organ instead of Farfisa, and tougher-sounding-guitars and vocals. This veers more into 1969-ish hard rock territory, which isn't a focus for me, or this book.

## THE ELECTRIC MESS (NEW YORK, NY, U.S.A.)

Formed in 2007, their self-titled 2009 album is a slickly-produced effort with some tasty organ flashes and a power-pop sensibility, too. It's that pop feel that differentiates the Mess from many others, but also makes it difficult to determine exactly where this combo fits into the neo-garage scene. Are they a pop act with '60s touches? A garage band with better production than many? Both ideas are probably accurate.

The "Falling Off The Face Of The Earth" follow-up (2012 on Groovie Records) continues the formula of slickly-produced garage-pop, and it is all very carefully crafted. This is highly polished stuff, and I just can't tell (at this moment) exactly where to place The Electric Mess in the garage hierarchy. The 2014 "House On Fire" album is also out on Soundflat Records in Germany, and perhaps it can help to answer my question.

## THE ELECTRIC PRUNES
(LOS ANGELES, CA, U.S.A.)

One positive product of the Internet age is the ability to connect with people in an affordable, instant way. No more long distance phone calls to Europe for me, as an example – staying in touch is now as easy as an interactive chat program or e-mail message. And so for the past 15 years I've been able to form an electronic friendship with James Lowe, vocalist for the Electric Prunes. He kept a re-formed version of the band active throughout the new century's first decade and a half, with U.S. and international shows, but also new records, videos (and DVDs).

A few of the most interesting of the 1960s originals – The Standells and Chocolate Watchband come to mind – have also continued to play and record with worthwhile lineups,

but few have captured their original essence like The Electric Prunes. Of course I must say that I consider The Electric Prunes the godfather of almost all the sounds I have ever written and recorded in my life – the band is more than influential to me. So I am delighted to hear that on their 2012 "Return To Stockholm" LP (a reference to their classic live 1967 recordings) that they sound as vibrant, energetic and freaky as ever.

New recordings, released on the band's own Prune Twang label, include the albums "Artifact" (2001), "California" (2004), "Feedback" (2006), and "WaS" (2014). Freed from what they considered creative shackles from their original major label years, these self-produced Prunes write and record whatever they wish. So some fans will find these albums less consistent (the band might prefer to say less homogenous) as the band's first two from the 1960s. James Lowe and the lads bravely take a lot of musical chances in these new recordings and sometimes they don't quite pan out – but there are many moments that hit the bullseye.

I especially recommend the 2003 "Rewired" video DVD, which captures the 21st century version of the band in a brilliant live performance, complete with colorful light-show. There are only a few stellar concert DVDs of original 1960s acts such as the 2003 Love "Forever Changes" and The Zombies' 2008 "Odessey & Oracle" set – and the Prunes offering is right up with them.

Long live the mighty Electric Prunes!

## THE ELEMENT 79 (FORT COLLINS, CO, U.S.A.)

The Denver 360 Twist label was way too short-lived, but when they were humming in the late 1990s they released some of the best garage records globally. This garage trio included the guiding forces behind the 360 Twist record label, but the "Dig Out With..." CD (and 10" vinyl) is not a vanity release in any way – it's one of the best garage records of 1997. There's a slight lo-fi edge to their '66-garage love, which brings special charm to "Leave It All Behind" and "Five Years Behind," especially.

Also highly recommended is a limited-to-300-copies 45 and 500-copy "I See You" 7" EP (both on 360 Twist) and the 1996 "My Love" 7" EP on Screaming Apple. Yep, I miss 360 Twist, and I miss the late, great Element 79.

## ELIO & THEE HORRIBLES
(BUENOS AIRES, ARGENTINA)

These wonderfully-named lads have a track on a 2002 compilation EP, and a 2001 debut album (on No Fun), but the track I've heard, "Texas," is dated from 2013 (so I'm guessing it's a re-mix). It is a rocking guitar and organ garage blaster, as is the only other song I've heard, the fine garage groover, "I Don't Mind."

The band reportedly split in 2002 and did a 2006 reunion show in Argentina. I've seen photos of Thee Horribles on stage dressed as various film monsters – Dracula, Wolfman, Mummy, etc – how can you not love that?

## THE EMBROOKS (U.K.)

It has been a long time since I have heard the massive amount of compression on a master recording that the "Our New Day" album (on Voxx, 2000) sports. Yep, it's that ultra-analog Toe Rag Studios production again, and all the colors are picture-perfect for The Embrook's 1966 mod-garage masterpiece. If you dig mid-60s Euro Freakbeat, then The Embrooks should be your selected destination.

Also out are at least six 45 singles and the "Separations" album on Dionysus (2000) and "Yellow Glass Perspections" (Munster, 2004).

The 2002 "Back In My Mind" b/w "The Time Was Wrong" 45 (on Butterfly Records) is another excellent slab of '66 Freakbeat pop. Absolute primo stuff here, lads.

## THE EXOTICS (MILWAUKEE, WISCONSIN)

The 1995 "Goofy Foot" EP on Tiki Tone Records is primo surf-instrumental, complete with beautiful ocean-blue vinyl. There is also the "Go Go Guitars" album from 1996 and "The Lost Album," also on Tiki Tone.

These Exotics (not to be confused with many other acts over the years) is the best surf band I've heard from Milwaukee. Just think about that for a moment.

## THE FAMOUS MONSTERS
(NEW YORK, NY, U.S.A.)

I love crappy music, and The Famous Monsters are crappy at its best. Estrus compiled a dozen tracks from various releases (there is at least another album and a couple 45s), and adds in the soundtrack to an actual "Monster Party" for their 1999 "Around The World In 80 Bikinis" CD. If you dig screaming chicks and fuzzy gits – or is that fuzzy chicks and screaming gits? – you'll groove to this. These are compliments, even if this was just a side band for a couple folks from White Zombie.

## FANTASY FACTORY (GERMANY)

A special commendation must be given to Cosimino Pecere and his Psych-Out Records in Italy. Not only has he made available a wide range of garage and psych sounds that otherwise might never see the light of day, he houses the vinyl releases in the thickest covers I have ever seen, in the old-fashioned 1960s pasted-on-board style, with nice, thick vinyl, too. And so the 2001 "Abracadabra" album is a perfect Psych-Out release, with stretched out spacey Euro-psych, colorful cover and a completely trippy ambience. There is at least one other CD album, titled "If I Like It, I Do It." That could be the slogan for Cosimino Pecere and Psych-Out, too.

## SHANE FAUBERT (U.S.A.)

There is something melancholy and haunting about The Cheepskates' vocalist Shane Faubert. I love how he phrases lines, how gentle and emotional he crafts his delivery. The "Squirrelboy Blue" CD (on Music Maniac, 1997) showcases all these fine qualities, and his expert songwriting, too. Much of this would feel right on home on a Cheepskates album, so you know that the pop sensibilities and song-crafting is all polished and in place. There are many highlights in this generous 18-track selection, and I love that final track, where Shane reads the "end credits" for the album! This is indie music at its best, and kudos to Gary "Pig" Gold for a fine production, too.

## THE FEENDS (AUSTRALIA)

The self-released "Jungle Man" 45 is enigmatic enough – no record label is even listed on the sleeve or label – but I "think" it was released in 1996 on Corduroy. Previously they managed the 1993 "Freek Show" and also a 1995 EP on Spinning Top titled "7 Scorching Tunes" (also released as a 10" on Dig!). "Jungle Man" is a fine fuzz and organ burner, by the way, with tongue firmly in cheek and fuzz pedal turned all the way up.

(This group is not to be confused with "The Fiends" from Canada, featured below.)

## I FENOMINI (ITALY)

The 2010 "Ora!" 7" EP is on Presto! Records, and my copy doesn't have printed record labels. It's an accomplished EP, with a fine cover version of Smoke's "My Friend Jack" (sung in Italian). The title track features some blistering psych-pop guitar. A really fine release.

## THE FIENDS (UPDATE)

The Canadian foursome's 7" on Greece's Dr. Mushroom Optical Illusion Records (1995) is one worthy discography addition. The North America-to-Greece connection isn't as strange as it seems – I've toured the land of ouzo myself, and have seen first-hand that the Greeks love this kind of garage rock mayhem.

Vocalist Greg Johnson hits his songwriting high-point with "She's Not Broken," yet another of his (not) sensitive and tender homages to womankind. (Oh, and there's plenty of fuzz guitar, too.) The B-side delivers a suitably warped Sky Saxon cover, plus the Zorba The Greek movie theme (re-titled "Zombie The Greek") delivered surf-style. Genius is too tame a word to describe whatever it is that The Fiends did. It is 1966-fuzz-garage fun in a nutshell. I have probably used the term "essential" much too often in this book to urge readers to search-out particular records or bands, but hear me now: The Fiends are essential for fans of the garage revival.

The "Gravedigger" CD (1998 on Dionysus) is another expertly crude garage classic, and I loved the band so much that I wrote the liner notes for their "In Scareo" CD (1996 also on

Dionysus). It is eerie for me now to see the photo of vocalist Greg Johnson in a coffin on the back cover – because he died in 2009.

Other highly recommended 7"s include "Zombie A-Go-Go" on Primitive, "She Looks Outta Sight" on Dionysus, and "Gravedigger" on Sonic Swirl.

I was working with Greg on an Ed Cobb Tribute album when he died (I did post it for free for a while online, in his honor), and had gotten to know him a lot more over the years. (My band, the Marshmallow Overcoat, had played shows with his bands in the late 1980s and early 1990s in Canada.) He was such a lovable, whacky and sincere garage friend. I miss him very much.

## FIFTY FOOT COMBO (BELGIUM)

"Go Hunting" (on MuSick, 1999) is more first-class (mostly) instrumental mischief, complete with go-go dancers, of course. Plenty of spring reverb, some fine fuzz, and a mysterious monsters-meets-spies at a cocktail party mood. I love the bands that have the talent to take '50s exotica, '60s surf and garage, spy and monster movies and mix it all up into a party soundtrack. There is sparkling production on this debut, too. There are at least four later albums, including "Evil A Go-Go" (2000), "Caffeine" (2002), "The Monstrophonic Sound Live At Ernesto's" and "Ghent-Bxl" (both 2004) .

## THE FINE LINES (SPRINGFIELD, MISSOURI, U.S.A.)

Springfield of course was known in the 1980s as the home of the awesome Royal Nonesuch, so it's fab to see other garage bands from that locale take up the garage gauntlet. But location is really the only similarity to the '66-fueled Royal Nonesuch.

The self-titled 2003 album, on Licorice Tree Records, is a purposely crude production. The trio kick out a decidedly lo-fi recording of basic garage-punk. I know folks who eat up this particular sub-genre of the garage sound, but a little of it goes a long way for me.

There is also the "Instrumental EP" (2008 on Wee Rock Records) that mines the same purposely scratchy lo-fi tone, one more album, and at least five more 45s.

## FLAMING SIDEBURNS (HELSINKI, FINLAND)

I almost don't care if any records actually exist on Bad Afro Records, because their graphic logo (of, what else, a "bad" afro haircut) is just so cool. But wait, their 1998 "Get Down or Get Out!" 45 by The Flaming Sideburns is every bit as fun as the record company's image. Burning boozy, pub-garage soaks this disc, as well as the 1997 "Close to Disaster" 45 on the Finnish Metamorphos label. Jesus, check out the lengthy contact info for Bad Afro; how long does an address have to be to get mail in Denmark?!?

There are a dozen other albums and countless 45s out there as well.

## THE FLASHBACK FIVE (UPDATE)

The Flashback V mine the classic guitar and organ garage sound I love so much – my favorite sounds in this book are centered around this classic formula. The "Not Exactly A Poem" LP (1996 on Guersson) picks up where their 7" tastes left off, displaying a maturing band ready to make a long player and succeeding with style and power. "Not Exactly A Poem" a true treat of the neo-garage era.

There is also the "Where Is Wally" four-song 7" EP on Misty Lane (1996), and it is a fine homage to the band's love of The Outsiders, Q65 and the Shadows of Knight.

## THE FLASHJUNKIES (GERMANY)

A two-piece garage punk band with a 1998 EP, simply recorded on a four track and based on improvised performances. It is certainly unique and experimental, while also fitting into a '60s sensibility.

## TONY BORLOTTI AND THE FLAVERS (ITALY)

This is one of those fine Misty Lane releases that you could swear was an original 1965 Euro-beat release. The 2000 three-song EP is 1965-true, down to the little details, and sounds like a garage-pop time machine. A spirited cover of The Kinks' "I Need You" shares space with another band original on the flip. Bravo!

## LOS FLECHAZOS (LEON, SPAIN)

A very active Mod band, with a dozen albums and a couple dozen 45s out from 1988 to 2007. There is a self-titled EP on the fine U.K. Detour label from 1996.

## THE FLESHTONES (UPDATE)

These NYC cats are one of the few garage survivors that trace their history all the way back to the punk rock 1970s. They have, somehow, managed to continue recording and releasing records – and more importantly for their legacy – tour relentlessly throughout the globe. There are way too many resulting releases to shuffle thought here, and they are more readily available than most found in this book. So get to it.

## FLIGHT REACTION (STOCKHOLM, SWEDEN)

The specific mixture of garage and psych that I love so well is a mysterious and tricky formula to concoct – it is just so darn difficult to get the mixture just right. And the wonderfully named Flight Reaction hit the mark perfectly in the few songs I've heard. The pop sensibility and diverse song structure is there, lots of tremolo and fuzz, harmonies and a driving beat. There's a reason why I always find myself going back to Electric Prunes and Strawberry Alarm Clock records, and it's the same reason why I have to go find some Flyte Reaction discs – this is what garage-psych is supposed to sound like.

There are four 7"s from 2010-2012 (on the CopaseDisques and 13 O'Clock labels), and the debut 2014 self-titled album (on 13 O'Clock Records).

## THEE FLYING CARPETS (LOUISVILLE, KY, U.S.A.)

The day that "Land Behind The Mirror" (2004 on Ear X-Tacy Records) popped into my life was one of unexpected surprise and pleasure. I had no idea that the Technicolor paisley garage of Thee Flying Carpets existed (and in Kentucky of all places!?!?), and this light-show-inducing album is one of my favorite self-released efforts from recent years.

The lysergia is of the playful kind, with plenty of Electric Prunes-meets-The Seeds moments. The title track "Land Behind The Mirror" is one of those garage-psych anthems that sounds better the louder you play it, too. I also appreciate that the Carpets don't try to mitigate their obvious love of the classic '60s psych –pop formula of fuzz, organ, backward sounds and shouted "HEYS!" They love this style of music— I love this style of music – and I love this album. It might be one of the best records in this book that most of you have not heard. There's a great bong-water sound effect before one of the songs, too. "Me Love You" is one great caveman garage song, and a perfect closer for this gem of an album.

## THE FLYING TYGERS (HOLLAND)

This is another Eric Geevers combo, formed in 2008 as a spin-off of the Raving Bonkers. The "Radio Action" album is a very lo-fi (and mono), and combines some '77 punk with some classic '66 garage covers, such as the fine "Where You Gonna Go?" and the always-wonderful "Suicidal Flowers."

There is also a split mono 45 on Tombstone Records (with both Raving Bonkers and Flying Tygers in all their crude garage splendor), another split mono 45 on Pure Coincidence (featuring the fine "Find My Way Back To My Mind," perhaps their best song), and a couple compilations, including a couple crunchy numbers of the 2008 "Westerpop" CD.

## THEE FLYPPED WHIGS (UPDATE)

The Washington D.C. area combo knocked around recording studios (and local clubs) for a few years in the mid-1990s, but without any vinyl making it out the door. They even put out an ad announcing their debut 45, but those tracks were scrapped as well. So it's with no small joy that I hold in my hands Thee Flypped Whigs' debut 1997 four song EP.

The untitled, picture sleeve-less 7" (on their own Charmkin Records) is a perfect reflection of their devoted all-Vox mentality, with plenty of snarl, snot and classic garage production. Just groove on the "Soapy"-like riff in their anthem "Don't Go Away Mad (Just Go Away)." It's all Vox, it's all energy, it's all fun! And Thee Flypped Whigs win my first "Best Fuzztone" award of 1997. These are all compliments!

## FOGBOUND (SPAIN)

The "Whispering Corridors" b/w "Come And See" 45 (on Sunny Day Records, 2014) is very vibrant and pulsating psych-pop, and several other tracks I've heard point to a promising explosion coming from Fogbound.

## FORTUNE & MALTESE AND THE PHABULOUS PALLBEARERS
(KALAMAZOO, MICHIGAN)

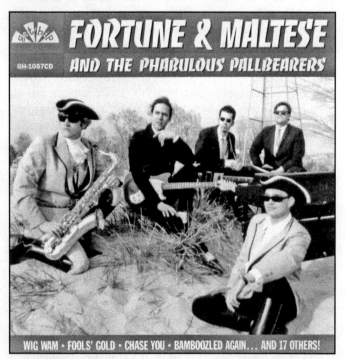

At the head of the class is the pride of Kalamazoo, Fortune & Maltese and The Phabulous Pallbearers. This high-octane quintet boasts stacks of quality wax, with their 1997 "Konquer Kampus" album on Hillsdale one of their best.

The matching uniforms and tri-cornered hats recall Paul Revere & The Raiders, but the grooves also spurt a

combination of Jan & Dean with the grit of Question Mark & The Mysterians at their lustiest. "My Baby's Hearse," "Cuttin' Class," and "Cuz I Want You" help explain why the F&M lads are a wall of Vox amps ahead of the competition, and each are highlighted by a rare and welcome commodity: glorious back-up harmony vocals and expert playing.

Fortune & Maltese are one of the few modern garage combos that often out-perform their '60s idols.

Get Hip did a fine job of releasing on CD previous vinyl-only releases from other labels, with the self-titled "Fortune & Maltese and the Phabulous Pallbearers" LP a definitive example. Dedicated readers will know F&M from my various year-end "best-of" lists, so it's no surprise how excited I was to find these tracks previously available only as a German import LP (on Screaming Apple).

Fortune & Maltese top themselves with what could be the best two 45s of 1990s. Their 1997 "Leave No Stone Unturned" b/w "Time Has Gone" single on Get Hip is a folk-garage-pop masterpiece, full of the expert songwriting and arranging that made their "Konquer Kampus" LP an instant hit. I love "Leave No Stone Unturned" so much that we included the wonderful music video for it on our "Knights of Fuzz" video DVD.

Their "Bewitched" 45 for Larsen is on the much grittier side, and just as effective as their poppier efforts. I love the Kinks' "I Need You" riff in "Don't Wanna Cry," and the Pallbearers take the fuzz to another level. Other highly recommended 45s include "Genie In The Lamp" (360 Twist), the "Wig Wam" EP (on Leppotone), "Bewitched" (on Larsen), "Sonic Sounds from Seattle" EP (Dionysus), "Fiddled While Rome Burned" (Keystone), and a rare Hillsdale promo 45 from the "Konquer Campus" LP.

A treat for the true F&M collector (like me) is also the limited bootleg-like "Live At Harvey's" vinyl album.

## THEE FOURGIVEN (UPDATE)

Of note is the 2006 "It Ain't Pretty Down Here" CD (on Dionysus), which deservedly reissues the fine 1984 album and adds a slew of cool bonus tracks, and a music video shot right here in Tucson, Arizona while the band was on tour. Thee Fourgiven remain one of the most criminally under-rated bands of the era. Shame on you if you are not cool enough to know it.

## THE FOXY RIDERS (ST. PETERSBURG, RUSSIA)

A mesmerizing pulse envelopes "Wise," from their 2014 digital four-song EP, complete with a very moody, trippy music video. While this certainly falls into the category of "modern" psych-garage, The Foxy Riders could still be of interest to the more progressive readers of this book. There is also a similar-sounding three-song digital EP available as well. Is there physical product available, too? I sure hope so.

## THE FRANTIC V (UPDATE)

This is another long-time garage survivor from wonderful Greece, which remains one of my favorite garage rock countries. The 1999 "Play The Quinta" 7" EP (on Italy's Teen Sound Records) shows the Greek combo playing traditional Farfisa-garage like it was 1966 and the Standells were in the wings waiting to come on stage. We would be so lucky.

The "Play The Fugitive!" EP (on Corduroy) is moody and dark, the "In The Bradford Mist!" EP (1996, on Golbin Records) is gritty and fun, and the 2001 "It's Frantic Time" 10" on Teen Sound tops them all with some fine production and a confident, mature band sound. I especially love the 10" vinyl format, and "It's Frantic Time!" is an example of the format at its finest, showcasing these Greeks at the top of the neo-garage genre.

The "Room 409" 45 was released by On Stage Records (2004); the same label also issued an album. Don't confuse this band with the similarly-named The Flashback V, another fine combo from Spain (described previously).

## THE FRED BISON FIVE: (U.K.)

This is Bevis Frond's Nick Saloman playing all the parts for the "Beat Roots" album (on his own Woronzow label) from 1992.

## FREDDY AND THE FOUR-GONE CONCLUSIONS (DETROIT, MI, U.S.A.)

A follow-up band from Freddy Fortune to his seminal Fortune & Maltese act, they issued the "Stand Up" b/w "Today" 45 on Get Hip in 2002. The A-side is a relatively unknown Del Shannon song, and Freddy and his new boys deliver a killer version. I loved it so much (and its video), that I selected it for the "Knights of Fuzz" video DVD. The song (and video) also feature Del Shannon's keyboard player, Max Crook. Another highly recommended 7" is "Gotta Give It Time" b/w "You're Just A Waste Of Time" (on Sounds Camera).

The "Wigged Out Sounds" CD (2002 on Get Hip) is lesser known than Freddy's F&M era, but it is one of the true gems of the neo-garage era. As always, Freddy's vocals are top-notch, and the production is full and sweet without ever feeling forced or slick. Few in this era understand how to balance a pop sensibility, melody and the garage spirit like Freddy Fortune, and this album drips with expertise. The aforementioned "Stand Up" is included, plus three CD-only bonus tracks.

Yes, I'll always love the crude fuzzed-out garage combos, but the pure quality that Freddy Fortune creates always rises to the top for me.

## FRIGG A-GO-GO (LAFAYETTE, LA, U.S.A.)

"The Penetrating Sounds Of..." (1997, on 360 Twist) is party-garage: it makes you get up and jiggle while drinking your beer *real* fast. Can any garage band even hope to achieve more than that? The production is practice-room perfect; good enough to blast but still organic, basic and in your face. A bit of that Louisiana feel creeps in, too, around the edges. "Explosion" is a stand-out, sounding in just over a minute like a long-lost unreleased Pebbles screamer from '66. Again, can any band hope for more? The answer, kids, is no. Also out is the "Everything Around Me" 45 on 360 Twist.

## THE FUZZ FACES (SAO PAULO, BRAZIL)

They formed in 2000, with the "We Don't Give a Fuck" EP appearing in 2001 and the "Voodoo Hits" album in 2003. They also have songs on Sonics and Fuzztones tribute albums. Their version of The Fuzztones' "Action Speaks Louder Than Words" is suitably fuzzy.

And speaking of The Fuzztones...

## THE FUZZTONES (UPDATE)

The Fuzztones, of course, ruled the black-leather garage netherworld throughout the 1980s, alternating their aural mayhem between New York City and Los Angeles. Their 1998 "Flashbacks" CD – also a double-vinyl LP – is fiery proof that the "paisley revival" has true lasting power, and that Sundazed could provide the same quality attention to the 1980s caveteen scene as it does for 1960s garagedelia.

"Flashbacks" isn't really a traditional "best of"; The Fuzztones released far too much quality material over more than 40 records to make a mere 70 minute distillation of their finest moments possible. The 22 tracks here instead opt for some choice LP cuts, alternate versions, demos and previously unreleased material.

Frontman and raven-haired lunatic Rudi Protrudi is the focus behind The Fuzztones' dark paisley sound. Protrudi's approach recalls an alley cat in the throws of vicious copulation, his guitar alive with buzz, his voice a groaning invitation. The Music Machine's Sean Bonniwell, The Mysterians' Question Mark and Steppenwolf's John Kay have nothing on Rudi Protrudi; perhaps he's the result of some DNA mutation/combination of them all.

Oh, and Moms, lock up the girls: Rudi & The Fuzztones reformed in Europe, and as of this writing are still lurking about, spreading the fuzz.

Sean Bonniwell joined Rudi for the "People In Me" b/w "I'm Gonna Make You Mine" 45 (1998 on Misty Lane). The cover of "People In Me," with Protrudi and Bonniwell trading vocals,

might be one of The Fuzztones' best recordings. It is both reverential to the original and expertly re-arranged. Just perfect.

By comparison, the "Lord Have Mercy On My Soul" b/w "They're Gonna Take You Away" 45 (2005 on Twist) might be one of their least-inspired. Recorded in California with a make-shift lineup, the A-side is – hold on to you hats, fans – a cover of a Black Oak Arkansas tune. I will say no more.

There are many, many, many additional Fuzztones releases to add to their discography since the 1995 version of this book, including "Salt For Zombies" (2003 on Sin Records), "Preaching To The Perverted" (on Stag-O-Lee, 2011), "LSD 25" (with an audio disc and video DVD, 2005, on Sin Records), 45s, many more compilations plus various Rudi Protrudi side projects. Especially recommended is the 1994 "Live In Europe" double LP on Music Maniac. Some other rare 45s worth searching for include the "Face Of Time" (on RAFR), "One Girl Man" (1998, on Sundazed), and the solo Rudi Protrudi "Gimme Danger" (on Twang!).

A footnote for Fuzztones fans is the curious "King Arthur's Quart" EP on Misty Lane. Rudi claims this to be tapes of his earliest sonic efforts, circa 1966, but others who have played with him over the years contend they are much later rehearsal tapes posing as a 1960s release. Whatever the source, its crude garage all the way!

The Fuzztones might be the most prolific band of the entire neo-garage era, with more than 30 years of output and still counting. There is so much Fuzztones music out there that even when a dedicated fan like me *attempts* to collect it all, it seems almost an impossible mission. The hit-to-miss quotient for Rudi's productions is also very high – you are guaranteed a quality time, with expert playing and a lot of lysergic garage effort, each time you find yet another new Fuzztones disc.

The "Snake Oil" two-CD set (2012 on The Third Ear Records, Israel) is a collection of rare 45 tracks, alternate versions and other obscurities in the spirit of the similar 1990 "Creatures That Time Forgot" collection. This is the rarities collection for the ultimate Fuzztones fan who thought he had everything! Hats off to Fuzztones-obsessed fan Moti Cohen for making this release happen.

The concept behind the 2013 "In Fuzz We Trust" album (on Stag-O-Lee) is unique for the neo-garage era: original 1960s garage-psych bands recorded Fuzztones songs, rather than the other way around! And there are some of the most important original garage band names here: The Shadows Of Knight (with a great "Gloria"-like track), Sky Saxon of the Seeds, The Pretty Things (helped by the fabulous Plasticland), The Monks (with a spine-chilling version of "Hurt On Hold"), The Electric Prunes with Sean Bonniwell of The Music Machine and Arthur Lee of Love, The Strawberry Alarm Clock, Question Mark & The Mysterians – a truly mind-numbing collection of bands.

I was worried that some of these venerable acts would sound tired and or no longer garage or psych enough, but Rudi made certain that some new blood helped where needed and that all deliver the goods. Tribute albums are a mixed bag, but this one surely puts the entire genre on its head. (Note that Rudi also released two other Fuzztones tribute CDs with more contemporary bands doing his songs.)

Whether you love Rudi Protrudi (and The Fuzztones) or not, when he finally hangs up his Vox guitar then the neo-garage era will officially end. Oh, garage and psych will continue unabated as a musical genre, but it just won't be the same without the mighty Fuzztones.

*In fuzz we trust!*

---

**NOTE: Remember to read the original 1995 book and the other book update chapters for thousands of other bands and records not featured in this update section.**

---

## THE GARAGE GODS (PORTLAND, OR, U.S.A.)

This studio concoction creates almost perfect '66-styled garage pop, and the 2009 "Had Enough Of Your Lies" b/w "She Don't Love You Anymore" (on Lost In Tyme) almost sounds like demos for the Monkees to cover. Yes, the fuzz and organ are right where they need to be, but it is a polished pop construction to the songs that really sets them apart. It is also highly unusual for the songwriter, here Gary Lalin, to play drums and deliver lead vocals.

I've also heard an unfortunately unreleased song "Lost In Tyme," (perhaps in honor of the fine Greek record label and zine?) and it is also a polished gem.

## ERIC GEEVERS (HOLLAND)

Eric has played in and formed so many worthy garage bands that I'll summarize them here under his own name. In the 1995 book (and at the start of this chapter) his Acetones are well-documented, but he also served stints with Link Wray (and the subsequent tribute band The X-Ray Men), The Bunny Club, The Counts of Three (a really inspired band name there), The Napoleons, The Paradogs, The Raving Bonkers, The Flying Tygers, Link Protrudi & The Jayman (and has played with Rudi's Fuzztones, too). You'll see Eric Geever's name throughout this book – he is one of those garage **True Believers** that I cherish so much.

## GHASTLY ONES (VAN NUYS, CA, U.S.A.)

"A Haunting We Will Go-Go" is another surprisingly worthy release on Rob Zombie's short-lived Zombie A Go-Go Records (a division of ultra-corporate Geffen Records). Yep, it's more reverbed '60s-styled instrumental surf-meets-hotrod-meets the Wolfman madness. (Interestingly, this LP was also released in 1998 by true indie Telestar Records.) The band survived their major label moment with at least three more albums and several 7-inchers, up through 2007. A big zombie thumbs up for these cats.

## THE GILJOTEENS ( STOCKHOLM, SWEDEN)

The Giljoteens play in the fine tradition of R&B garage, and the recording on the 2001 four-song 7" EP (on Teen Sound) is certainly period authentic – but it was the EP's final track, "The Summer Was Gone" that really grabbed my ears. It has that patented moody Swedish garage sound that must come from months of snow and darkness – something very foreign for me as I sit in sunny, baking Arizona.

There are at least two more 45s and 2004 and 2007 albums. Send them to me, please?

## GIRL TROUBLE (UPDATE)

Three decades on Girl Trouble keeps the down-home garage a-comin' from their Tacoma, Washington lair. I was lucky enough to play some shows with them in their native Northwest, and became a fan for life. I was even lucky enough to include their music video for their classic "Cold Shoulder" on my 2006 "Knights of Fuzz" video DVD.

In 2014 a documentary film titled "Strictly Sacred" about the group debuted, following their relentless, independent

and purely original path, with all original members, always as good as ever. A soundtrack album is out, and a video DVD release imminent.

There have only been a handful of groups in the history of rock music with the determination and sense of purpose like Girl Trouble. Put them on your "Must Hear" list.

## THE GLORIAS (UPDATE)

At least three records have since been released, with the 2000 "Goodtimes" CD continuing their Swiss garage dedication. Real kudos from me for their clever interpretation of The Roosters' classic "One Of These Days" – long a favorite folk-rocker from the proud Pebbles tradition. But is worthy originals that dominate the disc, and make it worth hunting for their records, waiting somewhere in the Alps.

There are also three more albums, dating back to 1987.

## THE GOBLINS (CHICAGO, IL, U.S.A.)

Gerhard Fluch has kept the Austrian garage fires burning with his long-running Rumble Radioshow, and also through his own Pure Vinyl Records. Here he makes sounds all the way from the U.S.A. available with the Goblins and their "Nightrockers" EP. They are pretty standard garage-punk, with only a slight nod to the '60s sound, but I'll include them here because of Darren Merinuk's fine and silly cover art of masked phantoms and the fact that all four song titles have the word "night" in them. Rock music is **supposed** to be silly, folks.

## THE GO DEVILS (JAPAN)

The 1996 "Wild World Of" 45 (on Dionysus) features a passable cover of "I'm In Pittsburgh and It's Raining," with a band-original curiously as the B-side. It's OK, too, but not spectacular. Dionysus honcho Lee Joseph is well known for enjoying all-girl garage groups, and perhaps that is one reason this Japanese female trio scored this 45 release. The audio production does, however, boast a fabulous low-end to it!

## LES GODZILLAS (FRANCE)

This all-girl group is another blast of European garage madness. Their 1997 self-titled five-song 7" (on Larsen) exudes the innocence and raw spunk of French garage, along with the goofiness that always keeps this stuff from getting dull. I mean, when "Rodan" is on organ, "The Bionic Monster" on bass and "Demothra" plays guitar, how could this junk be boring? Like many newbie garagers, Les Godzillas relied heavily on covers at their start, but it's the attitude and atmosphere that gives their debut a warm, fuzzy glow. There is also a three-song 7" EP (on Wiped Out, 1999).

## THE GOLDEN ZOMBIES (MADRID, SPAIN)

"The 24 Kilate Sound" CD (2000, on Munster) has a distinctly European instrumental feel to it, with plenty of nicely echoed guitar and organ. I love the instrumental version of the classic "Stay," which almost erases the bad memory of the famous Jackson Browne version. For some reason the last track on the CD is a compilation of the other nine songs together. I've never seen that on a CD before!

## GORE GORE GIRLS (DETROIT, MI, U.S.A.)

If you've read this far, then you know that garage sounds that make me smile are the best of all. Oh, nothing wrong with some good, gritty Sonics-styled nastiness – but at the end of any garage song I want to have had fun – and then want to have some more fun with the next track. And, thus, come The Gore Gore Girls. The garage here is on the punk side of town, more distorted than fuzzed, and played at a pace akin to running from the law. "Strange Girls" (2001 on Get Hip) is a fine first salvo, and "Up all Night" (also Get Hip) adds some classy visual style to their stew, with their happy trash intact. Jim Diamond's production (famous for The White Stripes, etc.) is stellar. There's another LP from 2007 and at least four more 45s, including "I'll Get You Yet" on Get Hip. Oh, I almost forgot – they are an all-woman band.

## THE GRAINS ( ITALY)

Teen Sounds strikes again: their 2005 "Just Our Flame" for the Grains adds another blast to the venerable '66 folk-garage tradition. Other Italian bands such as The Sick Rose and Head & The Hares seem to have been a good influence on The Grains, with an urgent delivery serving the album well. A nice thick organ sound and tight arrangements also make this a keeper. Pick hit: the power-poppy "Listen To Me." The "Heart Full of Rain" b/w "Wait A While" (two choice '60s covers done in a moody style) 45 is also out on Teen Sound.

## GRAHAM DAY AND THE GAOLERS (U.K.)

Of course Graham Day is a major name in the U. K. Medway garage scene, contributing to the Mighty Ceasers, Prime Movers, Solarflares, and many more. He is another of those rare **"True Believers"** I honor in this book – those lads and gals who remain dedicated to the garage sound over decades. It is in their blood, and it certainly raves on in Graham Day.

I've heard the "Begging You" 45 (2008 on Damaged Goods) and "Sitar Spangled Banner" is a wonderful fuzz instrumental in the best Prisoners tradition (and with no resemblance to the American national anthem). The "A" side is a brilliant garage-pop burner – I honestly believe a mainstream audience would groove on this as an infectious pop song if they ever had the chance to actually hear it!

As it is, even I have had to work to hear even a couple of their tunes. There are 2007 and 2008 albums (and singles), and what I've heard sounds like The Prisoners at their height – in other words, supremely crafted Mod pop in the finest U.K. tradition. Pure joy for me.

## GRAVYS DROP (BERKELEY, CA, U.S.A.)

Another of the Burger stable of interesting and enigmatic SoCal neo-popsters, with an audio cassette release (also on vinyl) including the 2013 "Gumball." Like most of the Burger scene, these cats defy an easy description, but there is enough of the garage ethos and approach to merit their inclusion here. Pick Hit: "Six Foot Babe."

## THE GREEN TAMBOURINE BAND
(EDINBURGH, U.K.)

It takes guts to name your band after a Lemon Pipers song and then play hushed, intricate psych pop, so hats off to these lads. The first track I heard from them is the magical "From The Seed Into The Flower." It is like an aural mediation, with glowing vocal harmonies, a mesmerizing hypnotic pulse, and a magic atmosphere, complete with backward cymbals.

It is truly intoxicating – though it took me a while to track down the fact that in 2014 it was released as part of an album titled "Let Yourself Be / Aum." I think this is a download-only release, but it is stellar, full of jangle, hushed vocal brilliance and a paisley glow throughout. I gotta get going and see if I can help get these boys a physical release, because this debut is just plain too good to be only a names of digital files on a hard drive.

Bands like The Green Tambourine Band are the reason I have spent the last 25 years compiling this book. Discovering such psych-pop brilliance makes all the work worthwhile.

## THE GREENFISH (UPDATE)

I really enjoy the do-it-yourself feel of the 1995 "Mass" four-song 7" EP (on DIG!). It has all the rawness of a practice-room recording, but with enough verve to distinguish it from a mere demo tape. A cover of the Pretty Things' classic "Midnight To Six" adorns the flip side. There is also the "Rise To The Bait" LP on Dig! from the same year.

## GREEN PAJAMAS (UPDATE)

Seattle's Green Pajamas are one of those bands that never breaks through, never gets that big break, never sells a million records. All they've done is make some of the most interesting, haunting pop records of the garage-revival era.

Fifteen of their rarest early salvos are collected on Get Hip's 1998 "Indian Winter," a wonderful treat for fans (like me) who have searched for tracks like "Peppermint Stick" and "Sister Anne" – songs that have been scattered on limited edition compilations and 45s. There's plenty of unreleased stuff here too, and almost all of it is spot-on.

Their 1997 long-player, "Strung Behind The Sun," continues their somber pop path cemented with 1990's "Ghost of Love." It is an Australian release (on Camera Obscura), but well worth the long canoe trip it might take to find it.

Vocalist/guitarist Jeff Kelly – the center of the Green Pajama's sound – remains one of the most original, thoughtful song writers knocking around the underground, and he shows no signs of drying up after years and years of quality work.

1998's "All Clues Lead To Meagan's Bed" (on Obscura) continues the Pajama's patented style; it's one of those records with great songs that I wish I had a crack at producing, because the recording sometimes doesn't serve the material the best (to my ears). Also available is "Strung Out" (1998) and the fine 2003 "Through Glass Colored Rose" solo best-of collection.

Kelly's solo effort "Ash Wednesday Rain" (on Green Monkey), is a welcome addition to their stack of pop melancholia for any Green Pajamas fan. It's a home-recorded "solo" effort that sounds better than most big-budget albums, and the quality of songs raises it far above a mere home taping.

It's not too late, kids; go find the 1990 vinyl version of the band's 1984 (originally cassette-only) "Summer of Lust" LP and get started collecting the Green Pajamas. And their

classic 1990 "Ghosts of Love" LP was re-issued on CD by Get Hip in 2000.

## THE GREMMIES (ALBANY, NY, U.S.A.)

Energetic, trashy hot-rod-ish instrumentals, just how I like them. I love the distorted tremolo on "Five Eyed Female," too, from the 1996 "Boss Now Sound Of" four-song 7" EP (on Cacophone Records).

## THE GRIM IMPERIALS (SAN DIEGO, CA, U.S.A.)

The band describes themselves as "Chuck Berry, Bo Diddley, Brian Jones-era Stones, Dutch Beat, Freak Beat, '60s Punk, Garage, Maximim R&B, R&R! and '70s American Punk" – that's a lot of junk to fit into one band's sound! The 2013 "Kicksville A.D." EP does display some of those influences, especially on "C'Mon," which slides nicely into a '77-meets-power-pop feel. I don't get much of a garage-punk vibe here, except on "Morningside Lane," so you garage purists would probably pass this by. But if you like your The Hives or Vines, then maybe this is for you.

## THE GRIP WEEDS (UPDATE)

The excellent "House of Vibes" album debut was followed by a couple seven-inchers (including the fab "We're Not Getting Through" on Twang in 1996), and the New Jersey quartet delivered their sophomore "The Sound Is In You" (1998, on Buy Or Die) four years later. Why the long gap between albums? Perhaps it's because The Grip Weeds take their time and perfect their songs, when most bands instead churn out undernourished, sloppy product.

The Grip Weeds polish their own Revolver-era Beatles-meets-Badfinger-and The Who sound and hit a bullseye for a majority of their tracks. As before, the band fails only when throwing in a misguided "hard" rock track or two, perhaps in an attempt to show they aren't pop wimps. These poppers don't need such balance, since their melodic side is the strength and joy of the group.

A tune comes along only rarely that makes me hum all day, and "Tomorrow" is my latest happy example of the "I can't get that song out of my mind" syndrome.

The 2004 "Giant On The Beach" album (on the sadly missed Rainbow Quartz Records) continues the Weeds' expertly crafted power-garage-pop. There are at least two other albums out on Rainbow Quartz, and another 45 as well on Twang.

A major label would destroy a band (and the sound) of an indie band like The Grip Weeds. Save them from future commercial "glory" and search-out their self-produced albums. They worked hard to make them all by themselves.

## THE GROOVY CELLAR (BERLIN, GERMANY)

The 1994 "Summer Of Falling Stars" 45 (on the venerable Twang! label) is the tradition of fine '60s Euro-pop, with a distinctive German edge to it. Nicely crafted and recorded, it'll bring a smile on a cloudy day.

## GROOVY UNCLE (CHATHAM, U.K.)

The "Monkey Trousers" b/w "Now Your Pain Is Over" debut 45 (2010 on State Records) is finely arranged and recorded Freakbeat pop, something State is especially adapt at capturing for their releases. Bassist Alan Crockford (formerly of the Prisoners and many other cool combos) joined up later, and three albums from 2011, 2012 and 2013 also exist.

## THE GROWL (SPAIN)

There is one classic organ and fuzz 45 from 1995, "You Don't Love Me" b/w "She Is Gonna Make You Blue." It took me 19 years to even hear the songs and maybe another 19 to find the actual 45.

## THE GRUESOMES (UPDATE)

The "Tyrants of Teen Trash" conducted some reunions (including a stunning appearance at the 2001 release show for "The Knights of Fuzz" CD-ROM in NYC) and also gave us a CD reissue of their debut album in 2008 (on Ricochet), plus a 1985-1989 best-of on Sundazed in 2003. There was more trash to share, too: the 2007 "Live In Hell" album (of a 1989 live show) confirms the garage mastery of the band, and the 2000 "Cave-in!" album was an awesome all-new outing. (Several reissues of early albums also are now available.) After all these years I can't find more superlatives for The Gruesomes – I've heaped so many on already there might not be any adjectives left. They remain simply one of the very most essential bands featured in this book. That's why they are the cover band for the 1995 paper version, why their video for "Hey!" is on the "Knights of Fuzz" video DVD, and why I listen to them on an almost continuous loop here at Garage Nation HQ. My love of The Gruesomes is yet another reason many people believe I am actually a Canadian. Thank you very much.

## THE GTVs (PHILADELPHIA, PA, U.S.A.)

This is Sam Steinig's post-Mondo Topless combo, with the "Sh'Bang" album out in 2014 on Teen Sound. It continues his mission to supply cool organ-fueled party dance music. I heartily approve.

# H

## THEE HAIRY FAIRIES (PESARO, ITALY)

The 1998 "Electric Fairytales" LP (on the Swiss Max Picou label) is a well-produced, meaty-sounding guitar-based garage affair, with lots of style to burn, too.

## HATE BOMBS (ORLANDO, FL, U.S.A.)

Denver's 360 Twist Records quickly became one of the most prolific garage-oriented labels in the mid-1990s, and quality

THE HATE BOMBS
HERE COMES TREBLE

comes with its quantity. The late-great Element 79 gave up the ghost with their blistering "Dig Out" eight songer, while fellow Denverites The Hectics spit out a welcome 16-song ode to crude, drunken punk rock.

Orlando, Florida's Hate Bombs – perhaps the best combo I saw "live" in the late 1990s – also deposited their 1997 "Here Comes Treble" LP on 360 Twist, with loads of high-octane sweat and fun. Garage and psych bands aren't adept at playing by the rules or painting by the numbers. And that's why I love 'em.

1999's "Hunt You Down" (on Dionysus) is just as aggressive and satisfying. The production captures the live-party feel, but this isn't some average sloppy garage band – The Hate Bombs balance that edge-of-their-seat sound with some fine playing. There are at least five more 45s that I haven't seen. Drat!

## HEAD AND THE HARES (UPDATE)

A shamefully few acts from the past three decades have mined the sweet chiming of folk-rock, but this Italian combo makes it their mission. Their 1992 self-titled debut LP appeared on the U.S. Moulty label – on vinyl only, of course – and it still rings joyfully for me.

The LP has been impossible to find almost since the day of its release, so Get Hip has thankfully reissued it on CD, with an extra track. Moody, affectionately simple and crudely recorded, the shimmering guitars and plaintive (teen) melancholy makes the debut a folk-rock goldmine.

Longtime fans like me are doubly blessed: Stanton Park issued in 1997 another Head and The Hares LP, "Autumn Songbook." Yes, once again it started as a vinyl-only release. Outer Limits in Germany also released the "Painted Air" three-song 7" EP in 1995.

Head and the Hares (another unrelated New England garage band from the 1960s held the same moniker) mix their 12-string acumen with well-chosen covers, including the three-brain-cell genius of "Velvet Illusions." I once thought the original U.S. 1960s version couldn't be topped, but when The Hares sneer, "We are the velvet illusions, so be-ware-air," you just gotta stop and tip your hat. Records this vital only come along every 30 years or so.

## THEE HEADCOATS (UPDATE)

Billy Childish's discography is longer than the daily U.S. Congressional record, crammed with a multitude of band and solo releases. Thee Headcoats are one of his longest running acts, but sound nearly identical to his previous Milkshakes or Mighty Ceasars of the 1980s (to my American ears). That means simple, crude recordings, English beat and R&B tinged songs – often lifted almost completely from other artists – and Childish's distinctive blurting vocals. Childish often

confuses proliferation with proficiency, however. More than 50 (!) albums into his runaway career, Childish needs to inject just a little more quality into the proceedings. (I played just one show on the same bill as Childish, in the mid 1990s, and I was a bit perplexed at the attention he garnered. The show wasn't memorable at all.)

Still, "Headcoatitude," his 1994 album on the U.S. Get Hip label, is worth finding. Also out on Get Hip is 1993's "W.O.A.H! – Bo In The Garage" and the very cool 1997 "Jimmy Reed Experience" 10" vinyl. Yes, I know for many (especially in the U.K.) he remains garage royalty.

## THE HECTICS (DENVER, CO, U.S.A.)

There have been many punk and garage bands named The Hectics over the years, but this example does the name justice. You gotta, just gotta, love a band that starts its debut album with its own theme song, and "Everything I Need" (1997 on 360 Twist) follows up with lots more fuzzy fun. This isn't purist '66 garage, but more of a modern punk outing with garage flavor. I love the fuzz bass on "Tokyo Hotel," and the direct Ramones-ish production. 360 Twist also released a four song 7" EP, too. This stretches the definition of garage, but is cool. So there.

## THE HEFNERS (LAWRENCE, KANSAS )

The Hefners returned in 1999 with a long-player of American crude joy, titled "Lay Off This Old Man's Private Poison" (on Middle Class Pig), which should satisfy the Billy Childish in all of us. I can see Billy Childish swinging by Lawrence, Kansas to pick up The Hefners if he ever needs another back-up band. They've got the fun/crude garage trio sound down pat, with plenty of spittle to spare. Throwing eight quick songs on one side of a white-vinyl 10" (split with a German band named Schwarz), The Hefners whet the appetite and beg for more. Recorded at the same studio that has spawned fine garage efforts from both the Element 79 and The Down-N-Outs (and sharing a similarly stripped-down sound), The Hefners look— that is, sound – to be winners.

## HELL ON HEELS (PHOENIX, AZ, U.S.A.)

The harder-rock credentials of Seattle producer Jack Endino (and involvement of guitarist Jeff Dahl) would seem to indicate this would land outside the garage genre. Wrong! All the punk guts and spittle is in there for this all-woman combo, but also some nice garage touches (especially nice keyboards). This is the follow up to the 2004 debut on Bomp!.

## THE HENTCHMEN (DETOIT, MI, U.S.A.)

The "Three Times Infinity" album (2002 on Norton) has that ultra-punchy Jim Diamond-produced sound as The Hentchmen perfect their '60s frat-rock-meets-punk rock meal. This album is actually somewhere in the middle of the band's very long career – there at least seven more albums and numerous 45s. My basic listing here isn't meant as disrespect; I merely haven't heard much of their output. I do know that their fans are dedicated and rate The Hentchmen among the best of the more-stripped-down, less purist garage acts. I did ask several hipsters, who claimed great love for the band, to write a longer piece about the band for this book, but none of them loved the band enough to actually write something! And thus an example of how easy it is to tell me, "You should have more about band "X" in your book," but so hard to accomplish when the fan peeps don't lift a finger to help.

## HERRERA AND THE HANDOUTS
(NEW YORK, NY, U.S.A.)

Guitarist David John Hererra, of the fine Cheepskates, assembled some of New York City's finest 1980s garagers (including the Optic Nerve, Fuzztones, Headless Horsemen, Mad Violets, and Blacklight Chameleons) for the "A Handout From A Cheepskate" album (1989 on Midnight). It isn't a very garagey record, though they do tackle a cover of the Optic Nerve's classic folk-rocker "Mayfair."

## THE HIGHER STATE (U.K.)

"Songs of the Autumn" is just about as perfect a 1960s pop-psych song as I can imagine. And, oh, as a writer and performer for decades in this genre I have attempted to imagine a lot of them. It is a startlingly beautiful blend of San Francisco harmonies, Electric Prunes sensibility and expert pop song construction. I would stammer on in praise further, but after a million or so words spent on other groups for this book I'm afraid I'm running a bit short right now. (The 45 is backed with "Precious Rings & Stones" on 13 O'Clock Records in 2010).

The A-side "I Just Pretend" (2012, also on 13 O'Clock Records) continues this hit streak, with another expertly arranged and performed folk-psych-pop winner. It's as if The Higher State was able to make a list of the best elements of '66-'67 pop-psych and then actually have the talent to combine them into their own songs. Oh, there is no "as if" about it – that's exactly what has happened!

Thankfully for the rest of us mere mortal musicians (who are competing for turntable time), the band isn't perfect, and their folk-rock take on "Aint It Hard" (best known by The Electric Prunes) doesn't quite hit the mark for me. Ah, but even saying that, I must admit it is an original interpretation.

The magic continues with the "Potentially Everyone Is Your Enemy" b/w "All Ties That Bind" 45 (2013, again on their own State Records). The A-side adds some well-placed fuzz into their jangle-pop-psych, along with their patented delicious harmony vocals.

It won't surprise anyone with ears when I declare that the

The Higher State are one of the most enjoyable and talented bands of the neo-garage post-2000 generation. They are a blessing for fans (and musicians) like me who love to hear this vibrant genre performed, recorded and written at an optimum level. I am simply stunned at how beautiful this music is.

Here is a list of other albums: "From 'Round Here" (2007 on Teen Sound), "Darker By The Day" (2009), "Freakout At The Gallery" (2011) and self-titled (2013) all on 13 O'Clock Records – and at least another half-dozen 45s.

*Also see the "Guest Authors" chapter for more on The Higher State.*

## THE HIGH LEARYS (PERTH, AUSTRALIA)

Another prime example that the garage genre still has some major steam as of this writing: Australia's High Learys. Their 2013 "Here Come" album (on Soundflat Records) is one of the finest to pass over my turntable in recent memory, especially as a debut. And an audio mixing and mastering note for you fellow vinyl enthusiasts: this vinyl record sounds really, really good! The bass is mixed up higher than most and this rich, full tone really gives "Here Come" a meaty sonic wallop.

Also, while only window dressing, I love good record album covers. What makes one good? Well, it should be simple, elegant, colorful and cool. Check, check, check and check: this is one incredibly satisfying total package.

Oh, but what about the sounds? Its '60s R&B-flavored garage at its finest, with perfect arrangements and a recording that sounds both vintage authentic and also clean and sophisticated. There's a real '64-Stones feel on many of the better tracks ("Idolize Your Woman" and "Let You Down" for sure), but there's also a good dose of garage fuzz, too in the nine originals – and the cover of the seminal "Sticks And Stones," done here in the Zombies' style. Keyboardist Michael Nutt does Rod Argent proud on that one, and he is excellent throughout the album.

You think I am gushing over this band? Just wait if I get a chance to see them play live. I'm betting that would be a night worth writing about.

Pick Hit: the garage anthem "Not Me (You've Got It All Wrong)."

## THE HIVES (FAGERSTA, SWEDEN)

I just had to include a shout-out for "Hate To Say I Told You So" from 2000's "Veni Vidi Vicious" major-label album. Its modern garage rock at its most infectious, even if much of their other work is more predictable (modern) pop-punk. They released many records over more than a 15-year span, and while I dig them – and similarly edged bands such as The Strokes – most of their material lands outside the spectrum of this book.

## HOLY WAVE (AUSTIN, TX, U.S.A.)

Yes, this is psych and yes there is a garage feel, but file this under the more "modern" label, because Holy Wave isn't worried about recreating a 1960s trip, they're working on their own. "Psychological Thriller" and "Night Tripper," from their 2014 "Relax" album, do have a kinship to their Austin cousins the 13th Floor Elevators, but it isn't obvious – it's a vibe in there somewhere.

There are two more albums, one from 2011 and another from 2012, compiled into the 2013 "Evil Hits," out on vinyl.

## PETE HOLLY (U.S.A.)

Pete Holly's very, very crude 2000 power pop "Wizard of Garage" CD (on Orchard, US) could be of interest to those who like homemade pop.

## THE HOODWINKS (SOUTHAMPTON, U.K.)

The 1998 "Hurtin Side" 45 is another authentic Teen Sound release, sounding very much like it slipped into Mod shops in 1965 or 1966. Both sides are tight, organ-fueled groovers, with the added distinction of both being longer than five minutes in length.

## THE HUNTINGTON CADS (CA, U.S.A.)

More space-age surf-meets-exotica instrumentals grace the "5...4...3...2..1...Cads Are Go!" four-song 7" EP (1996 on Dionysus). The "Thunderbirds Are Go" homage sleeve is a nice touch, too. There's a 1997 EP on Estrus, and two albums on Mai Tai Records in 1996 and 1998.

## THE HYMEN OF TONGUES (SWEDEN)

This is another of Crimson Shadows veteran Jens Lindberg's top-notch Swedish garage combos. The 1996 four-song 7" EP (on Misty Lane) is a more subdued effort than the Shadows' releases, with a moody feel throughout the four originals, and Lindberg's organ creating the somber mood. "Live And Learn" is top-notch.

## THE HYPNOMEN (HELSINKI, FINLAND)

The Hypnomen and their "Watusi '99" LP (2000, on MuSick) are truly unique. Instrumental music from Finland must be strange, right? But the Hypnomen rise above mere weirdness – they're one of the most original, genre-twisting acts to blow through these ears. The trio takes '50s exotica, '60s lounge and Davie Allan biker fuzz, throws it in the blender with some trance-like dub rhythms – and pow – get out the fire extinguisher! We're all too familiar with acts that dutifully ape one genre or another, but The Hypnomen raid the best from five decades of bizarro culture and graft it onto a totally contemporary context. When was the last time you could take one disc to a disco, garage party, and martini ho-down and have all three crowds dance!?!?

They formed in 1994, and have at least four more albums and a slew of 45s available.

---

*NOTE: Remember to read the original 1995 book and the other book update chapters for thousands of other bands and records not featured in this update section.*

---

## LES INCAPABLES (MONTREAL, CANADA)

The "1234 Succes" EP is on Teen Sound from 1997 is a twangy, crudely-recorded effort, showcasing a spirited cover of "Jezebel."

## THE INCREDIBLE STAGGERS (AUSTRIA)
(Also known as The Staggers)

One significant development since the 1995 version of this book is the much larger number of professional garage bands. By professional I mean very dedicated, rehearsed, well-equipped and talented bands writing original songs and also touring the globe over a period of years. While without major label backing, these bands have major talent, and can hold their own on any stage, with any band.

There were only a handful of these bands in the 1980s, and many more today – and The Incredible Staggers is a prime example. They released a slew of at least eight 45s and EPs, starting in 2004, and also the 2006 "Teenage Trash Insanity" album (on Soundflat) and the 2010 "Zombies of Love" album (on Wohnzimmer) – along with lots of gigging and touring (one report claims they have played more than 500 shows).

A record label at any level, especially the small garage indie – loves a band that actually goes out on the road, building fans across the globe. Add in a cool visual style and some very effective music videos – their 2007 "Little Sister" is everything a garage band could hope for – and you have a garage band monster called The Staggers.

Many "Pick Hits" here to choose from, but I'll point out "Be My Queen" for special consideration. The Incredible Staggers are another entry on your "Must Hear" garage bands list, kids.

## THE INDIKATION (NORWAY )

The original 1960s U.K. styled Freakbeat pop sounds rarely sounded as good as The Indikation on their 2004 "In Terms of" LP (on Teen Sound). Under the exactly appropriate analog production style of Toe Rag Studios (in London, of course), The Indikation sound late-1966 perfect. There are tinges of mid-period Kinks, Mod and all the best melodic U.K. pop. The Zombies are the perfect band for them to cover, and their version of "What More Can I Do" is both an homage and a manifesto of The Indikation's own great abilities. The smooth, sweet vocal mix also sets The Indikation apart from the pack. This is quite a stunning a debut, and I was surprised to find only three other 7-inchers available, all prior to the LP. "In Terms Of" will remain in my Top-10 for the 2000s. It is Essential, with a capital "E."

## THE INSECT (PLAINS, OH, U.S.A.)

These Buckeye-state lads take a less purist approach for their 1998 garage anthems on their 360 Twist album "The Detroit Sessions" (recorded by legendary producer Jim Diamond). The Ohio combo used the requisite Rickenbacker and Vox gear, but jumble it all up for their own distinct, lo-fi mess. (First-time readers take note: these are compliments.) One nod to their 1960s grandfathers is the wonderfully sloppy cover of The Dantes' "Can't Get Enough of Your Love." It's always good for a new generation to pay homage to bands that worked the same streets they do now; the near-legendary Columbus, Ohio group The Dantes is worthy of such respect. (Yes, I grew up in Columbus, Ohio. Go Buckeyes!)

## THE INSECT SURFERS (LOS ANGELES, CA, U.S.A.)

The "East West" 10" vinyl (1994 on Dionysus) is a fine example of blending traditional surf-hot rod instrumentals with a more modern recording approach. A couple "live" cuts show that these boys could shred in person, too.

## THE INVISIBLE MEN (LOS ANGELES, CA, U.S.A.)
(Also referred to sometimes as "The Legendary Invisible Men")

Including some members of The Bomboras, these costumed lads operate in a similar vein to the great toilet-paper-clad Mummies, though with a decidedly higher-fi recording.

The instant energy and infectious zing of this classic garage style reminds me just how timeless the Farfisa-Fuzz-Fun combination really is. "Who's Sorry Now?" (2000, on Blood Red) is pure modern West Coast garage. The halfway rip from Love's "Little Red Book" riff in "Journey" made me laugh out loud. As it should.

And what's this? The Men unmask themselves for the 2001 follow-up "Come Get Some" album on Dionysus. The '66 edge is a bit less "legendary" than on the debut, but some nice organ touches keep the band at least in the driveway of the garage. Pick hit: "Solidarity," a fine and punchy garage anthem.

There's also a 1996 four-song 7" EP on Dionysus, with a fine wrestling Elvis on the cover.

# J

## THEE JENERATORS (U.K.)

I have long had admiration for Twist Records honcho Mark Le Gallez. He somehow (with a lot of work and sweat is how) managed to release a slew of fine Mod-garage-pop records since the 1995 "Knights of Fuzz" book, all while headquartered on Guernsey, an island off of Normandy that is closer to France than the U.K. He has made so many other cool bands available that it can be easy to overlook his own worthy musical contributions, including Thee Jenerators.

A fine Mod groove permeates 2008's "The Kids Are Not Alright," kicking off with the cheeky "Who The Hell Is Frank Wilson." Nice horn work accentuates the clean production,

and a confident delivery shows that these are veterans who know their stuff.

The 2009 "Inside Outside" features a more polished vocal approach and a somewhat more guitar-oriented style that will satisfy the garage-oriented folks here. Some excellent horn work returns, though, and "Time" is a Mod showcase that is guaranteed to make you jump to your feet.

Thee Jenerators remind me that a band can ape a musical style because it is popular at that very moment – but only the truly dedicated can make records like these that ooze authenticity, passion and the joy of performing music. Oh, there are several other discs out there for you to find, too. You see, Mark Le Gallaz has a lot to say, and he's not waiting for someone else to say it for him.

## JEREMY (PORTAGE, MI, U.S.A.)

Jeremy Morris is one of those few fellows who make his love of making pop music more than a hobby – it's his obsession, his purpose, his calling. He's the honcho who runs Jam Records, which features modern power-pop acts (like his), and contributes also to the fine Lemon Clocks, described elsewhere.

The "Journey To The Center Of The Heart" (2009 on Jam Records) has a more traditional pop style to it (and with much shorter songs) than his subsequent work. It's jangle guitars and sweet vocals throughout, with a refined power-pop sensibility that reminded me a bit of The Knack on a track such as "Sweet, Sweet, Relief."

"From The Dust To The Stars" (2012 on Mals, a Russian label) continues this genre-stretching journey, with complex arrangements and a fearless approach to aural exploration. Pick Hit: "The Good Shepherd."

His "Searching For The Son" album (2013 on Mals) showcases Jeremy's trademark vocal layering and a thick, trippy production. These tracks stretch out – the shortest here in four minutes long – and twist and turn like a dream's soundtrack. I especially appreciate that while Jeremy's inspiration is obviously in the mid 1960s psych-pop sound we all love so much, it is also firmly planted in modern arrangements and recording techniques. No, this is not purist material, but for those who can stretch their perceptions of genre then there is much here for delight. The 11-minute opus "Wings Of The Wind" is a prime example, as it twists and bends through multiple styles and moods in a continuous groove.

There's also the 2014 "All Over The World" album billed to "The Jeremy Band." If you are more interested in how your psych music sounds than how the guys on the cover look, then Jeremy's output is for you. And for me.

## THE JUNIPERS (LEICESTER, U.K.)

The "Paint The Ground" album, originally released in 2012 and re-issued on vinyl by Sugarbush, is an elegant delight. It is sunshine harmonies throughout, jangly acoustic guitars and a quiet folk-pop-psych feel. "Willow and The Water Mill" is simply gorgeous, as is "Antler Season" and, well, there's no use in picking out highlights because this is one totally accomplished whole.

If the Byrds' harmonies on "Dolphin Smile" give you chills (like it does for me), then you'll get a similar endorphin rush hearing The Junipers' "They Lived Up In The Valley."

There is also a previous album, "Cut Your Key" and a 2013 four-song EP that might be download-only. It continues the Junipers' sweet-as-a-peach sound. Count me in, boys.

# K

## THE KAISERS (SCOTLAND, U.K.)

The "Squarehead Stomp!" LP was originally released in Britain in 1993, and Get Hip brought it to the Yankee shores in 1997. Recorded in one day at my favorite studio (which I haven't recorded in), Toe Rag, I don't have to tell you how lovingly crude it is, do I? The 2002 "Shake Me" album (also on Get Hip) continues the 1963-styled U.K. beat obsession, sounding very much like a fine opening act for The Beatles at the Cavern Club. If you love the original U.K. beat sound, then The Kaisers are essential.

The 1999 "Twist With The Kaisers" is a "live" vinyl album, recorded in Bloomington, Indiana of all places!

I asked Toe Rag Studios head-honcho Liam Watson (in an e-mail) about his approach to recording bands like this, which deserve authentic vintage analog production techniques. He responded to my e-mail – but said he would not answer questions for this book. That simply reminds me to make sure that I take the time for the next garage guy or gal who writes to me and asks for my help.

## KAROVAS MILKSHAKE (RUSSIA)

The 2013 "Freak Out" b/w "Factory" 45 is limited to 300 copies and is on Chickpea Records. It is psych-pop of the highest order, with a thorough U.K. 1967 Freakbeat sound, full of hooks, tremolo and style. There is also the more-basic sounding 2010 four-song "Low-Cow-Motion" EP, though it appears to be a digital download release only.

The future looks very bright for Karovas Milkshake, so remember to pour some more my way, boys!

## DE KEEMEN (SOUTHERN DRENTHE, HOLLAND)

Five 45s and two albums were created from 2009-2014, as the band formed from the remainder of the Miracle Men (see their entry elsewhere in this book).

I've heard "I Need Help" from their "Mirror Of Time" album (2010 on Dirty Water) and it is a blistering Nederbeat number, surely in the fine tradition of Q65 and other Dutch originals.

## THE KING MIXERS (TORONTO, CANADA)

It's Pavlovian, I know, but I just have to crack open a cold beer whenever I hear a band like The King Mixers. It's that unpretentious sound that invites me to tap my toes and swing my head from side to side, a wide smile stopping just long enough for another swig of delicious brew.

The Toronto trio's three-song 1998 debut 7" is a rave-up, revved-up, pop-garage treat, and I bet beer sales soared whenever they took the stage.

## THE KNACK (LOS ANGELES, CA, U.S.A.)

No, I won't re-hash the very popular history of these New Wave pop kings, but instead I tip my hat for their stellar 1998 "Zoom" album on Rhino. Long after their mainstream commercial life was over, The Knack was obviously playing music for all the right reasons: because they love pop songs. Rickenbacker, harmony and an obvious nod to the Beatles is saturated throughout, making "Zoom" a most surprising and satisfying power-pop comeback. "Can I Borrow A Kiss" and "Mister Magazine" are two of the band's best-ever tracks, and "Zoom" deserves a listen by even the most jaded garage fan who might want to dismiss the Knack as mere marketing hype. Miss this album at your own risk!

## THE KNYGHTS OF FUZZ (ALBANY, NY, U.S.A.)

Albany music veteran Brian Goodman told me his new combo took their name as a tip of their hat to this book – the kindest compliment a fellow musician could give me, to be sure. But their band name is also appropriate, since the Knyghts of Fuzz pay tribute to garage rock in general with their authentic '60s sounds.

A 2012 split-45 (with the punk band Bourbon Scum on the flip) on Carlton Records features beautiful yellow vinyl and two Knyghts songs: the grinding, chiming "Genny," which reminds me of a Mystic Eyes classic and surely could help to inspire the next generation of upstate New York garage bands. Their second song, the wonderfully titled "Fleshtones Saved My Life" explains how inspirational garage rock can be to those who open their ears and hearts.

The 2011 "U.G.L.Y." b/w "Let It Go" 45 (also on Carlton) is another slice of crazed garage energy. I salute these Knyghts of Fuzz and their crusade to keep the sound alive, one chord at a time.

## THE KUMARI (U.K.)

The Kumari formed in early 2012 with Alex Felstead on drums and Benjamin Craven on guitar (from the band Speak and The Spells), Claude Pelletier of The Vinyl Stitches (on vocals and guitar) and Phil Istine, known from the "Happening" club and Shindig! Magazine.

The 2013 debut three-song EP on Heavy Soul also features the Kumari's signature chiming guitar sound, and some wonderful vocals throughout. I especially like the cover of "Don't You Dare," with a warm, elegant production that seems like the tapes came out of a studio in mid-1966.

The follow-up four-song "Watching You" EP is on Lost in Tyme Records (Greece, 2013). "Watching You" is a fine, moody jangle-fest, with a touch of fuzz and a cool, retrained vibe throughout. It reminds me a bit of the Lemon Drops' "I Live In The Springtime" fuzztone, and that's a high compliment, indeed.

A 2014 three-song 7" is also on Hey Girl Records out of Spain, and for me The Kumari are a band to keep close tabs on, because I'm guessing they have some major jangle yet to share.

## THE KWYET KINGS (UPDATE)

Two releases on Dionysus are worthy additions: the 1999 "Been Where" Done What?" is satisfying power pop with the accent on the power, full of sparkling guitars and driving beat. So refreshing to hear an indie band recorded oh so well, too! If you enjoy the sunshine pop of The Someloves or DM3, then this LP will fit right on for you. The 2000 "Singles 'n' Shit" compiles other previous releases (there are many singles out there, including the 1995 "Somebody Like You" b/w "Still Searching" 45 on 1+2 Records in Japan) and is satisfying as a collection, too. I haven't heard the 1995 "Cherrypie" album (on Screaming Apple), but it must be great. It just has to be.

# L

## LANA LOVELAND (GERMANY)

The fine keyboardist from the 2010s German line-up of the Fuzztones struck out on her own (while remaining in the 'Tones) with the "Order To Love" album (2011 on Groovie and also Bellaphon), and it begins appropriately with her Vox-like organ. The album sounds very much like the Fuzztones with a female vocalist, and that's not a complaint. It is expertly arranged and performed, though Lana's vocal approach takes a little getting-used to. Pick Hit: "Bandit," with some nice Iron Butterfly-like guitar fuzz. There's also a 2010 7" on Butterfly.

## THE LAST (UPDATE)

Bomp rereleased the absolutely seminal and classic 1979 "L.A. Explosion" album on CD in 2003. Their follow-up 1980 "Look Again" album shows a natural and worthy progression for the band and deserves to be heard – though it became with time difficult for the band to escape the reputation of their monumental debut.

## LAUGHING SKY (NEW YORK, NY, U.S.A.)

Dino Sorbello is another of those prized individuals I like to call **True Believers**." He helped create some of the U.S. East Coast's best neo-psych-garage with the Mad Violets, then the Blacklight Chameleons – and then with his powerful trio Laughing Sky.

The "Free Inside" album (1999 on Bomp, 2005 on Tripwave) shows that he hasn't stood still, either. The songs are trippier, longer, more blistering and oh, so psychedelic. This isn't fashion-posing-psych, this is guitar psych of the, um, **highest** order. The original songs sizzle, and the cover songs are inspired: "Lucifer Sam" sounds like it was teleported from Syd Barrett's brain, now orbiting somewhere off of Saturn. The modern approach to "Tomorrow Never Knows" also breathes life into what would simply be a jam in lesser hands. Bless Dino Sorbello and his psychedelic visions. They are real.

The 2012 "Divine" album follow-up continues Sorbello's distinctly unique trip, and it takes but a moment to recognize his signature guitar tone on the "Electric Circus" opener. I think it is a special compliment to a guitarist to recognize his style just after a few notes, and Dino Sorbello's garage-psych mastery on guitar always makes the hair on my back stand up and take notice. His work is seriously blistering on the album title track, and then shows restraint and range on the mesmerizingly beautiful "Hyperswirl," as apt a song title as I'll find in this book.

Both sides of the "Arms of the Sun" b/w "Take It" 45 (self-released in 2012) are on the 1996 CD, though these vinyl versions are new recordings.

## THE LAZY SUNDAYS ( SPAIN)

The "A Shade In The Light" b/w "Gong With The Luminous Nose" was on Subterfuge Records in 1996. The B-side was not on their "The Texture And The Flavour" album.

## THE LEARS (UPDATE)

One of the Misty Lane label's 1997 missionary projects was to help Florida's finest folk-rockers, The Lears. This on-again, off-again outfit squeaked out a few 45s on other European labels – teasing us with their Rickenbacker sweetness and addled '66 psych energy – and deliver more delightful racket with the "Her Magic Smile" and "Don't You Know" single. The folk-rock side of the global garage equation has been sadly missing for the most part, and The Lears do their finest at filling the void.

My eyes also light up at the sight of any new Lears disc, and "The Story So Far" CD on Get Hip was instantly in my "Top 5 Best Albums of 1998" list.

The Lears were one of the few bands which understood the beauty of Rickenbacker-fed folk rock, and the 14 tracks here are a stunning extension of the best that genre has to offer. Almost half of the album is from earlier, hard to find 45s and EPs, dating from 1989-1994. The other half is made up of unreleased tracks that push my estimation of the band from merely great...to deliciously fabulous.

Imagine The Byrds trapped in a garage (with a car running and the doors closed), and you can start to appreciate The Lears' own folkadelia. And it's been far too long since I saw/heard an album with a song titled "Electric Mushroom Voyage."

## THE LEMON CLOCKS (SWEDEN & U.S.A.)

This book is jammed with thousands of worthy garage greats who mine endlessly the wonderful world of fuzzy three-chord bliss. I love them all. But I also have great respect for the very few bands of the revival era which have the musical prowess and developed sensibility to offer new explorations in the pop side of psych-garage. Ah, bless The Lemon Clocks!

The Lemon Clocks are a bi-continental creation, with band members in both Sweden and the U.S., combining their talents for one of the most distinctive sounds I've heard in many years. There is equal respect for both the jangle and the power of trippyness within the Lemon Clocks, as the eight-minute "Rainbow Bridge" depicts. But don't mistake these cats for some droning jam band – the songs are all tightly arranged, expertly performed and well recorded pop gems.

Jeremy Morris (who also has a fine line of his own bright sunshine pop releases available as "Jeremy") layers his lush vocals throughout, and Stefan Johansson adds in everything from guitar to drums and bass (along with third member Todd Borsch). There are so many highlights on their debut "Now Is The Time" album (on Jam), with the shimmering "Life Is Like A Dream" delivered as if "Pictures Of Matchstick Men" was played by Oasis. So the balance of original '60s inspiration and modern pop sensibility is intact, and makes for the tastiest of original compositions.

I love the sound of a Rickenbacker 12-srting guitar so much I could listen to it tuning up all day (a bit of an in-joke for those who have spent time tuning one up), and when The Lemon Clocks is chiming away they remind me a lot of Sweden's fine jangle-masters The Rhinos. "The Man Who Lost The Time" is one of those ringing tunes that you'll be humming long after first listen. Another Pick Hit: The sunshine jangle of "The Bright Side."

This is as fine a debut as any band could ever promise, and a second album is in the works as of 2014. I'll set my alarm and wait for it.

## LEMMUS LEMMUS (ISRAEL)

The band's self-titled 2008 album is a quiet, subdued folk-psych affair, with some sitar augmenting the acoustic feel. The songs take their time, are meditative, carefully arranged and also feature nice backward guitar, sometimes erupting into dynamic louder compositions. This album is perfect for a rainy day, looking out a window, slowly chewing on a mushroom or two. Highly recommended.

There is also a similar 2004 "Chameleon Mood Swing" album.

## THE LET DOWNS (SAN DIEGO, CA, U.S.A.)

The 1997 "Atlanta" b/w "Flash & Crash" 44 on 360 Twist is a two-sided garage winner. The practice-room-styled recordings are just good enough to capture the bursting garage energy, and you can almost see the beer cans vibrating on top of the amps as the band blasts through their numbers. Thank you, garage rock. Thank you.

## LIGHT BULB ALLEY
(*See the "Guest Authors" chapter for more information.*)

## LINK PROTRUDI AND THE JAYMEN
(UPDATE)

As with the Fuzztones, even the most rabid record collector such as me can be utterly frustrated when attempting to find and hear all of his side-band The Jaymen. Frontman Rudi Protrudi continues to seemingly release records almost constantly – and let's just say there is more out there to find, including "Drive It Live" (1992), "Hashish" and the wonderfully-titled "Naked Crisco Twister Party," the last two in limited CD-R quantities on the self-released Sin Records.

A limited 300-pressing 45 on Skoda Records, featuring members of the Acetones, is an excellent live recording, showing the band's serious musical muscle.

## THE LINKERS (UPDATE)

Across the pond, The Linkers steadily became one of Europe's hottest garage combos in the late 1990s; and their 7" "Outer Limits" EP (1998), is a fab effort. Plenty of Farfisa and grit, plus solid songs, make this a must-have. They also have a cut on a 200-copy four-song split EP with the Slow Slushy Boys, Sidewalk Stroll and The Brambles from 1995.

The 200-copy album "Dusty Memory Lane" was issued in 1999 (on Time Warp).

## LIQUID GENERATION (UPDATE)

An entire 80 minutes of recordings have accumulated, in addition to the 1985 single described in the original book, though no release of the compilation has occurred yet. Here is the band's more complete history, written by guitarist Bob Blackburn:

"Liquid Generation was a Seattle, Washington based 'neo-psych' band that existed in 1984. Formed originally by Randy 'Rubato' Nash (drums), along with John Branin (lead guitar) and then 17-year-old Jeremy Meyer (singer).In late 1983 they recorded a version of 'Little Girl' by The Syndicate of Sound, and I (Bob Blackburn) joined on rhythm guitar and organ. I had played bass previously with Seattle's The Colorplates from 1979-1982 and released my own solo 45 in 1983, 'Bombsights Over Amerika' b/w 'Black Leather.'

I also brought in roommate John Conrard to play bass. Drawing initially on more obscure 'Nuggets' style songs the band developed a set list that included gems from The Remains, The Chob, the Ugly Ducklings, The Choir and more plus B-sides by The Kinks, The Troggs, Them and Northwest bands like The Wailers, Don & The Goodtimes, and more. We felt a strong link to the classic bands of the Pacific Northwest and were proud to expose local audiences to some of those songs which for many had been forgotten or lost.

We played a handful of shows at local rental halls and punk venues like The Grey Door. Green Monkey Records released our only single in 1985, the year after we broke up, 'I Love You' b/w '1/4 To Zen.' We etched into the run-off wax on the 'A' side, 'To Brian Jones' and on the 'B' side, 'Save The Sixties.' We re-formed for a one-off 25th reunion show in Seattle in 2009 for the release of the Green Monkey Records two-CD anthology titled 'It Crawled From The Basement,' which included our song 'I Love You.'"

## THE LIQUID SOUND COMPANY
### (ARLINGTON, TX, U.S.A.)

The 1997 debut CD, "Exploring The Psychedelic," is one of the heaviest, freakiest, trippiest blurtings of the 1990s. Pink Floyd meets Hendrix at a happy hour booze-a-thon with Spacemen 3 manning the mixing board – how's that for a thumbnail view? This stuff is truly demented, alternating between four and 10 minute-plus excursions into an acid freak-out. Not for the faint of heart, and obviously even more impressive while floating outside of your body, naked, covered in chocolate syrup. I've done it – believe me, it's fun.

The 2002 "Inside The Acid Temple" brings us another heavy dose (on Swamp Room). It seems appropriate for this to be on a German label, since they seem to understand and appreciate the heavier side of psych. While for most of the releases in this book I use the term "psych" to mean more of a pop-song tradition, The Liquid Sound Company is psychedelic in the more traditional 1960s heavy sense. The eight-minute

"The League For Spiritual Discover Lives" clues you into their approach – take your time, create a mood to envelop the listener, then add enough blistering fuzz guitar to poke holes in the universe. Now, c'mon, kids – you do understand that these are compliments of the highest order from me, right?

There is also a 2011 EP titled "Acid Music For Acid People." I bet you can't figure out what that sounds like.

## THE LIVING ROOM (GERMANY)

A short-lived acid-psych sextet that had one private limited edition vinyl release in 1997 titled "Chambers." I've heard "Rising Dawn" and it is seriously swirling and authentic 1960s psych, with a soaring Syd Barrett-era-Pink Floyd-in San Francisco feel. "Just A Little Song" has a lilting female vocal and some nice sitar, too, in an intoxicating folk-psych stew.

It looks like there is a more recent CD album titled "Time Like Lakes" that includes these songs, but I'm not sure if the 1997 release is also included.

## THE LIVINGSTONES (SWEDEN)

I don't know how I missed the 1987 "Fastest Car Around" b/w "You're Not A Better Man Than I" 45 (on Sunlight Records) the first time around for this book. The A-side is a primo 1965 Sunset Strip-like hot rod burner, and the flip an angst-ridden teenage jangler, and together they form yet another primo slab form the Swedish garage. Bless you, my Swedish friends!

## LOBOS NEGROS (SPAIN)

They look like Spain's toughest rockabilly ho-dads – and there's nothing wrong with that – but Lobos Negros create a racket closer to the Ventures than Gene Vincent. Their 1997 "Instrumentales" CD (on Fiebre) is just that, 18 slabs of pure instrumental fun, with meaty, muscular arrangements and a startling number of fine original songs. Many of the current instro freaks lean too heavily on regurgitating the old masters, but Lobos Negros can stand on their own. Yip, yip, ahooo! There are also many other releases, stretching from 1987 through at least 2013.

## THE LONG RYDERS (UPDATE)

The band re-formed in the 2000s for some shows, and a 40-song, two-CD retrospective was issued in 1998 (on PolyGram). If you missed all the original 1980s vinyl, then this is a handy collection, documenting their brilliant debut and then slow evolution to a much less-interesting country-rock act. That first EP and debut album, though, will remain ranked right up there at the top, though.

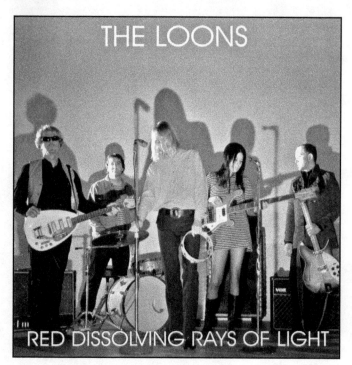

THE LOONS
RED DISSOLVING RAYS OF LIGHT

## THE LOONS (SAN DIEGO, CA, U.S.A.)

Few have the long-standing history in the neo-garage era of Mike Stax, who has contributed to the growth of the scene through his fine bands (Tell-Tale Hearts, The Hoods, and more) and through his seminal 1960s fanzine Ugly Things. In many ways he is a "garage-rock elephant" – learning and storing all the knowledge of generations, like a pachyderm, and then passing that on to others down through the years.

The Loons are his longest-running musical outfit, forming in 1995 and releasing three albums and a half dozen 7"s, in sporadic bursts, over the years.

1999's "Love's Dead Leaves" (on Get Hip) has more of a Mod and pop feel than Stax's previous output, but with plenty of his love of R&B for balance. He's joined by fellow-former Tell-Tale Heart Eric Bacher for some fine guitar work, too. Pick Hits: the gentle '65-'66 slightly-Stones feel of "Thursday's Child" and "Flying Up Into The Floor."

Bacher was gone by the second album, and Stax's wife Anja, (formerly of the excellent Diaboliks) picked up bass duties for 2004's "Paraphernalia" (on their own UT label). I especially dig the teen-folk-rock chime feel of "Follow The Rain Down." There's high energy and some nice harmonica accents on "Turned To Stone," and some sweet fuzz and a cool vibe on "The Search." A 10-minute-plus "Another Life" is the closer, and by far is the most overtly psych item for the band, feeling a bit like a pop-Seeds freak-out. All together, I think this follow-up has more individual character than their debut.

The 2010 "Red Dissolving Rays Of Light" album found The Loons on the venerable Bomp! label, with a less-obvious '60s feel and more of a power-pop vibe. The title track is a nice, grooving rocker, "Stowaway" also delivers plenty of hooks, and "The Losers Win" is a fine album closer.

The band is still blasting strong as of this writing.

## LOVE ME NOTS (PHOENIX, AZ, U.S.A.)

I first came upon the very slick Love Me Nots just as my "Knights of Fuzz" DVD was released in 2006. I liked their live show so much that I would have invited them to be on the DVD if I had known about the band sooner. They mine a very professional style of gutsy '66 garage, with some tasty Cramps and New Wave flourishes as well. Their very measured commercial approach could be a turn-off to fans who like their garage a bit more spontaneous. There are several albums out, and as of 2014 they were still performing.

## THE LYRES (UPDATE)

Jeff Conolly's Lyres seem to rival Billy Childish in the realm of proficiency – both seemed to release a 45 every other week in the 1990s. Besides driving collectors crazy, Conolly and company make sure each of these vinyl slabs are essential tastes of garage-punk-pop delight. Norton Records has established itself as one of the most consistently quality-conscious indie labels over the past decades, and on "Those Lyres" they thankfully collect six Lyres 45s onto one 1995 CD, with 14 1993 "live" concert tracks as a bonus. The 45 tracks are mostly pure genius, with Conolly's take on the obscure "Baby It's Me" summoning a particularly potent spine tingle. Was garage music ever supposed to be this good?

Conolly still performs in the U.S. and Europe as The Lyres, with make-shift lineups, including the Sick Rose as his back-up band on one European jaunt.

---

*NOTE: Remember to read the original 1995 book and the other book update chapters for thousands of other bands and records not featured in this update section.*

---

## LA MACCHINA DEL TIEMPO
(The Time Machine) (ITALY)

The 1993 "Non Ti Votero' Ma!!!" four-song EP on Destination X is a blistering slab of garage, with a fab cover of "Aint No Friend Of Mine" and also Max Frost & The Troopers' "Shape Of Things To Come," which made me instinctively sing along. The flip has two originals, and they are full of spit and vinegar, all sung in Italian, with loads of energy and attitude to spare. Brava!

## THE MAD VIOLETS (UPDATE)

NYC's Mad Violets remain one of my favorite of the original wave of neo-garagers – their "Psilocybe" on the 1984 "Battle

Of The Garages Vol. 2 " compilation remains in my all-time Top 10 – but a collection of their earliest (and best) work was never released until the "Season Of" CD in 2003 on the band's own Tripwave label. Yes, "Psilocybe" is there, along with unreleased gems such as "Quetzalcoatl" and the "Mad Violet Theme." The Mad Violets deserve to be held in the highest esteem, and this compilation should be found immediately if you want to understand that colorful initial blush that helped launch the garage-psych movement discussed in this book.

The colorful Wendy Wild – the heart and soul (and vocalist) of the group – died in 1996 from cancer.

## MAGGIE'S MARSHMALLOWS
(PRAGUE, CZECH REPUBLIC)

I've only heard the magnificent 2014 fuzzer "Come Along" from this trio, full of buzz and some distorted vocals along with a killer hypnotic guitar riff. For obvious reasons I am partial to bands with the word "marshmallow" in their title, especially those that spell the word correctly. Once again, dear friends, there is no "e" in Marshmallow!

## THE MAGGOTS (SWEDEN)

Swedish garage royalty is all over The Maggots history, with former members of the Crimson Shadows and the Wylde Mammoths at various stages. The Maggots sound on "Get Hooked" (on Low Impact) is no less frenetic, or full of fury, and even won a Swedish record industry award for best indie release of 2001. It is 100-miles-an-hour garage fun from start to finish. I especially love the Bo-Diddley feel on "Five Finger Shuffle." If there was a purity sticker on this album it would read "100% meat, no filler!" There are at least two more albums and 45s out there in garage-land (including a four-song 7" EP on Low Impact). (**NOTE:** This band is not the 1980 punk group with a recently re-issued 45, or any of the other many Maggots-named bands around through the years. Damn all those other maggots!)

## THE MAGNETIC MIND (LONDON, U.K.)

The "Maybe The Stars" b/w "Laser Fingers" 45 (2012 on Heavy Soul) is a stellar debut of gentle psych-folk-pop, full of heavenly harmony, melody and a tight, driving arrangement. They are certainly evocative of a San Francisco 1967 act, but with a pop sensibility and energy all its own.

The 2014 "When The Morning Comes" continues the U.S. West Coast-like journey, with some fuzz added in. The band's cover of Love's "Alone Again Or" takes a couple listens to appreciate how they de-constructed it for their own interpretation. I think it's rather groovy.

It takes a great deal at this late date to get me excited about a new band. I am excited about The Magnetic Mind!

## THE MAHARAJAS (SWEDEN)

Also on Teen Sound comes a 10" from The Maharajas. The eight-song mono slab features all four band member tongues firmly in cheek, but also some infectious garage grooves. They returned, with an altered lineup, in 2001, with the "H-Minor" LP on Teen Sound. The Maharajas displayed a seasoned, mature Euro-beat-pop command on the long-player, with an exceptional vocal blend of Jens Lindberg and Mathias Lilja. The song-crafting and performance is so authentic that the "H-Minor" album certainly would have gone down in history as one of the finest Eurobeat albums of 1965 or 1966 – if it had actually been recorded then.

There are also 2004, 2005 and 2007 albums all out on Low Impact, plus at least four 45s on Loser, Chaputa and Crusher Records. A new album is slated to appear in late 2014 on Low Impact – and perhaps a two-album "best of" collection, too.

Obviously I will have a lot more essential sounds to include in the next book update!

## THEE MAKEOUT PARTY (ANAHIEM, CA, U.S.A.)

Sean Bohrman and Lee Rickard, the head honchos of the currently ultra-hip Burger Records, are behind this guitar power-pop SoCal party, starting up in 2001. The "Play Pretend" album saw the light of day in 2008, plus a 45 on their own Burger and a couple other slabs of vinyl and compilations. "Resonars Love" is a fine tribute to the great Tucson power pop act The Resonars (which is also on Burger), and dig the smirk about bubblegum songs in "Dreams" and the Love-vibe in "Listen" – both from a six song set titled "The Lost Album" which I don't think has seen actual release.

## THE MALARIANS
(NORTHAMPTON, MA, U.S.A.)

Originally active 1984-1990, The Malarians reformed in 2010. The 2010 CD on Chunk Archives is a compilation of the 1988 "Know" EP and the "live" 1989 "Finished In This Town" album. It starts with a fine cover of the manic, addled "Good Times," and the moody "Once Upon A Time (In Your Mind)" is an original highlight. There is a nasty, almost-out-of control feel here that is always welcome in good garage music. It sounds both together and solid, and also like it could spin out of control at any moment. Ah, yes, that's good rock and roll, my friends!

Their version of "What's New, Pussycat" sounds like a circus band on LSD, all on unicycles, racing down a mountain, while being chased by tigers. Consider that my highest recommendation.

The "live" portion of the album is well-recorded, and the playful, energetic and twisted delivery confirms that the studio tracks captured the spirit of the band. This isn't purist '66 garage, but it sure is real garage music, if that makes sense.

There is also the 1986 album "In The Cool Room." As of this writing, band leader Mal Thursday hosts a variety of essential garage rock audio radio shows and podcasts.

## MAN OR ASTROMAN (UPDATE)

These lads toured the universe several times since the 1995 book was issued, and released a slew of other releases, too. The only one I found in my massive stack was the 1995 "What Remains Inside A Black Hole" (on Au Go Go). It is another fine venture into their surf-and-movie sci-fi alternative world. There are as many as 10 more albums, lots of 45s, and numerous compilation appearances out there in outer space, too. Now go find them!

## MANDRAGORA LIGHTSHOW SOCIETY
(BERLIN, GERMANY)

We're back in the realm of real psychedelia here, German style. That means the sound is dark and not afraid to stretch out past three minute pop standards into the netherworld. The two-CD "The Mindexpanding Triprock Compilation" (1997, on Patina) is exactly that – a collection of previous releases packed into one massive wallop of modern psychedelia.

This is as opposite the vibe as you can get from the three-chord Pebbles-covering garage bands that grace so much of this book – and that's OK with me. There's plenty of room in my paisley music room to sit back and sink into the world of the Manda Lightshow Society. The 1999 "Beyond The Mushroom Gate" (on Liquid Sound) continues the eclectic, eccentric trip, stretching out past the usual genre trappings even further into modern psychedelia. I tip my hat to the nine-minute opus "Magic Rushroom," (yes you read that correctly). There is also a 10" vinyl picture disc (2001 on Swamp Room). Shine on, you crazy diamonds!

## MANUAL SCAN (UPDATE)

The 1997 21-song best-of (on Get Hip) is the definition of essential, and includes a complete band history in the CD booklet that beats anything I can add here. Was Manual Scan the most important Mod band in the U.S.A. in the 1980s? Yep.

## MARK & THE SPIES (HOLLAND)

Do you remember that instant when a new song comes through your speakers and after just a few seconds you realize it is one of the best you've ever heard? Do you know that excitement and surprise when discovering a new gem that will soon be a garage classic? Yep, that's the thrill I had the first time I heard Mark & The Spies' 2007 four-song 7" EP on Butterfly Records.

The opening "Everything I Need" is certainly one of the top pop-oriented tracks I've heard in the neo-garage era, and it sits along side some of my favorite original '60s tracks. Imagine the sweet vocal harmonies of the Everly Brothers superimposed on a revved-up power-pop Easybeats, and the appeal of Mark & The Spies should be obvious.

There are at least two albums (2007 and 2009) on Screaming Apple and at least three more 45s – so obviously there are a lot more thrills for me to go out and discover.

## MARSHMALLOW OVERCOAT (UPDATE)

It is now another 20 years later and I've written another half-million words about other garage bands. And so, as I write this last entry for the updated "Knights of Fuzz" book your humble author will add a few words about my own band, The Marshmallow Overcoat.

And like before, what I have to say is as much about all the other garage bands in this book as it is about my own experiences. You see, I have lived all the good and bad that every other band in this book has experienced. I know the joy of bonding musically with other musicians – for a brief time they are your brothers – and then becoming one with an audience. I know the hard work it takes to write and record songs and then somehow get them released. *Somehow!*

I know the satisfaction of seeing friends help in our struggle, and the sadness of realizing how many simply watch and enjoy our struggle. I've been drunk and happy after giving encores to wildly enthusiastic crowds – and I've been on stage when there was not a soul in the building who wanted to hear my songs.

"No, we will **NOT** play 'Free Bird!' I have yelled. "Here's one from The Music Machine!"

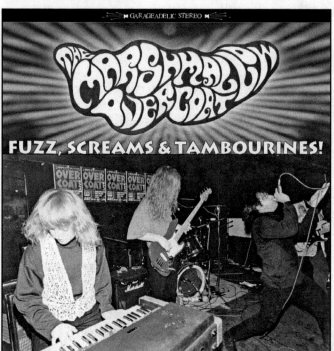

I am one of you, garage brothers and sisters. I have seen it all. And it is glorious. It is rock and roll, the giver of pleasure and pain – the ultimate proof that we are still alive – and the undeniable proof that we all die too soon.

And now the statistics: The Marshmallow Overcoat re-formed in 2001, and we made it all the way to our 25th anniversary in 2011. Most rock bands aren't meant to survive one year, so that milestone is one that seems remarkable, especially to me.

Along the way we completed the 2002 "Psilocybic Mind" EP, the vinyl reissue of the live "Fuzz, Screams & Tambourines!" LP (both on Psych Out), the "Fly Away" b/w ""(Can't Stop) Thee Hands Of Tyme" 45 on Sound Effect in Greece, and a two-disc 2005 "best-of" titled "26 Ghosts" (on Dionysus). That one had an audio CD and then a video DVD, too.

In 2008 we released the "Light Show" album (CD only) and then a fan-only limited CD with new sessions that I thought was the band's swan song. But we soldiered on to our 25th anniversary, and I was delighted that in 2014 the two-album vinyl collection "The Very Best Of" saw release. Oh, all of those releases didn't just happen – they were the product of so much blood, sweat, and especially tears.

Imagine starting the band you always wanted to be in, and then somehow guiding them through 25 years of making the sounds you love, and then seeing it condensed into a double-album that we hope will survive the ages.

Yes, indeed, I have seen it all. And yes, my dear comrades, for those of you who can understand this – *it is glorious.*

## LOS MARTES (SPAIN)

I have heard a cool late 1990s demo tape. Yes I have.

## THEE MARTIAN BOYFRIENDS (BELGIUM)

The self-titled 2010 album on Lost In Tyme is a fuzz festival – I love the distorted cover of the classic "I'm Cryin'," which transforms from a R&B number into a garage-punk blaster. The instrumental "Red Planet Groove Attack" is perhaps a signature tune, with its Leslied organ and a distinctly European-flavored garage attack. I also love the cheesy sci-fi movie graphics and feel taken from "Invasion of the Saucer Men" and "This Island Earth" – there's no doubt this album is supposed to be fun.

## THE MARVELOUS BEAUHUNKS
(OSWAHA, CANADA)

Forming originally in 1990 – and then re-formed in 2010, they display some polished Mod power pop, and have a 2013 CD and 2014 tracks available as a digital download.

## MATERIAL ISSUE (CHICAGO, IL, U.S.A.)

The much more mainstream pop band is mentioned here mainly because of their fine cover of The Green Pajamas' classic "Kim The Waitress," done in a most pleasing power-pop style on a 1994 major label single.

## MAZZY STAR (UPDATE)

The dreamy, quiet world of Mazzy Star continued with another album in 1996 (amazingly, on major label Capitol), "Among My Swan," and then returned after a long layoff with "Seasons Of The Day" (2013).

## McFADDEN'S PARACHUTE
(ROCHESTER, NY, U.S.A.)

I know firsthand how garage and psychedelic music can take hold of one's mind and heart, and create a devotion that is all-encompassing. Witness the millions of words I've spewed over the decades about this music, plus the countless garage-psych records I've made for proof of that devotion.

Darren Brennessel is another of these true blue devotees, or **"True Believers"** as I call them. Darren has a calling to make this kind of music – he must make it. And so he needed a band to contain this calling, and McFadden's Parachute was born in Rochester, New York, famously known as the birthplace of The Chesterfield Kings – perhaps the finest garage band of all time. The Kings influence would play a large part in McFadden's Parachute, as stellar former Chesterfield Kings guitarist Rick Cona joined the band lineup for a time.

Darren recorded and still records some of his material as a one-man band, but he did sport an actual live lineup for part of the band's history.

Altogether he has recorded more than a stunning dozen albums worth of garage-psych material since 1991, interestingly, only a few of these albums have seen even a nominal commercial release – The 2001 self-titled album and "Allison Crow Is Dying" (2002) on Garage Pop and the "Sweep Out The Brainfog" (2004) and "Flashback To My Hometown" (2012) albums on Jargon. I had neither seen nor heard of these albums – whether commercially released or not – so I fear most garage fans haven't either.

The remainder of this incredible catalog of material is mostly self-released CD-Rs, in limited quantities and with little distribution. So in 2014 the garage-psych world as a whole has not discovered McFadden's Parachute – but that is all about to change. You see, I declare that this is some of the finest, most vibrant, most colorful garage-psych of the entire neo-garage era, and no real garage fan can say they understand the genre if they don't have some McFadden's Parachute on their shelf.

Yes, it is time to bring Darren Brennessel and McFadden's Parachute to the people! Calling all record labels!

## THE MEANIE GEANIES (ATHENS, GREECE)

The 1998 "I'm On My Way" b/w "You Left Me Blue" 45 is on Action Records, and I can't think of another garage band that is made up of four girls and a guy. The results are strangely mesmerizing and unique, as these Meanies create a gentle 1965-66 combo sound that would fit in believably on any Pebbles collection of 1960s teenage angst. I believe there's another 2009 45 on Fuzz Overdose, and a self-released CD-R album from 2006.

## THE MEAN THINGS (FRANCE)

The "Out Come The Freaks" album (2007 on Lost In Tyme Records, Greece) comes complete with more stellar Darren Merinuk monster-cartoon cover art, and the welcome fuzz and Farfisa in the grooves. This is a groover from start to finish, with "Don't Let Me Be Blue" a special toe-tapping favorite of mine. "Mean Machine" is a fine homage to "We're Pretty Quick," but it's one of the few moments where another song comes to mind – while this is purist garage the originals here truly are original. I can listen to classic garage albums like this all day, all night, and then start over at dawn.

There are a few very trusty Greek garage labels that will never disappoint when it comes to '66 garage, and Lost In Tyme is one (and their brothers at Action and Sound Effect also come to mind).

There is also the "Change Our Ways" 2011 album on Soundflat Records.

## THE MERRY MELODIES (VIGO, SPAIN)

The "Eye On" EP is on Animal Records, 1996, and I am still searching for it!

## TME MERSEY SECT (ITALY)

The "Slushy Ruin," vocalist from French garagers The Slow Slushy Boys, combines with the Italian combo The Mersey Sect on the 2000 four-song 7" EP on Larsen Records. It is an authentically-sounding 1963-ish Merseybeat EP, with three originals and a cover of the Remo Four's "Lies." Nicely done, lads.

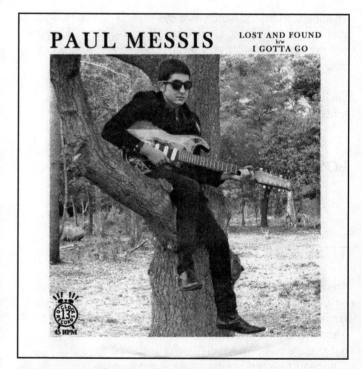

## PAUL MESSIS (BILLINGHURST, U.K.)

The bass player for The Higher State also issues his own discs, and the rest of his usual band backed him for the "Stuck In Society" b/w "'The World Is Square" 45, which was issued by (the band's) State records in 2009, limited to 500 copies.

13 O'Clock then issued in 2009 the "Lost And Found" b/w "I Gotta Go" 45. Everything about it has the feel of a 1965 New England teenbeat 45, with its moody tone and authentic 45 label. Details, kids, they count!

The "Time Will Tell" b/w "When You Pass Me By" 45 was issued by State in 2010. The A-side is a wonderfully chiming piece of garage pop, supported by period-perfect production and a fine arrangement. Simply top-notch in all ways, and my favorite of his solo 45s. And what is that weird 12-string Paul is holding on the picture sleeve, a beautiful, vintage Burns?

But wait – I made that 45 my favorite before hearing the transcendent "Sunflower" b/w "As Nightmares Turn To Dreams" 45 (on State in 2012). Together with guest Jessica Winter on vocals, Messis suddenly created the absolutely perfect 1966 pop-folk-psych 45. The sitar-blessed "Sunflower" is a colorful trance, and the San Francisco-ish B-side an angelic flip. Oh, I didn't see this coming, to be sure!

This last 45 will spin on my turntable continuously for the next 12 hours or so, so we'll suspend "Knights of Fuzz" operations until then. Carry on.

## THE MIDWAYS (CANADA)

The "Manners Manners" album (2007 on Screaming Apple) is garage party music, plain and simple. And that assessment isn't meant to minimize the importance of the record – just the opposite – any album that can create an instant party on hitting "play" is a special experience. The energy, urgency and "I gotta dance" feeling that albums like this create are priceless. It is well known that I am partial to garage combos that have an organ included, and it adds a lot of flavor in the Midways sound, too.

I love the cover of The Rooks' "A Girl Like You" – man what a wailing fuzz guitar tone there! – and "No Thanks For Nothing" takes its place in the snotty girl-done-me-wrong hall of fame. Yep, next time I'm feeling down I need to remember to pop in "Manners, Manners," grab a beer, and jump to my feet!

There is also at least one more album and one more 45.

## MINDBURGER (PALATINE, IL, U.S.A.)

This is the kind of handmade music I love, especially when it comes straight from a fume-filled garage. In this case, Mindburger is also filtered through the flashing strobe lights somewhere in the fog, too. The "Reflections Of Infinity" b/w "Cheeseburger To Go" is the definition of Do-It-Yourself garage rock, a bit on the heavy side, and 100% fun.

The handmade Xerox sleeve shouts, "Remove socks before listening!" Relax, get that Lava-Lite boiling, and **GO!**

## THE MINDERS (PORTLAND, OR, U.S.A.)

There is the "Right As Rain" b/w "Up And Away" 45 on Earworm from 1999, an album titled "Hooray For Tuesday," and reportedly a few more 45s.

## THE MINDFLOWERS (COPENHAGEN, DENMARK)

I've only heard a couple tracks, the first is "Down The Line," from a 2014 split-45 with the Roaring 420s. It's guitar-based garage, with a good nod to the 13th Floor Elevators. That trendy facial hair on the trio's band photo, though, sure will look silly after the current hipness of that look wears off – in about just one more week if my hipness calculations are correct. You heard it here first!

There is also a 2013 track, I believe download only, titled "Japanese Hills," which I prefer – it has a dreamy, vibrating feel to it and has a more distinctive feel to it than the split 45.

## MIND KIOSK (GERMANY)

The 1997 five-song self-titled CD (on Twang!) is '60s-tinged pop, with a big production style, sung in English with a slight German accent. This might be too "pop" for garage fans, and not pop enough for mainstream listeners. Good stuff, nonetheless!

## MINERS OF MUZO (UPDATE)

This Dutch band has been very active since the 1995 book, with a plethora of releases. The "About Time" CD (1993 on Music Maniac) is garage-psych tinged, not in a revisionist way, but you gotta love a song titled "Vampire Tiger (From Outer Space)." At least I do.

The band is alive and very kicking on the "Really...Is That Fact?" CD (2013 on MOM Productions). There is certainly a lot of rock fire left in their bones, but probably only of marginal interest to garage fiends.

The 1985 "Hey Gipsy Woman" b/w "Sandman" 45 on Spliff Records has more of a garage-psych vibe to it, with two finely crafted songs that defy in many ways a genre classification. And that's OK, many of the most original bands can't be easily slotted into a category, and I think that might define The Miners Of Muzo most accurately: difficult to categorize.

At least five more albums and various 45s also exist.

## THE MINKS (PHILADEPLIA, PA, U.S.A.)

This unpretentious trio – a guy on drums and two chicks up front (for their album at least) – play their garage with straight-forward crunchy guitar toughness. For some this might be a bit too "punk rock," but there's enough '60s garage in there for me. Their 2005 "Are You Ready Now?" album (on Steel Cage) never lets up , and the sneering attitude reflects their hard-scrabble Philly home. Pick hit: the "love song" for The Woggles, "I Wanna Do A Woggle."

The three-song "Plaything" EP does veer a little too much into generic punk for my tastes, but the four-song "Songs About Boys" EP on Steel Cage is another winner. How can you not like a song titled "Cavegirl Love" that includes the lyrics, "I'm gonna put him in a cage in his underwear"? And it's on beautiful pink vinyl, too – and I like pink, if you know what I mean.

## THE MIRACLE MEN: (HOLLAND)

Tough folk-rock-garage in the classic Nederbeat style is the order of the day on the "They're Coming" album (2006, on Teen Sound). I like it a lot – reminds me a bit of The Kliek. A 2005 EP on Kuriosa is also out there. The band evolved into De Keemen, also with releases on Kuriosa.

## THE MIRRORS: (PORTLAND, OR, U.S.A.)

The instrumental "Summer Spell," from the Mirrors' 2014 debut "On The Rise" EP, has a distinct 1967 Country Joe & The Fish feel to it, something I don't know if I've heard in exactly the same beautiful way elsewhere in the neo-garage-psych era. Moody, colorful, wonderfully arranged yet simple and evocative. That is my kind of psych pop!

## THE MISTERIOSOS
(BOSTON, MA & PHILADELPHIA, PA, U.S.A.)

I make no bones about loving self-released albums like this debut 2005 CD (on Trip Tone). A band has to really believe in itself – even when no one else seemingly does – to make and somehow release their own music to a hyper-critical and snobby music world. The Misteriosos boast former members of The Datsuns, The Greenhornes (and later Seeds and Electric Prunes-related projects), and they are well-versed in fuzz, swirling organ and trippy elongated psych bursts. Pick hit: "Any Wonder."

## MMOSS: (BARRINGTON, NH, U.S.A.)

I would put the modern psych vibe of Mmoss in a category with bands like Holy Wave – mesmerizing, certainly psychedelic, but reaching out for their own sound and so not really able to be categorized. "Grow Down," from the 2011 album "i" has the feel of The Strawberry Alarm Clock jamming with the U.S. version of Kaleidoscope. Oh, that is a very good thing, kids, just trust me and select the sugarcube of your choice here.

The 2012 "Only Children" follow-up continues the band's exploration of creating dense, psychedelic soundscapes, and this time out I hear some Iron Butterfly in there, too on a track

like "Spoiled Sun." Not to worry, it isn't the pretentious, heavy Butterfly, but the precisely arranged, powerful 1967-ish sound.

My Pick Hits: the somehow pop yet trippy "Another Day" and elegant "Another Dream."

No, the purists won't touch Mmoss, and all that means is that they are missing out on some vibrantly expert psychedelic music.

## MOD FUN (UPDATE)

My appreciation (and knowledge) of original 1960s Mod sounds and their modern descendants has increased greatly since the original 1995 book, and Mod Fun are one of the bands that I've since really enjoyed. Their 1995 "Past... Forward" compilation on Get Hip is especially satisfying, with expert pop songs and some fine covers, such as The Zombies' "Just Out Of Reach" – a Mod staple. There are so many other Mod Fun releases worth finding. As soon as I add another mirror to my scooter I'll go looking for them.

## MONDO TOPLESS (PHILADELPHIA, PA, U.S.A.)

Named for Russ Meyer's epic 1966 nudie film, Mondo Topless thrived from 1992-2011. Thick, swirling organ and party-time vocals from Sam Steinig set the band apart from many others. The wonderfully-titled debut "Fifty Thousand Dollar Hand Job" (on Twist, 1996) is direct, thick-sounding garage heaven. "I Want You" is a pulsing groove monster that stands the test of time.

The "In The End" 45 appeared on Dionysus in 1996, and then the "Get Ready for Action" (on Dionysus, 1998) is a fine beer-fueled follow-up, with "Too Late" a fuzzy toe-tapping delight. The 2002 "Go Fast" album (Get Hip) emphasizes that Mondo Topless was built to be a live-gig animal, with lots of hip-shaking fun afoot – dig "Futility Dance."

Two more albums on Get Hip also appeared, "Taking It Slow" in 2006 and "Freaking Out" in 2010. The wonderfully-named "Panty Sniffer" 45 also appeared on Get Hip. Steinig went on to form The GTVs with an album on Italy's fine Teen Sounds Records.

## THE MONKS (GERMANY / U.S.A.)

(Yes, The Monks were an original 1960s band – but they re-formed in the late 1990s/early 2000s and had their legendary 1960s recordings re-issued, hence their inclusion here.)

The Sex Pistols didn't know it at the time, of course, but they were a decade late. Their brand of iconoclastic mayhem had already been invented, chewed and spit out in 1966 by a quintet of weirdos named The Monks. Smash cut to 30 years

The original 1960s German vinyl of "Black Monk Time" trades for several hundred bucks, and it's been bootlegged on vinyl and CD several times over the years. Polydor finally licensed a legit Euro CD, but American's subsidiary Infinite Zero produced the definite re-issue version in 1997. The recordings are stunningly powerful, with every fuzzed squeal and thumping rhythm stabbing the listener like a knitting needle in the eye. These are crude four-track recordings by today's digital standards, and I'm confident that "Black Monk Time" is also the best produced album you could hear in 1997. So take your 96 track penthouse recording studio and shove it up your noses – The Monks don't need no stinking technology!

The topper is the reprinting of Mike Stax's glorious mini-biography of The Monks, reprinted from his "Ugly Things" fanzine. Stax's portrayal of The Monks' world brings new dimensions to the music itself, and is simply one of the finest pieces from a rock music fanzine I've ever seen.

Add it all up, and "Black Monk Time" isn't simply a re-issue; it's a document of the first modern punk rock group. It makes the best from 1997 look like the weakened beer-commercial soundtrack that it is, and might never be topped.

later, and suddenly "Monkmania" hit with the first official U.S. release of their lone 1960s LP, "Black Monk Time."

What major label in the 1990s would touch these freaks, sporting noose neck-ties, real shaved monk haircuts, fuzzed banjo and enough distorted angst to sink a battleship? American Records, of course, the home of Johnny Cash and Danzig. The folks there obviously had their fill of Offspring sound-alikes, and had the smarts to track down some real punk rock, 1966-style.

The short-list requisite bio: The Monks lived their bizarre lifespan in Germany, where the five American ex-GIs had been stationed. Beatlemania, in all its "Yeah Yeah Yeah" harmony glory, had swept the globe – except in the Monks' rehearsal room. Ominous was the prevailing tone in the Monk's camp, right down to their undertaker stage outfits and their stark jet-black album cover. Songs such as "Shut Up," "I Hate You" and "Drunken Maria" began to take form, and soon The Monks were scaring the hell out of kids and parents alike throughout Europe. Sensing that twisted fuzz punk would eventually outsell The Beatles, (wrong!) Polydor snatched up the group. They eventually scored several Euro-hits and even toured with The Kinks.

The kids' reactions to all this rage were curious. Mainly they jumped up and down furiously, causing journalist to tag the group as making "Hop Music." To you '77 purists, that would be "The Pogo," only a decade early. A wonderful time capsule of the band was made at the band's peak, when they performed three songs on a 1966 German TV show. The kids, weaned on Beat-era white R&B and pop, practically stand mesmerized by the undulating, absolutely sinister Monks, blurting, "Cuckoo, cuckoo, who's got my cuckoo," and "Complication, people die for you!" This was pop music from hell, and The Monks meant what they said 100 percent – no gimmick joke band here. "Pussy Galore is coming down, and we like it!"

## THE MONTGOMERY CLIFFS
(BALTIMORE, MD, U.S.A.)

This is certainly more guitar-pop-ish than most everything in this book, but I dig the classic pop-song construction and fine vocal work – so in the book they go! "Christmas Lights," from the "Christmas Stocking Stuffer" EP (1999 on RPM) is catchy as heck, and the 2001 self-titled album also has many fine hooks.

## THE MOONSTONES (MADRID, SPAIN)

Forming in 2005, The Moonstones claim direct inspiration from the first wave of garage revivalists such as The Chesterfield Kings and The Lyres. Yes, the neo-garage scene has been around for so long – we define it for this book as starting circa 1980 – that the new generation of bands looks to the 1980s bands perhaps as much as the original 1960s bands. I have to say, for me it is both perplexing and a great compliment to hear a band today playing one of my songs from the 1980s or 1990s. The music will live on!

And so it is also odd to hear The Moonstones playing a cover of the Chesterfield Kings' "She Told Me Lies," note for note (though sung in Spanish) on their 2014 album "Cuando Cae La Noche" (on Soundflat Records). Oh, it is an excellent version, but why try to better a masterpiece? The entire album is so well recorded and performed – see my notes elsewhere about how amazingly professional many of the latest bands are in comparison to their 1980s cousins.

The 2013 three song EP "Eres El Diablo" (on KOTJ) is also cool, with the toe-tapping "Gunslinger" my favorite. The 2011

"Fuzz, Farfisa y Fiesta" album (on Soundflat) is another 1966 Kings-like party, with some nice harmonica to keep things R&B-ish. The thumping "Seras Mia" is my fave here, sounding a lot like The Miracle Workers, circa 1986.

## THE MOSQUITOS (See the 1995 book and the "Fan Submitted Updates" chapter for more information.)

## THE MOUNT MCKINLEYS (UPDATE)

The discount vinyl bin at the Haight-Ashbury record store was chock full of garbage. There was plenty of death-metal and phony alt-rock, but I kept digging anyway; every vinyl-junkie knows that persistence has its rewards. I almost passed by two 45s by a group I'd never heard before, The Mount McKinleys, but I paused long enough in 1998 to give them a chance – for a whole U.S. dollar.

It's proven to be one of my wisest investments. Since then I've ferreted out every scrap of lo-fi noise with the Mount McKinley's banner on it, reveling in their instrumental-dementia and poinging reverb madness. The Mt. McKinleys 1995 debut album of crude and spirited dementia, "Portrait of a Mindbender," delivered on the promise of their previous stellar 45s. Bug the cool cats at Get Hip for that one.

So, I just about leapt out of my shoes when the McKinleys' "Indescribable High Rise Sounds of Today!" debut LP fell in my hands, all the way from Switzerland.

The McKinley lads hail from Pennsylvania, but the Swiss fans at Max Picou Records got the honors of releasing the 16 track LP – and it's on the thickest vinyl I've ever seen on a modern album. Modern, in this case, meaning since the 1980s.

The band is tighter and more manic than ever, with their irreverent humor and simple trash approach intact from my cherished earlier discs. I just hope **you** don't have to travel to Switzerland to find the LP.

There's more – 360 Twist also barfed up a 1997 single from the Mount McKinleys. The whole wreck of a band spits out the fun on the "No Come Down" 45, and Get Hip followed up with the 1999 "Stacked Up (And Get It!)" album. Now you have a lot of sounds to go find – good luck getting them for a dollar.

## MOURNING AFTER (UPDATE)

The 1996 self-titled vinyl album (on Mystic Beat) displays the exact garage formula that I enjoy the most: it is spiked with liberal amounts of 1966 paisley and psych color. The garage snot is tempered with a pulsating psych mood, and the whole event coalesces into a vibrant, colorful, audio stew. There are a few bands in the neo-garage era that poke up above many others, and The Mourning After have always been one for me.

There is also the 2002 "But You Promised You'd Withdraw" album on Corduroy and the 2013 "Tall, Dark and Gruesome" album on Screaming Apple, and a whole slew of 45s, too. You read my mind: I want them, too.

## THE MOVIEES (ROCHESTER, NY, U.S.A.)

The Chesterfield Kings' Andy Babiuk and Greg Prevost mentored The Moviees, producing their debut album "Become One Of Them" in 2000. Unfortunately mired on the under-publicized Sundazed Records, the expert blend of power-garage-pop didn't bubble out of the underground. It is expertly arranged and performed, with plenty of nods to Mod-era Who and other classic Brit-pop (along with their U.S. garage sound). Pick Hit: "Sunny Day" and their cover of the 1960s classic "Queen Of The Shadows."

There is also the "Come On" b/w "You Got What I Want" 45 on Living Eye.

## MR. ELEVATOR AND THE BRAIN HOTEL (LOS ANGELES, CA, U.S.A.)

The 2013 "Dreamer" b/w "Are You Hypnotized" 45 is out on Resurrection Records, and the band garnered lots of hipster attention for their 2013 "Nico… and Her Psychedelic Subconscious" cassette (and CD-R) on Burger.

This is post-modernist garage-psych – in other words taking some of the genre elements of original 1960s garage (like some wonderful organ) and mixing it with arty meanderings, noise, jazz and non-genre elements. It is eccentric, trippy and crudely (simply) recorded.

"Mermaid Song" sounds like Captain Beefheart jamming with the Doors in Venice, circa 1966, but even that description is probably too coherent to capture the ephemeral nature of Mr. Elevator And The Brain Hotel.

Pick Hit:" Grape Jelly (Jam)." Tasty.

## MUCK AND THE MIRES (BOSTON, MA, U.S.A.)

Forming in 2001, this long-running professional garage act has spit out at least seven albums, mostly on the European Soundflat and Dirty Water labels. It is almost a U.S.A. garage tradition in the revival era to not be appreciated by local record labels and instead find homes in Europe. So be it, and thank you, Europe!

Legendary music scene nutcase and promoter Kim Fowley (along with Maria Baglien) produced their 2009 "Hypnotic" album, and described the band as "The '64 Beatles meets The Ramones." I hear more garage-pop in their grooves than that, but the point is valid – there is a lot of 1960s pop beat and '70s punk energy mixed into the very professionally arranged and delivered Muck and the Mires.

There are at least six other albums and a clutch of 45s and EPs out there, too.

Unlike many bands of the revival era that only play the occasional weekend gig, these cats tour – a lot.

## THE MYSTIC BRAVES (LOS ANGELES, CA, U.S.A.)

Starting life as The Blackfeet Braves, this (currently ultra-hip) L.A. band changed to The Mystic Braves for a 2013 45 and download-album, and the 2014 "Desert Island" vinyl album. This is modern guitar-based psych-pop, with a slight nod to the warbled mystery of early Country Joe & The Fish and the hushed strumming of Love, but not in a reverential 1960s style.

As of this writing, in 2014, they are at the center of a mini-psych-revival in Los Angeles, with other similar-sounding acts (in the Burger and Lollipop Records circle). Will their heavily-echoed L.A. sound stand the test of time and remain interesting a year or even two from now? Ah, kids, you know that while I am not interested in being hip that at least I'll still be here to see and hear for myself about the fate of bands such as The Mystic Braves. I wish them well!

My Pick Hit: "There Is A Pain" from "Desert Island."

## THE MYSTIC EYES (UPDATE)

The "Little Girl" b/w "She's Gone" 45 on Get Hip was added to the wonderful legacy of the Mystic Eyes, still one of the finest and most under-rated (by others) of the groups featured here.

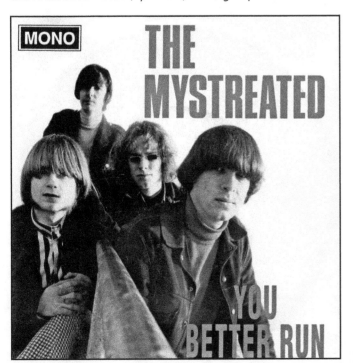

## THE MYSTREATED (UPDATE)

One of my favorite of the U.K. revival-era bands, The Mystreated remained one of the planet's best at mixing a lysergic feel without slipping into aural mush. Their fuzz-box garage devotion rarely wavers, and is augmented wonderfully with the sweetest of jangle and melody. They remained one of the 1990s best through many releases, all of which are highly recommended, including their final album, the 1997 "Love Sunday Dreaming" LP on Twist Records.

The 1996 "This Is..." 10" on Twist is another knock-out, with a beautiful 10" cover, and a slew of 45s have seen the light of day as well. Among them is the beautiful chiming 1997 "What's In Your Mind Today" b/w "I'll Be There" 45 and the stunning 1998 "Contrasts" b/w 'Right Here" 45 (both on Detour.) Both of these later 45s demonstrate a musical maturity (and wonderful analog recording) and are among the best of the neo-garage era.

Put the Mystreated at the top of your international garage-record shopping list.

*NOTE: Remember to read the original 1995 book and the other book update chapters for thousands of other bands and records not featured in this update section.*

# N

## THE NAPOLEONS (HOLLAND)

These Dutch garage-believers are in the basement, kicking over empty beer bottles and scrambling to find the light switch. Yep, The Napoleons revel in the crudest of the crude on their debut four-song 1998 "In Sound Shape" 7" EP (on Tombstone). Led by Eric Danno, late of The Acetones, this Dutch trio probably won't play any guitar that doesn't have rust on the strings. Yes, I like this a lot.

There is also a split" EP on Tombstone (with Dr. Reverb on the flip), where The Napoleons fit four blasters on one side of a 7"disc!

## THE NEANDERTHALS (U.S.A.)

A thick, solid recording stands out for these garage cavemen on their 1999 "The Modern Stone-Age Family" album (on Sundazed). With party tunes such as "I Go Ape" and "Flinstone Flop" you know you're in for some toe-tapping fun. A frat-rock '60s style permeates the proceedings, and there's nice fake-fur leopard-skin outfits, too! There at least three other albums and a half-dozen 45s out there dating to at least 2005. The lineup included guitarist Eddie Angel of Los Straitjackets. **Ooooga-booooga, baby!**

## THE NEATBEATS (OSAKA, JAPAN)

Another of the rare long-term survivors of the new-garage era, this Japanese combo has racked up at least 15 singles and a half-dozen albums of their own unique Merseybeatish sound from 1997 to 2014. The 1998 "Far And Near" (in mono, of course!) has an authentic (though better recorded) Liverpool feel to it, circa 1963. They sing in English, with only a slight accent, and the 1999 "Mercurial" album (also on Get Hip) continues the Big Beat joyride. Extra points for matching outfits and a real sense of cool '60s clothing style. Pick Hit: an enthusiastic cover of "Long Tall Sally," done Neatbeat-style. Essential stuff, me thinks.

## LOS NEGATIVOS (UPDATE)

A beautiful reissue of the seminal "Piknik Kaleidoscopico" album was released on CD by Mushroom Pillow records in 2005, complete with four bonus demo tracks. It remains one of the most important records of the neo-garage era, and one of the finest to be released in Spain in any era.

The "Dandies Entre Basura" album was issued on CD in 2009 (and again on vinyl by Butterfly in 2012), and it adds to the band's legacy of '66-Revolver-esaque garage pop. The title track is a soaring garage-pop anthem, full of the band's patented evocative vocals and expert arrangement, while other stand-out pop gems include "Plaroid Nocturna & Peronal" and "Flash!" Yes, it is all sung in Spanish.

Other album releases include "18º Sábado Amarillo" (1987), "Las Cintas De Thule" (1996), "Puzzle" (1996) and at least eight vinyl 45s.

It is my sad duty to report that Los Negativos singer Alfredo Calonge died in May 2014.

## THE NEPTUNES (UPDATE)

Fans of Australian guitar pop such as the Stems and Hoodoo Gurus recommended to me highly the "Godfish" six-song 12" EP (1991 on Citadel), but I found it to be rather bland indie-pop, even after a few tries. Perhaps they had more fire and grit at their live shows?

## THE NERVE (UPDATE)

I only heard a couple songs on cassette of The Nerve during their initial run in the early 1990s, so it is yet another great deed that Detour Records has done for the garage-psych public by collecting all their sounds for the 2001 "Seeds From The Electric Garden" album. It has the tracks from their two 45s, compilation songs and more, painting a complete picture for these authentically 1968-ish U.K. psych-popsters.

Starting the album with a cover of The Nazz's "Open My Eyes" was a curious decision, since the band's original material is much more confident and vibrant, so let that needle keep moving to discover treats a-plenty. The package is lovingly delivered in a colorful cover and elegant inner sleeve, complete with band history. Reminding me at times of the similarly colored The Tyrnaround (from Australia), The Nerve are certainly one of the most distinctive Mop-psych-pop acts from the U.K. in the 1990s. I am delighted that their history is collected on one LP to keep their sound alive.

## THE NEUMANS (SANTA ANA, CA., U.S.A.)

The 2012 three-song "Fuzz Filled Dreams" 45 is on Wild Records. The title "A" side is pure 1966 Pebbles territory, so authentically recorded you'd think it was actually transferred from an original 1960s vinyl 45. Yes, that is a grand compliment from me. All hail authentic 1966 garage rock, the inspiration at its core for this book.

Their 2014 debut album is on Screaming Apple in Germany.

## NICK NICELY (UPDATE)

The 2004 "Psychotropia" CD (on Castle Music) compiled all four sides of Nicely's very rare early 1980s 45s and adds in another 14 demos and other more recent tracks – exploring thickly layered distorted vocals, tape loops and other weirdness. The classic "Hilly Fields" is still the pop-psych highlight here, but I also dig some of the trippier sounds, as if they were outtakes from the background music from the darkly hypnotic film "Blade Runner." A 2014 45 also appeared.

## THE 99th FLOOR (UPDATE)

Luca Re continues to write Italian garage band history with his seminal band The Sick Rose, so perhaps it is easy for some to forget his other fine garage band, The 99th Floor. I certainly do not forget them – I was able to witness their magic in person in Italy, and I still rate them among the most important garage bands of the 1990s.

The "Electric Ragoo" album (1996 on Misty Lane) stands on its own as a neo-garage classic, with the perfect blend of fuzz and Farfisa, along with Luca Re's definitive garage vocals. There are expertly crafted originals throughout, capped off with picture-perfect covers of "Flyte" and The Blues Magoos' "Albert Common Is Dead."

If you are reading this book to find more great garage music to love, then here is first assignment: go out and find some 99th Floor records. And then turn it up. You'll thank me later.

## THE NOBLE KRELL (TUCSON, AZ, U.S.A.)

Sessions for a debut 45 were recorded in 2014, with a jangly 12-string Rickenbacker A-side and Electric Prunes-ish psych freakout B-side. Yes, I was the producer for this new band's sessions, and I hope to help get these tracks released. As their B-side screams, *"Beware The Noble Krell!"*

## THE NOCOUNTS (SWEDEN)

The 2001 three-song 7" EP on Fast Lane Records is very authentic '66 garage, though, in the best neo-garage Swedish tradition. That means it's loud, proud, and blasts in the best way possible. A cool picture sleeve completes this treat.

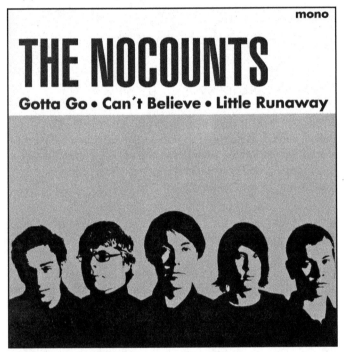

## THE NOGOODS (MEPPEL, HOLLAND)

I've heard "Wonder," from their 2009 Kuriosa 45 (b/w "Maureen and limited to 300 copies). It is strong Dutchbeat in the tradition of Q65 and the Outsiders. I'd love to hear more!

## THE NOMADS (UPDATE)

There are just far too many releases by this seminal Swedish act to even try to keep track of – always an issue when a band has produced records for more than three decades! I will point out one cool rarity, the "Raw & Rare" 10" (1996 vinyl on Estrus, on CD in 2006). It is worth the price of admission alone for their version of the classic "I Wanna Come Back From The World Of LSD." While the band has long moved on from a strict '60s garage feel, the continuing influence of The Nomads can't be under-estimated in the neo-garage world. Their "Outburst" LP continues its residency on my turntable some 30 years after I first heard it. Thank you, Nomads!

## NOM DE GUERRE (SWEDEN)

This Swedish pop band might bristle at being lumped in with the garage bands in this book, but their elegant pop-punk, with the heavy emphasis on the pop, owes its sound to the heritage of 1960s pop. Sparkling production and sweet vocal acumen are the focus here for the "La La La" album (2007) with a wink and a grin that makes this debut infectious. There's a slight hint of late-period Zombies in their approach – the highest of compliment coming from me. Maybe it's my appreciation of bands that can really, really write and play well that is the biggest difference in my taste since the 1995 version of this book came out. I still love a good, sloppy two-chord garage band, but the sweet pop joy of bands like this make it more and more into my personal playlist. The "Love They Neighbour" 2010 follow-up is also available, with more expertly-crafted pop-garage.

## THE NORVINS (FRANCE)

The Norvins have that magical combination of fuzz, organ and garage urgency. Their "Time Machine" debut album (2008 on Soundflat) is a blast-furnace of garage rock energy, balancing both a respect for the original 1960s sound while also feeling contemporary and new. This isn't the "modern garage" I mention somewhat reluctantly at times in this book – the Norvins are still rooted fully in the R&B garage tradition that purists love, but they aren't hung up on being a music museum – they have too much rocking to do in the here and now.

"Fleshtones In Your Head" is a perfect example – paying homage to the seminal Fleshtones while sounding original and new. Some nice harmonica throughout also keeps it all grounded and gritty. I love their sweaty version of the classic "Abba," too.

Soundflat also issued their next two albums. "Yoga With Mona" (2011) sports very cool and trippy cover art, and the sound inside shows The Norvins even sharper as performers, more polished, with a more refined recording as well.

This is garage music that forces you to your feet to dance. Even the most jaded music fan must turn into a sweaty mess at a Norvins show – I find it impossible to sit still as they blast their garage sacrament through my speakers. Hard for me to pick out just a couple tracks as standouts since this is a solid winner throughout, though I especially dig "Monk's Hangover," the anthemic "You Can't Comin'," and the infectious "Keep Me Posted." I'm a sucker for chimes and sitar, so "Better Of Dead" (not "off") also makes me smile.

"No Tyme For Tears" (2014) continues The Norvins' mastery of the garage spirit, as if they merely took a few minutes to rest after "Yoga With Mona" and then went back into the studio to capture their next set. Plenty of pop hooks in here as well, as "Dark Avenue" and "Are You With Me" shows. There is also the "I Wanna Shake You Girl" b/w "TV Program" 45 (2013 on Howlin' Banana) – both sides are on the brilliant third album.

I put the Norvins at the front of the garage-rock class – they are one of those primo bands that give me hope that garage music can continue to flourish in the 21st century.

## THE NUTHINS (UPDATE)

The Nuthins survived the U.K. for much of the 1990s, depositing disc after disc of wonderful fuzz and pop-garage. Two 1997 EPs help cement their reputation as one of Europe's best: The "Cemetery Chemistry" EP on Italy's For Monsters Records mines the perennial "I just dug up my girlfriend/boyfriend" motif, while their untitled 7" on Detour continues to build on their already sizable output of prime garage muck.

The "One Step Forward" LP (1995 on Twist) is another aural treat. The cover gives a winking homage to The Beatles' "Rubber Soul," the grooves instead contain the band's own U.S.-meets-U.K. garage sound. The emphasis is on originals, but the cover of The Barbarians' "Are You A Boy Or Are You A Girl" is a real winner. I also dig the garage-surfish sound of the "Hang 9" instrumental. Here's a hint to all of you insiders: go find some Nuthins records before some other caveteen beats you to them.

## THE OGRES (OAKLAND, CA, U.S.A.)

The 2013 "Acrid & Misanthropic Sounds Of" album is a perfect release for Hillsdale Records, which specializes in crudely-recorded basic rock that sound like it was cut in 1963. "Don't Tell Me No Lies" actually sounds like it could've been played in the Cavern, circa 1963, but don't get the wrong idea about a Beatles-esque pop group hiding here – this is nasty, mostly simple, stomping garage music, with some fuzz and of course a tongue planted firmly in cheek. Sounds good to me!

## JAMES RICHARD OLIVER
(BLUE RIDGE, GA, U.S.A.)

The four-song "Rocket To Nashville" 7" EP (on his own Illbilly Records) circa 1992 probably doesn't belong in this book – it isn't '66 garage at all – but sounds more like Mojo Nixon doing Cramps covers. But it makes me smile, is crude in its own way, and I liked the songs about the "Forty Foot Elvis." So there.

## THE OKMONIKS
(TUCSON, AZ & OAKLAND, CA, U.S.A.)

I heard word in the early 2000s that there was a new verifiably 1960s-ish combo here in my hometown of Tucson, Arizona. I then heard a side or two from a 45 and it seemed true – Tucson finally had a new garage band worth talking about! I contacted them to sit down and fill me in on their band, their releases and to just say hello. "Oh, we don't have time for anything like that," came the e-mail reply. So – I'm on to the next band listing...

## THE OMEGA MEN (Lebanon, PA, U.S.A.)

MuSick Records' 1997 "Spy-Fi Sounds of The Omega Men" LP is especially worthy of praise. Featuring three former members of the mid-1980s Cellar Dwellars – whose lone 45 remains cherished in my vaults – The Omega Men add a devilish Mod tone and martini atmosphere to their alternating instrumental/vocal attack. Stir one for me – I'm out of Schlitz.

## THE OMENS (DENVER, CO, U.S.A.)

The 2008 "Make It Last" b/w "Won't Be Ashamed" 45 on Hipsville Records is a super-crude garage blast on cool purple-marbled vinyl, limited to only 250 copies. There are at least two more 45s on Hipsville, and the 2012 "Fuzz, Fades and Escapades" LP on Soundflat.

## THE 1-2-5 (UPDATE)

The 1-2-5 capture a near-perfect blend of Euro-beat and U.S. garage styles on their 1997 self-titled album on Misty Lane. The trio crams 16 songs onto the long-player, with half of them a good selection of covers that compliment their own sound. Of course there is the Haunted's "1-2-5" on board, and "It's Cold Outside" is fine, too. The recording wavers between crude and cruder, which doesn't detract from the true garage spirit.

The band reunited in 2001, and stayed together until 2008. During this period they released two songs "Rumble on Mersey Square South" on the compilation "Snaps - The Primitive Compilation Vol. 1" CD (2004), and "What You Don't Know" on the CD "Fuzztones - Illegitimate Spawn" CD (2006). In 2008 they recorded seven songs which have not been released as of this writing.

The 1-2-5 is pure garage for pure people. Dig.

## THE ORANGE ALABASTER MUSHROOM
(UPDATE)

Three vibrantly pulsating psych garage releases have appeared since the 1995 book: the 1996 "Psychedelic Bedroom" EP on Paisley Pop, the Earworm label 1998 "The

Slug" 45 and "Space & Time: A Compendium Of The Orange Alabaster Mushroom" (on LP in 2000 on Earworm and on Aha!). All are extremely rare and fetch large amounts if ever appearing for sale. I am proud to have helped with the production on the band's signature tune, "Your Face Is In My Mind," which remains as catchy as all those years ago.

## OS HAXIXINS (SAO PAULO, BRAZIL)

This very cool Brazilian band has a debut self-titled 2007 album, the 2008 "Depois De Um LSD" b/w "Espelho Invisível" 45, and the 2010 "Under The Stones" album (all on Groovie). The 2010 "Noites Brancas" four-song 7" EP is on 13 O'Clock.

*See the "Guest Authors" chapter for more on Os Haxixins.*

## THE OTHERS (UPDATE)

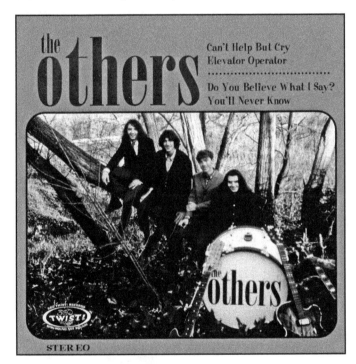

The Others remain one of the entire garage revival era's finest practitioners of garage mayhem. These Italian mop-tops slide easily between fuzzy-punk to soaring 12-string folk-pop, and effortlessly add their own classics next to their letter-perfect cover versions. They've spit out countless records, with their four-song 7" on Germany's fine Screaming Apple label another worthy effort.

I was fortunate to visit The Others' head-cheese, Massimo del Pozzo, in his native Rome years ago. I witnessed the Others' furious on-stage action; if a Vox teardrop guitar is your altar, then the Others are your temple. Massimo also still runs the always-cool Misty Lane (and Teen Sound) label and fanzine. His labels spit out countless gems, with a couple fine compilations of modern garage noise: the 1997 four-song "Teen Scene!" 7" and the "Transworld Garage" LP especially recommended. Both overflow with pimple-tinged excitement.

Italy's Psych Out Records releases only authentic-sounding 1960s garage and psych made by the coolest (and most obscure) acts, and their vinyl album releases ooze with purist commitment. Check out the thick cardboard sleeves and even thicker vinyl, and you'll understand that sometimes CDs just don't cut it. The Others clocked in with a collection of rehearsal studio demos on Psych Out that kick the shit out of almost every "real studio" record of the past 30 years. Fuzzed, reverbed folk rock is the flavor, and The Others are at the top of the international garage heap with their 1997 "Dreams" LP.

I hear that some monks (or The Monks!?!?) are suggesting Massimo Del Pozzo be named Italy's garage-punk saint; his constant batch of essential releases surely open the pearly gates to '60s fuzz nirvana. His band The Others is one of the best European garage groups of the 1990s, and their 1998 "So Far Out" 10" and "Everything's There" LP (both on Misty Lane) help argue the point. Raw energy, snot, 12-string folk-angst and plenty of hair make The Others an essential sacrament of fuzz.

Of special interest also is the 1999 "Yellow, Purple & Green" album The Others made with Rudi Protrudi of the Fuzztones and Craig Moore of The Gonn. You simply cannot find anyone in the garage world more dedicated to the authentic sounds than Massimo and The Others.

The Others also reaffirm their position as garage-folk royalty with their 1997 four-song EP on 360 Twist (the U.S. label, not to be confused with the U.K. "Twist" label). "Can't Help But Cry" is simply one of the most beautiful folk-pop songs in garagedom, and The Others have yet to record a clunker of any kind. There's also the fine 1997 "About My Town" b/w "Gimme Love" 45 on Detour, a 1996 Screaming Apple 7" EP, and the 1995 "Going Around With " EP on Misty Lane – The Others sport a large back-catalogue of other releases, and they are all uniformly brilliant.

## THE OTHER SIDE (UPDATE)

The 2000 "In A Haunted House" CD is a compilation of many of the band's essential tracks from various compilation albums and 45s, and was one of the "Knights of Fuzz" series made in cooperation with Inbetweens Records. You must love their 1984 live recording of The Left Banke's "Walk Away Renee," which sounds like the original must have at gigs, circa 1966, without the strings of the studio recording. The Other Side have that special "it" for me that makes them a very special band of the revival era.

## THE OUT-FOUR (FRANCE)

I had never heard of the Out Four before the "Drive It Slower, Live" album (1998 on Where The Action Is) arrived at my door – and I am surprised that they were new to me, because these "live' and studio tracks from 1995-1997 show a polished, high energy Mod-garage outfit. The album sleeve writes, "This one is dedicated to all the fuzz and Hammond addicts," and those fans will certainly approve. You must love a band that covers the Shadows of Knight's "Potato Chip" with reverence, too.

## OUTRAGEOUS CHERRY (DETROIT, MI, U.S.A.)

The venerable Del-Fi surf label came back to life in the 1990s with multiple re-issues of their 1960s heyday, but they also released new acts such as Outrageous Cherry on their 1999 "Del-Fi 2000" label. The band's fourth album, "Out There In The Dark," took echoed vocals and dreamy distorted melodies to an ultimate level. This stuff is hard to pigeonhole, thank goodness, but I'll slap a "bubble gum Velvet Underground meets the Laughing Soup Dish" tag on them to help the readers who have gotten this far in the book. Outrageous Cherry would sound great on a double bill with Tucson's best current act, The Resonars.

Active since 1992, O.C. boats at least eleven albums. "Our Love Will Change The World," (2005 on Rainbow Quartz) adds some tasty horns and a more refined pop sensibility (evident on the title track). O.C. probably have survived for so long because more general fans in the indie music world see them more like a Brian Jonestown Massacre or Jellyfish genre-brother than being part of a neo-psych movement.

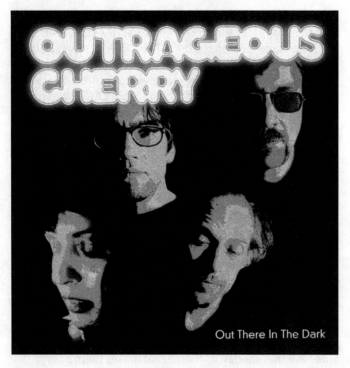

Out There In The Dark

# P

## PAINTED AIR (UPDATE)

There is also a 1997 five-song 7" EP (on Swamp Room), and the "Born Without Mistakes" LP (on Swamp Room). Both are

very dark garage-psych, distinctively German in its moody approach, and maintaining Swamp Room's practice of releasing unique sounds that are difficult to pigeonhole.

## THE PAINTED BRUSH (ITALY)

The "Made In New Mexico, U.S.A." album attempts to look and sound like a vintage 1967 garage recording from the southwest U.S.A. – but it's actually a 2009 recording from Italy and a band named I Fenomini. The crude recording style and expert arrangements do sound like a 1960s U.S. band effort, and this album is highly recommended. Just ignore the phony band credits and enjoy the recreation of the classic garage-psych era.

## THE PANDORAS (UPDATE)

The 1999 "I Didn't Cry" b/w "Thunder Alley" 45 (on Dionysus) appeared in 1999. These aren't "new" Pandoras tracks – The A-side was released on a CD compilation previously, and the B-side on the "What Surf" compilation. Still, fab to have them on vinyl here, and a reminder of just how vital the early and mid-era Pandoras were to garage music.

A 1993 Voxx CD combines the seminal "It's About Time" LP with EP and demo tracks, and Rhino issued a limited CD version of "Stop Pretending" in 2003, also with bonus tracks. "Essential" is the only word for both releases. Former band members were reported in 2014 to have recorded new tracks, but without leader Paula Pierce (who died in 1991), of course these new efforts are not the late, great, Pandoras.

## PIERCED ARROWS (See the "Fan Submitted Updates" chapter for more information.)

## THEE PHANTOM FIVE (TN, U.S.A.)

Tennessee is well-known for its surf instrumental combos (um, no), and Thee Phantom Five are obviously king of those hills. (This combo is not to be confused with the New Jersey band from the mid 1980s, The Phantom Five, with one less "e" in their name.) Their 1997 "Guitars Galore" four-song 7" on Dionysus is a must-have for those instrumental-freaks who seemed to pop up everywhere in the late 1990s and early 2000s – even in Tennessee.

## THE PHANTOM KEYS (SPAIN)

"The Real Sounds Of" album (2011 on Screaming Apple) is snotty R&B garage, with some wailing harmonica and an authentic Euro-beat vibe. "I'm Still A Mess" is a fine lead-off, in the Crawdaddy's tradition, followed up by a full set of teen garage. "Even If I Try" has a more refined feel, complete with cool "Under My Thumb" fuzz guitar. I am quite certain that a house party with the Phantom Keys would be a satisfying affair, and would lead to much beer sipping, dancing, screaming and a full day's rest after collapsing. Screaming Apple has a knack for finding more and more R&B-fueled garage bands, and this is another winner.

At least three other 45s exist.

## PLASTICLAND (UPDATE)

Milwaukee's Plasticland is only now receiving their full due as one of the planet's best psychedelic pop acts. They released a plethora of vibrant and expertly produced singles and albums over their 15+ year history. Many of their earliest releases were limited edition instant collector's items, and "Mink Dress And Other Cats" (on Timothy's Brain Records) collects these aural nuggets together on this 1995 CD for the first time, along with some essential outtakes. It should be noted that the songs that Plasticland consider "outtakes" are more interesting than most other band's actual releases – that's a testament to Plasticland's high standard of creative achievement.

## PLASTIC MAN (FLORENCE, ITALY)

The 2013 four-song 7" EP on Teen Sound is an eclectic, eccentric psych-pop debut. I salute bands like Plastic Man because they have the courage to search out their own sound rather than simply ape their musical heroes. That, of course, makes it more difficult for listeners who like to know what they are getting in advance of actually hearing a record. So I suggest turning off your expectations and try to give bands like Plastic Man a try – there are rewards for hearing bands following their own path. Pick Hit: the darkly vibrating "Atlantis."

## THE POETS (BOLOGNA, ITALY)

There are very few bands in the neo-garage era with the vocal and songwriting skill to actually pull off a pop sound, but The Poets are a great exception. Self-described accurately as a cross between The Beatles and The Kinks (circa 1965 to my ears), the 2001 four-song 7" EP on Teen Sound is a true gem.

The lead-off track "When You Were By My Side" is a real winner, and I would've believed it to be a real 1960s track if I didn't know better. The band followed this EP with the "Surrealistic Rain" album (also on Teen Sound) in 2002.

## POVERTY STINKS (HELSINKI, FINLAND)

This guitar-pop will be way too sweet for many readers here, but there is some great charm to much of the 1992 "Another

World" album (on Snap). The jangle and smile of "There Must Be" is truly timeless – it still sounds bright and right more than 20 years after originally released. "Hitch-Hiker" is another jangle gem, and "Don't Follow Me Down" another head-bobber. There are least six other albums, and an early single was released by CBS in the homeland.

## THE PREACHERS (UPDATE)

The 2008 "Preachin' at Psychedelic Velocity" is a powerful garage effort, sounding very much like a tough Fuzztones release. One song (the wonderfully creepy "Turn Me Out") is even co-written with Fuzztones frontman Rudi Protrudi, so the comparison seems to fit. This album also reminds me how much better-recorded many of the more recent garage bands are. With digital technology making recordings more affordable – even at home – the bar has definitely been raised for how good a garage record can sound. The Preachers reach a good compromise of sonic quality without it detracting from their gritty garage sound. Pick Hit: "Wild Girl." Preach on!

## THE PRIMATES (UPDATE)

The band was successful at perpetrating a publicity stunt that even made it into the 1995 version of this book: they told everyone they moved to Los Angeles from Cleveland, Ohio. They didn't – they were always from Manhattan Beach (L.A.), California. They band thought it would give them some garage street credibility if folks thought they moved all the way from Ohio to be part of the Cavern scene of the mid-1980s L,A. We corrected the hometown in the band's main listing found elsewhere in this book, by the way.

## THE PSYCHOTIC REACTION (U.K.)
The 2000 four-song 7" EP on Detour is certainly full of colorful freakbeat style, echoed in the cool color picture sleeve. The three band originals display some nice production and plenty of garage spirit, and the cover of the Five Canadians' classic "Writin' On The Wall" is fine, too. Vocalist Peter Feely would go on to be a very accomplished creator of custom-made Mod and psychedelic clothing, and remain one of the coolest-looking cats around as of this 2014 writing.

## THE PURPLE MERKINS (UPDATE)

Yes, this is another of the author's own bands, this one a pure, crude, beer-fueled '66 garage combo. Picking up from the 1995 book entry, we placed our cover version of "Cock-A-Hoop" on the 1998 "Battle Royal" compilation LP and CD, and had Greek compilation appearances on a 2007 "Lost In Tyme" magazine CD and a 2008 "Rumble Skunk" magazine CD.

All of our EP tracks, plus an unreleased "live in the studio" session were collected for the "Merkinmania!" album, released on vinyl in 1998 on Psych Out Records in Italy, and then on CD in 2006 (on PCMP/Dionysus, with different cover art). PCMP, by the way, is the media label which later became Garage Nation Records.

All Purple Merkins songs were re-mastered and released in a special digital download edition in 2013. So even you, kids, can now submit to "Merkinmania!"

And with the Internet it should take you just a moment now to discover what a Merkin actually is. Enjoy.

## THE PURPLE OVERDOSE (UPDATE)

This Greek band has flourished since the 1995 book, with the "Reborn" album (1999, on Action) a shining example. Sitar, soaring vocals and swirling keyboards take the best of The Strawberry Alarm Clock and add in a distinctive middle-Eastern and Greek tinge. "Fortune Teller" is one of those classic psych tunes that demand you fire up the Lava Lites and burn some incense (and peppermints). This is truly trippy, colorful, intelligent psychedelic music. The Purple Overdose can stretch out their songs, too, without becoming heavy, boring or "jammy." The recording here is stellar, too. There are at least six more albums up to 2012, and The Purple Overdose stand very high on the ladder of true psych bands of the revival era.

## QUESTION MARK & THE MYSTERIANS
(BAY CITY, MICHIGAN)

It isn't often that The Garage God – whomever or whatever he, she or it is – knocks on my door and sits down for a chat. I checked my old Polaroids, and "TGG" has popped in on me unannounced only a dozen or so times in my rock music lifetime.

So pardon me if my eyes swell with joy while I discuss one of The Garage God's best visits to me, which was also an excuse for him/her/it to deliver to me the 1998 Question Mark and The Mysterians "Do You Feel It Baby?" live LP.

Norton Records, which earned its spot in the heavens eons ago, heads to the front pew with "Do You Feel it Baby?" Recorded (almost entirely) at a New York City Cavestomp festival, Norton delivers a package that is long on quality and short on hype; scores of eye-watering '66-era Mysterians photos grace the excellent booklet and the sounds themselves are, well, like heaven on earth.

All the Mysterians' classics are here, spit out with a frenzy and passion that belied the band's then 50-ish age demographic. It's no small detail that all five original band members sizzle

through this "live" album, and it should be no surprise at all for fans to hear that Mr. Question Mark might still be the embodiment of the perfect rock front-man. (Mick Jagger, for comparison – whose geriatric jiggles tempt me to call him Mick Chicken – looks and smells like a lunch that went bad several decades ago.)

I've seen scores of twenty-something rock "singers" attempt to muster 1/10 of the honest, raw, exhilarating emotion that ? exudes naturally. He's simply got "it," and thanks to Norton and the Cavestomp's producers, David Mann and Jon Weiss, there's plenty to go around.

Next up was a new studio album to complete the comeback. "I was a little leery at first, because almost always these groups can't reclaim old glory," said Jon Weiss, co-producer of those new LP sessions. "But this is one of those one-in-a-million times. This stuff shreds."

Norton tantalized us first with the 1998 "Sally Go Round The Roses" b/w "It's Not Easy" 45, a taste from the LP. My ears did a double take – these new sessions have all the energy, attitude and garage grit of the band's 1966 hey-day.

The best garage record of 1999 then was Question Mark and The Mysterians' "More Action" double CD (on Cavestomp). The 21 songs feature the entire original lineup of the 1966 garage legends, and prove that the then 50-something Mysterians were better than any band their grandsons and daughters could create. Question Mark himself is in fine vocal form, and seems as nasty as ever. Yes, there are two versions of the band's signature "96 Tears" (one in Spanish), but "More Action" isn't a retread of dusty memories – these guys sound mean and lean.

A couple bonuses round out the package: the band's first two 1966 demo recordings appear for the first time, and a video for "Sally Goes Round The Roses" fills out disc one. This comeback was destined to go one way or another – up to sweet success or to the bottom of the bowl. The only ones flushing would be any band foolish enough to go on after Question Mark and the Mysterians in the year 2000.

---

*NOTE: Remember to read the original 1995 book and the other book update chapters for thousands of other bands and records not featured in this update section.*

---

## THE RAMONETURES (STUDIO BAND)

I have an idea: Take the instrumental-guitar frenzy of The Ventures and mix it in with the pimply punk of the Ramones. Out of that oven comes a band called The Ramonetures and their 2000 debut LP on Blood Red. It was the brainchild of

The Phantom Surfers' Mel Bergman, and includes 1960s fuzz guitar legend Davie Allan, too. This stuff is more fun than watching a beach-party movie with a keg of beer, and who can't love the imagery of the Ramones and Ventures jamming on "The KKK Took My Baby Way"?

There's a second 2001 album that gives the instrumental treatment to seminal 1980s punk band X.

## THE RAZZLES (BUFFALO, NY, U.S.A.)

Nice buzzy power-melodies drip all over "3x3" EP; imagine if The Ramones chewed up The Knack and Green Day for breakfast. (That's not a bad idea, really.)

## THE REACTIONS (CLEVELAND, OH, U.S.A.)

This power pop trio released the "I Want You" b/w "Frenzied" 45 on St. Valentine Records in 1986.

## REEFUS MOONS (UPDATE)

The one-man-band that is Reefus Moons continued to impress me with the "Roar" album (1995, on Insect Eye), not only because all the playing is so well executed, but because the psych-pop songwriting is again among the best in the genre. The Syd Barrett-meets-Robyn Hitchcock sound is still there, with distinctive eccentric English-accent vocals and plenty of sparking guitar. The liner notes state, "This album was made by accident," but nothing could be farther from the truth. This is expertly arranged and performed psych-pop at its best. If you enjoy your U.K. psych eccentric, unique and distinctive, then Reefus Moons is for you. It is most definitely for me.

## THE REPLIKAS (ISTANBUL, TURKEY)

The 2014 "Biz Burada Yok İken" album (on Dionysus) is one of the most unique records featured in this book. It is filled with covers versions of Turkish garage and psychedelia from 1965-1975, the originals which I didn't even know existed. A Turkish garage band is weird enough, but a Turkish garage band from today doing Turkish garage from the '60s is an additional layer of weird. (This is actually The Replika's sixth album, dating back to 2000.)

OK, so that is good shtick, but what does it sound like? Well, I guess it is like I imagined a Turkish garage band would sound – there's some R&B in there with distinctive eastern flourishes. "Suya Giden Alli Gelin" sounds a bit like "Blues Theme" played at an Istanbul coffee-bar. Definitely unique!

## THE REPROBETTES (MELBOURNE, AUSTRALIA)

An all-girl band that was touring and recording their debut album as of this 2014 writing. If they sound as cool as they look then all will be well.

## THE RESONARS (UPDATE)

Lead by the songwriting muscle of Matt Rendon, The Resonars have been one of the desert's best kept secrets for years – and one of the best western U.S. bands. After years of honing their pop-garage craft, the band finally started releasing vinyl in the late 1990s, and are more popular and more active now (2014) than ever before. The debut 1997 "So Below" b/w "Sleep Don't Travel" 45 on Star Time is a tasty first bite from a band which has a sinful amount of good songs. The follow-up "Flood Lamp Eyes" b/w "She's In Love With Her" (also on star Time) is even better.

Vocalist and guitarist Matt Rendon also accumulated scores of songs that mostly didn't make their way onto the crowded playlist of The Resonars. He collected home-made recordings of 12 of these little gems for this cassette-only release titled "The Kilgore Trouts." Most bands scratch and claw for enough original material to pull together an only somewhat interesting set, but Rendon and The Resonars are not cursed by such a creative drought. They're overflowing with musical ideas, as 1995's "The Kilgore Trouts" attests. "A Waste Of Honesty" uses kettle-drum effects, "wooing" back-up vocals, jangly guitar and an echoey somber mood to form one of the highlights. Like most of this tape, Rendon's eclectic rock/folk/psych stylings are unlike anything else being attempted in Tucson. Good for us.

The subsequent Resonars albums are among my very favorite, beginning with three albums for Get Hip: "Bright & Dark" (1999), "Lunar Kit" (2002) and "Nonetheless Blue" (2007). Those were followed-up by the Burger Records LPs "That Evil Drone" and "Crummy Desert Sound" and also an EP and tongue-in-cheek "best of" album for Trouble In Mind Records.

The very best of the Resonars is chiming classic 1960s pop – I selected "If She's So Great" for the "Knights of Fuzz" audio compilation album years ago, and it still sounds like one of the finest Rickenbacker12-string songs of all time. "Everything You Said," from "Lunar Kit," is a jaw-droppingly-emotionally-charged song worthy of "Pet Sounds." Add in loving nods to The Who, Paupers, Association and any other cool 1960s band you can think of, and the result is a Resonars sound that is both respectful of the genre yet creative, modern, and unique.

Yes, that Matt Rendon is one very talented guy. Now if I can only get him to play in a band with me. Oh, wait, I did. Lucky, lucky, lucky me.

## THE REVELLIONS (DUBLIN, IRELAND)

There is a 2008 self-titled album and the 2014 "Give It Time" album (both on Dirty Water), plus another 45 as well. Their unique approach is equal parts finely crafted pop and '60s garage overtone, encapsulated on a track from their first album such as "Bitter & Twisted."

Things get moody on "One Of A Kind," and a bit more garagey on the toe-tapping "Ain't No Fool." There is wonderful orchestration on "Drip," which makes me think (hope?) that The Revellions could actually poke out of the underground into a hip more-mainstream pop mentality. Ah, I can dream.

I really enjoy bands that can both take the best elements of the '60s sound and then graft onto it their own identity. The Revellions can sound familiar to fans of '66 garage, yet sound utterly unique and original in their own way. Well done, lads.

## REVERB (U.K.)

Ochre Records is also the U.K. home for a bright and snappy British pop outfit called Reverb. (They shouldn't be confused with The Reverbs, a mid-1980s American pop duo from the U.S.) Their "Pedal" b/w "Swirl" 45 is the first taste I've heard of the band, and it's a pleasing exercise in jangle and melody. Reverb also has another 7" housed in attractive fake cow hide, plus the strong track "Metamorphosis" on the Ochre "Voyage To The Cosmic Underground" 12" sampler.

England always seems to breed these kind of fun guitar-pop acts – remember The Dentists? – and Reverb are another fine addition to the sunny heap.

## THE REVOLVING PAINT DREAM
(LONDON, U.K.)

The "Flowers In The Sky" b/w "In The Afternoon" is an early Creation label release from 1984. It was limited to 1000 copies and Andrew Innes who went onto Primal Scream. There was another 45 and two albums up to 1989.

## THE RHINOS (SWEDEN)

The 2003 "Year Of The Rhinos" debut album (on Rainbow Quartz) is a Rickenbacker 12-string guitar-fan's dream – an entire platter of the joyful, ringing jingle-jangle. The lush harmony vocals are there, too, making this a modern Swedish Byrds-influenced gem. "Stop The Time" kicks off the album and is the obvious highlight, but there are many more bright moments throughout. A promo only release precedes this album, and a second 2008 album, "In Rhi-Fi" also was released on Rainbow Quartz, though I haven't seen or heard either. That's a shame (for me), because I love bands that sound like The Rhinos.

## THE RIOTS (YPSILANTI, MI, U.S.A.)

Oh, there have been many punk bands named The Riots, but these hepcats are squarely in the 1966 garage, courtesy of Freddy Fortune's excellent Sound Camera Records. Freddy produced the 2005 "Love After" long-player. It's full of pop-tinged mod-garage fun, highlighted by spirited organ and energetic vocals. The Riots must've been a wailing good time at a house party – they sound like a party waiting to happen. Pick Hits: "Broken Man" and "Hold On Me."

## LOS RIPPERS (ITALY)

At least nine 45s and four albums are out and about from 2003 to at least 2012, though somehow every last one of them have avoided arriving at my stereo! What I have managed to find and hear is very energetic R&B-based garage, expertly played and well recorded, too.

And there was another "Rippers," but from Argentina. All I've seen is one very crude and drop-out riddled video of the band playing live, I believe in the early 1990s, an addled version of the '60s classic "99th Floor" – ironically, a song that the Italian Rippers also played live!

## THE RIVIERA PLAYBOYS
(ROCHESTER, NY, U.S.A.)

"Generic" is not one of those review terms I ever like to use – if I lay it on a release it means that I don't hear a unique flavor or feeling that makes me want to spin it again and again. And that is the word I am forced to use for the 2005 "Ambassadors of Rock-N-Roll" album on Screaming Apple. It is surprisingly flavorless, despite its fine personnel (including ex-Projectile Dave Anderson and ex-Chesterfield King Walt O'Brien). I tried, I really did, and went through this long-player until the "generic" tag stuck in my mind. It's kinda garage, but more so just kinda rock. Generic.

There's also a 1997 album on Jargon and a 2003 45 on Northern Alliance.

## THE ROAD RUNNERS (STOCKHOLM, SWEDEN)

The "'I Believe'" EP (on Uppers) was released as a five song CD of originals in 1997, reportedly in the style of "Get The Picture"-era Pretty Things.

## THE ROAMIN' NUMERALS
(NEW YORK, NY, U.S.A.)

The Stockholm, Sweden Beluga label released the "Fruit Of The Day" b/w "Buckle Up!" 45 in 1998. The wonderfully-named Roamin' Numerals included ex-Fuzztones and Headless Horsemen member Elan Portnoy.

## THE ROARING 420s (DRESDEN, GERMANY)

The 2014 "What Is Psych?" album has a dark garage-psych sound, with some sitar and organ, and a mesmerizing beat. It is difficult to categorize them exactly, which is a good sign that the Roaring 420s have their own sound. My Pick Hit: the elegant, fluid "These Woods of Stones," which has a 13th Floor Elevators-meets the Electric Prunes vibe for me. Yes, that is a good sign.

## THE ROOKIES (ITALY)

How does Massimo Del Pozzo keep finding all these great Italian garage bands for his Misty Lane and Teen Sound labels? The 1998 four song EP is a nice band introduction, highlighted by their lone original track, "Setting Of Despair" – a moody number featuring some soaring viola.

The 2000 four-song 7" EP features more moody garage covers, highlighted by the Warren Zevon classic "Outside Chance."

There's a good power-pop sensibility behind their guitar-garage attack on their 2005 "Out Of Fashion" album, with "You" a prime example of their expert approach. The Rookies sound like a revved up Sick Rose, with high energy as their top priority. The energy here doesn't let up – I got sweaty just listening to it!

## THE ROUTES (OITA, JAPAN)

The Routes certainly have a unique story: U.K. ex-patriot Christopher Jack, living in Japan, collects a variety of bassists and drummers (only one of each at a time) to make garage and instrumental records, released on labels all over the world. Yep, garage is a global phenomenon!

Their debut "Left My Mind" album (2007 on Motor Sounds Records) has a Billy Childish R&B feel to it, complete with (purposely) distorted vocals. The "Alligator" album (2009 on

Dirty Water, U.K.) is a slightly less distorted affair, though still in a Headcoats R&B garage style. The tile track is a highlight here.

The Routes start to hit their stride with the "Do What's Right By You" b/w "Love Like Glue" 45 (on Dirty Water). The sound is basically the same as previous releases, but the songs are tighter and catchier. The Kinks-ish "Don't Want To Know Your Name" and "Everybody's Talking" from the "Better Off" 2013 four-song 7" EP (on Groovie, Portugal) is another step forward (though the record labels list the wrong song order).

The band tackles two classic 1960s covers for the 2011 "Stormy" b/w "Willie The Wild One" 45 on Groovie Records, and both performance and recording improved yet again. A great photo picture sleeve makes this a winner, too.

Then Chris Jack made an interesting choice for the band: the next Routes LP was all-instrumentals. It is titled, of course, "Instrumentals" LP (2012 on Groovie Records) – and it's really a fine record! Kind of Davie Allen-meets-Yardbirds in approach, it surely is a bold move for a group that was just finding its own garage voice in previous releases.

The "I Got A Feelin'" 45 (2013 on Action Weekend Records) is next, and tackles (with vocals) a couple more '60s covers in fine form. There's also another cool instrumental, "Montohihi Mama," on a split 45, with Los Wakamonos and The Paralyz, on Go Ape Records (U.S.A.). The band has produced some really fun music videos for their best tracks, too.

The latest release I have is the "The Hole In My Soul" four-song EP on KOTJ Records (Spain). It probably is my favorite Routes record, with four new band originals – two fine garage punkers and two surf-instrumentals. This was released with two separate 45 cover sleeves, each version limited to only 150 copies. So snatch it up if you see one!

I eagerly await what sound (and lineup) that Chris Jack unleashes on forthcoming Routes records. What continent they will be released on will be a good guess, too.

## THE ROYAL FINGERS (JAPAN)

The 2000 three-song 7" EP on Estrus features one of my favorite color covers in recent memory, and the grooves are darn cool, too. It's primo Japanese instrumental hot-rod stomp, authentic in every detail. There is also a 2000 "Wild Eleki Deluxe" album issued in Japan, available in the U.S.A. on the venerable Del-Fi Records.

## THE ROYAL FLARES (MUNICH, GERMANY)

The debut "Tales Of Sound & Fury" (2013 on Copasedisques) is garage made just how I like it: snotty, fuzzy, and driving. It's pure '66 fun here, with a clean, thick production and a good selection of covers to augment the band originals. This German combo does a fine job with The Squires' uniquely American "Going All The Way" and also captures the headlong fury of The Del Vett's "Last Time Around." The original "Signifying Nothing" has a driving stomping beat that defines garage punk – good and mean.

Pick Hit: the original "This Is Why I." You say you like '66-styled modern garage punk? Then go find this disc (available on vinyl and CD).

## THE ROYAL HANGMEN (ZURICH, SWITZERLAND)

Their self-titled album (2012 on Screaming Apple) is in the fine Euro-beat garage tradition, with its R&B leanings augmented with cool organ and harmonica. "Get Out Of My Way" has some fine Entwistle-like distorted bass, too. The production is slightly more raw than others in the same vein, perhaps to give the proceedings a bit more of an authentic '60s feel. One CD bonus track, "Back Where I Belong," packs a wallop – dig that bass drum oomph – and is one of their best originals.

The 2009 "Mary Jane" b/w "You Better Tell That Girl" 45 on Lost In Tyme is another solid driving garage platter.

# S

## SABROSITAS (TUCSON, ARIZONA, U.S.A.)

Scott Moody headed up the Tucson, Arizona "Star Time" record label, which featured fine locals The Resonars and Al Perry among its small roster. This 1999 lo-fi desert-surf style

CD release, which most instrumental-garage fans probably still have no idea even exists, is so cool in its simplicity. Recorded on a cassette 4-track, this classic Alfie McNabb production has some groovy organ warbling throughout its instrumental runtime. For folks who wonder about surf music in Arizona – we have lots of beach here. Just no ocean.

## THE SATANS (SWEDEN)

If these guys are all Satans then Hell is gonna be a lot of fun. It's pure teenbeat Pebbles-garage time here, kids, and I dig it very much. The 2001 three-song "Girl In My Dreams" 7" EP (on Loser Records) is a fine debut, and I love the matching devil-red coats on the picture sleeve. Also from 2001 is the "Bad Woman" b/w "You'll See Me Cry" 45 on Zorch Productions – and it is an almost perfect 1966 single.

"Bad Woman" (a band original, though it conjures up so many other similar tunes) has the sound of an instant garage classic, with a driving riff, snotty vocals and fabulous production. The B-side is a New England teenbeat styled moody counterpart.

Why do so many fabulous '60s-styled records come from Sweden? Is it the dark, cold winters, when kids are forced inside to listen to Pebbles volume #3 over and over? Whatever it is, you crazy Swedes, keep doing it.

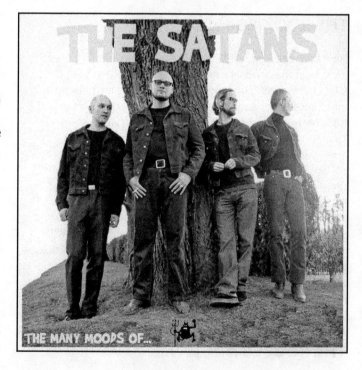

## SATAN'S PILGRIMS (PORTLAND, OR, U.S.A.)

Starting in 1992, the band remained dedicated to surf-ish instrumentals, with at least a half dozen albums and a half-dozen more 45s during their long run. I especially enjoy their 2009 "Psychsploitation" album (on SP Records and reissued in 2013 on Merlin's Nose in Germany), recorded after a long band hiatus. It's like a fake 1966 biker movie soundtrack, with plenty of fuzz and pop-psych touches instead of their usual surf-ish styles. "Kaleidoscope," "Colours Of Your Mind" and "Psycle Pswami" are all period-perfect soundtrack send-ups, maybe even better than the originals in fact.

## THE SATELLITERS (GERMANY)

The Satelliters grew to become one of the most prolific and enjoyable bands in the time since the 1995 printing of this book, starting in 1994 and all the way up through 2014. There are at least 11 albums and more than a dozen 45s available, with no end in sight. I gave up trying to collect it all – there is that much Satelliters product out there!

At least five of the albums are on Dionysus, which nurtured the band along considerably by making them available in the U.S.A. as a priority for the label. I was happy to produce the "Why Do They Know" music video clip for the 2007 "Where Do We Go?" album, and that song remains one of my favorites from the 2000s garage-psych era. While the earlier Satelliters releases are more distinctly (and deliberately) in the lo-fi recording category, the band developed their sound and production technique as time went along – and their songwriting blossomed as well.

The albums "Wyld Knights Of Action" (1997 ), Sexplosive," (2001), "Hi Karate!" (1996) and "Shake, Shake, Shake" (1998) are all recommended – and I'm certain I'd praise highly the remainder of their catalog if those discs were here in front of me.

The aptly titled "More Of" album from 2014 (on Dionysus) is the latest as of this writing. My Pick Hits: Gotta Get You (Out Of My Head)" (which sounds a lot like label mates The Creatures Of The Golden Dawn), "Girl It's Over Now" and the 12-string "Part Time Passions."

The Satelliters are one of the must-not-miss bands of the garage revival era. They combine an expert knowledge of the original '60s sound, blend it with their own musical personalities and a keen sensibility, and deliver solid garage-pop (and some occasional psych) of the highest order.

## THE SATURN V Featuring Orbit
(SAN FRANCISCO, CA, U.S.A.)

The frat-rock party atmosphere of the Saturn V is infectious, and the 1997 "Give Her Lovin'" b/w "So The Syracuse" 45 (on Dionysus) and 1999 four-song 7" EP (on Teen Sound) are a blast. There's some garage royalty involved, too, with Johnny Bartlett from the Phantom Surfers and Ron Silva and Tom Ward formerly of the Gravedigger V and Crawdaddys. There are at least a couple more 45s and two albums out, from 2002 and 2004.

## THE SCARECROWS (UPDATE)

It was reported to me that the band's singer, Yves Eve Pollart, has passed away. I've also heard a live version of the band, circa 1983, doing a scorching version of the Castaways' classic "Liar Liar."

## THE SECRET SERVICE (UPDATE)

Very active on the U.S. east coast during their mid-1980s heyday, the 1999 "Power and Volume" retrospective CD (on Snap, Crackle & Pop) shows that the Long Island lads were masters of their Mod sounds. The 28-songer includes the 1988 "It's all Happening" EP, studio tracks from 1985-88, and live tracks from the span of the band's life. The Secret Service (like Mod Fun) are a band that I've come to appreciate greatly more as time has gone on – and that is as good a testament of a band's worth as anything. "Its All Happening Here," baby!

## THE SELLWOODS (PORTLAND, OR, U.S.A.)

The 2013 four-song 7" EP on Smash Records is good, very basic, no-frills single-guitar garage rock. I like the touch of Theremin on "Mini Skirt Mob," too. Three chords and mono almost always sounds good, kids!

## SHAKE BEFORE US (See the "Guest Authors" chapter for more information.)

## THE SHAMBLES (SAN DIEGO, CA, U.S.A.)

Another of Bart Mendoza's sparkling pop-mod-garage treats, The Shambles picked up where Manual Scan left off – that means guitar-based catchy pop tunes, full of hooks and sweet vocals. "Fire" kicks off the "Reviving Spark" album (1996 on 1+2 Records) on a sunny note, and the garage feel arrives with a fine cover of "Louise," with lead vocals from the always-excellent Ray Brandes. Other San Diego garage mainstays Bill Calhoun and, David Klowden also make worthy appearances. I'm sure Bart groaned when he saw that the songwriting for The Zombies' "You Make Me Feel Good" was credited to him on the CD sleeve – he writes enough quality songs himself that he doesn't need credit for that classic! There are at least six other albums and more singles available, too. Go get 'em.

The 1996 "Innocence Becomes You" b/w "Nadie Te Quire Ya" 45 on Get Hip is more meaty Mod-pop, with the B-side sung in Spanish.

The 2013 "Live At The Casbah" is a limited CD compiling "live" performances at the band's hometown Casbah club from 2003 and 2004. The performance and sound quality of this in-the-room recording is pretty good, but I would've liked to hear a more direct feed of Mendoza's fine vocals.

## SHUTDOWN 66 (AUSTRALIA)

The "Welcome To Dumpsville" album (on Get Hip, 2001) is a U.S.A. re-issue of the 1998 Australian release. It's Euro-beat garage all the way, with plenty of wailing harp and some fine, warbling organ riffs. If you like your garage in the early snotty Stones-white-R&B style, then this satisfies. There are at least two more LPs on Corduroy in Australia and at least ten 7-inchers.

## THE SICK ROSE (UPDATE)

Long-time readers of my garage reviews know that I class Italy's The Sick Rose among the top echelon of garage bands from any continent, in any era. Amazingly, they have survived all the way through this 2014 writing, and are playing a live show even as I write this. While moving away from the more purist '66-garage sound into a very pleasing power-pop guitar style, The Sick Rose also saw the reissue of their seminal 1986 "Faces" LP on Teen Sound in 2008. It included the 1986 "Get Along Girl" EP tracks, too, and is one of the most essential releases I'll ever write about for this book. **No excuses, kids: if you love garage music you must obtain and cherish the "Faces" album.**

There is also a 2001 7" picture disc on Swamp Room that is as wonderful to look at as to hear.

The 2005 "Blastin' Out" LP (also on Teen Sound) showcases their power-pop expertise, with The Stems' Dom Mariani producing – so you know it has shimmering guitars and lots of pop hooks. A newer "best of" CD is also available to help a new generation understand how important The Sick Rose remain. We are so fortunate the band is still vital and strong – the band celebrated its 30th anniversary in 2013, and are still touring. Anyone within their earshot has no excuse to miss them.

## THE SIDEWALK SCENE (SAN DIEGO, CA, U.S.A.)

This is Tell-Tale Heart alums Ray Brandes and Eric Bacher (and Mark Zadarnowski and Joe Piper of The Crawdaddys, plus Paul Carsola from the Hedgehogs) in full 12-string folk-rock mode. There is a self-titled a four-song 2014 CD EP, including a tribute song to Gene Clark, and a cover of "Know My Rider" done Byrds-style.

## THE SILENCERS (DETROIT, MI, U.S.A.)

The Silencers mine a more traditional California surf sound, and their own "Link Wray heaved through Dick Dale's living room window" description beats anything my fingers can peck out. The Detroit trio also earn an extra hotdog and beer

from me for emphasizing original sounds on their 1997 debut disc for Total Energy, though each of their fiery numbers bring to mind a menu of earlier seminal surf and burn tunes. That's OK, there's plenty of hotdogs to go around, and some sand in between the toes sounds good just about now.

The Silencers followed up 1997's promising debut with a much more authoritative and gritty "Cyclerific Sounds" LP (1999, on Total Energy). Instrumental-fuzz, a la Davie Allan, is the recipe here, and I just love the rap about how "The man is everywhere, and he's gonna bust us!"

"Guaranteed to blow the squares' minds." Yeah, baby!

The 2001 three-song 7" EP on Pure Vinyl has a heavier "Love Theme From Motorcycho" (yes, that spelling is correct) plus a couple vocal tracks on the flip, including an Alice Cooper cover, all recorded at the hipster Ghetto Recorders by Jim Diamond.

## RON SILVA AND THE MONARCHS
(CA, U.S.A.)

The 1994 four-song 7" EP (on Get Hip) looks every bit like a 1964 U.K. release, and the four vintage R&B covers are convincing and period-perfect, too. Ron Silva (and Tom Ward) are veterans of The Crawdaddys, Gravedigger V, and Saturn V, so you know this is the real deal.

## THE SIRES (U.K.)

These U.K. cats first delivered two worthy blasts, with the "It Ain't Happening Anymore" 45 (on Smart Guy) and their 1998 debut LP "Rulers Of Your Hearts" (on Twist). When I last saw Domi and Andy in the early 1990s, they were spewing out twisted French garage in Limoge with a band called Thee Turkee Necks; then they invaded the U.K. – and The Sires are a worthy and logical extension for their mayhem.

All of this junk was recorded at the infamous Toe Rag studios in London, so you know that it has all the snarl, guts and energy that's required to make a dog's ears bleed. Yes, these are compliments!

The Sires also put a super-nasty attitude to fine use on a pair of four-song EPs: the "High & Mighty" 7" EP (1996 on Twist) and the "Sires Rule!...Okay?" four song EP (1997 on Twist). Primo and essential stuff.

## SIT N' SPIN (UPDATE)

The 1996 three-song 7" EP on Pure Vinyl is wonderfully produced '60s girl pop (recorded at the home studio of pop mavens The Grip Weeds), with "Dance With My Baby" a bouncy gem. The B-side "El Guapo" is a tasty instrumental, too. It's a shame that more Sit N' Spin hasn't crossed through my doorway – I dig their sound. At least three other albums and more 45s also exist.

## THE SIXTY SECOND SWINGERS
(LA ROCHELLE, FRANCE)

If you've read this far then you understand how important I think a good keyboard player is for a garage band. Whether it is a Vox, Farfisa or some wheezing cheap-o knock-off (which are sometimes even better), the organ is a garage act's secret weapon. And so it is with the wonderful "Better With Fuzz Babe" album (2013 on Soundflat Records).

All the perfect '66 garage elements are in place here: snot-filled vocals, fuzzy, buzzy guitar – and my fave, those wiggling organ tones. The band is named after a song by Little Phil and The Night Shadows, and it fits them well, because within one minute you will be hooked. I love the very basic recording here – not too crude but still raw, and the boys are fortunate to have some fab originals and only a smattering of covers. Their take on "City Of People" is the best since Canada's mid-80s Ten Commandments, but it is the originals that really blast and shine. Pick Hit: "Please Don't Let Me Down" (a showcase for that keyboard I love so much) and the stomping "I Got Something."

Important playback note: this 12" runs at 45 rpm! Without this detail the band sounds a bit depressed if played at the usual 33 1/3 RPM.

There are at least two more 45s out there as well, which I will start searching for now.

## THE SLEEPWALKERS (ITALY)

The fuzz-and-snot meter heads all the way into the red for the 1998 "I Wanna Eat Your Brain" b/w "Go On Leave" 45 (on Psych-Out). This is snarly, gritty garage-punk in beautiful mono, and I truly believe the Sleepwalkers want to eat my brain.

## SLOW SLUSHY BOYS (UPDATE)

France's Slow Slushy Boys kept cranking out the crude joy with two new 45s, one their own Larsen label and the other on the Italian 3M&P outfit; a three-song 7" EP on Pure Vinyl (Austria), and a four-song 7" EP on Psych Out also appeared.

The "Play And Sing 10 Slushy Hits" 10" (1995 on Larsen) has a live-in-the-studio party vibe to it, highlighted by a fine cover of Phil & The Frantics "I Must Run" (itself a good rip of the Zombies' "I Must Move"). The "Boogaloo" album (2000 on Larsen) has an even more authentic 1960s party vibe to it, courtesy of Toe Rag Studio's U.K. mono sound. File The Slow Slushy Boys with your other garage true-believers.

And more information from the band: " The boys made a small French tour early in 2007 and played at the great Soundflat Ballroom Bash in Leipzig, with Curlee Wurlee, the Montesas, the Cool Jerks, the Satelliters & the Staggers. Four new tracks were recorded at Larsen studio, and a new single is out on B-Soul, "Move your hand" b/w "Don't Look Back." The fourth single for Butterfly Records (and twentieth for the band!) "The Duck" b/w "The Worm" was planned for 2008.

2012 - After four silent years, the band was back on stage, with a new line up and a new set : A nine piece band, including a horn section (two trombones, trumpet & sax) and a funky rhythm section played only new material (except a few old slushy hits like "Dance On Thru," "Move Your Hand" or "Why.") This lineup went into the Larsen studio to record a new album.

2013 - 16 new songs were recorded and the eighth album, "Live Together," was released. The band started again to tour, as a nine piece band, or as guitar, drums, bass, vocals.

More discography additions: LP "Move Your Hand" (Benny Gordini & Friends) 2009; France LP "Live Together" on Larsen Records, 2013; France 7" "Move Your Hand" B/w "Don't Look Back" on B-Soul, 2007, France; 7" "The Duck" b/w "The Worm" on Butterfly Records 2008, Espagne; 7" "Paint It Green" b/w "Mobile Blues" on B-Soul 2014, France.

## SMALLSTONE (LOS ANGELES, CA, U.S.A.)

Their 2000 self-titled debut was on Bomp! – It was a good initial power-pop effort, which also has enough muscle to fight away the flab that infects similar bands. Flashes of melodic brilliance ("Perfect Day" and "Sunshine Girl") and a seductive, sleepy atmosphere make Smallstone an act to discover.

## THE SMELL OF INCENSE (UPDATE)

The four-song 1997 "Through The Gates Of Deeper Slumber" EP (on CD through September Gurls Records) is centered around the 25-minute opening track "A Floral Treasury." The extended time allows the band to create a mystical and hushed world in five parts. Plenty of Mellotron and sitar highlight this epic – one of the most accomplished high-concept psychedelic recordings of the revival era. For those who enjoy a folk tint to their early Floyd-styled psych (like me), this is the pinnacle of colorful expression.

The 1994 "Smell of Incense" b/w "A Visit To Ashiya" 45 (also on September Gurls) is a slab of vinyl that took me several years to find. The band's cover of the seminal 1960s classic "Smell of Incense" is a true neo-psych classic, showing why the song title is worthy to be taken as the band's moniker. I also have a test pressing for a 1995 three-song 45 with the handwritten titles "Why Did I Get So High, "If Not This Time" and So I Coming Down."

There is the "All Mimsy Were The Borogroves" album from 1994, a 1997 10" and also the 2007 "Of Ullages And Dottles" LP, though I haven't tracked them down yet.

## KENDRA SMITH (CA, U.S.A.)

The "Five Ways Of Disappearing" title of Smith's 1995 full-length solo debut might comment on her exit from music since the late 1980s. The bassist, guitarist and gentle vocalist helped shape such seminal acts as The Dream Syndicate, Clay Allison and Opal – and then left music behind. 1995's "Five Ways" (on 4AD) touches thematically on all of her previous pioneering, while also experimenting with odd or unconventional instrumentation and arrangements. Her trademark hushed vocals and restrained presence are also omnipresent, and stand-out tracks such as "Temporarily Lucy" and "Valley Of The Morning Sun" showed that Smith had been away for much too long.

## THE SMOGGERS (SPAIN)

Fernando Smogger is one of those few "True Believers" I mention throughout this book. You know, the guys who actually live their garage rock passions: Caveman haircuts. Bone necklaces. Vox Phantom guitars. They believe so fervently in the pure beauty of 1966-styled garage rock that they must start their own band, write their own garage anthems, and then take the garage sacrament to the people.

So Fernando plays guitar and shouts for The Smoggers, the ultimate demonstration of his garage faith. Attitude is so important in any genre of rock music, and check out Fernando's vibe – his playful sneer on the cover of the 2013 "Join The Riot" LP (on Clifford Records) for instance. Yep, there is garage rock punk attitude to spare in The Smoggers, who seem not to care one bit what anyone thinks about them.

They gotta do what they gotta do.

And make no, mistake, I do like The Smoggers, a lot. They have a barely controlled feeling of mayhem about them, as if the band will start smoldering and explode at any moment. That kind of dangerous feeling makes for very exciting garage music, and the appropriately-named "Join The Riot" album oozes with musical danger. They sing in both English and Spanish, and it sounds just as nasty either way. Highlights include the anthemic "No Estare" and the pounding "You'll Never Know Us," full of the fuzziest fuzztone and stomping drums. Yep, "True Believers."

The A-side of their 2011 EP "A Day With You" (b/w "Come On Now!" and "One More Time" on Grit Records) is an almost perfect 1966 garage fuzzer, and worth digging to find.

The 2012 "Chinese Food" 10" (on Clifford) is crude fun, but doesn't yet emanate the unbridled energy of their subsequent LP. That palpable lunacy is apparent on the 2012 "Shame On You" three-song 7" EP (on KOTJ Records). The 2013 "Breaking Your Boots With" four-song 7" EP (on KOTJ) is also trashy fun. Ah, that word – fun – an essential element to the best garage music and also of The Smoggers.

Bless those few bands that have entered the Kingdom of Fuzz and shall be rewarded throughout garage eternity. So bless the mighty Smoggers – I am a true believer in them.

## THE SNAILS (GREECE)

Some really cool fuzz guitar – always my favorite – highlights the debut 2009 four-song 7" EP on Action Records, but for The Snails and their distinctively Greek garage sound my favorite is the more subdued, dramatic and paisley-tinged "Won't Let You Go."

The 2011 self-titled album (on CD again for Action Records) finds the band sounding much more confident and accomplished, aided by a much-improved studio recording, too. That wonderful fuzz guitar is an ample supply – "Sidewalks," "Wyld Child" and "Universal Soldier" are all supreme fuzzers, but once again I like even more their moodier side as typified in the vibrating, wonderfully moody "Dove." Oh, and some beautiful cover art completes this album package.

Around since 2005, it seems The Snails are still taking their time to deliver their sounds to the world, but it is a wait worth the effort..

## THE SNYDES (U.K.)

The four song "Four Sydes Of" 7" EP (2000 on Twist) is a rather polite Mod-pop-garage affair, highlighted by a reverential cover of "The 13th Floor Elevator's "You're Gonna Miss Me," complete with some electric jug-like sounds. In mono on beautiful white wax, too!

## THE SOLARFLARES (U.K.)

Many fans point to The Milkshakes as the early 1980s Brit-garage-pop act that turned them onto the entire U.K. scene, but for me The Prisoners did the trick. Ex-Prisoners Alan Crockford and Graham Day are also two-thirds of The Solarflares (with drummer Wolf Howard), who blasted back with the 2000 "Psychedelic Tantrum" LP and "Can't Get You Out Of My Mind!" single (both on Twist). I can't fully describe how difficult it is for writers/performers like Crockford and Day to sound fresh, inspired and excited after two decades of work, but The Solarflares pull it off in a bloody brilliant fashion. This is the power side of pop, with the single especially showcasing the wonderfully analog tones of the infamous Toe Rag studio – many fans' Mecca of fuzz.

The Solar Flares' second long player for Twist, the sardonic "That Was Then...And So Is This," (2000) elevates their power-Mod-pop attack to new levels. These garage veterans know you can't keep a good melody down. Highly recommended!

## THE SOUND EXPLOSION (UPDATE)

A 2014 split 45 on Lost In Tyme with fellow Greek band The Basements is available – with the Sound Explosion offering the marvelous "Every Day And Every Night." It is classic driving 1966 fuzz n' Farfisa, and instantly went onto my "Best Garage Songs Of All Time" list. (The Basements song on the split 45, "Stop Rolling," is fine, too.)

The Sound Explosion remain one of the finest Greek garage groups of all time. There is also a "Last Recordings" EP from 2000 since the last edition of this book.

## THE SPACE COSSACKS
(WASHINGTON, DC, U.S.A.)

The 2000 "Tsar Wars" album (on MuSick) followed up their 1998 debut "Interstellar Stomp" LP (also on MuSick). It's space-age instrumental fun here, well-produced and fitting in nicely with MuSick's roster of instro specialists. At least three vinyl 7-inchers (including a split 45 with The Fathoms) were launched before the band departed our orbit in 2000.

## SPANISH MOSS
(SANTA CRUZ, CA, U.S.A.)

The "Kelp" album (2012 on Spot-On Sound) is a heavy guitar-based modern psych assault, with the lead-off track "Fuzz Puzzle" landing at almost 10 minutes. They remind me a bit of Plan 9, and I'm betting they pack a wallop in person with a wall of fuzz and fury.

## THE SPECTORS (UPDATE)

The 1992-1996 compilation "Beat Is Murder: Cockfights & Cakefights" (2002 on Get Hip) is a fine introduction to the energetic garage-pop of yet another band that should of, could of, should have been heard by a lot more folks than the underground could muster. The Spectors aren't retro-purist at all, which should've helped their cause with a more mainstream audience, but they'll just have to be happy with leaving some fine tunes behind in their wake.

## THE SPIDER BABIES (UPDATE)

The "I'm Dead" b/w "Treat Me Right" 45 (1994 on Tombstone Records) is a true garage-punk treat, from the mono sound to the straight-ahead three-chord fuzz and organ onslaught. "I'm Dead" is a true garage classic, and when they sneer "I'm dead, how 'about you?" I just have to smile. This is garage rock, baby!

By accident I saw that the band played a few shows in Europe as late as 2014, a full 20 years after this 45. *There are at least a full 10 more 7"s out there I haven't seen, plus at least seven albums, dating up to 2012. Gulp!*

## THE SPINNS (CHAPEL HILL, NC, U.S.A.)

The irony of the fabulously homemade "Lost Colony" album (2005 on Demonbeach) is that while the band does not look overly purist in their 1960s style, the recording has a distinct and authentic "Back From The Grave" 1966 garage band vibe to it all. Many crappy-but-hyped indie bands have come out of that area of the U.S.A., but here's an act that *deserved* some attention and praise! There are a couple 7"s as well. It is fabulous and uniquely original garage heaven to my ears.

## THE SQUARES (UPDATE)

The "Squarification" album (1995 on Get Hip) is a worthy snot-filled chapter of the band's reign of mayhem. Pick Hit: the distorted vocal punch to the mouth of "Baby."

## THE STEMS (UPDATE)

At this late date I'm not sure how many bands I have on my "All-Time Ten Best Bands of the Neo-Garage Era" list – maybe 20 or 30 crowd the list now. But move them all out of the way, because I have to make sure that The Stems are always in there. While main Stem Dom Mairiani kept busy with various other bands and recordings – a special shout-out to the wonderful and mainly instrumental Majestic Kelp while I think of them – fans were especially delighted with the band's reunion halfway through the new century's first decade.

The 2007 "Heads Up" album (on Invisible Records) showed why fans longed for their return. "She Sees Everything" showcases Mariani's special pop-garage touch, while Dave Shaw's "Surround Me" continues the band's legacy of jangly pop. It is all simply fabulous garage-pop, expertly performed and produced.

A vintage 1986 live show also saw release as "Weed Out" on CD and LP in 1997 (on House Of Wax), and it also explains why the Stems' star continues to burn bright long after many of the other bands from this era have faded.

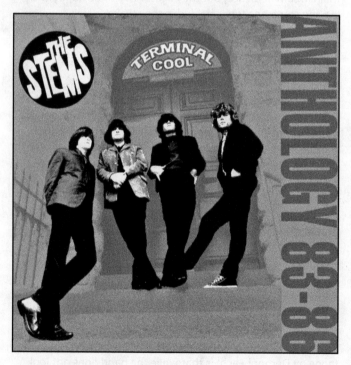

## THE STONEAGE HEARTS (AUSTRALIA)

There is a slightly distorted power-pop feel to the early 2000s four-song 7" EP on Butterfly, with the bouncy cover of "The

Bitter Thoughts of Little Jane" actually my favorite. There are also 2002 and 2004 albums on Off The Hip and at least one more 45 – and with Dom Mariani of The Stems involved, too!

## THE STORMCLOUDS (UPDATE)

My praise of this quiet U.K. combo was mainly based around a few 7" releases and cassette tapes, so I'm delighted to report that at least two CDs have since found their way to me ears. "Nightmares In The Sky" (1996 on Rainfall) and "Sleep No More" (2000 also on Rainfall) are full of the quiet psych that I love so much, propelled by ringing guitar and sweet, quiet vocals. Listeners who don't take the time to delve into these very personal and unique songs might tag them as a Mazzy Star-ish act, but the comparison is only superficial.

While both mine a reverbed, hushed world, The Stormclouds have a distinct English feel to them with a dash of folk. It makes perfect sense that one of my other favorite U.K. psych faves, Reefus Moons, guests on the "Sleep No More" album – the two bands share production styles and feel. This later album also is more upbeat.

Both are an acquired taste that demand some time and attention to penetrate their cloak – and both are worth the effort.

## THE STEWED (UPDATE)

Also from England comes a trio of long-haired weirdos called The Stewed. Their first two seven inchers showed promise but not much spark – but that element is in abundance on their 1995 "Deep Down Thing" LP.

The Stewed recall those few minutes in late 1968 when Led Zeppelin's over-amped blues treatment hadn't tipped over into arena rock redundancy and excess. There's more of a MC5 or Stooges feel here, along with some garage junk and slight metal tinges, but The Stewed seem adept at keeping all of these influences in balance.

They also add some wailing harmonica and frantic sax on top of their mega-distorted guitar, taking chances with formulas rather than delivering on expectations. "Hate Reducer, "Star Spangled Lie" and She's My Witch" all have that aforementioned spark, and I get the feeling that I'd be screaming along with them after a few pints at the pub.

## LOS STRAIGHTJACKETS
(NASHVILLE, TN, U.S.A.)

A slew of instrumental bands have flooded the garage underground since the original 1995 book, and some have found an easier time gaining a more mainstream foothold in the marketplace. Perhaps the mere idea of "retro surf" isn't as challenging as garage punk, but for whatever reason, a few instrumental acts have succeeded (relatively speaking, on a commercial level) where many others have not.

It is with that introduction that I observe that Los Straightjackets might be "too professional" an outfit for the garage genre. Expertly arranged and performed – and complete with Mexican wrestler masks – Los Straightjackets are slick entertainers that know exactly what they are marketing.

There are many, many releases available (at least 15 albums and a whole bunch of 45s from 1995 to 2014) as of this writing, and 2003's "Supersonic Guitars In 3-D" (On Yep Roc) seems a typical example – well produced and performed instrumental tunes bridging surf, hot rod and exotica. It's not that any of this is bad – just the opposite, the band is quite fun and pleasing. It's just that it also strikes me a bit *too* calculated and commercial. It's not their fault, and it might not make much sense, but perhaps they also are too good of a band for garage fans?

## THE STRANGE FLOWERS (UPDATE)

The 2005 "Ortoflorovivaistica" album – write that five times fast – on Beyond Your Mind Records shows the band's expert psych-pop coming to fruition. The Syd Barrett-meets-The Byrds feel remains, with "John On The Moon" a beautiful, smooth and melodic meditation. The 17 minutes of "Strange Girl" shows the band also able to stretch out into an inspired psych plane as well.

The wonderfully-titled "The Imaginary Space Travel Of The Naked Monkeys" album (2007, also on Beyond Your Mind) isn't as trippy, and loses some of its obvious 1960s influences, but with some fine melody on "Drops Of Light" and "Pleased When You Come." The 2008 "Aeroplanes In The Backyard" (on Teen Sound, in their native Italy) is a more upbeat affair, without as much of the guitar jangle that highlighted their earlier work. There are also at least three more albums dating up to 2001 which I'd like to hear.

## STRAWBERRY SMELL (FRANCE)

You should know by now that I have the softest of soft spots in my music heart for Beatles-like 1966 pop songs. They are my ultimate goal to write and also to hear. And so The Strawberry Smell's "Zen Song 9" makes my heart skip a beat each time those harmonies kick in. It's from the 2002 "Odorama" album (on Bip Bip Records).

There are also 1994 and 1997 seven-inch releases, and the 2003 "Strawboscopic" album – which has a much more mainstream modern pop-electro feel to it, and thus is less interesting (to me).

## THE STROLLERS (SWEDEN)

These lads continued the unlikely tradition of gritty Swedish garagers with their 1998 four-songer on Low Impact. These boys do everything right for their debut: trusty mono grooves, bowl haircuts and a picture sleeve worthy of the Pretty Things make this EP one of those little treasures that I'm thankful for stumbling upon.

The follow-up "Bring her Home" b/w "Stay Away" 45 (also on Low Impact) is another essential Swedish garage winner – the A-side is a three-chord killer and the flip an organ-hooked toe-tapper. Simply awesome, in mono, too.

The Strollers then delivered a knock-out punch with their 1999 debut long-layer, "Falling Right Down!" (on Low Impact). I never thought a band would ever come along to take the Swedish crown from such 1980s masters as The Creeps or Stomachmouths – and I was wrong. "Falling Right Down!" doesn't only match up with the best of Swedish garage, it's one of the best debut LPs I've heard. The fuzz, snot, tough and guttural production – and original songs – are all there in force. It doesn't hurt that these guys look cool, very cool, in a way that makes me thankfully forget Abba ever existed.

The follow-up album, "Captain Of My Ship" (2000 on Low Impact) is also distinctive, and fits in with the best of Swedish garage royalty. "Not Good Enough For You" is a moody beat ballad that would've fit perfectly into a 1966 Zombies' concert, and the title track is another garage stomper in the best tradition of the early Creeps. Bravo! There's another 7" on Teen Sound from 2000, too, with another fab Swedish garage legend, Jens Lindberg.

## STRYPES (IRELAND)

I know, this book isn't about major label bands like Strypes, but they received so much attention in both the mainstream and the garage underground as I wrote this 2014 book that I felt I needed to add something here. These very young lads mine a very slick '60s blues-based rock, bringing some comparisons to an early Stones or Yardbirds. They have been deemed by media and fashionistas to be very hip.

There's only one problem: to me it all seems so calculated and emotionally empty. For me, it's just more major label product, packaged to look like something new and shiny. Go ahead, roll your eyes at me – I remember friends doing that to me when I raved on in the early 2000s about how much I liked The Strokes. Yes, there are commercial marketing similarities here, but for whatever reason, The Strokes connected to me on an authentic *visceral* level that these kids do not.

But then, I've never cared about what is considered hip anyway. And by the time most people read this the goal-line of what is "hip" will have been moved on us all once again. Ah, but an actual 1965 Yardbirds rave-up is forever, man.

## SUMMER SUNS (PERTH, AUSTRALIA)

Once I get in power-pop mode it's difficult to shake me out of it, so I'll give a grateful nod to Get Hip for issuing the Summer Suns 10" EP (in 1998). The Australian combo featured luminaries from a score of other great mid-'80s acts – including Dom Mariani from my fave Aussie act of all time, The Stems, and now the DM3. These tracks were recorded in 1986 and at the time were "released" only on cassette. Some of the songs were later re-recorded and officially released, but this eight-song EP is the vinyl debut of the originals.

This stuff is all hooks and hum-able choruses, shimmering guitars and soaring vocals. Ahhhh, the joys of power-pop!

## SUN DIAL (See the "Fan Submitted Updates" chapter for more information.)

## THE SUNNYBOYS (SYDNEY, AUSTRALIA)

The "Happy Man" b/w "Tomorrow Will Be Fine" 45 was released by Mushroom in 1981, and was a precursor to the Australian guitar-pop revival of the 1980s.

## THE SURF SLUTS (U.K.)

The parody of the Beach Boys' "Pet Sounds" album cover (complete with pot leaf) lets listeners know this isn't a reverential stab at surf music. The idea of a British surf band is silly enough, but the "Pot Sounds" album (2000, on Delerium) is full of party-woops and none of it takes itself seriously one bit. It's not really surf music anyway, but a mish-mash of '60s frat rock, surf, some fuzz, and of course, stoned humor. Bless you, Surf Sluts!

## SURF TRIO (UPDATE)

Garage fans are a picky bunch – keep strictly to the genre or die, many say. Ironically some of the best garage acts defy mere carbon copying and take on the scorn of purists – and create more interesting sounds as a result. Enter Oregon's Surf Trio, which both revered and destroyed the surf-garage genre beginning in 1985.

"Moxie and More" (on Blood Red, 2000) collects EP and 45 tracks from these past 15 years, and displays a band with enough wit, humor and chops to both pay homage to surf roots while also fucking up the whole thing when needed. Their "Forbidden Sounds" (on Dionysus) shows the Surf Trio better than ever, with an expert balance of melodic instro-surf ("Clatskanie" and "Foglifter") and snot-fun punk ("Party In My Dorm"). They don't dress right – they play right.

## THE SWIV-O-MATICS (BALTIMORE, MD, U.S.A.)

"The Return of The Fezman" (1998 on Bad Go-Getter) mines the fuzz-meets-surf sub-genre, and must've been a real hoot at house party gigs. This kind of fun instrumental stuff always is better after a few cold ones, in the middle of a sweaty dance floor. Yep, you know you are still alive, because the Swiv-O-Matics are still playing.

---

*NOTE: Remember to read the original 1995 book and the other book update chapters for thousands of other bands and records not featured in this update section.*

---

# T

## THE TABLES (OSLO, NORWAY)

A circa-2000 early Pink Floyd tribute vinyl 45 features covers of "See Emily Play" b/w "Arnold Layne" by this Norwegian group, in an edition of only 200 copies on Two Zero Records. Their versions are quite good – I wish I could find the actual 45 to own myself.

To my surprise I find there are at least seven other 45s and two albums (on Perfect Pop) out beside this 45. The only other track I've heard is from the band's 1988 debut and is in a more indie-pop vein.

## TEE AND THEE CRUMPETS
(SAN FRANCISCO, CA, U.S.A.)

A flat, bland production style mitigates the excitement of "Introducing Today's Young Hitmakers" (2000 on Dionysus), which needed a bit more flavor to accentuate singer Tee Emmerich's snotty front-woman contributions. A lady front-person is still rare in garage rock circles, and Dionysus is well-known as fans of girls in the garage (literally, with their compilation series of 1960s girl-group albums). Friends would sing to me the praises of the Crumpets' live show, in the early 2000s, so I'm guessing in person they enraptured the listener in ways this sole album doesn't quite achieve.

## LOS TELEPATAS (BUENOS AIRES, ARGENTINA)

The 2013 "Vs El Mundo" album (Rastrillo Records) is classic organ and fuzz '60s garage, sung in Spanish. Seems they actually formed way back in 1989, with a debut disc appearing in 1994. The song I've found from that debut, "Mejor Tomate 2 Vasos De Whisky," is a wild garage fuzzer.

## TELL-TALE HEARTS (UPDATE)

As a certified Tell-Tale Hearts fan myself I was delighted to see that some live recordings found the light of day on vinyl, and I was surprised to actually find the 1997 "Live Vol 2 – Later That Night In Springfield" album on Corduroy. Unfortunately the sonic quality of these recordings is just plain crappy, and even as a fan I don't get a lot of enjoyment out of LPs where I have to recall in my mind the original recording of "Satisfy You" by The Seeds in order try to recognize that it is the same song being played on my turntable in this muffled "live" recording.

I do understand the enthusiasm in wanting to make more vintage Tell-Tale Hearts sounds available, but instead of enhancing their reputation this release was just a disappointment. So, no, I don't need to track down the "Volume 1" album with more crude recordings from this 1986 show.

## TEMPLES (U.K.)

"Shelter Song," the kick-off of the 2014 "Sun Structures" album (on Heavenly), features a wonderful chiming guitar hook and mesmerizing vocals wrapped around an hypnotic beat, a la Abbey Road circa December 1966. Maybe I am the only one who thinks this also sounds like a Micky Dolenz outtake from The Monkees' "Head" album – which is a compliment from me, though others may piffle at the reference. The Revolver-era meets Dukes of Stratosphear vibe continues throughout, and man, do they know how to use compression and limiting in the studio – this album (especially the drums) sounds loud!

The amount of catchy hooks and expert melody separates Temples here from others who replicate a dreamy psych mood but without much form to the songs themselves. This is lovely pop-psych music, beautiful and lush, modern yet also vintage.

I do think, though, that Temples' follow-up will reveal much about this band – is this a one-trick pony, or a new leader for more mainstream U.K. psych-pop in this new century?

## THE TEMPONAUTS (ITALY)

"A Million Year Picnic" (2007 on Teen Sound) opens with an exciting Mod-pop burst, and reflects perfectly the bright and colorful album art. This is garage pop for a walk in the park on a sunny day – upbeat, catchy, bright and fun. Pick Hit: the delightful and hook-laden "(She's An ) Animal, " which would fit right in on a song list for the great Stems.

## LES TERRIBLES (PARIS, FRANCE)

The "Ils Sont Formidables!" 2009 album (on Screaming Apple) is one of the most purely European-sounding records in this book, at least to my Arizona ears. Yes, the sensual female singing in French is one aspect, and I get a feeling that these cats and one kitten might sip good French wine instead of swizzle German beer. It's all a bit more refined (on this recording at least) than the usual garage outfit, especially the bachelor-pad-vibe backing vocals. It is difficult at this late date for me to hear a band that certainly fits in the garage genre yet still surprises me, and Les Terribles certainly do that. And is that a Plastic Bertrand cover I hear in there, too?

There is also a 2005 album on Dionysus that seems a bit more raw, a 2011 45 on Hillsdale, and the "Quelque Chose Comme Ca" album (2012 on Screaming Apple). This last album is less slick-sounding, too, and has more of a traditional garage feel for me, so I prefer it to the 2009 release. There some catchy originals ("Chou-Chou" and "Je Rentre Tard" especially) but it is Les Terribles' cover of the We The People/Chocolate Watch Band classic "In The Past" that is my favorite, full of pulsating vibe and wonderfully delivered.

## THE THANES (UPDATE)

Lenny Helsing has endured the decades to become a garage legend. There are only a few bands, in any era, which can compete as practitioners of authentic 1960s U.K. beat music like his band The Thanes. There are numerous other releases available, and their "The Complete Undignified Nobleman Sessions," (2005 on Teen Sounds) compile the 1996 sessions at Toe Rag Studios – surely the most appropriate place in the world for Lenny and the boys to lay down tracks that you would swear came from 1965. It took me a half-a-minute to realize that their cover of the early Syd Barrett gem "Lucy Leave" wasn't actually the original! Such love and enthusiasm for the genre oozes from every Thanes release, not as a museum piece, but as a living, breathing garage animal.

More pick hits: The "Downbeat And Folked Up" album appeared on Screaming Apple in 2003 and the "A Night In Great King Street" on Larsen in 2007, plus a whole load of 7-inchers since the original book documented their early years.

The Thanes sound absolutely masterful on the "She's Coming Back To Me" b/w "Love Is Fading Away" 45 (2013 on State Records). I've been watching a lot of the early 1960s U.K. "Ready, Steady Go" TV show recently, and "Love Is Fading Away" sounds like it could have been from an appearance by The Searchers on that show, circa 1964.

"Dishin' The Dirt," from the Dirty Water 2014 45, has a great fuzz and organ hook, and "I Don't Want You" an infectious groove that doesn't quit. It comes in a deluxe gatefold 45 sleeve, though the graphic design curiously doesn't really take advantage of such a luxury. That's a piffle of complaint from yet another top-notch release by a great treasure to garage music: The Thanes.

The Thanes are one of those watershed bands that will stand the test of time and inspire future generations to start a band. You can count on that.

I've avoided listing discography updates in this edition of "The Knights of Fuzz," but Lenny & Company deserve one:

**Honey I Need,** on Not So Pretty – A Tribute To The Pretty Things LP/CD, Corduroy Records And Detective Agency, Australia 1995
**Shipwreck/Dissatisfaction**, on freebie 7" Split EP (with The Others), Misty Lane magazine, Italy 1995
**I Would Love You**, on Transworld Garage Scene LP, Misty Lane, Italy 1995
**Thanes Of Cawdor** 10" LP – A reissue of the debut LP - omits the 5 cover versions from the original issue, Minotaur, Greece 1996
**Better Days/Never Make Me Blue** 7", Larsen, France 1996
**Undignified Noblemen** LP, Misty Lane, Italy 1997
**X+Y=13/World Of Pauline Lewis**, on 7" Split EP (with The Slow Slushy Boys), Do The Dog, France 1999
**Don't Say Why**, on 7"compilation EP (with The Chocolate Watchband/Tyme Society/Rookies), Misty Lane, Italy 2000
**Now It's Your Turn To Cry**, on 7" compilation EP (with Bangtwister/Firestone/Grease Monkeys), BMB-The Big Psych-Out, U.K. 2000
**It's Just A Fear/Sun Didn't Come Out Today** 7", Living Eye/Sundazed, U.S.A. 2000
**One Night As I Wandered On The Moors...The Best Of The Thanes** 2 LP vinyl only set, Corduroy Records And Detective Agency, Australia 2001
**Downbeat And Folked Up** LP/CD, Screaming Apple, Germany 2003
**No No No No/What More Can I Do** 7", Larsen, France 2003
**Evolver** CD only, Rev-Ola, U.K. 2004
**She's Coming Back To Me/Love Is Fading Away**, State, U.K. 2013
**Dishin' The Dirt / I Don't Want You** 7", Dirty Water, U.K. 2014

## 1313 MOCKINGBIRD LANE (UPDATE)

This Albany, NY group released a string of uniformly fine garage-punk records, beginning in the late 1980s. Their 1995 "Devil's Weed" b/w "Tamala" 45 on Germany's Screaming Apple is another gem, full of unbridled enthusiasm and beer-soaked spittle. Their "Naked (And Waiting)" b/w "Backwash Beach" 7" is even better, with vocalist/guitarist "Haunted Hausmann" screeching up a storm.

It's satisfying to hear Americans that can still make garage-punk rock the good-old fashioned way – with a couple of guitars and a tape recorder.

1313 Mockingbird Lane finally called it quits in 1997, but there's some good news in with the sad: 1313 left behind almost eight years of the best garage punk available. Countless 45s and two LPs are topped off with their farewell 1996 "Problems" 45. Yep, Albany, New York's finest went out on top, because "Problems" ranks up with their own best tracks. The energy couldn't be any more fever pitched, and the captivating "Drambuie" B-side tops off the R.I.P.

If pumping Farfisa, red-in-the-face vocals and fuzzy, fuzzy, fuzzy guitar are your thing, then spend some time flipping through the indie music bin for some 1313 Mockingbird Lane. And if that's not you kind of thing, then go back to reading a vapid People Magazine and leave the rest of us alone.

## THE THREE O'CLOCK (UPDATE)

A wonderful surprise was the reunion of The Three O'Clock, with live dates in 2013 and 2014 and the issue of a vinyl-only "Live At The Old Waldorf" album (from a poor quality 1980s live tape) on the ultra-hipster Burger label. Burger also issued in 2014 the vinyl-only "Aquarius Andromeda" LP – a collection of early tracks culled mostly from the 2013 "The Hidden World

Revealed" CD (on Omnivore). It is wonderful to re-introduce the band's sparkling early work to a new generation, and even better to hear the band back in top form.

What a surprise it was to see them in April 2013 on a U.S. national TV late-night show performing "With A Cantaloupe Girlfriend," sounding as good as in 1983!

## THE THUNDERBEATS (MOSCOW, RUSSIA)

This Russian band's self-titled album (2013 vinyl on Teen Sound from Italy) is also issued in their own country on CD and titled "66." Interestingly, the CD version uses a slightly different cover photo and also includes some really primo bonus tracks.

"Wyld," from the CD, is alive with fantastic fuzztone (a highlight throughout), pure energy and a powerful delivery. Yes, this is '66 garage punk from one of the more recent entries into the worldwide garage beat, Russia. "Sing It To Me" has a slight Russian flavor to it, but the main influence seems to be classic U.S. '66 Pebbles-compilation-type sounds along with some classic U.K. mod. The boys sing in English, too!

The Thunderbeats go to great lengths to sound '66-authentic, and the results are convincing and inspiring. This is one of the most authentic '60s sounding records I've heard in a long while, while also still sounding sonically impressive. In other words, it sounds really good! I especially love "Confusion," (with a fine organ riff and lead guitar break), the elegant "Let Me Go" and the CD-only fuzzer "Things That You Do."

The album liner notes mention some of the band members' previous Russian revival-era bands, including The Rogers, The Mods, The Sticky Fingers, Dans Ramblers, Stone Shades, The Crushers and Tom & The Phantoms – all unknown to me. So I am so happy that I do know The Thunderbeats' debut album – it is one of the most unique and one of the very best neo-garage records I have had the pleasure to hear in these past 35 years.

There is also a 2012 45 on Groovie (both sides are on the album) and a split 45 on Chickpea.

## THE TIKI MEN (SACRAMENTO, CA, U.S.A.)

Yes, I enjoy my crude Mummies records as much as the next garage guy, but I never got into the whole "lo fi" vinyl trend of the early 2000s like some garageniks. Some bands and labels were seemingly attempting to see who could release bad recordings on vinyl that sounded the absolute worst, and while that's a funny shtick, it doesn't inspire much repeated listening. And so the "Twelve Dusty Diamonds" album on Hillsdale fall into this hole for me.

There are a variety of in-jokes on the back cover boasting the fidelity and precision of the recordings, which are instead a

treble and distortion festival. I do understand the purposeful post-modern irony of releasing music that is as far away from digital purity as possible, but if I can't actually hear the music then the shtick overtakes the music, and thus my record needle moves on to other releases.

There are several 7" releases, too, and I'm happy to report that the sound is much better on both the four-song 7" EP "The Good Life" (on Estrus, with a beautiful color cover) and the "Cattle Prod" b/w "Surfin' Senorita" 45 on Hillsdale.

## TIKI TONES (UPDATE)

The "Suburban Savage" album is yet another lovingly beautiful mixture of exotica, surf and garage, complete with perfect vintage cover art and perfect spring-reverbed production. There is no way a band can make this music without an absolute love for it – true respect for the instrumental bands of the past ooze through every note of "Suburban Savage," a title that itself pays homage to the best of late 1950s exotica records.

This album also has one feature that is maddening for a collector (or journalist) – no mention anywhere of what year it was released. The intention is to make the record timeless, not stuck in 1965 or 1995 or any one specific era, and several prominent garage labels use this technique on their record sleeves. I understand the coolness of this approach, but it isn't helpful for collectors! (This album was released in 1997, I eventually determined.)

The four-song 7" EPs " Songs For Rum Drinkers" and "Enchanted Tiki Tones" (both on Dionysus) are also primo instrumental slabs, and feature fabulously colorful covers, too.

## THE TIME BEINGS (UPDATE)

Only cassette demos had made their rounds as of 1995, so it was a fabulous surprise to see the "Journey To Tyme" album (2007 on Dino Records).It blasts with a fab original "Where I Come From," and adds fine '60s classics such as the title track and "Time Will Tell" to the mix. The production is muscular, confident and everything I love about garage music – albums like this exist because the band loves this music so much that they must – *they must* – record songs and share them. It is a compulsion, a dedication, a necessity. The lords of fuzz have blessed the Time Beings.

The 1996 "Visions" b/w "Louie Go Home" 45 also appears on the always great Stanton Park label.

## THE TIME LODGERS (NORWAY)

The 1991 three-song 7" EP (on Perfect Pop Records in Norway) is the only vinyl I have from these lads, though there are at least three albums from 1992-1994 also available. The EP is pleasant guitar-based Mod-pop.

## THE TOL-PUDDLE MARTYRS (AUSTRALIA)

There are not many bands from the original 1960s era that stayed away from music for decades – then re-appear with new records in the 2000s. The Tol-Puddle Martyrs have a deserved reputation for their seminal 1967 and 1968 singles, and then burst back onto the underground garage scene with 2007's "Freak Out U.S.A." album.  It's a modern-sounding pop psych effort – perhaps too modern in production and delivery for garage purists.

2009's "A Celebrated Man" follow-up tread similar ground, and while there are some quality songs, a more sympathetic (more organic, raw, and analog) production style could've have helped add some flavor. Perhaps the band was overly preoccupied with a desire to appear modern rather than as a vintage original 1960s act – if so, it is a miscalculation. A 2001 Christmas EP and the "Flying In The Dark" album also appeared.

## THE TREBLEMAKERS (MONTREAL, CANADA)

The "Versus The Doomsday Device!" album (1999 on Dionysus) follows up two previous albums from 1997 and 1998. With that band name, do you expect anything but

echoed guitar, surf-styled instrumentals? Nice production and an energetic delivery separate these boys from many others, and they sport some fine Fender gear, too.

## THE TRIPMAKERS (ITALY)

The 1999 four-song 7" EP on Psych Out is crude blues and punk based garage, and surprisingly not very '66-sounding for the venerable Psych-Out label. Interestingly, label head Cosimino Pecere gets the producer credit for this one.

## TRIP WAVE (NEW YORK, NY, U.S.A.)

Dino Sorbello made some of the best U.S. east coast psych-garage music with the Mad Violets and Blacklight Chameleons, but he wasn't done stretching the conventions of the genre in the 2000s. Tripwave is certainly genre-bending, and Dino's blazing guitar is at the forefront, and the 2005 self-titled CD starts with an unexpected version of "Psilocybe" – one of the Mad Violet's signature songs. There's plenty of electric sitar and very psychedelic effects throughout, along with an aggressive, frenzied delivery – this is certainly psych music for a new century. The debut ends with a six-minute live track, the sprawling, shimmering psychedelic "Bardos."

## EL TRONS (SPAIN)

The 2009 "El Que Queda De Mi" four-song EP covers four '60s classics, and it is quite odd to hear backing tracks that sound similar to the originals in Spanish. My fave here: their Spanish version of "I Ain't No Miracle Worker."  The 2011 "7 & 7 Is" four song EP (also on Butterfly) has four more classic '60s garage covers.  "Outside Chance" is probably my favorite here.

There is also a 2010 four-song 7" EP on Butterfly – and my hope it that is finally has some originals songs on it.

## TRUE WEST (UPDATE)

The 1998 "The Big Boot" album (on Bring Out Your Dead) is an OK-sounding live recording of the band during their best era, circa 1984. "And Then The Rain" is a highlight (as it is on their debut EP), and since I saw the band during this same time period I can attest that it is a good document of their sound at the time, though perhaps this album is satisfying most to diehard fans like me.

## THE TWISTAROOS (MOSS, NORWAY)

There are a bucketful of rock genres mixed into the "Twisted" album (2010 on Screaming Apple). You have some '50s rock, some rockabilly, some power-pop, a little garage and the gutsy vocals of Vibeke Saugestad. Vibeke is a girls' name, in case you don't know much Norwegian, and it's her pipes that make this release distinctive.

This is light-hearted fun, without pretension, designed to get you to dance, have a beer and relax for a moment. I dug "Everybody Say Hey," and its anthemic power-pop-garage attack.

There is also the 2010 "Twist and Shake With" EP on Ghost Highway.

## THE TYME SOCIETY (ROME, ITALY)

This is another top-notch fuzz and jangle band from Misty Lane head honcho Massimo Del Pozzo. There is a three-song EP on Butterfly Records from 2001 with songs "When I See Her Eyes," "I Gotta Know" and "Marion The Painter."

---

*NOTE: Remember to read the original 1995 book and the other book update chapters for thousands of other bands and records not featured in this update section.*

---

# U

## THE UBANGIS (SILVER SPRING, MD, U.S.A.)

The 1997 four-song 7" EP on Pure Vinyl would sound very much like a Cramps record – the sensibility, at least is very similar. As it is, Brian Horrorwitz (also of Date Bait) paints similar pictures in "I Want To Drink Your Blood Tonight" and especially "I'm a Ubangi, Baby." There are also two 45s from the early 1990s and two albums, from 2006 and 2008.

## THE UGLY BEATS (AUSTIN, TX, U.S.A.)

The Ugly Beats has been a focus of Get Hip since at least 2004, with three albums and another 45, and a 2014 album as well. And there's good reason for the confidence from Get Hip – The Ugly Beats are an expert garage act.

Unlike many revivalists, the Ugly Beats can mix up their sound, from straight-ahead garage to folk-pop to a Tex-Mex regional 1960s garage sound. They've also toured extensively and appear to be deserving of my **"True Believer"** status that I confer on only a few devoted souls. Any band that soldiers on for more than a decade while maintaining their '60s sound obviously loves what they do.And the proof is in the grooves.

## THE ULTRA FIVE (UPDATE)

Band leader Bob Urh kept the sounds of the venerable Ultra 5 alive through all these years, and the "Denizens of Dementia" album (2004 on Green Cookie) is a massive 24-song compilation to get fans up to date. Lots of highlights in there, but I have a special place for "Psychedelic Soul" on my playlist. There are also EPs out in Zebra Records (1996) and Tryptic (2009). Bob Urh is one of the survivors of the first neo-garage generation who still exudes the same energy and creative spirit of the 1980s scene – and his many solo efforts through the past few years also prove this out.

## THE UNCLAIMED (UPDATE)

The Unclaimed remain one of the absolute unsung heroes of the early 1980s garage revival. I was delighted to hear that in 2013 original band leader Shelley Ganz re-formed the group and along with more original garagers such as Dave Provost (The Droogs, Dream Syndicate, Davie Allen and many more) and Lee Joseph (Yard Trauma and many more).

Lee Joseph commented to me in 2014, "It's a trip to be playing with Shelley again and great this time around, not feeling trapped by the concept of the band now, in fact loving it – and giving Shelley a lot of respect for his vision and songs."

Dave Provost added, "Shelley Ganz has always surrounded himself with members who could easily lead their own bands, and many later did: The Long Ryders, Yard Trauma, Thee Fourgiven, Tommyknockers and Boardwalkers to name a few. We've got a strong Unclaimed lineup now, Lee Joseph and Shelley Ganz are a creative force and I'm proud to be a part of it."

The re-formed Unclaimed have been playing shows and recording new songs, due for release starting in 2014. I can't wait, and I am sure a whole new generation will come to see and hear The Unclaimed as one of the original bands deserving of the title "Knights of Fuzz."

## THE UNHEARD OF (UPDATE)

The 2001 "Revoxination" album continues this U.S. band's low-fi dark psych campaign, this time aided by the sympathetic tones of Plasticland's Glenn Rehse. This is so distinctively American in nature – the murky recording, dark fuzz guitars, oddball songs and moody atmosphere are unmistakable of the U.S. garage underground. This time the time machine seems to be set for 1968, so it's a little heavier than most, but still with enough psilocybic fumes to keep the proceedings moving upward. Yes, these are the kinds of records that become legendary with time in the garage underground, and deservedly so.

I must also point out the heroic efforts of Cosimino Pecere of Psych Out Records for finding and releasing so many unique sounds that otherwise would never see the light of day. You will never find a 12" vinyl record cover heavier or thicker than a Psych Out release, too. Thank you, again, Psych Out!

The four-song "Metaphysical Carnival" release on Psych Out is actually two 7"s – how cool is that – in one EP sleeve, and continues the dark and fuzz-laden trip for these Wisconsin originals. A band could have a million dollars and all the studio time in the world and still could not recreate the unique world of The Unheard. They are the real deal, and in my garage world that counts for a whole lot.

## UNITED SPACE LEAGUE (DETROIT, MI, U.S.A.)

The 2010 "You Told Me A Lie" b/w "Water Under The Bridge" 45 was issued on Freddy Fortune's Sound Camera label.

## UNTAMED YOUTH: *See the "Fan Submitted Updates" chapter for more information and also the "Knights of Fuzz" DVD, where "Supercharged Steamroller" is featured.*

## THE UPBEATS (U.S.A.)

All I've heard is one side of the 1986 45 released on the Sun Valley label – a fine "girl-done-me-wrong" garage banger titled "Forget About You." There's Vox organ and Phantom guitar, Rickenbacker and some vocal snot, so what's not to like?

## BOB URH AND THE BARE BONES
(LOS ANGELES, USA)

The force behind the Ultra V Has also released some very unique solo records, and the self-released 2005 "Boom Boom A Zoom Zoom" b/w "Ramblin Man" 45 is an evocative opening salvo. Swampy blues is as much an influence as garage, and Urh's version is moody, murky and a bit addled. If you dig the dark, moody Ultra V then this will be both a departure and also a logical extension of Bob Urh's own sound.

Three albums are on Green Cookie Records (Greece) from 2005, 2007, 2011.

## VIBRASONIC (UPDATE)

The 1997 "Instrumental Vibrations" album (on Yep Records) is not what I expected from the very psych album cover art. It's a collection of instrumentals that cover the range of 1960s styles, from surfish, to exotica, with some garage and psych thrown in, too. The "Fiddler On The Roof" Broadway musical standard "If I Were A Rich Man" is an odd choice for a cover, to be sure, and the low-end psych overtones in "The Vibratremble" must've been a challenge for the lacquer-cuter to get on disc. Interestingly, this is one record where the venerable vintage Toe Rag studios doesn't seem quite the right match for this band's sounds. Yes, this is an odd and unique release, which I believe is the goal of most bands in this book.

## VIBRAVOID (DUSSELDORF, GERMANY)

Centered around guitarist Christian Koch, Vibravoid is sparkling modern psych-pop. There are at least seven albums dating from 2000-2013 (with many compilation appearances and a few singles, too), and the demo I have features the shimmering track "Into Sunshine" that I can't easily find on any of them. It's pulsating guitar pop-psych at its best, sung in English, but with a distinct Euro-flavor.

## THE VICE (MOSCOW, RUSSIA)

Leave it to the Italian Teen Sound label to find a group of Mod-popsters from Russia who sing in English for their 2013 four-song 7"EP. I am delighted to find some Russian garage-related groups for this book update, and the polished pop of The Vice is another fab surprise. My Pick Hit for the EP is the wonderfully melodic "Rain Came Down," complete with some sweet harmonies.

## THE VICE BARONS (UPDATE)

The 1995 three-song" EP on MMPM Records is more fun and crude surf-meets-garage mayhem.

## KYLE VINCENT (LOS ANGELES, CA, U.S.A.)

OK, I've made great efforts to explain why so many fine bands don't quite fit into the scope of this book, but then I bend my own rules to explore the pure pop of Kyle Vincent. One reason is the fact that Vincent didn't move into the mainstream media consciousness like contemporaries The Ravonettes or White Stripes, etc., so he deserves the attention here. Another reason for his inclusion is simple: I love beautifully-written and performed power pop. And Kyle Vincent delivers the goods on his debut self-titled album (1997, on Hollywood Records).

There are nods a-plenty to the best of 1960s pop – and 1970s Raspberries-esque pop, too – with an emphasis on Vincent's personal lyrics and emotional singing. This might be too sweet for many garage fans here, but those who appreciate The Nazz, Badfinger or even the more recent and mainstream pop Gin Blossoms will find much here to fall in love with. The debut album did gather some mainstream attention – it was on a major label after all – but he was soon dropped and his 1999 self-produced follow-up "Wow & Flutter" lacks the focus and production budget of his debut, but still with plenty of fine songs to pull you in.

If you appreciate real songwriting craft, vocal excellence and bright guitar pop, then sneak a little Kyle Vincent in between those listening sessions with The Beatles or Association. You might be surprised how much you like him.

## THE VINES (SYDNEY, AUSTRALIA)

It perhaps isn't fair to lump modern major label bands such as The Vines in with others like the Hives as "fun but outside the range of this predominately '66-styled book," but like The White Stripes and others mentioned in passing here, mainstream information is readily available elsewhere for them ad nauseam.

## THE VIPERS (UPDATE)

The current garage scene is in the midst of an ironic retrospection: looking back we realize the height of the 1980s revival is the same distance in the past, about 20 years, as the original '60s sounds were when rediscovered in the 1980s. Those 1980s garage-psych bands are now looked back on by many as the "old masters" inspiring yet another wave of Beatle-booted, Vox guitar maniacs as much as '60s icons The Seeds and Sonics.

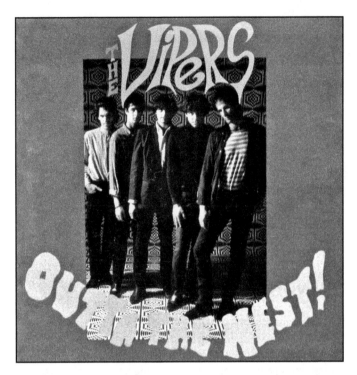

The Vipers were (and remain) one of the absolute best of that 1980s crop. They were one of the few "revival" acts that balanced expert musicianship and top-notch original songwriting without losing their garage inspiration. Their debut 1984 vinyl LP, "Outta The Nest," has been issued several times, but it made its first CD appearance on Cavestomp (2000) just in time to inspire a flock of garage newbies.

This LP was one of the first of the 1980s New York garage scene recorded with a "real" budget in a "real" studio, and The Vipers didn't blow their chance. The veritable anthem for the garage movement, "Nothing From Today," shimmers as if the Beatles were from Times Square, not Liverpool; It still sends shivers up my spine. Gentle melody sparks "Tears (Only Dry)," while lysergia pulses through "Now I Remember."

Eight bonus tracks add to the Vipers legacy, and the enhanced CD features a couple video clips from the long-gone and missed Night Flight TV show. (One of them is also on our "Knights Of Fuzz" video DVD.) I remember watching those clips when they aired the first time, in the middle of the night, back in 1985. Seven years later on tour with my own band I rolled over in my bunk bed in Germany, only to find graffiti from the Vipers greeting me on the wall. Yes, they paved the way for many of us back then.

## THE VIRGINEERS (CHICAGO, IL, U.S.A.)

The self-titled 1999 album (on Liquid Sound) mines a distinctly modern psych-pop landscape. Mainly the duo of Ken Zawacki and Bruce Lash, the sound is awash with flanged vocals and heavy reverb and delay effects. Heavily relying on digital recording technology, the arrangements could have benefitted from a more organic in-the-room recording rather then the very clean straight-into-the-board approach. Still, this is a fine debut. Pick Hits: the fine "Floating" and "Lost

Balloon." A second album, "Love Soldiers," was rumored as late as 2010, though I haven't found it.

## THE VOLTA SOUND (CLEVELAND, OH, U.S.A.)

Perhaps only marginally associated with the more purist psych sounds heralded in this book, this eclectic act – they describe their genre somewhat enigmatically as "Kraut Rock with harmonies" – skirts the alt-Americana, Velvet-psych territory. Those who like Brian Jonestown Massacre and associated acts will probably find this of more interest (than I do). There are two albums from the early 2000s on Orange Sky, and more from 2012.

## THE VON ZIPPERS (CALGARY, CANADA)

Four albums and at least nine 45s have been issued since 1995. All that I've heard has been in an ultra-high-energy garage punk mode, with the emphasis on the punk. Yes, there's some cool organ in there at times, and some distorted vocals, but the Von Zippers (named of course for the infamous 1960s beach party movie character) aren't a strict revival act. For one thing, they have a sense of humor and the absurd, and certainly don't take themselves too seriously.

I get the idea that a double bill of The Von Zippers – perhaps in leather beach party cycle gang outfits, and The Mummies – in their toilet paper mummy outfits – would be quite legendary.

## THE WAISTCOATS (GRONINGEN, HOLLAND)

The 2000 "Explosion!" album on Larsen Records has everything that Toe Rag Studios is known for: rich, mono, analog sound, and a mid-1960s feel that could only be equaled by a trip in an actual time machine. The sounds? Primo 1965 Eurobeat all the way, perfect in so many ways. The four-song 7" EP "Live @KUT90.5FM" 7" EP on Butterfly Records is a good-sounding set from their appearance on an Austin, Texas radio station in 2001.

The 2004 four-song 7" EP on Pure Vinyl is also a Toe Rag production, and is another winner, with a 1965 Who-ish feel to "It's Not True." They switch to a '64-Kinks feel for the fine "Shaggy Dog," which has a killer groove.

There are a bunch of other 45s and at least six more albums up through 2010 for this fine combo.

## THE WARLOCKS (LOS ANGELES, CA, U.S.A.)

My good old friend Greg Shaw of Bomp!/Voxx Records just plain loved this band, and he championed them and their 2000 debut. Greg was enamored with the new generation of less-reverential psych that sprang from the then-new Brian Jonestown Massacre-family of bands. The sound is loping, droning (some would say "shoegazing") psychedelia – so 1960s purists beware. The band amazingly stayed together and released at least five albums up through 2013, and have toured the globe. This style probably appeals more to the fans of The Dandy Warhols, BJM et all, and that scene, more than garage-psychsters. But Greg Shaw loved them all the same.

## WATCH CHILDREN (UPDATE)

"Blessed be the weirdos." The whacked-out, bleary-eyed Watch Children bring such imaginary musical commandments to mind. The Ocean, N.J. combo were uncrowned kings of the late 1980s cassette-only demo world, with only a few spatterings of their dementia making it to actual vinyl or CD compilations. It took a Norwegian label, Perfect Pop Records, to finally spit out some much deserved vinyl, and "The Kinda Retarded Tapes" double 7" (from 1997) was worth the sleepless wait.

The 10 tracks add up to almost an entire album's worth of home-recorded ultra lo-fi fun, full of verve and effortless bizarreness. Marc Saxton's sense of twisting melody is the glue for Watch Children, holding just enough reason to counter the band's puzzling rhyme.

"Lonely Marmalade" is one of my fave titles, but it's "I'm In Love With Your Mother" that bakes the proverbial cake. The atonal masterpiece was conceived as a "phony" '66 garage track, intended to be passed off as a vintage recording for inclusion on one of the "Back From The Grave" reissue compilation LPs. It didn't make it there, but it's a classic here; dig the percussive power of a beer bottle banging on a toilet seat! Ah, yes, **Blessed be the weirdos!"**

## THE WAY-OUTS (BELGIUM)

It's weird to hear current bands (in the 2000s) recording covers of 1980s garage bands, but the Way Outs do justice to the Miracle Workers' "I'll Walk Away" as the B-side to their 2005 "Can't Take No More" 45 on Lost In Tyme. The A-side, written by garage veteran King Koen, is also in the classic Miracle Workers' fuzz 'n Farfisa driving style. There is also a 2006 album and another 2007 45.

## THE WHAT 4? (FORT COLLINS, CO, U.S.A.)

This is not the German band of similar moniker; these Colorado lads deposited a four-song 7" EP on Max Picou

Records in 1998. It's good, crude, guitar-based garage that makes me want to find a beer and guzzle it. That, kids, is a true garage compliment.

## WHIPPED CREAM (GOTHENBURG, SWEDEN)

Power-pop garage is a personal favorite sub-genre for me, and Whipped Cream delivered some sweet examples in the early 1990s. "& Other Delights" sounds as fresh and shimmering today (2014) as in its original 1990 release. Not many recordings sound as vital and "now" as 25 years ago, so this is a remarkable debut, indeed. Pick Hits: "Explosion." The follow up "Tune In The Century" (also on Snap) doesn't capture me like their debut. The 1994 "Horse Mountain" is said to be heavier and less satisfying as well, though I haven't found it yet.

## THE WILDEBEESTS (U.K.)

Another Lenny Helsing outfit, with the 2000 Norton Records "Rudolph's Ruin" 45 in my stack. Christmas garage records never go out of style, and this one is a doozy with some nutty, echoey, mono production. I may have only this 45, but there are at least five albums and a dozen more 45s from 1995 up through 2010. Amen, brutha!

## WILL-O-THE-WISP (GREECE)

The 1998 self-titled album on Action Records is a true gem – expertly arranged, recorded and performed, it is an artistic entry in the quieter folk-related psych genre. There are only a few albums in the neo-garage era that attempt a similar quiet mood and feel, and there are two main reasons why there are so few examples: 1) it is difficult to write and record contemplative psych music and 2) this music demands that listeners take time to let it develop and then envelope the listener. Not many garage-psych fans have that kind of patience, but they will be rewarded if they can track down this LP. A beautiful gatefold sleeve completes this fine release.

## THE WOGGLES (UPDATE)

Manfred Jones (better known perhaps as "The Professor") is a rock and roll evangelist. He is determined to spread the gospel of the sound, and thank goodness his dedication is to the garage flavor of the scriptures, because he delivers his message so well. His band, The Woggles, has deservedly grown in stature in the garage world exponentially since the 1995 version of this book. They tour the globe and have released an onslaught of records that no one label could possibly keep up with. Of course, neither can this humble reviewer.

"Wailin' With The Woggles" (1998 on One Louder) is a representative showcase for the Woggles brand of garage fun. Their collective tongues are cemented in cheek for the joyous "Ramadan Romance," a track that seems to capture the actual sweat of the blistering performance. There are more than a dozen other releases from recent years, all drenched in that same kind of holy sweat that only true-believers can muster. The Woggles are, and will remain, true "Knights of Fuzz." Put them in your Top Ten all-time neo-garage groups, kids, and get hep like me.

## THE WOODY PEAKERS (UPDATE)

The "Beat Solution" CD (on Soundflat) is a fine compilation of their 1988 and 1990 output, and it all sounds better than my very worn vinyl. Yes, I dug the Woody Peakers back in the day, so this collection, with five bonus tracks, is very welcome. The previously unreleased originals "Out Of Mind" and "Dear Freddy" are both boss, making me wonder why it took so long for them to hear the light of day. This is primitive, crude, teenage-garage punk, just how it is was always meant to be. Remember, these are compliments. *Compliments!*

## THE WOOLY BANDITS (LOS ANGELES, CA, U.S.A.)

Beginning life as a backing band for legendary Seeds vocalist Sky Saxon, in 2004 they started playing and recording as The Wooly Bandits. "Say Hello To My Little Friend" (2005 on Dionysus) was their debut, and it isn't nearly as retro-purist as one might have expected from their history playing Seeds tunes. Oh, there's a mighty '60s vibe throughout, but with a modern punk energy to push it all along. As a smirk to their former Seeds life, there's also a very fun punkish version of "Pushin' Too Hard" as well. Pick Hit: "Let Me Know."

There's at least another album (2009's "Woman Of Mass Destruction") with a new vocalist (and a very slick commercial approach and look that does not impress me), and more is rumored for release as of 2014.

## THE WRONG SOCIETY (HAMBURG, GERMANY)

Their song "Gone And Dead" has a straight-ahead '66 combo sound, and they released their debut 2013 four-song 7" EP, limited to just 250 copies.

## THE X-RAY MEN (HOLLAND)

There is a split 10" with the unfortunately-named Boogie Punkers (2004 on El Beasto Recordings). Another Eric Geevers band, The X-Ray Men deliver appropriately Link Wray-ish cover instrumentals and one original.

Despite their band name, The Boogie Punkers actually hold their own on this split release, and their smooth, surfish instrumentals are actually pretty good.

## YESTERDAY'S THOUGHTS (ATHENS, GREECE)

The quality of garage-psych that continues to come from beautiful Greece constantly surprises me. Yesterday's Thoughts' debut "Searchin' In Shadows" album (2002 on Sound Effect) is an instant classic, with each Seeds-ish addled fuzz note perfectly in place.

Their previous four-song 7" EP on Action Records (from 1998) gives us even more primo, moody, authentic '66 garage psych. Few bands nail the '66 band feel while still sounding fresh and authentic. Just one taste of "Jungle's My Place" and you'll understand that these Greek cats aren't posing as a 1960s band – they practically *are* one.

The "Let's Take A Ride With..." album (2004, on Sound Effect) is the second long-player from these fine Greeks, and fittingly the CD features a photo of the band with Seeds singer Sky Saxon (who is also featured on two tracks). "Wasting My Time" has a great 1966 garage groove, and the fuzz is fine on "Walking To Your Grave."

The 1966-Seeds vibe is alive on the self-titled "Yesterday's Thoughts," and lovers of the classic U.S.A. garage feel will find much to enjoy. The final album track, "Build Yourself An Aero Plane" (with Sky Saxon on vocals), is actually one of the most coherent post-Seeds tracks ever recorded by the infamously erratic singer. It truly does have a feel of a Seeds track, circa 1967 or so. There is also the "A Moment To Pray" album (2009)

The 2009 "A Moment To Pray" album is also on Sound Effect, and the boys prove they have perfected their Seeds-mania. A perfect blend of Farfisa and fuzz, Yesterday's Thoughts remind me why I love garage music so much – it's fun, it's evocative, it's snotty, it's lysergic, it's beautiful.

Put Yesterday's Thoughts on your must-have list.

## THE YOUNG PLAYTHINGS
(LOS ANGELES, CA, U.S.A.)

The "Pick Up With..." debut (2005, on Dionysus) is a lo-fi punk-pop effort, and otherwise unremarkable, though the vintage organ gives the proceedings a slight vintage feel. This fits more into the late 1970s Los Angeles power-pop revival feel than the garage bag, me thinks. They broke up soon after the album saw release – any record label's worst fear. A 45 also exists.

## YUM YUMS (UPDATE)

The three-song 7" EP on Screaming Apple is some fine guitar-based power pop, and reminds me of an early 1980s single that Greg Shaw would have put out on Bomp! Records. That's a great compliment for fans of indie punk-pop rock!

---

*NOTE: Remember to read the original 1995 book and the other book update chapters for thousands of other bands and records not featured in this update section.*

---

# COMPILATION ALBUMS UPDATE

## BE A CAVEMAN

More than 30 years ago Voxx Records trumpeted the garage revival, so it makes perfect sense that history repeats itself with their 2000 "Be A Caveman" compilation. The CD picks the best from that label's impressive 1980s garage catalog and packages it into one tidy introduction for a new generation that missed out the first time around. Sound familiar? Yep, compilations like this one brought the forgotten sounds of '60s caveteens to the kids of the late seventies – and the paisley revival was the result.

Voxx honcho Greg Shaw – who almost single handedly jump-started the global garage revival – picked a glorious selection of Voxx nuggets for this literal retrospective. Seminal cuts from The Unclaimed, Pandoras, Miracle Workers, Vipers, Chesterfield Kings and Cynics should turn on the light bulb over the heads of a new generation: That's right, it's time once again to ignore the corporate playlist and dig some real sounds, made by real caveteens.

## BEAT-O-RAMA AT ITS BEST

Germany's Music Manaic Records released this live-concert compilation in 1994 of the Beat-O-Mania festival, which boasted a fine lineup including The Strange Flowers, The Others and The Fuzztones' Rudi Protrudi. Recording quality is excellent and the performances spirited. This concert is so far in the past – now decades ago – that this CD seems like quite a significant historical document.

## BLOOD ON THE SWITCHPLATE '65

A U.K. compilation from On Motor Sounds records, including tracks from The Routes, The Urges, Secret Agent Men, The Keepers, and a bunch more. I'm not sure what the connecting theme between the bands and songs is, other than they all fit in the raw side of garage & punk, circa 2006.

## BLOOD RED BATTLE ROYAL

This 1998 album and CD on Blood Red is full of spit and vinegar, from The Hentchmen to The Woggles, to the Fiends, Hate Bombs and always-fab Girl Trouble. One of my own acts, The Purple Merkins, also makes an appearance among the 16 boss tracks.

## BLOW THE FUSE

Quebec in Canada is one scene that hadn't been documented like others around the globe, so the Blow The Fuse label collected 15 local acts to save for posterity. There's Tricky Woo, Smash-Up Derby, Les Secretaires Volantes and more lesser-known nuggets for us Anglophones to discover on this 1997 12" platter.

## CAVESTOMP! Volume 1

The continuing Cavestomp! Garage festivals are now legendary, and this 1998 album features live tracks from 1997 (and one from 1998). Some of my fave acts are representing with fine-sounding live tracks: The Brood, Cheepskates, The Fuzztones and Chesterfield Kings – plus some surprises like The Smitheereens and Question Mark and the Mysterians. Energetic and essential.

## CHILDREN OF NUGGETS

See the "Garage Feature Articles" chapter, and the piece on the original Nuggets compilation CD re-issue, for comments about this attempt to use the venerable Nuggets name for this disappointing neo-garage compilation.

## DELPHONIC SOUNDS TODAY

The classic (mainly) 1960s surf label attempted an image update in the late 1990s, and this compilation showcases then-current bands covering vintage Del-Fi releases. So you get The Brain Jonestown Massacre doing "I Fought The Law" (but Bobby Fuller's original version won), The Jigsaw Seen doing an unfortunate interpretation of an early Arthur Lee track "Lucy Baines," and Baby Lemonade (who backed Arthur Lee over many years before his death) doing a fine version of an early Barry White tune, "All In The Run Of A Day." A very uneven collection, but I give credit to bands for attempting their own takes on some classics.

## DUTCH GARAGE ROCK EXPLOSION

This 2013 vinyl album on Kliko Records is really a compilation of indie and underground sounds, though the always-trashy Flying Tygers make an appearance. Other than that, it's more punk-garage than garage-punk, if you get my meaning.

## AN EVENING IN NIVRAM

"An Evening in Nivram: The Music of The Shadows" is a tribute to the venerable early 1960s act. The Boss Martians provide the only vocal track, and they are, as always, a highlight. This is a happy hour buffet for MuSick artists with their own releases, including the excellent Space Cossacks, Fathoms and The Omega Men.

## FORTY ONE SIXTY: The Sounds Of The Shambles

This 2009 Shambles tribute album on Blindspot / Jam Records is a fine testament to the San Diego band, especially the stellar songwriting of Bart Mendoza. I really dug Mark Le Gallez & The Eddies' version of the anthemic "Don't Know Where To Start," and Afterglow's very British-sounding version of "Of Heart & Soul," one of Mendoza's most enduring Mod-pop tunes.

## FUZZY LOGIC

The RPM label's 1997 "Fuzzy Logic" compilation plays it loose with their definition of "garage rock," and perhaps a less flavorful "power-punk-pop" would better describe the bulk of these 26 tracks. There's plenty of grit per minute, though, and Greece's Walking Screams stand above the rest with a score of perfect 10 on the 1966 fuzz-o-meter. Maybe ouzo has the same effect as LSD.

## HOT RODS TO HELL

The surf/trash/dragster craze continues to spit out a surprising wealth of worthy sounds, and Blood Red's "Hot Rods to Hell, Volume II" (1998) serves a platter of the globe's best. I haven't heard "Volume I" of the series, but the sequel boasts a bundle of my faves, including The Boss Martians, Surf Trio, Space Cossacks, and Phantom 5ive. The collection jumps off the line with a bang: the distinctive, fuzzy, thumping sounds that can only come from Davie Allan & The Arrows. *Vrrrooooooom!*

Like other Blood Red comps, this one is chock full of quality – topped off by primo cover art from Canada's finest UFO/rock'n'roll/monster illustrator, Darren Merinuk.

# INSTRUMENTAL FIRE

The MuSick label has spawned an impressive catalogue, focusing mainly on cool non-vocal sounds. Their 1998 debut compilation long-player, "Instrumental Fire," spotlights most of the globe's best surf-instro combos, with Los Straightjackets and Man or Astroman? perhaps the most recognizable, but with The Bomboras and Tiki Tones raising my bamboo the highest.

# THE INTERNATIONAL LEAGUE OF TELEPATHIC EXPLORERS

This 2001 Free City Media sampler gets my award for album title of the moment. It features Nick Bensen (reviewed here elsewhere) and other sympathetic sounds such as Bevis Frond and Mandra Gora Lightshow Society among the more and a dozen acts. This is label-defying psych-pop-rock, with as much modern and vintage inspiration. So only tread here if your garage-psych dogma can stretch to consider things you've never heard before. Yes, that is an invitation.

# IT WAS 40 YEARS AGO TODAY: a tribute to the Beatles

These kinds of cover-version albums are cyclical, and this 2004 two-CD effort (on the Canadian Bulls Eye Records) joins the ranks of a seemingly countless number of Beatles tributes. The 50 bands here are mainly underground, though Andrew Gold and Al Kooper certainly are notable exceptions. I do give credit to the acts attempting to make these classic songs sound like their own, but most simply remind us why the original band – The Beatles – where so much better than most mere mortals.

# LAS VEGAS GRIND 2000 EP

Several labels released special records to coincide with larger garage festivals or shows, including this Dionysus platter, including The Boss Martians, The Surf Trio, The Tiki Tones, Freddy & The Forgone Conclusions, and The Hate Bombs.

# THE LUSTRE KINGS / PROFESSOR SCHMIDDY & THE ELEMENTS

This 1995 split 45 EP does its best to paint the combos as actual 1964 instrumental entities, and while the sounds and recordings truly are authentic, I must tell you these were modern acts. If you enjoy that moment before The Beatles changed how American teenagers listened to music, then this EP is for you. It's primo instrumental joy, on Happy Hour Records.

# MISTLY LANE FEST EXPO 2000

Misty Lane released a special 7" EP for their 2000 garage festival, featuring The Chocolate Watchband, Tyme Society!, Thanes, and Rookies.

# MONDO DRIVE-IN

All you hipsters, of course, know that the instrumental-surf-garage scene has exploded since 1995. Blood Red Vinyl's 16-track "Mondo Drive-In" CD (from 1997) collects many of the finest of this sub-genre, complete with 3-D cover art and red-blue glasses! A sample from garage's royalty, The Chesterfield Kings, is represented by their "Muscle Beach Party," and the always-excellent Tiki Tones contribute several other prime minutes of pleasure. The Surf Trio, Boss Martians and Insect Surfers also deserve high praise. Have a hard time finding music being made just because it's fun? "Mondo Drive-In" is the place to start.

# MONSTER PARTY 2000

The horror-themed compilation is also a 1960s legacy, revived successfully once again with neo bands on "Monster Party 2000" (on MuSick). Dependable instro-kings The Tiki Tones and Los Straightjackets anchor the creepy collection along with MuSick regulars The Hypnomen and Fifty Foot Combo. It's time to "Frankenstomp."

# MOTOR CITY BURNIN'

Total Energy unleashed an interesting twist for its two compilations of Michigan rock, "Motor City Burnin' Volumes One and Two"— they each include sounds from 1968 up to the present. Kinda strange to see recent acts such as The Hentchmen and Big Chief rubbing shoulders with veterans Iggy Pop and Destroy All Monsters, but the concept works somehow. There's a cool 1990s live track from ? and The Mysterians on Volume Two.

# MUSHROOM MUSIC MONOLITHS

OK, this compilation wins my award for one of the best titles. It is a 1999 compilation from Swamp Room (Germany), with a lavish printed inner sleeve and colorful cover. Swamp Room's garage and psych interests are wider than mere purists, and the sounds range form the punkish Dead Moon to their own trippy Mandra Gora Light Show Society. There's plenty of weirdness to go around, and then the power-pop of the Grip Weeds, too. Well-played, Swamp Room.

## NOTHING BEATS A ROYAL FLUSH

Heading even further south in sophistication (and that's OK with me), let's head even further north geographically for Canada's "Nothing Beats a Royal Flush" compilation CD (1998, on Roto-Flex). When the sleeve says "18 Classic Canadian Crap-Outs," it doesn't lie, with plenty of texture and fiber to boot. My faves: The Shinolas' "Aqua Vulva," The Fiends' "Just in Case You Wonder" and The Tonics" "Mindbender."

## NOW PUT ON YOUR FACE AND JOIN THE RACE

This is a 1994 four-song 7" EP by the Belgian Demolition Derby label, featuring The Squares, The Perverts, Percolators, and Sin Alley.

## OOK LEU.K. OM TE HOREN!

This 2004 CD collection from Delft, Holland, has a whole bunch of vowels in its name – a bunch of unremarkable indie bands, and one crunchy punk number with The Napoleons.

## POP ON TOP

Bomp's 1997 "Pop On Top" collects 20 Australian power-pop acts, with a whole slew of jangly highlights.

## POPTOPIA

Rhino Records pioneered the art of rock & roll re-issues, and their 1997 box set "Poptopia!" display that their loving care for rock's past hasn't lost its passion.

"Power pop" has been around since before the Beatles uttered their first "Wooo!," but the genre of two-minute-long, melodic, catchy, pimple-inducing tunes was only getting its (commercial) due in the 1990s. Reflecting a groundswell of interest, Rhino's "Poptopia!" set features 54 power pop songs spread over three CDs, split into the decades of the 1970s, 1980s and 1990s.

The artist and track selection veers between the hits and the obscure, making this box set an illustration of the difference between a "compilation" and a "sampler." A compilation of the best power-pop from the 1970s through the 1990s would have many more of the charting songs and much less of the underground acts – and it would also be nearly impossible to produce because of the song licensing expense.

"Poptopia!" goes the sampler route, delivering a wider taste from the genre without attempting to include every absolute must-have song.

So, in the spirit of understanding what it *is* rather than what it isn't, "Poptopia!" is sheer delight. So many of the guilty pleasures from the '70s, such as The Raspberries, Cheap Trick, The Records, Bram Tchaikovsky – and yes, even The Knack – bring taps to the toes and a smirk to the lips.

The New Wave '80s disc also deliver prime slabs from The Romantics, Plimsouls, Hoodoo Gurus, The Smithereens – and The La's "There She Goes" ranks right up there with the all-time "Songs You Can't Get Out Of Your Head."

The '90s disc is a bit less satisfying, perhaps because we're still too close to the sounds to judge what the hell should be included. Many of the "right" acts – Matthew Sweet, Jellyfish, The Rembrandts and Redd Kross – are there, but perhaps with the "wrong" songs. Beauty, like song selection, is in the eye (or ear or record-label-checkbook) of the beholder.

"Poptopia!" as a whole hits the right harmony buttons.

## POWER CHORDS, HARMONIES AND MISTLETOE

A 2011 Twist Records Christmas-themed compilation featuring The Shambles, Jeremy, The Risk, Skid Roper (of Mojo Nixon fame) among the 21 tracks. This isn't another collection of Christmas standards, but instead original songs, with lots of chiming guitars and the promised harmonies.

## ROOTS OF POWER-POP

Greg Shaw used this 1996 CD as a way to re-introduce fans to some of his earlier pioneering work on his Bomp! Records with then-unknown pop groups such as The Romantics and The Shoes. The Barracudas, Plimsouls, and Stiv Bators each add fine cuts, and the more garage-oriented acts such as The Pandoras and The Last are here, too. Of special note is a CD appearance for "The Trains," by The Nashville Ramblers, still one of my favorite original songs of the garage revival era. It has a magic and mystery that still haunts me, decades after my first listen.

## ROOTS OF SWEDISH POP
### The Garage Days Volume 2

This is a wonderful collection of many of my favorite Swedish garage acts of the 1980s (on Uppers Records, 1996) including The Creeps, Backdoor Men, Crimson Shadows, Stomachmouths, Cornflake Zoo and more. Interestingly, even though most of these songs were only a decade old or so when this CD was released, most of the tracks are transferred from the original vinyl releases. Yes, it is now decades since these sounds first burned their way onto my cerebellum, and now it is time for kids today to re-discover what I already know to be classics.

## SANTA'S GOT A GTO!
### Rodney On The ROQ's Fav X-Mas Songs

I don't even need to hear the audio to know that this 1996 Dionysus effort will be fun – Rodney Bingenheimer in a Santa suit is enough for me. Oh, but there are songs, too – The Wondermints' "Ski Party" is fine, as is the classic Wednesday Week's "Christmas Here" (sounding like it was transferred from a copy of the 1980s vinyl Midnight Records Christmas album it originally came from). Holiday rock music compilations are one tradition I can always get in the mood for.

## SLOW SLUSHY BOYS / KRAVIN A's

A cool split-45 on Larsen Records, 1996.

## SOUTH AMERICAN TEENAGE GARAGE PUNK

The 2002 four-song 7" EP on Butterfly Records features The Tandooris, Los Peyotes, Flio & The Horribles, and The Supersonicos. A second volume was released in 2005, though I haven't seen that disc.

## THE STORY OF TONIGHT'S HALLUCINATION GENERATION

The always enigmatic and freaky Swamp Room Records in Germany released this 1997 compilation of its artists, most notably including Fit & Limo and Madra Gora Lightshow Society.

## STRAIGHT OUT OF BURBANK

Many indie labels have made it commercially bigger than Bomp! – the tiny Los Angeles label that helped change how underground and indie music is made and heard. But that's OK, Bomp! still survives, even if founder Greg Shaw is no longer with us to hear the musical children of all his efforts. This 1999 two-CD collection covers a broad spectrum of the Bomp! heritage – with one album sampling Bomp/Voxx releases and one CD of the newer Alive/Total Energy (more punk) acts. Of interest to the gargeniks here are vintage tracks from Nikki & The Corvettes , Surf Trio, and DMZ. The much more garage-oriented songs are on the "Be A Caveman" compilation (reviewed above) – this collection covers the more punk side of things.

## SURF MONSTERS

Del-Fi released this 1999 snapshot of modern surf-related acts, with faves Man Or Astroman, The Bomboras and Tiki Tones among the 20 acts. Modern instrumental sounds reach back to exotica and forward to space age and fuzz, so this is a worthy snapshot of the genre, circa the turn-of-the century. I do wonder – will these types of sounds still be sought after in the next turn-of-the-century?

## A SWAMP ROOM HAPPENING

At least four volumes of the German Swamp Room label exist – I have the 1996 Volume 4, which features Mandra Gora Lightshow Society, Something Weird, Head Colours and Milford T. I also have a 1997 EP for the "Event At Café Glocksee."

## SWINGIN' CREEPERS

MuSick Recordings also delivered more 1990s instrumental acts, this time paying homage to The Ventures with 1999's "Swingin' Creepers!" The line up is a who's-who of instrumentalist bests, with The Space Cossacks, Boss Martians, Bomboras, and Tiki Tones leading the way.

## TALES FROM THE BOOT

This 1995 Misty Lane album highlights the wealth of (then current) garage talent in Italy, including The wonderful 99th Floor, The Hermits, Hairy Fairies, and of course the legendary Others. Italy remains one of the most dedicated countries to the garage sound, and Misty Lane continues to keep that faith alive.

## TEEN SCENE Volume 1: Spain

A 1996 four-song 7" EP on Misty Lane featuring The Flashback V, Mocking birds, Doctor Explosion, and Gravetones. "Volume Two" featured Greek bands, though I haven't seen that disc.
.

## TEEN SCENE Volume 3: Canada

A 1997 four-song 7" EP on Misty Lane featuring Canadian acts The Gnostics, Polyester Explosion, The Knurlings, and Polaris.

## THEE CAVE COMES ALIVE

The What Wave fanzine in Canada released an amazing collection of audio cassettes with their paper issues throughout the 1980s and into the 1990s, and the best of them are collected for this vinyl LP on Action Records from 2004. The highlights are many, including The Royal Nonesuch, Gruesomes, Mystic Eyes, Beatpack, Projectiles, Creatures, Ultra 5 and more. Hats off to Action (and Dave and Rena O'Halloran at What Wave) for this important garage monument.

## THE THUGS / THE SATONES

The cover on this split 45 from 1997 says, "File under garage-surf-sci fi-rock," and that says it all for both The Thugs and Satones, who belt out four crudely-recorded instrumental tracks. How the heck did I find a disc from Blue Man from Uranus Records, anyway?

## TIGERMASK

This 1998 Dionysus compilation highlights bands that played the California "Tigermask" club in the 1990s (here with mostly studio cuts), including The Neanderthals, Loons, Boss Martians, Bomboras, Untamed Youth and Hate Bombs. Fun stuff, but as for the club, well, I guess you had to be there!

## TIME MACHINE

Enough time elapsed for fans to finally look back at the 1980s garage explosion, and the 1997 "Time Machine" CD was one of the first retrospectives to chronicle the Canadian scene. The 28 tracks are clunker-free, with The Gruesomes, Ten Commandments, Fiends, Nights Stalkers, Cryptics and Chessmen all registering knock-out punches. Beautiful Darren Merinuk artwork and extensive liner notes make "Time Machine" a winner in every detail.

## TOMORROW'S PEBBLES TODAY

In 1995 Mike Korbik of Twang Records put together an impressive package to put an exclamation on his many years promoting '60s-styled music in Germany: a clear-vinyl 7" 45 and a two-CD set housed in a twenty-page 45-sized paper booklet. The highlights of the 44 bands represented include The Chud, Slow Slushy Boys, The Stormclouds, The Petals, The Gripweeds, Crusaders, The What...For! and many others.

## TRANSWORLD GARAGE VOLUME 1

This is a 14-song LP (1995 on Misty Lane) featuring The Thanes, 1-2-5's, No Counts, Flashback V, Nuthins, Doctor Explosion, Perverts and more. Another solid piece of garage heaven from Misty Lane.

## TRANSWORLD GARAGE VOLUME 2

The 1996 follow-up LP from Misty Lane pits the U.S.A. vs. Europe. The U.S.A. is represented by the Woggles, Flypped Whigs, Fortune and Maltese, and Hate Bombs, among others. There's a fun goof here: my own band The Purple Merkins contribute a track, but are misidentified as my other band, The (Marshmallow) Overcoat. Europe weighs in with The Nuthins, Others, Frantic V, Flashback V and more. Who wins this great garage battle? You, dear listener. You win.

## A TRIBUTE TO THE ROKES

A split 45 with The Kartoons and The Waistcoats, on Larsen in the year of our fuzz 2000.

## UNSOUND

Gary "Pig" Gold and Shane Faubert are also long-time garage "True Believers" – together and apart – releasing scores of memorable discs year in and out. They also collaborated on a CD compilation series of home recordings titled Unsound.

The debut volume, 1998's "Pop," jams 24 tracks of living-room recordings into its digital grooves. I've long-admired the ambiance that home-tapers achieve, capturing more true creativity on their cassette 4-tracks than all the 96-track Fleetwood Mac/Hanson/Spice Girls luxury sessions combined. (OK, a small feat, I admit.)

Such lo-fi genius permeates "Unsound: Pop," which boasts a boatload of highlights. The compilers put their guests up-front, but my ears zeroed in on Faubert's own "Anybody Like You" for my early favorite. There's just something about Faubert's sensitive songwriting, arranging and vocal sensibility that strikes the sweetest of chords with me, and I find something new to appreciate about his work with each new release.

Such praise will probably bring an embarrassed blush to Gold and Faubert; their intention with the Unsound series is to expose other artists, not beat their own drums. Not to worry – there's plenty on the Pop disc from others to make listeners tap their toes and sing along.

## WINNIPEG RIOT

Garage fans will have seen ace illustrator Darren Merinuk's artwork on countless releases, whether you know his name or not. You may not know that he also compiled this compilation album of Winnipeg, Canada punk-garage acts. I have been to Winnipeg, and let me tell you, a band has gotta be tough to make music in that very northern little city. This is much more a punk collection than a '60s garage collection, and documents the universal joy of figuring out some chords (or not) and laying down some tracks. Great fun, no doubt, eh?

# MORE FANZINE COMPILATIONS

Many fanzines created audio CD-R compilations of then-current bands (and some original 1960s tracks on occasion) to include with their paper publication, including Misty Lane Magazine (Italy) , Garage Band Revisted (France) , The Continental (U.S.A.) , Rumble Skunk (Greece) , Larsen (France) , Gew-Gaw (Greece) Lost In Tyme (Greece), Peace Frog (Greece),  and Ptolemaic Terrascope (U.K.).

# Garage Feature Articles

## by Timothy Gassen

# THE JAGS: power goes pop

## by Timothy Gassen (2009)

*The late 1970s power-pop and "New Wave" movements helped pave the way for the 1980s rediscovering of 1960s-styled garage, pop and psych – so the example of The Jags is especially illuminating.*

The term "one hit wonder" is often used as cynical criticism, usually by those who have never had even one song of their own climb the charts. What jaded music fans don't understand is that bands which carry the weight of the "one hit wonder" tag often have a full catalog of other fine work that never reached a larger pop audience. Many pop listeners are just too lazy to search for anything but their spoon-fed Top-40.

That means many power-pop fans still don't realize that The Jags remain one of the New Wave era's most accomplished acts – and that their sound only starts with their 1979 smash "Back Of My Hand."

Record labels and radio in the U.K. were grudgingly forced to allow new wave and punk sounds to edge onto the airwaves in the late 1970s, long before their U.S. big brothers would even consider such an experiment. The young public's interest in these startling sounds meant a new breed of U.K. bands needed to be cultivated, signed and promoted – and quickly. The Jags were perfectly suited to seize that moment.

"The Jags started in 1978 when Nick Watkinson (vocals & guitar) and Neil Whittaker (drums) went to Wales to rehearse with John Alder (lead guitar) and me," said original bassist Steve Prudence in late 2007. Watkinson and Alder were the band's busy songwriters, with plenty of original pop material to develop together. (The Jags' John Alder is no relation to The Pink Fairies' drummer of the same name who is also known as "Twink.")

"The beginning was really idealistic, rehearsing in the Welsh hills," Prudence continued. "To me it's not so much 'sex and drugs and rock and roll.' – it's 'sweat and tears and rock and roll.' I could fill a half pint glass with sweat from my jacket after a gig.

"After moving to London, the band signed to Conspiracy Management and played the London pubs and college gigs," Prudence said. Luck struck them quickly when Island Records honcho Chris Blackwell found The Jags and immediately signed them – a major coup for any new band.

Then the problems started.

According to published reports from 1979 and from band members in 2008, Blackwell saw the band perform at another show soon after the signing – and Neil Whittaker walked right through his drum set over to Nick Watkinson and punched him so hard that the singer was sent flying off the stage.

Thinking their shot at stardom was quickly dashed by such a public disaster, the band was relieved that the Island Records deal was intact after Whittaker left the band. Solid drummer Alex Baird was installed behind the skins by April 1979 – shortly before recording their power-pop classic track "Back Of My Hand."

The Jags sound in 1979 was jangly and based around clean, ringing guitar, with slashing rhythms, quick musical changes and expertly precise three-minute arrangements. Their original songs were upbeat, full of hooks, elegant melodies and guttural rock energy – a perfect model of power-pop New Wave fun.

They claimed their favorite bands included Rockpile and Thin Lizzy, while Beatles references also creep into their press clippings. A close listen reveals all of these influences in the band's original output, especially a healthy dose of 1960s-styled pop sensibilities. This mixture wasn't a target for early criticism, but the U.K. press corps had a much deadlier poison in their pens: they quickly tagged the band as "Elvis Costello imitators" – an unfair, simplistic and damaging accusation the band would never shake.

Bassist Prudence, who counted Paul McCartney as a major influence, commented about the critics to journalist Shirley Stulf in 1979, "If the Beatles re-formed and started playing sixties type music again, they'd get slagged off, too."

One positive constant of the band's early press coverage is the assertion they were one of the most professional, musically tight and entertaining live acts on the U.K. New Wave punk-pop circuit. Great rock and roll lives on stage, and by all accounts The Jags were a great live band.

It should be also explained to American readers that the U.K. music press has the deserved reputation in some circles as being vicious and just plain arbitrary. Then, as now, they can saddle a band either as a "next big thing" or as unworthy of any attention – and then hammer the public relentlessly with their pontification. By 1979 Costello had been anointed by the U.K. music press as a pop savior, with all others to be seen as unworthy of even attempting his singular style. The Jags were easy targets as industry newcomers.

But Costello hadn't begun to make a dent in the U.S., and Jags singer and frontman Nick Watkinson slyly told the Record Mirror in their September 29, 1979 issue, "We've got to make it over there (the U.S.) before Costello does. Then everybody will say he's copying us!"

Police guitarist Andy Summers was announced as The Jags' audio producer in that same issue of the Record Mirror, but he wasn't in the studio to direct the band's initial sessions. "We recorded at Olympic studios in London with producers John Astley of The Who fame and Phil Chapman," Alex Baird said in 2007.

Those initial sessions would become the band's debut release: a four-song 12" vinyl EP in July 1979 containing "Back Of My Hand," "Single Vision" (both later on the debut album in different versions) and two tracks only available on the EP, "Double Vision" and "What Can I Do."

Island certainly sensed that The Jags' "Back Of My Hand" would be the band's breakout hit, and actually released three significantly different versions of the track. The 12" EP version was also released as a 45 (with similar cover art) in the U.K. and has the first mix, which is very "dry" and the most basic. A completely re-recorded version is on the U.K. version of the debut album "Evening Standards," and it has more of a live-in-the-studio feel to it.

Finally, an extremely different mix of the EP recording is on the U.S. version of the debut album and was also released in the U.K. and the U.S. as the single that would hit the charts. It is this last version of the "Back Of My Hand," mixed by The Buggles' Trevor Horn and Geoff Downes, which is the best – with a slight synth addition to the open and a fuller, more reverb-laden production style. It is 1979 power-pop record production at its best.

"I don't think any of the band was aware that the U.S. album contained the 'Buggles mix' of 'Back of My Hand,'" Baird said in 2007 after I informed him of the switch. "I wonder who made the decision to swap that track for the one we did on the UK album? And I agree that the 'Buggles re-mix' was indeed superior to the others."

The "Buggles version" of "Back Of My Hand" was a U.K. hit well before the band's debut album was ready, and the single hung in the U.K. charts for 10 solid weeks, reaching #17 in October 1979. It would be the highest chart position ever for the band, but no one could have guessed it at the time since the band's original material was so strong.

They played the hugely influential U.K. TV music show "Top Of The Pops," and also made a music video for the subsequent

"Party Games" track from the debut album. Alex Baird also remembers more TV. "It was a show called 'The Old Grey Whistle Test.' We did two songs from the album, 'Tune into Heaven,' and 'Evening Standards,'" he said.

"When we started work on the album (at CBS studios in London) we recorded 'Back of My Hand' again along with 'Double Vision' and some other stuff I can't remember," drummer Baird said in 2007. "We then continued recording the remainder of the album at Marcus Music Studios, again in London."

I remember clearly in early 1980 how stunned I was when I first heard my promo copy of the debut "Evening Standards" album. I was, indeed, an early fan of Costello and his band the Attractions – but I thought The Jags take on the new power-pop sound was all together different. Watkinson was right – if he could get to U.S. music fans and journalists like me, then comparisons to Costello would not be so important.

Watkinson told U.K. journalist Des Moines at the time, "We're not a Mod band, we're not a punk band. People will probably find it difficult to identify with us." As for Costello, he continued, "Look man, I'm no cheapskate Elvis Costello. I've never tried to impersonate him. For a start, we're more humorous, more tongue-in-cheek than him. He's more bitchy and venomous, like a middle-aged child."

But the music critics did not accept that The Jags could develop and play their own sound. It was much easier to simply call them Costello copycats. "Any group that can mimic Costello's tricky changes and melodic uppercuts this skillfully shouldn't have to imitate anybody," Rolling Stone commented in their review of 1980's "Evening Standards" debut album.

"The problem with critics, they're not musicians," bassist Steve Prudence said in 2007. "So they can't hear that the way The Jags played bears no resemblance to The Attractions, and that the influences were diverse, from "Woman's World" (Thin Lizzy) to "Evening Standards" (The Clash) and maybe even The Boss (Bruce Springsteen) on "Party Games.""

Two "live" recordings of The Jags from the era of the first album show a band bursting with energy, and confirm the band's status as expert performers. An early 1980 concert recorded in London's Paris Theater for BBC radio displays the band at their apex: meaty, powerful and prime for a larger audience. That audience was in the U.S., and in the summer of 1980 they made their sole tour of North America.

A July 1980 radio broadcast from that tour, of a "live" show in Houston, Texas, shows the band starting their transition to their second album's sound, with a keyboard in tow. This show has advance peaks at some material for that next album, plus two fine original songs they never recorded in the studio: "Love In A Telegram" and "Love And A Song." (Both of these songs are listed incorrectly with different titles on a recent CD bootleg.)

"'Love In A Telegram' was Nick's Thin Lizzy influenced tune," Alex Baird said in 2007. "The vocals are very 'Lizzyesque.'"

Bassist Steve Prudence left the band in March 1980, before the U.S. tour, and other changes were afoot for the recording of the follow-up album. Michael Cotton took over bass duties, while Paddy O'Toole added keyboards for 1981's "No Tie Like A Present." Despite the new blood, the relentless Costello taunts and subsequent chart failings seemed to stagger the confidence of the band in the studio. While members to this day explain they never consciously attempted to sound like Elvis Costello, drummer Alex Baird did say to me in 2008 that for the second album the band consciously worked not to sound like him.

"When we went into Compass Point Studios in Nassau (in the Bahamas) to start the second album, we had just finished a two and a half month tour of the U.S.A.," Alex Baird said in 2008. "We had spent a week rehearsing in L.A. to work out some ideas for the album and I remember it was awful. It was actually quite worrying – There seemed to me to be no direction."

The band set up in the Bahamas to record and feverishly worked to pull together new material. "We also had the guidance of Alex Sadkin as producer, who was amazing," Baird said.

The sophomore album suffers from an uncertain stylistic goal – the New Wave and power-pop exuberance of the first album is muted, replaced by a more scattershot approach. "Being in the Bahamas with an American producer who had little knowledge of our past and being away from our usual surroundings – out of our comfort zone – it's hardly surprising we sounded a bit different," Baird continued.

While many Jags fans scratched their heads over the group's attempt to diversify, the band itself was pleased with the growth. "Personally, I preferred the variety on the second album. If I had to choose one of them to listen to, it would be the second," Baird said in 2008.

But in 1981 the album didn't chart, was met with indifference by the press and public – and The Jags seemed finished.

Former Jags members were polite and reserved in their recent comments to me about the problems surrounding the end of the band from 1980 to 1982. They simply say the band did not end with all on good terms, with legal disputes concerning management – and that looking back reminded them of the unpleasant memory of the death of original drummer Neil Whittaker. Baird explained in 2008, "He threw himself under a train. I think it was at Clapham Junction station in London. I think he had a few problems and never, I suspect, got over his departure from the band."

By 1982, after two albums and many fine tracks behind them, The Jags were also no more.

Band members today still believe The Jags were only beginning to reach their potential, and they miss the exhilaration of the special times when their music worked and the future was theirs to make. "Playing live was pure adrenaline," said drummer Baird. "I'd never experienced such a rush. I was devastated when we split up."

The Jags' signature "Back Of My Hand" has since been included on many New Wave compilation albums, and is regularly referred to as one of the highlights of the era – but the remainder of the band's output was out of print until a 1999 "Best Of" CD issued by Spectrum Music in the U.K.

Not an edited collection, this CD is actually a compilation of the band's two U.K. albums. (The song order for the "Evening Standards" album is different than the 1980 US version.) The CD does not include the band's two non-LP B-sides or two extra EP cuts, and includes the U.K. album mix of "Back Of My Hand" rather than the "Buggles re-mix" that was a hit on U.K. and U.S. radio. This fact has infuriated fans who bought the collection specifically for this one hit, only to find an alternate version included.

Of the missing B-sides, the first-album-era "Dumb Blonde" is a pulsing, marching, power-pop gem. It was backed with "Woman's World" as the A-side (which hit the U.K. charts for one week in 1980, at #75) from the "Evening Standards" album. The other B-side not included on the CD, "The Hurt," might be the band's least representative track (though a favorite of at least one band member). It was backed with Island's last-ditch single for the band, "The Sound of G-O-O-D-B-Y-E" from the 1981 "No Tie Like A Present" LP.

The audio mastering of this CD is quite harsh in the high end, as if the master tapes were transferred without attention to proper EQ. The cursory liner note information in the CD booklet is also flawed, crediting the "Here Comes My Baby" single to Jags members – it was actually written by Cat Stevens and was a #4 hit in the U.K. in 1967 for the Tremoloes. One more error: the standout original instrumental, "Silverbirds," has an incorrect songwriter credit, and should read "Watkinson/Leaf/Alder."

Fans of pure power-pop should not be dissuaded by any of these quibbles, and should hunt the bins for all Jags output, especially the early vintage vinyl. Newcomers to their sound will be delighted with a range of power-pop that few – including Mr. Costello – ever achieved.

But after all of the praise and clarification I offer here, even I admit that it is difficult to erase fully the miscalculated perception of The Jags by most music journalists. Reviewer Allan Jones was prophetic when he wrote, circa 1980, "Costello remains a phantom they still have to exorcise."

# LIVE AT THE CAVERN CLUB

## by Timothy Gassen (2007)

*In 2007 Bomp! Records asked me to produce two albums worth of material for a proposed "Live At The Cavern Club" set. I combed through dozens of tapes of 1980s performances recorded by Bomp! head honcho Greg Shaw at the Los Angeles club, and cleaned-up and compiled a couple dozen of the best cuts. These albums have yet to be issued, but here are the liner notes I penned for them.*

*Also, while I only performed myself at the Cavern Club once, with The Cryptics (pictured below, I'm third from left), I visited the club often and I cherish my memories there.*

It was natural for a home base to form in the media mecca of Los Angeles as interest in the new garage music sound grew in the early 1980s. KROQ disc jockey Rodney Bingenheimer had tried a '60s-themed night dubbed "The Cavern Club" at the trendy Club Lingerie in 1985, but it didn't muster much interest. Bomp! and Voxx Records honcho Greg Shaw revamped the idea in a new location, and while this Cavern Club was a hit, it couldn't have been more opposite of its famous original 1960s Liverpool namesake. This Cavern wasn't in an English cellar at all – it was upstairs at 6419 Hollywood Boulevard, near Cahuenga Boulevard.

Interestingly, from 1958-1964 the building had been home to the seminal rock 'n roll radio station KFWB. Though subsequently used as a Hollywood costume museum of sorts named "The Haunted Studios," show-biz glamour was not evident in the building for the club's 1985 debut. The stuffy, sweaty interior sported cheap wood paneling and an almost warehouse feel.

A running joke among bands was the club's inadequate audio system. Plastic Radio Shack-brand microphones and a tiny vocal speaker set-up seemed more like toys than part of a workable club audio system, yet bands somehow made it work week after week. There was no real stage, and only minimal lighting separated the band from the audience – but none of the crudeness mattered: fans were there for the cool sounds and a '60s sense of fashion.

And how the kids looked was all important. While Greg Shaw was the godfather of the weekly club, acting as host and guiding oracle, he brought in the always-fashionable Audrey Moorehead to spin '60s records between bands and act as a groovy hostess. (The teenage Moorehead must have been quite the sight, hauling crates of albums with her on a public bus to the club, in her full-on '66 wardrobe.) Boys sported perfect bowl haircuts, stove-pipe pants and Beatle boots; girls in go-go boots, Mod Mondrian dresses and long, straight hair. These hipster kids, reflecting the best mop-top looks a full 20 years after the first garage explosion, even inspired the wry "Psychedelic Boy" single from The Leopards. "A psychedelic boy never wonders, about the recent past that he plunders," the song slyly commented.

Not strictly fuzz garage, the club also was popular for Mod bands and their fans, and Greg Shaw even tried booking eclectic non-genre acts like the punkish Lazy Cowgirls and glam Donovan's Fairies for variety. But it was the true-blue garageniks such as The Unclaimed, Tell-Tale Hearts, Pandoras, Morlochs and Untold Fables who were the club favorites, and rightfully so.

It was the unavoidably cliquish nature of such a small scene that eventually turned away some of its most fervent supporters. "It got close-minded as it went along," Yard Trauma bassist and Dionysus Records chief Lee Joseph said in 2006. "It was great fun at first, but after a while we got tired of the same little scene week after week."

When it was new and fun, though, The Cavern was the place to be in California for garage music. All the best local and touring garage acts played there, and since it was a rare all-ages club (with no alcohol served and no smoking allowed), it drew enthusiastic teenagers, too. (I should note that while drink was not apparent in the club, it was readily consumed outside in the parking lot, much to the constant consternation of the police.)

**The Untold Fables blast the fuzz at The cavern in 1986. (photo by the Author)**

**Legendary Seeds singer Sky Saxon performed several times in the mid-1980s at L.A.'s version of The Cavern Club, shown on a typical gig flyer (above).**

I saw many shows at The Cavern, and was fortunate to perform at the club once in the summer of 1986, with The Cryptics. (Members of The Cryptics would go on to form with me the initial lineup of my 25-year-plus garage act, The Marshmallow Overcoat.) I remember the horror of not being able to hear a word I was singing, and later being told that was absolutely normal for the club.

The scene generated mainstream interest with Los Angeles newspapers and the national magazines Creem and Newsweek – and People Magazine even ran a photo of many of The Cavern regulars in their September 1985 issue. Greg Shaw, sensing that "something was happening," as he told me then, smartly recorded every act that played The Cavern – and he accumulated more than 150 hours of rough club recordings. To call the master tapes raw is an understatement – the piles of cassettes are full of hiss, distortion and dropouts. These recordings are raw and crude by any standards, but they exude a primal passion that perfectly reflects The Cavern scene.

Greg Shaw told me in 1986 that I would compile a "best of" album from the tapes for Bomp!, and more than 20 years later I finally have. Our goal with these two "live" albums (designed to be one bonus disc in each of the two "Battle of the Garage"

CD re-issues) is to finally document the wide variety of styles that Greg brought to the Cavern Club in 1985 and 1986 – from purist '66 fuzz garage, to rave-up R&B, to heavier rock, to melodic pop-psych.

The audio challenge was huge: tapes of most performances were technically unusable, and the tape cases showed only the name of the band, with no song titles! But we've sorted through the wild times at The Cavern and cleaned up (as much as possible) a sampler of performances. The songs still sound raw and nasty – just like it was at The Cavern the first time around.

Greg Shaw died in 2004, and for me these albums (still unreleased as of this 2014 writing) are a little "thank you" for all he did to mentor not only me but the entire garage music world.

The weekly Cavern Club closed in the fall of 1986, but rock historian Domenic Priore revived it briefly for four more monthly shows before it finally rested. It was strange in 1987 to realize that the 1966 wave of teenage go-go mania had returned to Hollywood 20 years later – and was gone yet again.

Now (in 2007) it is 30 years since that 1980s Cavern revival has passed. But as long as Beatle boots, fuzz guitar and fun exist, there is always a chance that yet another Cavern Club could sprout up in another Hollywood alley.

*Special thanks to Audrey Moorhead, Domenic Priore, Amy Etra, Lee Joseph, Suzy & Patrick and all at Bomp! for their assistance with this piece.*

**Inside Hollywood's Cavern Club, circa 1986 (left to right): Bomp! and Voxx Records' Greg Shaw, The Miracle Workers' Dan Demiankow, Yard Trauma's Lee Joseph, and the author, Timothy Gassen.**

# THE DOORS OPEN WITHOUT JIM

## by Timothy Gassen (2003)

*The 1980s revival of interest in The Doors mirrored the resurgence of neo-garage bands, and the influence of the band on the new generation is significant. Keyboardist Ray Manzarek told me during this interview that he was encouraged by the new interest in the 1960s sound, and here we discuss the idea of psychedelia in a new century.*

"We've opened the doors of perception; we've broken on through to the other side," keyboardist Ray Manzarek says, "and here we are."

Part of that "other side" is a new century for Los Angeles' defining band of the 1960s, the Doors. Frontman and poet Jim Morrison died in 1971, the remaining band members never replaced him, and they were effectively frozen without him.

Smash cut 30 years later, and guitarist Robbie Krieger, drummer John Densmore and Manzarek suddenly appear for a 2001 "VH-1 Storytellers" TV special with a parade of guest vocalists.

Most of the interlopers were current-flavor novelties, but one — Ian Astbury of the Cult — struck an exhilarating chord with his erotic rendition of "Back Door Man." There was murmuring from fans that a new Doors tour, with Astbury, would do the band justice and give a whole new generation the chance to experience the Doors' concert magic firsthand.

"The same thought came to us," Manzarek says with a chuckle. "We know we don't have Morrison. But we have the guys, Manzarek and Krieger, who created the music with the Doors. And we have a guy who comes from the same psychic space as Jim Morrison (Astbury). Like Jim, he understands the shamanic state and has that Dionysian quality to him."

But the fairy tale return has been bumpy. The VH-1 performances reportedly damaged Densmore's fragile hearing, and he bowed out from more reunions. Undaunted, Manzarek and Krieger added ex-Police drummer Stewart Copeland for the band's live concert return in September 2001 at the Ontario (California) Motor Speedway.

Manzarek, now 64, acknowledges that the triumphant return was intoxicating — despite Densmore's pending lawsuit against his former band mates. "Feeling the electricity shooting up and down your spine when we took the stage definitely made me want to do this again," he says.

After a few more shows, Copeland was also out, also filing and then settling a lawsuit with the new Doors. Sidemen Angelo Barbera (bass) and Ty Dennis (drums) fill out the current touring band, and Manzarek is delighted that the newly assembled shamans are on the road.

The act — officially dubbed "The Doors of the 21st Century" — is performing classics "L.A. Woman," "Love Me Two Times," "Break on Through," "Soul Kitchen" and 1967's "Light My Fire." But the group won't touch the dark masterpiece "The End."

"That song is sacred to Jim," Manzarek says gently, seriously. "We'll leave that song to Jim Morrison."

Manzarek has been such a constant and vocal proponent of Morrison's unique contribution to The Doors that his forming of this new lineup is most surprising.

But the virtuoso keyboardist sees the Doors as an evolving concept — a band with living people making changing music, not historical photographs hanging on a wall.

"People are afraid of change because you have to step into the unknown, and that is dangerous," he says.

"Some people say we should honor Jim Morrison by doing nothing," Manzarek adds. "But I say we're honoring Jim by playing — carrying on his legacy and the legacy of The Doors."

Lawsuits and band mate squabbles aside, Manzarek's focus remains on those magic moments when the music matters. "When you're on stage and you're having a communion with the audience for that two-hour ritual we call a Doors show, that's my vindication. The energy that goes back and forth is overwhelming."

A devilish grin then seems to reach through the phone receiver. "You want to take a trip?" Manzarek asks. "Come and see a show with the 21st-century Doors."

A 1968 Japanese 45 sleeve, with keyboardist Ray Manzarek at center. Manzarek died in 2013.

# MINING HIDDEN ROCK:
## The Nuggets Box Set

## by Timothy Gassen (1998)

*The garage-rock compilation album is taken for granted today – but the scores of albums, sporting the most obscure garage sounds of the 1960s, wouldn't have been possible without the original 1972 Nuggets collection.*

---

It's late 1966, and Gonn set up their band equipment in the back room of a Burlington, Iowa electronics store. Two microphones are hung from the ceiling and plugged into a tape deck. No one knew it, but they were about to make garage rock history.

The resulting song, "Blackout of Gretely," didn't sell a million copies or get them a big record contract. It merely cemented Gonn in the pantheon of garage band immortality – just like the other 115 or so bands on "Nuggets: Original Artyfacts From the First Psychedelic Era, 1965-1968."

Nuggets was originally a two-LP set released in 1972, and it single-handedly defined the genre of "garage rock." The songs from that original compilation comprise the first CD of this new Nuggets box set, with the other three CDs mining similar delicious obscurities and fuzz-laden AM radio hits.

"We didn't know we were recording a classic at the time, of course," says Dick Dodd of The Standells, which contributes the 1965 punk anthem "Dirty Water."

"We were recording pop music with guts, but I had no idea it would stand up to the test of time like it has."

"Dirty Water" is one of the archetypal garage rock songs, full of snotty attitude, guitar buzz, and a solid thumping beat. "It still gets my blood pumping," says Dodd of his signature song. "That era of music still has vitality, honesty and attitude that can't be beat."

Paul Revere and the Raiders might be the most commercially successful act on Nuggets. Their expertly crafted R&B/garage/pop hits still haunt oldies radio, and they deservedly land two tracks on the box set.

"Everyone knows we had a lot of success in the '60s," says vocalist Mark Lindsay, "but I remember thinking during the recording of our first album, 'We are so lucky to make it this far. I sure hope we get a chance to make another record!'"

Most of the bands on Nuggets only made one 45 or so, playing to regional fans for a few months before fading away. Lindsay says Nuggets deservedly shines the spotlight on these unknown rock heroes.

"We got to be on TV and make lots of albums, but that doesn't mean these other bands were any less important," Lindsay says. "The bands on Nuggets made great music – they were keeping the spirit of rock 'n roll alive."

The songs from these lesser-known bands – such as The Chocolate Watch Band, Del-Vettes, Squires, Daily Flash – all burst with the energy of rock 'n roll true believers.

That raucous garage spirit lives in Lindsay, who still performs onstage constantly. "I'll know I'm old when this music doesn't excite me anymore," he says with a laugh. "I can still play this stuff, crank it up, and have a blast. That's my definition of a good time."

The Music Machine represents another end of the garage rock spectrum. Dressed in all-black, with jet-black bowl haircuts and sinister scowls, The Music Machine invented punk rock a decade before it had a name. Their 1966 top-15 hit "Talk Talk" ironically defined garage rock as a form with intellectual potential, with its staccato structure and moaning vocal. No pop song before or since has approached its unique combination of addled attitude and throbbing ambience.

"Some people think 'garage' means that a band doesn't know how to play," says Music Machine vocalist and leader Sean Bonniwell. "The Music Machine was blessed with incredibly gifted musicians. We became so close that we could sense each other's creative intentions, and communicate musically with each other and the audience.

"So yes, we were a garage band, but in the best sense of the word," he says. "We were sincere, we meant what we played."

Countless new garage bands – we're deep in a third generation of garage and psychedelic music – rely on groups like The Music Machine, Raiders and Standells as a road map to the golden garage era.

Nuggets has already influenced generations of bands and listeners. Now it's time to do it again.

***NOTE: in 2005 Rhino released a 4-CD set they titled "Children of Nuggets," supposedly representing the neo-garage movement to that date. It is a shoddy misrepresentation of the garage-psych revival of the 1980s and 1990s, and it is not reccomended for a variety of head-shaking reasons.***

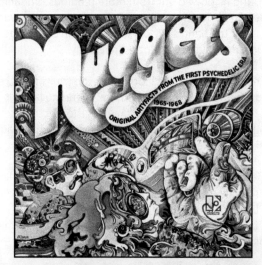

# AN ORGY FOR YOUR EARS:
## Dionysus Records

## by Timothy Gassen (1995)

*No one can appreciate how difficult it is to operate an independent record label and survive. Lee Joseph has accomplished this for decades, and his Dionysus Records was a vital link in the 1980s-1990s rekindling of interest in the garage-psych sound.*

---

Music throbs through Lee Joseph as his life's blood. "I grew up collecting records, and radio in the 1960s made music an integral part of my existence," he says. "My Mom has photos of me as a two year-old running around with a 45 in my hand."

The former Tucsonan continues to run around with 45s – he's celebrating the decade anniversary of his own Dionysus Records label. The 37 year-old music fanatic has also retained his sense of humor and perspective through the hard years of independent record company work. "The theme of our anniversary is 'A Decade Of Decadence,' and the theme for the next 10 years is 'A Decade Of Dollars'," he chuckles easily.

Laughs aside, making ends meet in the cut-throat Los Angeles music business has been a continuing struggle. "Dionysus has survived for 10 years because I've kept part-time jobs and because the mail-order catalog really supplements the label," notes Joseph.

"It's never been a problem getting our records into 'mom & pop' stores, but there are a lot of cities, a lot of markets where chain stores are the only place to buy records," he explains. "The mail-order part of my business has filled that void."

Joseph honed his entrepreneurial spirit while still in Tucson, Arizona in the early 1980s, managing the now defunct Roads To Moscow record store and marketing his own Iconoclast International cassette-only label.

He was already a talented musician with a world-wide following through his band Yard Trauma, and the exodus to Los Angeles in 1984 led directly to forming his own record company.

"Dionysus was definitely a garage label, partial to what some people called 'retro-'60s' stuff, and that's why I started the label," he remembers, "because there were a lot of great bands doing that music.

"For me the interest in rock music from different eras has never been nostalgia – music is something that's eternal," he adds energetically. "People don't think of classical music as being 'retro,' for Christ's sake!"

Joseph slowly built his label and reputation, and soon expanded releases to include a wide range of styles. "Later on, I started releasing anything I liked, and that's when we decided to start the 'Hell Yeah' subsidary label," he says.

Described by Joseph as "over the edge and out the window," Hell Yeah's output is definitely more abrasive, eclectic and less specifically genre-oriented.

The dedicated music collector also became a major player in the growing re-issue market. "Bacchus Archives is my re-issue label," he says proudly. "At first it included just stuff from the 1960s, but that's really branched out."

A big hit now for Joseph are his re-releases of 1950s "exotica" music. The mostly instrumental genre, which colorfully melds Polynesian and Afro-Cuban rhythms with small orchestras, is "basically popular music from the 1950s, pop music of the day." The current interest in "exotica" has pumped new life into all of Joseph's labels.

"Dionysus is now going to be a full-time label," says Joseph excitedly, "with the day-by-day operations run by Aime Elkins. She also has hired my ex-wife, who's doing promotion and the remaining mail-order."

The label has become more assertive, and is poised to make the giant leaps that other independents are now making. "What I've been doing with Dionysus for 10 years is just now starting to catch on. People like garage music now," he says triumphantly.

"There's also an awareness of indy labels," he continues. "People are more open-minded than ever, thanks to the fact that kids want to trace the roots of punk rock, because it's been around for 15 years. So they're interested in the roots of garage and surf and rockabilly -- it's Americana."

Joseph is also not blind to the fact that The Offspring's "alternative" sales are nearing the 10 million mark. "I'm not expecting any Dionysus artist to sell millions of records, but you never know," he says with another laugh. "Our new Hot Damn album is going to be a hit, I can tell you that."

The acclaimed producer and songwriter stresses that he certainly doesn't need to hear any more demo tapes. He's set his label roster firmly, and has learned from his decade in Los Angeles not to waste time on bands that won't work as hard as he does.

"I've had many run-ins with musicians who think that the world owes them something," he says with a smirk. "I like level-headed, down-to-earth people, but that's hard to find, because I think that anyone who is creative also has a chemical imbalance."

Add up the struggle, sweat and personal sacrifice, and Joseph still comes out far ahead on the ledger with his more than 200 releases.

"I like being able to crack open a release from one of my labels, then put it on the turntable and say, 'Man, this is a cool record!'"

# STILL TOPS OF THE POPS

## by Timothy Gassen (1995)

*The Smithereens are one of the most commercially success bands that proudly display their roots in 1960s pop. By this 1995 interview the band's top-40 career had ended, but they were beginning a new phase that continues today: simply playing the garage-pop sounds they still love.*

---

Smithereens guitar wizard Jim Babjak thinks back over 15 years of smoky bars, echoing theaters and faceless arenas. "It really does seem to me like we started yesterday," he says. "There's no real difference now, I think, except we get more stuff on the (backstage) rider now, more beer I guess," he snickers.

More has changed for the power-pop kingpins than an extra six- pack a night – Capitol has just released a 16 song "best of" for the band titled Blown To Smithereens. That's quite a jump for childhood friends who in 1971 started a band literally in their garage.

"I don't know how I feel about the 'best of'," says Babjak. "It wasn't our decision to put it out. At least they were nice enough to ask for a little input, like some of the old photos."

The new package attempts to condense the band's history into a mere 60 minutes, offering a somewhat compressed overview of the band's divergent pop abilities.

"The 'greatest hits' isn't the best representation of the band, though I suppose it could be an introduction for people who haven't heard us before," agrees Babjak. "There are a lot of styles that we do that aren't on the 'best of.' There were some of the softer songs like 'Cut Flowers' that should have been on it. That's a great song that wasn't ever really heard."

The band was asked for some input on track selection, though Babjak adds with another laugh, "I wish I had a little more input, because I would have added one of my songs!"

As it stands, Blown To... features 15 of vocalist/guitarist Pat DiNizio's stand-out originals plus a sparkling cover of the Outsiders' '60s gem "Time Won't Let Me," which was also featured in last year's Time Cop movie.

"I think that our version of 'Time Won't Let Me' should have been a hit," says Babjak about the most recent track represented on the CD. "I think radio complained because there was no soundtrack album. Our track was the only song in the movie."

Despite the new release, Babjak says that promoting "hits" isn't the band's #1 priority for the moment. "This tour is fun because we're not really pushing a record. There's the 'best-of,' but that's on our former label, so when we get on stage we do whatever we want to do," he says. "We're also doing a lot of songs we haven't done for years, and that keeps us on our toes. It's like in the early days when we'd take requests from the audience."

The U.S. current tour covers 37 dates in just seven weeks, culminating in a monster outdoor extravaganza at the new Denver airport. "They expect like 200,000 people," says Babjak matter-of-factly. "I hope we do O.K."

The Smithereens have been doing more than simply "O.K." for the past decade and a half. Few bands – R.E.M. comes to mind – have stayed with their original lineup intact for their entire career over such a long stretch, and few bands have so harmoniously produced quality pop music with such effortless ease.

"It's because we're sort of like a family," says Babjak. "You see, I've known Mike (Mesaros) our bass player since 1964 – we were neighbors and we both had the same accordion teacher! This is when the Beatles were just coming out.

"He knew (drummer) Dennis (Diken) already, but I didn't meet Dennis until 1971 when we were freshmen in high school," Babjak continues. "We started playing together the second day after we met. Mike picked up the bass – it was the only instrument left, and we finally met Pat (DiNizio) from an ad in a local paper in 1980," he says. "So like three months after we had been together we released that first EP, and it gelled. It's been working ever since."

What has been working is the Smithereens' blending of classic 1960s Beatlesque melody, hooks and jangle with meaty lyrics and a timeless pop sensibility. The band is also known for their happy-sounding upbeat songs about melancholy subjects.

Explains Babjak with a laugh, "That's because in the old days, when I played on the records, I never listened to Pat's lyrics! So I didn't know what the hell the songs were about, I was just playing how I felt. But The Smithereens 'sound,' I still don't know what the hell that is."

The band's sound has been shaped over the past five LPs mainly by two producers with opposite methods. "Our first producer Don Dixon likes to work fast, and we like to work fast too, but then we started to word with Ed Stasium, and it seemed like it took forever in the studio.

"I mean, Blow Up took like four months," he says of the band's fourth album. "That was ridiculous – I like to get in and get out. So that's what we did with the latest record (1994's A Date With...), we went in with Don again and did it in three weeks.

"Ed likes layers and layers of tracks," he says. "On songs like 'Top Of The Pops' I'd put six guitar tracks on the thing, while on our new LP we have basically one or two guitars, I didn't layer anything.

"Sometimes when we're in the studio we have a day left over, so we'll just knock out some 'live' tracks, and we've been doing that for years," Babjak also notes. "As a matter of fact, Capitol will be releasing a 'B-side' collection too. We've done Kinks and Beatles songs, a lot of different things," he says excitedly.

"We did a version of The Beatles' 'One After 909,' not the 'Let It Be' version, but in the earlier style. It was kind of goofy, Pat and I were drunk and we both sang on that."

The Smithereens jumped from Capitol to RCA after 1991's Blow Up, and will start work on their second RCA disc this summer. Record company politics are admittedly not Babjak's cup of tea. "Sometimes I don't know what record companies are thinking," he sighs. "Do they just want the quick buck or are they interested in bands like us that have longevity?"

The whims of media outlets such as MTV also raise Babjak's ire. The band was once one of MTV's hottest bands – with

1989's blockbuster 11 album – but now they find it difficult to find screen time with the trend setting network.

"In a way it's amazing that we've been able to continue without MTV support," he says. "They told us not to even bother to shoot a new video, because they wouldn't show it. This is the same station that once had us in heavy rotation, but then would only show our other videos once or twice."

In the scheme of the band's 15 successful years, MTV's acceptance – or lack of it – is merely a footnote. "We've always done what we love to do – it's just fun, and that's probably why we're still together, despite label changes and changes in radio styles," concludes Babjak, getting ready to skip off to yet another gig.

"I think we'll always be around, whether we have hits or not."

**The Smithereens, in an early promo shot, never forgot their Beatlesque inspiration, even in their commercial career.**

405

# ROCK REDUCED TO PEBBLES
## Greg Shaw Mines The Garage

## by Timothy Gassen (1995)

*Many garage rock fans and musicians – including me – first heard the wonderfully unique sounds of 1960s garage bands via the venerable Pebbles compilation albums. The series' name – a winking nod to the seminal Nuggets compilation – is still an essential bible for garage music.*

---

Bomp Records' Greg Shaw has always been at the forefront of the re-issue game – but not in anything as obviously marketable as "pop" music. Instead he's pioneered the field of compiling obscure 1960s garage and psychedelic rock with his Pebbles album series.

The Pebbles family of vinyl re-issues stretches over 100 albums, and is known by several other titles – including Highs In The Mid Sixties, Rough Diamonds, Electric Sugarcube Flashbacks and English Freakbeat. The vinyl collection began in 1979, eventually selling more than 30,000 copies a year, and peaked a decade later. They're now making a gradual conversion to the digital domain.

Pebbles has also paved the way – artistically and commercially – for other labels to dig deep into the closets of 1960s garage rock. There are now literally hundreds of other competing garage re-issue compilation series (on vinyl & CD) from the U.S. and Europe. It is obvious that more garage music is now available than ever before, and much of the groundwork was laid by Shaw.

Anywhere from 15 to 20 songs by different bands fill the grooves of each Pebbles, occasionally with more than one song from each of the obscure groups. The quality of the songs is remarkably wide in both performance and recording – from excruciatingly dismal to remarkably brilliant.

None of these forgotten songs were hits, most were never heard outside the band's home town, and almost all came from band-released 45s in batches of 500 or less. Compiled together, these garage rock artifacts reflect a vibrant cultural underground that is only now being appreciated.

Greg Shaw recently talked about the phenomenon of the garage rock re-issue.

**Timothy Gassen:** When Pebbles first appeared, collectors were excited to have obscure garage music available in any form, even if the transfers from original 45s were sometimes crude or scratchy. Now it seems that fans are more demanding.

**Greg Shaw:** The standard in this field has really moved on from where it was when Pebbles started. Now there are labels like Sundazed and quite a few others that are going to original

sources (master mix and multi-track tapes) and doing a really thorough job. I continue to try and fill the gaps, because I don't think it's the role of Pebbles to compete with those people. There are as many different ways of doing this as there are people doing it.

**TG:** The CD versions of Pebbles sound "better" than the original vinyl re-releases. You obviously are trying to address the collector's concerns for aural quality.

**GS:** In the past I've mastered from scratched (vinyl) copies and on occasion even from cassette. I won't do that for the CDs – they have to be from mint copies or original tapes.

**TG:** How did you decide originally what material you'd use for re-issue?

**GS:** What I did is I went through every known ('60s garage/psych) song and I made a working list database on my computer. I listed which songs exist, with a description and rating grade, what the sources are, who has the record – if I knew that or if I had them myself – and then I organized it by region. I've got about 50 regions that I'm tracking that way, and there are several hundred records on each of those regional lists that are under consideration for future re-issues. There are certainly 15,000 to 20,000 songs of sufficient quality that could be on my work list.

**TG:** Besides correcting some of the vinyl-version liner notes, adding new photos, artwork and previously unreleased songs, you've also combined under the Pebbles name songs from other series .

**GS:** This isn't really a resuscitation of Pebbles and Highs of the Mid Sixties on CD – it's really a new series. It's a distillation of the whole field, my compilations and everyone else's, and things that haven't been compiled yet.

**TG:** Do you have an idea of what kind of people are buying these records and CDs?

**GS:** It's hard for me to know who the audience is, but generally the people who buy these are not insulated from the culture of it. If they like this stuff enough to buy it they probably buy other garage stuff, probably read some of the fanzines, and they gradually get involved in whatever scene there is around this music. Sooner or later they adopt the values of this scene – and they have to collect 45s because a lot of the new bands making this kind of music make 45s. I think they're aware of vinyl.

**TG:** Has the re-discovery of these old garage records become a way of life for some people?

**GS:** There is a real lifestyle issue with some of the people who are into this stuff. Some people, even some of the younger ones, are obsessed with this caricaturized '60s lifestyle. The re-issues they buy are the soundtrack for their lifestyle of haunting thrift shops for old clothes and pretending that they live in the world of (the cheesy 1967 teen exploitation movie) Riot On Sunset Strip. This is a fantasy world that I don't share with them.

**TG:** Why do you think that this music captures the imagination so strongly?

**GS:** This stuff definitely comes from some weird place, and you can't even lump it all together except to say that it all comes from left field. It's like another dimension that it's coming from. Each one of those tracks is such a unique vision of somebody.

**TG:** Do you think this music as important now as when it was being made almost 30 years ago?

**GS:** I think that once something passes beyond its creative phase into a preservation phase, it becomes something different, like a lifeless artifact or a museum piece, and it's no threat to anybody. And the first time around this stuff was so intense and disturbing that it was a threat to the status quo in a lot of ways. And I think that was its purpose, to piss people off and to make a statement.

**TG:** Does garage and psychedelic music remain a rite of passage for some young people?

**GS:** I think so. You go through a phase when you're young where you want to reject the culture of your parents or the establishment society, but you can't invent a whole new culture of your own unless you're a visionary, so you join some kind of counter-culture. We do have these kind of pre-fab alternate cultures, and because they're small and very stylized and self-limiting they appeal to young people who want to belong to something – but in a manageable scope, where they feel they can have a place and a feeling of status.

I think it serves a valid role, and I think this type of thing has always taken place.

Legendary Bomp! and Voxx Records maven Greg Shaw.

# ALL YOU NEED IS MARTIN

## by Timothy Gassen (1994)

*We take for granted one important fact: the original garage -rock explosion of the 1960s (and therefore the 1980s and beyond) would never have happened without the success of one band – The Beatles. In the mid-1990s their music was being released digitally for the first time, creating a new wave of enthusiasm for the sound we all love.*

---

The filthy, dank night clubs of 1961 Hamburg held no hint that The Beatles would change the world. It was tough enough for the Liverpudlians to get a record company audition, let alone an actual deal. Aspiring bands note – The Beatles were turned down by every major label twice before meekly signing with EMI in 1962.

So thirty years later the numbers remain numbing for their 1964 U.S. invasion – 30 million Beatles records sold, covering 14 different songs in the "Hot 100" chart and the top five spots at one time. Forty percent of all singles sold in 1964 were by The Beatles.

"I'd been working for 14 years as a producer at EMI, and I was very aware of the dominance of the American market over the British market," says Beatles record producer George Martin recently in a phone interview. "English records just didn't sell in the States at all. So this breakthrough of 'I Want To Hold Your Hand' was enormously significant, not just for The Beatles and me, but for the whole record industry and indeed the economy of Britain."

Boxes of John, Paul, George and Ringo have blazed off British loading docks ever since, the product seemingly immune to changing trends and the passage of time. Among their massive list of Guinness Book-bests are the most #1 albums of all time (15), most #1 singles on the pop chart as a group (20), and most top-40 singles for a group (48). No one is quite sure exactly how many records they've sold throughout the globe, but the figure is in the hundreds of millions.

Despite their status as commercial icons, Martin believes the Fab Four's true importance is as accomplished artists.

"I think the genius of The Beatles lay in their songs and their song writing," he says with his trademark British tone. "They had such a wonderful abundance of genius in writing these songs. There were over 300 songs they wrote, and most of them were brilliant, and that was the basis of their greatness."

Martin remained the band's studio taskmaster for the whole of their glory years, helping to shape them and, in turn, the entire pop music world. "The Beatles were great people to work with in the studio," he continues humbly. "I mean, obviously we had our problems and wrangles and frustrations, but listening to those recordings again I am amazed at the quality of them, particularly the quality of the songs."

The classically trained pianist-turned-producer has been busy of late re-mastering original Beatles master tapes for the CD generation. "I did a television program not long ago (The Making Of Sgt. Pepper), and for the first time I went back to Abbey Road (recording studios) and listened to the old tapes. I found it astonishing, traumatic, but also extraordinarily fascinating.

"It's true that when we made these original recordings we were making them for vinyl. There is a kind of 'softer' quality (to analog recording) I suppose. CDs have been accused of being 'clinical,' and there's a kind of feeling you get on CD.

"You do have to 'cook' your 'vinyl sound' to make it sound on CD like vinyl. It's a paradox, but you do have to work at it. It's pretty subtle."

The latest of Martin's digital entrées is the re-release of the two most famous Beatles "best-of" albums. Commonly referred to as the "red" and "blue" albums, they cover highlights from 1962-1966 and 1966-1970 respectively. Martin's recipe for transferring the old analog tapes to CD works beautifully, capturing the warmth and brilliance of the originals while adding clarity and depth.

The only downside is the CD's packaging and price: they're sold separately as double-CD sets for about $30 each. The price gouging by Capitol Records is obvious, since all the tracks could have fit onto a total of two CDs.

None of this detracts from Martin's meticulous efforts to present these cherished songs at their best. His attention isn't on marketing, but on The Beatles' music, and his recollections remain vivid.

"Nostalgia is a pretty powerful thing, especially as you get older, and listening to those records does bring back an enormous amount of memories," he says while rustling over the CD track listings.

"'Norwegian Wood' was written by John when I was with him (and Lennon's wife Cynthia) on holiday. A lot of people thought we were raving and night-clubbing and so on, but after our skiing we'd go back to our rooms and play Monopoly and had hot cocoa. Very, very boring.

"'Strawberry Fields Forever' is got to be one of my favorite songs, and a lot of other people's too," he notes. "A unique song, something that John broke so many frontiers with, and it was the beginning of Sgt. Pepper, it was the first song we put down for the new album.

"It was gorgeous, terrific," he whispers with almost hushed reverence. "I loved the word-imagery, I loved the harmonic changes. I think it was a new kind of art form."

He singles out the epic Sgt. Pepper closing track "A Day In The Life" as a special moment for him and the band. "It was an extraordinary song and recording. A little bit bizarre, but of course the way John sang the song, it still chills me to hear it. His voice is the most wonderful thing to hear.

"And what a memory 'All You Need Is Love' gives to me," Martin sighs, revealing that some of the recordings evoke bittersweet emotion. "It was a live (TV) broadcast, and the 350 million people watching was a truly staggering figure. That week was absolutely horrendous for me, because my father died two days before the show."

The lads had evolved from yeah-yeah-yeah-ing mop tops to the gurus of altered consciousness, with the even-keeled Martin as their studio guide. He credits their dedication to originality as a key to the evolution. "I can't think of any other group ... who were able to create, actually create new material so well. The teamwork was amazing, and they were greater than the four parts.

"They had enormous curiosity," he continues, "and they were never satisfied with sticking to one style, one format, one sound. They were not just a group, but a multitude of groups. I'm still amazed at the wideness of their range, the brilliance of their talent."

All commercial record, film, video and merchandising success since the 1960s has been gauged against The Beatles' standard. The question has become an industry mantra: who will be the "next" Beatles?

"I don't think we should look for 'another Beatles'," Martin offers with his usual reserve, "but we should look for another great talent. It will only come when young people realize that it isn't just a matter of dressing right, looking right, moving right. I think it's a question of writing enough great songs as well as being good performers. The material itself is the fundamental part, and once you have that you have everything."

Critics and fans alike debate endlessly why The Beatles phenomenon continues after three decades. Social theories aside, Martin has his own insider opinion about their enduring influence.

"There isn't an answer to 'why them?' except that they were great, and that they were the greatest. The Beatles were the greatest performers and writers ever," Martin says, "and I think that's why we're still talking about them."

**What was the name of that band again? Oh, yeah, yeah, yeah, it is The Beatles, on the set of the Ed Sullivan TV show that began Beatlemania in the USA, in February, 1964.**

# BIRTHDAY BYRD

## by Timothy Gassen (1994)

*The Byrds, along with the Beatles and The Doors, remain three of the most influential bands for the garage sound. You can trace much of the neo-garage bands' style to these three bands – but few can current musicians can match the majesty of Roger McGuinn's 12-string Rickenbacker.*

Roger McGuinn's 22nd birthday wish in 1964 was probably simple: some kind of lasting success for his newly-formed band, The Byrds. They were about to issue a first single, and the jury was still out on the combo's commercial potential.

No one knew that soon enough they'd be crowned as "The American Beatles."

Thirty years later – today is McGuinn's 52nd birthday – it seems ludicrous that The Byrds were once considered a long-shot for stardom. Now they sit among the most influential musicians of their generation, and McGuinn's name is synonymous with the jingle-jangle of the electric 12-string Rickenbacker guitar.

"I'd been playing a 12 (string guitar) for a long time, starting back in my folk days in Chicago," McGuinn says. "When I saw A Hard Day's Night I noticed George Harrison was playing an electric one, so I went out and got a Rickenbacker, and I've been with that ever since."

The idea of seeing McGuinn without his trademark guitar is now unthinkable. He's so identified with the instrument that the Rickenbacker company introduced the "Roger McGuinn model" of the classic guitar in 1990, complete with his autograph.

McGuinn hit the road to guitar-hero status in 1961 with The Limeliters, then paid dues with The Chad Mitchell Trio (1962), Bobby Darin (1963), and Judy Collins (1963).

Yearning for a band of his own, he stumbled upon Gene Clark and David Crosby, and formed the embryonic Jet Set. Bassist Chris Hillman and drummer Michael Clarke were soon recruited, and The Byrds were hatched.

The first major task for the fivesome in the summer of '64 was to create a pop arrangement for "Mr. Tambourine Man." The Bob Dylan original held no hint of the eventual 1965 Byrds version – the soaring vocal harmonies and McGuinn's stately chiming were about to be invented.

The term "folk-rock" swept the globe with the tune's release and instant #1 charting, while the follow-up #1 "Turn! Turn! Turn!" cemented their oldies-station top-40 placement for decades to follow.

Several more hits ensued, but by 1968 The Byrds veered off into a genre that simply didn't yet have a commercial audience – country-rock. McGuinn was the only remaining original member of the band when The Byrds limped to an end in 1973.

Five subsequent solo albums showed only glimpses of McGuinn's guitar brilliance, while two late '70s McGuinn-Hillman-Clark LPs offered some commercial success but little artistic merit. Ironically, McGuinn's commercial influence flourished through other artists in the 1980s, while he sat without a record contract.

"I ran into this guy, Ramblin' Jack Elliot, when I was on The Rolling Thunder tour (Bob Dylan's 1975 traveling musical circus), and he told me about a time he went on the road with just his guitar, and he had the time of his life, so I thought that would be fun," McGuinn said.

Without a major-label deal, McGuinn spent the 1980s stockpiling original material while leisurely performing solo acoustic concerts in small venues.

Very little recorded work subsequently appeared, with McGuinn playing only on a handful of other artists' tracks, including The Beach Boys' 1986 remake of California Dreamin', and Elvis Costello's 1989 Spike LP. One highlight from the period is a concert appearance with Australia's Crowded House, dubbed "ByrdHouse" for the occasion. The resulting three-song CD features a blistering version of the 1966 Byrds classic "Eight Miles High," with McGuinn in top form.

He also popped up on stages with R.E.M., Tom Petty, and mentor Bob Dylan; he kept just close enough to the mainstream music industry to eventually snag a contract with Arista Records.

His subsequent 1991 "comeback" LP, Back From Rio, is a showcase of McGuinn's accumulated talents, and in a way a refresher course on the past 25 years of pop history.

"Back in the '60s I changed my name from Jim to Roger, and a lot of people didn't know that. They thought that Jim McGuinn was my brother, and that he went to Rio," McGuinn said.

"People would come up to me and say 'We really liked Jim McGuinn, he was a great guitar player,' and I'd say, 'Well, that's me, I just changed my name,' but they wouldn't believe me! So (the album title) is a joke about 'Jim' coming back from Rio."

Tom Petty and all but one of The Heartbreakers make up the backbone for many of the LP's tracks. Petty has perhaps capitalized most significantly on the groundwork first laid by McGuinn and The Byrds, and he returns the favor here with obvious gratitude.

The most interesting pairing on the LP, however, is that of McGuinn and the bitingly acidic Elvis Costello on "You Bowed Down," a powerfully angry song of disillusionment.

"I met Elvis about five years ago when I was playing in New Orleans," McGuinn said in 1991. "I asked him if he had any songs I could use ... He went home to Ireland and wrote this song, saying it was about these two guys who grew up together, and one was telling the other he had sold out – 'You Bowed Down.'

"He wanted me to sing it like a combination of (Dylan's) 'Positively Fourth Street' and 'My Back Pages.' Only Elvis would give you all this direction for a song!" notes McGuinn. The results are powerful, reminiscent of Costello's revitalizing collaboration with another rock legend, Paul McCartney.

Back To Rio's release coincided with The Byrds' tension-filled induction into the Rock and Roll Hall Of Fame. Bitter legal battles had been pitting McGuinn, Hillman, and Crosby vs. the other original members, vocalist Gene Clark and drummer Michael Clarke.

To many fans' dismay, Clark and Clarke had toured for years jointly and separately, billing themselves (and disposable back-up musicians) as "The Byrds."

McGuinn, Crosby and Hillman countered by performing a limited number of concerts in 1989 and 1990 also billed as "The Byrds," in a failed legal move to retain the name. The 1990 four-CD Byrds box-set further fueled the controversy, since it included new tracks recorded without Clark and Clarke.

Still, all five original Byrds stood amiably on the podium in January, 1991 to accept their reward. There was optimistic talk later of an upcoming official reunion, but all McGuinn would say of the induction ceremony meeting was, "The good news is that we all sang together and did three songs."

A Byrds reunion soon became sadly impossible – Gene Clark died in 1992, followed to the grave the following year by Michael Clarke.

McGuinn's influence hasn't faded with the deaths of his former bandmates. The adjective Byrdsian remains a common description for a wide variety of current pop and country music. Newcomers such as The Mavericks and Blackhawk continue to chart with stabs at McGuinn's recipe of jingle-jangle and sweet harmony – his guitar heritage has never been more evident.

Despite McGuinn's claim that he plans "only about six weeks ahead," it's obvious that birthday wish of 1964 is still being heard.

**The Byrds, with Roger McGuinn top left.**

# Guest Authors

*Music authorities share their views on the global neo-garage & psych music scene.*

# CANADA UPDATE

## by Dave O'Halloran (Canada)

*Dave O'Halloran was hypnotized by the unpredictable sounds of 1960s AM radio, only to be bored for most of the 1970s until punk rock returned music back to reality. From there he and his wife Rena produced the What Wave fanzine (and record label) from 1984 to 1996, and since 2004 has been sharing those deranged sounds via a weekly radio show titled Radio What Wave.*

My name is "WhatWave Dave" and back in the 1980s to 1990s I was co-editor of What Wave magazine (along with my wife Rena O'Halloran), the first Canadian zine dedicated to the new garage music scene. But here we're going to talk about the year 2000 onward in the Canadian garage/psych music scene. I've tried to include as much as possible, but Canada is geographically huge and the scenes are still regional – even in this era of instant and constant communication.

Back in the mid-1980s the Canadian garage scene was a happening affair, with the likes of The Gruesomes, The Ten Commandments, Dundrells, Purple Toads, Deja Voodoo and many others whose records would show up in the national college radio charts here. Packed sweaty clubs were the norm during this reign of garage rock, as paisley, turtlenecks, pointy shoes and pegged pants disappeared from the racks of the second hand clothing stores. As the 1990s arrived, grunge took over the clubs and radio, eventually taking over the mainstream, yet diehards continued to support the bands and scene as it slowly shrunk and went back underground.

Garage bands with their roots in 1960s punk survived across Canada as each city has its tiny yet extremely dedicated underground scene, oblivious to most others. Toward the end of the 1990s a new form of garage rock appeared: high energy, low fidelity, primitive sounds with roots in 1960s and 1970s punk as well as 1950s rock'n'roll.

Montreal was a primary site for this sound with bands such as Les Sexareenos, The Spaceshits, Del Gators, Scat Rag Boosters, The Daylight Lovers, BBQ, and many others creating a new scene. Some members of these bands continue to this day with an even newer form of this primitive garage-punk, some influenced by mind altering substances and with band names such as Demon's Claws, Red Mass, Sunday Sinners, Bloodshot Bill, CPC Gangbangs, Skip Jensen, Mark Sultan (BBQ) and many others. Attempts were made to bring the scenes and sounds together, but these garage festivals met with varying results.

A huge outdoor garage festival was planned for Southern Ontario, just southwest of Toronto, Canada in the summer of 2003. Among the bands invited were the cream of the crop in garage and psych at that time: The Gruesomes, Brian Jonestown Massacre, Orange Alabaster Mushroom, The

Sights, The Chains, Les Sequelles, The High Dials and a host of others.

The bash was called "The Wilderbeat Weekender," but unfortunately the weekend of August 14, 2003 turned out to be the weekend of the second largest widespread hydro-power outage in North America! As the early arrivals were just getting ready to rock on Friday, the power went off for several days in most of Ontario as well as the northeastern United States. Some acoustic performances were given, but many could not even get to the festival due to the lack of power. A lot of planning ended up being defeated by forces beyond control.

Flash forward to August 2009 and the "Wooly Weekender" in Montreal packed crowds in for three nights of garage rock and psych featuring a lineup of Canadian and American bands. Les Breastfeeders, The Gruesomes, Saffron Sect, Sunday Sinners, The Hypstrz, Muck and The Mires, The Electric Prunes, Question Mark and the Mysterians, The Higher State, A-Bones, Morlocks, Flakes, Alarm Clocks, and Nag all performed on the large stage.

There was a smaller stage at another location during the Saturday of the "Wooly Weekender" and some of the up and coming and noisier garage type bands played: Sonic Avenues, Tuetonics, Jinxes and a special appearance by The Nashville Ramblers attracted a devoted crowd. Members of Love were slated to play, but got stopped at the U.S. border, a somewhat common occurrence for touring bands coming to Canada from the U.S. The real sad part was that Sky Saxon was to play the "Wooly Weekend," but passed away a couple of months prior. His passing went almost unnoticed in mass-media as it was the same day Michael Jackson died!

Many of us had so much fun we were hoping for another edition of the "Wooly Weekend," but that was not to be. Teenbeat Takeover, which ran the fest, is no more, as its head honcho has moved to the west coast and settled down to married life.

Prior to that, Teenbeat Takeover brought some of the U.S. touring garage bands up for a few shows in Ontario and Quebec, including The Cynics, Ugly Beats, Reigning Sound, A-Bones, Muck and the Mires, Dex Romweber and others for us diehards.

One of the headliners at the Wooly Weekender, Canada's greatest export of the 1980s garage years – The Gruesomes – still do the occasional live show, usually in hometown Montreal or Toronto, where they are still well known and revered. And The Gruesomes records have all been re-issued, with lots of rarities in CD form, by Ricochet Sound, a label that specializes in current garage music. Not only have they released The Gruesomes CDs, but former Gruesome Gerry Alvarez's two solo releases, as well as garage combos Lightbulb Alley, and The Hook Up.

Toronto's record label, Boppa Do Down, has also released many singles and CDs featuring modern garage bands:

The Bon, Blue Demons, The Above, and Von Drats to name a few. Other Toronto labels include Ugly Pop (1960s and 1970s 7-inch vinyl reissues), Optical Sounds (psychedelic) and Bamalama (modern garage).

And the What Wave archives were dug into for the release of the "Thee Cave Comes Alive" LP, released by Action Records in Greece in 2004. This LP consisted of some of the more '60s oriented garage sounds that were originally released on cassettes that came with the What Wave paper magazine back in the mid-1980s to early 1990s. Some of the songs were re-mastered and some were slightly different versions, making it a necessary purchase for the collectors. Big thanks to George Rigas for his behind-the-scenes work on getting that LP released.

There are many tiny regional scenes across Canada and we'd need another whole book to write about them all – but we will take this opportunity to list some of the garage/psych bands from circa 2000 onwards we are aware of, starting with the Toronto area: The Midways, The Primordials, The Bon, The Chickens (placed in the top three in one of Little Steven's battle of the garage bands), The Leather Uppers, Tijuana Bibles, Smokestack Lightning, The Evil Eyes, Crummy Stuff (they back up touring legends like Mono Man, Peter Zaremba, Chris Masuak and others when they do mini tours in the area), Blue Demons and The Von Drats, and many others.

And the highly populated area of southwestern Ontario, surrounding Toronto, has always had fine garage bands, such as: The Fine Print, PsychoDaisies, The Mongrels, The Square Root Of Margaret (1960's UK psych influenced), Simply Saucer (proto-punk meets psychedelic), The Noble Savages and The Ride Theory (remodeled as Young Rival). The city of Hamilton has even started a monthly garage night titled "Kissin' The Carpet" (where many of these bands get to play to appreciative crowds) at a local club to try and keep things happening. And further east in Ontario, The Glads, Midduns and Orange Alabaster Mushroom have all played.

Montreal has been home to garage bands since the days of The Gruesomes, among them: Les Breastfeeders, Sunday Sinners, Le Chelsea Beat, Les Sequelles, The Chains, The High Dials, The Milky Ways and Fuad and The Feztones (which just might include some former Gruesomes).

The west coast of Canada has always had its share of garage combos, among them The Fiends (R.I.P. Greg Johnson), The Smugglers, Green Hour Band, Trap Doors, Thee Manipulators, The TVees and Raised By Wolves. Heading across the prairies, regional combos like The Forbidden Dimension, Von Zippers, Heuvos Rancheros, The Pygmies, Cripple Creek Fairies, The Mants, The Brewtals and The Angry Dragons have kept the spirit alive.

And we can't forget Canada's east coast which The Stance, The Stolen Minks, The Baketones, Sweet Tenders, Their Majesties, and others all call home. Oddly, almost all these bands site The Gruesomes as an influence as they recorded

their "Live In Hell" cassette (now on CD) on Canada's east coast many years ago.

There is one surviving print magazine, Mongrel Zine, based in Vancouver, which covers some of the newer garage combos, does artist profiles, and occasionally covers garage bands from the 1980s among lots of other crazy and cool stuff.

And we should mention we've released what is probably the last ever edition of What Wave zine, as we did a complete London, Ontario band history from the mid 1970s to early 1990s, encompassing the 1980's garage scene. Included with this tome was a 90-minute cassette of unreleased London, Ontario combos, including many that were garage related.

The sound of things

415

# UNITED STATES UPDATE

## by Dennis Dalcin (USA)

*Dennis was editor and publisher of the punk fanzine Useless Information between 1977 - 1978 and Kaleidoscope Magazine between 1986 - 1991. He was also owner of the Direct Hit Records label and guitarist/vocalist in The Shades (1977 - 1981) and The Lears 1990 - 2000. The Lears remain one of the most important jangle-garage groups of the revival era.*

The 1960s were of course the pinnacle time period for garage-pop and psychedelia. Groups were all over the world – so many great bands in fact that it was hard to keep up with them all. By the 1970s most of those bands were gone or had changed their style into some other form. Disco and southern rock ruled the commercial airwaves through most of the 1970s, even though glitter-glam rock and punk rock managed to make some inroads on tightly controlled and strictly formatted radio stations. Power pop and then new wave bands later on also broke through and had a few hits worldwide.

Then in the early 1980s came the second great flowering of garage-pop and psychedelia around the world. Most of the bands were in the style of garage or garage pop with a fewer number playing psychedelic, garage-psychedelic or power pop music. By the 1990s, and with the advent of the grunge movement out of Seattle, most of the bands were gone or again had changed music styles to a new harder-edged rock sound that was more acceptable to the masses. Gone too it seemed, were the hook filled choruses that made songs from previous decades stick in your head for days after hearing them only once or twice.

The new century arrived and again there were a small number of musicians, who were disenfranchised with the prevailing styles of rap-hip hop and/or corporate rock and pop of the day, and who chose to borrow from an earlier time when music was free, fun and "fab." These new bands also had a knack for penning fabulous hooks in their songs just like in years past. And as the 2010s began one could again see the beginnings of what might just turn out to be the third great flowering of garage-pop and psychedelia!

Not only are we seeing older 1980s bands reunite and release new albums (The Bongos, No Strange, The Liars among others) – and some with a new sound like The Sick Rose (Torino, Italy) who changed from garage to power pop – but we're also seeing a rise in brand new bands creating their own brand of worthy garage sounds such as:

The **High Learys** (Australia), **The Woolly Bushmen** (Orlando, FL, USA), **The Ugly Beats** (Austin, TX, USA), **Thee Wylde Oscars** (Adelaide, Australia), **Os Haxixins** (São Paulo, Brazil), **Sultan Bathery** (Vicenza, Italy) and the all-girl band **The Splinters** (Berkeley, CA, USA). There's bands who combine garage/folk/psych into their own style like **The Belltowers** (Orlando, FL, USA), **The Quarter After** (Los Angeles, CA, USA) and **Paul Messis** (UK); as well as new psychedelic bands like

**The Sufis** (East Tennessee, USA), **The Paperhead** (Nashville, TN, USA), **Pond** (Perth, Australia), **Temples** (Liverpool, UK), **Vibravoid** (Düsseldorf, Germany), **Boogarins** (Brazil), **Jacco Gardner** (The Netherlands), **Eternal Tapestry** (Portland, Oregon, USA), **Hookworms** (Leeds, UK), **The Liміñanas** (Perpignan, France), and **The Striped Bananas** (Baltimore, MD, USA).

One cannot forget the new mod-garage groups like **The Mergers** (UK), **The Routes** (Japan); and young R&B bands picking up from both the 60's and 70's like **The Strypes** (Ireland). New power pop artists like **Radio Days** (Milan, Italy), **Exploding Hearts** (Portland, Oregon, USA) and **Lannie Flowers** (Kennedale, TX, USA) have also released fine albums.

These bands and others like them will have to struggle against the tightly controlled media outlets such as radio and TV and mega recording corporations who are run and controlled by lawyers and businessmen (aka the dreaded "suits") who know little or nothing about what goes into making great art or music.

Bands now have to slug it out for pennies rather than dollars in income. This changes the way every musician creates his or her music and in a very detrimental way stifles true creativity. I believe that musicians will continue to choose to market themselves and their music through social media Internet sites like ReverbNation, Bandcamp and others where their music can be bought directly from the artist who created it.

This will allow artists to create the type of music they want – without the interference from labels and/or corporations trying to tell them which style of music will sell or not – and make it available (at least in theory) to the general public.

As we race toward the middle of this decade (2015) let us all keep a watchful eye on the bands I mentioned above (and new ones yet to form) – and hope that we will once again see a great flowering of garage-pop and psychedelia throughout the world.

We may even hope that one day great music will once again flow forth from FM radio stations worldwide rather than just on the internet!

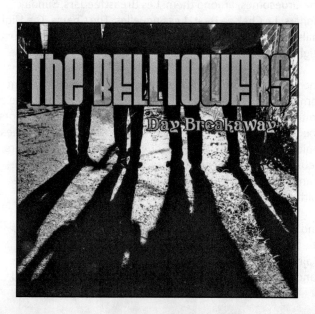

# DEAD MOON

## by Eric Geevers (Holland)

*Eric Geevers is a longtime fixture on the Dutch underground rock scene, playing in the Ace-Tones, Link Protrudi and the Jaymen, Link Wray's band, The Napoleons, with Robert Gordon and Chris Spedding, The X-Ray Men, The Raving Bonkers, and his main band Flying Tygers.*

Dead Moon's unique and amazing story is a tale of defiance against all odds. It is the story of Fred Cole (vocals/guitar), his wife Toody (bass/vocals), and Andrew Loomis (drums and "entertainment"). It is a story that has also spawned some of the best rock music since the original 1960s garage beat explosion.

First of all, it is not fully correct to see Dead Moon as a "garage revival" band. Although they emerged in 1987 (first gig on September 17), Fred had never really stopped playing in bands since the 1969 demise of The Lollipop Shoppe, whose key song "You Must Be A Witch" has been a staple of garage bands' set lists ever since.

The Lollipop Shoppe, originally named The Weeds, weren't Fred's first band either. Born in 1948, he's been in bands since he was 13, backing Frank Sinatra Jr. in 1964 (while playing bass with The Lords), gigging in strip clubs while still under age, hooking up with the legendary producer Larry Williams, recording as Deep Soul Cole with backing vocalists The Blossoms.

It's safe to say that by the time The Weeds were firmly going places Fred had enough notches on his gun not to suffer bigwig music industry bullshit. So when manager and scenester "Lord" Tim Hudson changed the band's name to The Lollipop Shoppe on the album's record sleeve without the band's consent (or knowledge), and with silly stuff going on like Fred and Toody having to keep their marriage a secret "to protect the band's image," the writing was on the wall.

When the band was pushed into a less underground sound by their label, The Lollipop Shoppe called it quits. Being at loggerheads with the music business suited the Do-It-Yourself ethic of Fred and Toody perfectly. In fact when they avoided the U.S. military draft (and the Vietnam war) by going to Canada, they built their own cabin there – from scratch. With two little kids. You want to hear about primitive? Talk to Fred and Toody – or their kids (and grandchildren).

Returning to the U.S., they opened a music store (named Captain Whizeagle), Fred doggedly forming band after band (Zipper, King Bee, The Western Front, The Rats, and The Range Rats). Fred released a string of lo-fi but heartfelt records on their own Whizeagle label, with Toody picking up the bass in 1979 for The Rats.

The Rats was the band that connected the 1960s songwriting and attitude seamlessly with the 1970s punk energy and D.I.Y.

rebellion. However, the Rats came to an end after drummer Louie Samora quit (being the third drummer already). Then they remembered someone who they'd asked previously to play in a western-style band that didn't work out ... and enter Andrew Loomis: drummer, bartender, 15 years younger, sharing their love for rock'n'roll, Jack Daniel's whiskey, and cigarettes.

Things firmly started to roll when Toody bought a Presto-88 disc cutter for Fred's 39th birthday – the same machine that once cut the original "Louie, Louie" 45 for The Kingsmen – and in 1987 they released a 7" by their new band, now named Dead Moon.

Now Fred had enough equipment to record those songs himself with Dead Moon, mix the recordings, master them and even cut the record, have them pressed and sell them – all on his own terms.

This sound is sometimes called "lo-fi," but all too often I have heard that term given to bands that make deliberately bad recordings to gain notoriety. Not so here – this approach was simply because the recordings were done at home, with simple gear, amps in one room, drums in another, wires all over the place, hoping nothing would break down before the songs were done. The urgency of getting it on tape oozes from those recordings. And, of course, the songs are straight from the heart, and brilliantly so.

In 1990, a handful of 7-inchers and three albums had been released on their own label, Tombstone Records (after the new music store they hand-built themselves, Western style, called Tombstone Music).

Then, out of the blue, they were invited to play a couple of gigs in Europe, with the Dutch/German record label Music Maniac releasing a compilation LP of the Dead Moon catalog to that point (titled "Dead Moon Night"). The first couple of gigs and the first proper tour launched a word-of-mouth snowballing effect, resulting in an explosion of Dead Moon shirts with their famous skull-in-a-moon logo (designed by Kelly Manahan) being worn all over Europe.

The 1990s would see Dead Moon returning to Europe, playing famously long sets in long exhausting tours, for a growing and growing audience, with band rituals that became a firm part of the Dead Moon folk lore, so to speak. Once seen, never forgotten: Andrew and his sparse drum kit at the front of the stage, with Toody immediately to his left and Fred immediately to his right (audience view), both using straight mike stands, amps on the floor right behind them. Whether in a small venue or a huge festival, this would be their stage set-up, not to be messed with.

The inverted Jack Daniel's bottle with a burning candle on top of the bass drum all covered in wax. The floor tom being perfectly level, for Andrew to pour a couple of beers on it during the intro of "Johnny's Got A Gun" (showering the front rows in beer for the next few songs). Fred breaking a string, the band not missing a beat while Fred is furiously changing the string, tuning up quickly, and – after a nod – carrying on exactly where he left off.

The looks exchanged between Fred and Toody (a married couple since June 14, 1967) when singing the line "and I still don't know you…" in the song "Clouds Of Dawn." The encore, usually consisting of another whole set (and then some, until a Country & Western classic says "that's all folks"). The dressing room, always full of friends and fans. The tattoo of the band logo on Fred's face. Yes, on the side of his face. Toody's laughter, loud, and incredibly contagious. Her hollow-body Vox "Wyman" bass, covered in stage tape and re-glued back together by Fred after every couple of tours. Fred's own Guild guitar, modified to hell and back (with some interesting side tours), looking like a train wreck but sounding terrific.

Drummer Andrew, behind his kit, drinking Jack Daniel's or whatever 40% liquor is on hand, handing the bottle to friends in the front row to pass around (his finger drawing a line, "leave this for me"). His on and off stage behavior is legendary. Everyone seems to know Andrew, somehow. Everyone seems to like Andrew – hotel staff included. (A claim that he had trashed a hotel room in rock star style was proved completely false.) He'll take the piss if you treat him like a rock star. He's set you straight when you behave like an asshole. He doesn't give a fuck – instead, he cares a lot.

Dead Moon would simply never have happened without Andrew Loomis, and that's a fact.

A steady output of albums (with every now and then something extra, a single, EP, or bonus disc) and a tough touring schedule made the band a household name in venues and festivals all over Europe, and in the 2000s their homeland discovered this "best kept secret form Portland Oregon."

Worldwide, bands name-checked Dead Moon as being very influential, and even bands like Pearl Jam were covering Fred's songs (notably "It's OK"), and in 2004 Last Chance Records released a double CD, titled "The Cole Mind," where 40 bands from across the globe played Fred Cole songs (most of them from the Dead Moon catalog).

Did they start recording in stereo? Nope. Bigger amps? Backup guitars? No such thing. Hey, "we won't change, not like that," they sang (as early as 1990).

Then, in 2006, SubPop Records released a double CD that compiled the whole Dead Moon story, to raving reviews. Magic Umbrella released an amazing insight in the world of Dead Moon with their documentary "Unknown Passage – the Dead Moon Story," directed by Kate Fix and Jason Summers and filmed at the Coles' home and during one of their endless European tours.

It was buzzing, and this could "break" Dead Moon to a wider audience.

Then, for most people, completely out of the blue, came a short announcement: "After 20 years, Dead Moon is retiring.

It has been a journey we will always treasure and (we) feel that a worldwide family has emerged in its place. Dead Moon became much bigger than the band itself, it became a D.I.Y. underground, hopeful for a lot of people. The candle is still burning!" – (signed) Fred Cole.

Tour after tour, Dead Moon was the best live band. The albums underline the songwriting genius of Fred Cole in gloriously raw mono. Their work ethic is illustrated by something I witnessed somewhere in the early 1990s in Rotterdam, the Netherlands. The Marshmallow Overcoat (on tour from Tucson, Arizona) was to play a cool-and-yet-hot little beat cellar, and before I boarded the train to the show, I got a phone call. Dead Moon, being on tour, had a rare night off, and were coming to go and see their fellow Americans – and hey, they had thrown their guitar cases and a couple of drumsticks in the trunk … you know, just in case. And sure enough, in between two Marshmallow Overcoat sets, Dead Moon were happy to play a set, cut short by Toody breaking a bass string.

What's more fun that watching a band? To start a band and play yourself! I wonder how many bands have been formed over the years by people who saw Dead Moon and saw the light? Many, that's for sure.

Oh, and if you have read all this and you feel bummed out because you missed Dead Moon live – check out Fred and Toody in their latest band: Pierced Arrows.

Fred Cole (bottom) Toody Cole (middle) and Andrew Loomis of DEAD MOON.

# SAN DIEGO AND BEYOND

## by Bart Mendoza (USA)

*Bart Mendoza is one of the truest of true believers in pure pop and rock music. As a writer, singer, guitarist and producer his discography is 13 pages long, chock full of brilliant releases with Manual Scan, The Shambles, True Stories and many more. But what really separates Bart from other talented garagers is the tireless work he puts in to help other bands. Whether it's mod, garage, pop, or simply rock & roll, for decades Bart Mendoza has taken action to help other bands get shows, make records and then get attention though his excellent written reviews and feature pieces. Bart is a true treasure in the world of garage music celebrated in this book – and his contributions both in front of the microphone and offstage have not been trumpeted nearly enough.*

Garage rock? Alive and well my friend. I'm talking about the purist stuff, not the Spin Magazine, or some such modern definition thereof, but the sixties-inspired, Chelsea boot-wearing, sometimes Farfisa-toting combos that aspire to Nuggets or Pebbles inspired greatness.

Perspective and context is important. Looking back over the past decade plus, the entire music industry, from smoke belching conglomerates to guys borrowing their moms money to put out a single, has continued to downsize. That said, today the proof isn't in record sales. Go to an online video service like YouTube and type in "garage rock," or whatever combination describes what you want to hear, and countless new disciples to the sound appear.

Certainly San Diego has never had a shortage of sixties inspired and influenced combos. While there are new bands out there, it's also heartening that many of the original crop of revival musicians are still playing out there in ever shifting combinations – and still sounding great. In San Diego, there are several combos that fit that template.

**The Loons** continue to go from strength to strength, the key to their sonic gifts being a mix of Mike Stax's songcraft and manic front man persona with the rhythm section of bassist Anja Stax plus drummer Mike Kamoo's propelled rhythms and studio work. In addition to the band, Mike publishes the legendary **Ugly Things** magazine, runs a music label, promotes shows, and is involved in more cool projects than anybody this side of Andrew Sandoval.

Meanwhile, Anja Stax has also been making waves of late with her own group, **The Rosalyns**. It's an all girl, all star combo, which includes guitarists Amy Gore and Diana Death, organist Birdy Bardot and drummer Lety Beers. They've also recently recorded tracks for an upcoming EP with Mike Kamoo.

Another new group featuring familiar names features two of Mike Stax's former musical partners from the Tell Tale Hearts: Ray Brandes and guitarist Eric Bacher are now part of **The Sidewalk Scene**. The quintet includes bassist Mark

Zadarnowski (from The Crawdaddys) alongside guitarist Joe Piper, with a wonderful sound that takes in The Byrds, The Kinks and more. As of early 2014 the band recorded four tracks for a EP, with David Fleminger at the board. Of the new groups, two are standouts.

**Shake Before Us** is probably the current San Diego band that has the most direct **Nuggets** influence. Their self-titled 2011 album was produced by Rocket from the Crypt's John Reis – no gimmicks just great rock and roll. Well, they do use a Theremin pretty extensively, but they use it well.

The other band that seems to be making a big splash and draws pretty well are the **Creepy Creeps**. Like great bands, such as The Mummies, before them, The Creepy Creeps come from the costumed side of things, making them extremely visual. I'll start by mentioning that the frontman-keyboardist plays an instrument housed in a coffin.

But they are not a one-shtick pony. Besides the de rigueur go-go girls, the band has a variety of costume options, ranging from Dr. Jekyll and Mr. Hyde personas to reptile aliens and my favorite, Mexican Day of the Dead skeletons, complete with Mariachi band outfits. The music can be pretty primitive riff rock, but its never less than a fun time.

Also, very sixties influenced, from the Ronettes-look to their sixties pop sound (which seems to be diminishing as the releases continue) **The Dum Dum Girls** have quite a few good songs, but it's material like "He Gets Me High" that probably appeals most here.

Outside of my San Diego back yard, there appears to be a healthy amount of great music being made. **The Ugly Beats** immediately come to mind, as do **The Cynic**s, but one recent favorite, especially after playing at Ugly Things 2013 anniversary shindig, is **The Neumanns** from Orange County.

The message is clear: Amongst seemingly insurmountable odds, the kids are (still) alright.

# THE TIMELESS GARAGE

## by Glynis Ward (USA)

*Glynis Ward is a DJ, record fan, and go-go dancer, and as of 2014 one of the radio hosts of "The Fringe Factory Radio Show" on AM1690 in Atlanta, Georgia.*

My interest in garage music started as a child, when I heard local bands such as the Ugly Ducklings on the radio in my hometown of Toronto, Canada. Back then they were of course merely called a pop band, a local rock 'n roll outfit – and there was no categorization such as "garage." If anything they'd also be called "white r'n'b," but even in Toronto, dividing lines between styles of music weren't looked fondly upon by local musicians and fans (and thus began the "Toronto sound," a mish-mash of everything popular at the time).

However, perhaps if only out of the sheer volume of music I've been exposed to, I find myself categorizing bands for my own sanity. As a fanzine writer in the 1980s & '90s when I published "Feline Frenzy," I needed categories to keep the fanzine focused on the 1960s-influenced garage music we all love – yet still the fanzine featured some other garage and psychedelic bands for good measure. And during the ten years I hosted "The Fuzz That Wuzz" radio show on CHRY in Toronto, I felt the need to categorize bands simply because, once again, the radio show was about *garage* music.

Today many of those similarly like-minded bands would blur the lines of what I deemed garage, psych or surf music back then. Even each of those small genres has classifications within themselves. For example, there are psychedelic bands such as The Night Beats (which is my favorite modern band of the 2000s) which is stripped down and play real Texas '60s-influenced styled psychedelia.

I tend to be drawn much more to bands of this ilk than I am of the psychedelic-influenced groups that are more "stoner rock" or electronic '80s indie pop and "shoegaze" influenced. But what remains the same for all eras of '60s-influenced bands is that the musicians playing the music have always been influenced by *all* the past music they have heard.

So as time goes along, more and broader influences sneak their way into the music – for better or for worse. There are always a few bands, such as The Higher State, that remain incredibly close to the original 1960s sounds. For bands such as this I find it's the songwriting subject matter that often becomes broader and keeps the group sounding vital.

So what does that synopsis of the "current scene" (through my eyes and ears) mean? It means that I still absolutely love garage music (and surf, and psychedelia) and have enjoyed seeing the creative transformation that the music has made over time. To think back to the 1960s, who'd ever think that the music made then would have been "a thing" during the first "Knights of Fuzz" revival in the late 1970s-'80s? Even in the first revival era, who'd ever think it would still be a "thing" and even picking up in popularity now? Certainly not me!

It amazes me that I can still go see bands I loved in the 1980s such as the Fleshtones and The Cynics – these bands that haven't stopped playing and putting out records. But what gives credence to this whole genre of music are the original '60s bands like the Alarm Clocks or the Sonics getting back together and playing again, not just once or twice, but regularly, and making new music that sounds *great*!

Garage music has become timeless – especially when many facets of rock 'n roll are often termed as "dead," garage band fans of yesterday are still keeping rock 'n roll alive and well, and ushering in whole new generations of musicians and fans.

---

# P.J. CRITTENDEN'S DIRTY WATER (UK)

*P.J. Crittenden's Dirty Water Records label continues to release fine garage-related music, and his Dirty Water Club live band nights in the UK are the stuff of garage legend. Here is a list (in alphabetical order) of some garage-oriented bands he recommends, many from the UK, and mostly not featured elsewhere in this book:*

Blackout (France)
Chrome Yellow
Deadly Long Legs
Graham Day & the Gaolers
Janey & the Ravemen
Jarvis Humby
Leighton Koizumi & the Born Losers
Les Bof (Scotland with French singer)
Les Terribles (France)
Little Bare Big Bear
Lord Rochester
Los Chicos (Spain)
Los Cretinos (Spain)
Los Explosivos (Mexico)
Los Idiotas (Spain)
Los Mutagénicos (Spain)
Lulu's Marble (Japan)
Mark & the Spies
Minnesota Voodoo Men (Japan)
Muck & the Mires (USA)
Neil's Children
Peter Berry & the Shake Set
Phantom Keys (Spain)
Quant
Seven And Seven Is

Speak & the Spells
Teddy Boys From The Crpyt
The Baron Four (ex-Vicars)
The Black Rash
The Bo Linksters
The Boonaaaras (Germany)
The Branded (British but based in Sweden)
The Bristols
The Carpet Sellers (France)
The Cogburns (USA)
The Creepy Morons
The Crushers
The Cryptics (Channel Islands, UK)
Thee Cybermen
The Dee Rangers (Sweden)
The Diaboliks
The Dilemmas
The Dirty Burds
The Dorktones (Netherlands)
The Draytones
The Dukes Jetty
The Electric Fayre
The End of the Beginning
The Exit
Thee Exciters
The Fabulous Penetrators
The Federals
The Felines
The Fingertips (France)
The Flakes (USA)
The Fore
The Freaks
The Fumestones (Spain)
The Gas Mach V
The Gideons
The Giljoteens (Sweden)
The Graverobbers
The Green Hornets
The Guaranteed Ugly
The Hi-Class Joes
The Hypno-Twists (USA)
The Hypnotic Eye
The Immediate
The Jeckyls (Germany)
The Knights of the New Crusade (USA)
The Ladybugs (Japan)
The Launderettes (Sweden)
The Len Price Three
The Lysergics
The Madame Cats

The Madd
The Maggots (Sweden)
The Masonics
The Mean Things
The Midnight Kicks
The Misbegotten
The Missing Finks
The Mobbs
Thee Northcoats
The Nuns (all girl Monks tribute group)
The Orangu-Tones (USA
The Pacifics (Ireland)
David Peter & the Wilde Sect (Denmark)
The Phroggs
The Priests (USA)
The Revellions (Ireland)
The Rippers (Italy)
The Sly Tones
The Stags
The Subcandies (Austria)
The Surrounds
The Teamsters
The Unchayned
The Understanding
The Urges (Ireland)
Val's Basement
Thee Vicars
The Vinyl Stitches
The Voladoras (Sweden)
The Witchdoktors
The Wobbly Lamps
The Wonkey Monkees (France)

## THE HIGHER STATE
self-titled album
13 O'Clock Records, 2013

## by Colin Mason (UK)

This is the U.K. band The Higher State's fourth album and third for Austin, Texas label 13 O'Clock Records.

13 O'Clock is a new label that has seemed busy recruiting talented groups and performers from around the globe, mostly European, I may add. Their roster also includes Paul Messis, who is the new bass player for The Higher State, The Flight Reaction (from Sweden), Os Haxixins (from Brazil) and Arsene Obscene (from France).

They also reproduce wonderful thick card album sleeves and use heavy vinyl. Satisfaction is guaranteed for the purveyor of a quality record. If this wasn't enough, The Higher State has recorded their new long player in mono and it all sounds sublime.

The album was officially released on the 12th November 2013 but I got a sneak preview of its folk-rockin' greatness via a very limited edition promo CD that The Higher State's drummer Mole kindly sent me during October.

2013 was quite busy for The Higher State. They replaced bass player Ben Jones with Paul Messis. I have exchanged many emails with Paul over the years and I can say for certain that he was thrilled to be joining such an amazing group, after all, The Higher State are the U.K's foremost exponents of authentic folk-rock.

With this album Kent's finest have gone all out to create a purist '65-'66 Los Angeles-Sunset Strip folk rock masterpiece. It's a direction that the've hinted at ever since they began recording, but in 2013 it seems that The Higher State focused their efforts wholly on this style of music.

The music is expertly recorded by Marty and Mole at Sandgate Sound Studio where they have custom built an eight-track recording facility. All twelve songs have beautiful multi-layered harmonies over the soundscapes of Rickenbacker jangle, tambourine splashes and drum patterns that are at the very least the equal of anything laid down at the "epicenter of jangle" during mid 1965 to mid 1966.

It's difficult to pick my favorite cuts from the album as I dig them all, they really are stupendous and ooze a classy commercial folk beat. Back when The Byrds was having their hit records these boys would surely have also hit the big time. They have received rave reviews in the notable music magazines and fanzines as well as online blogs etc., but underground critical acclaim aside, The Higher State have already hit the big time in my "forever mid-60s" world.

Paul Messis provided one song in the set, the driving folk rocker "Why Don't You Prove It," which adds clattering Keith Moon style stick work and stellar guitar tones. Marty's opening gambits "Need To Shine" and "Jagged Words" are sublime and so too is his mournful "Sky Clears To Blue" which sounds like the same kind of 12-string moody trip the original 1960s combo The Roosters were so adept at recording.

Side two opens with the exciting single "Potentially (Everyone Is Your Enemy)" and continues on an unrelenting folk jangling trip until the powerful "Try Slowing Down," where Marty spits out some insightful and thought provoking words seemingly about "plastic people."

*"But look here comes another trend*
*Now you look just like your friend*
*Where will it end - where will it end.*

*You've laughed at me for all these years*
*It helps to divert from your fears.*

*Get the latest style from the salon*
*as the band wagon rolls along - rolls along."*

The Higher State released one more song in 2013 when they provided a cover of the classic "Don't Run And Hide" for the Fruits de Mer label Hollies tribute titled "Re-Evolution."

I believe in 2014 that they have been active in the studio cutting a couple of 13th Floor Elevators covers for a forthcoming Fruits de Mer 7" box set titled "7 And 7 Is."

**line-up:**
Marty Ratcliffe (12 string guitar, harmonica, vocals)
Daniel Shaw (guitar, vocals)
Mole (drums, percussion, vocals)
Paul Messis (bass)

---

## OS HAXIXINS

"Depois De Um LSD" b/w "Espelho Invisivel" 45
Groovie Records, 2008

"Under The Stones" album
Groovie Records, 2010

## by Colin Mason (UK)

Os Haxixins are from Sao Paulo, Brazil, and their debut 45 was limited to 500 copies on green vinyl.

Both sides are fine and purist examples of 1967 Los Angeles groove. These guys have got The Doors and Iron Butterfly heavier psych sound down on vinyl perfectly. Other groups have tried this combination in the past but none have come close to matching Os Haxixins. They even add some wild fuzz guitar in the mix for good measure.

I've been playing their second album, "Under The Stones" for the last few days and the songs are really burying deep in my mind.

They're clearly fond of mid '66 garage sounds but have combined this with some spooky Doors like organ. I was actually very intrigued by the organ sound and I'm led to believe that they're using a Diatron.

Also in the mix is a heavy use of fuzztoned guitars and reverb. Most of the songs (apart from the two covers) are sung in their native language which is a huge bonus, for me anyway. No need to criticize unusual or wrong pronunciation of English words.

Hard to pick out a favorite as the whole album runs along smoothly, most songs have a fast tempo, there are no ballads. I'm not sure if Os Haxixins could pull off a slow love-song or ballad. I don't think it's their style.

## "FAVORITE" LISTS
## by Spiros Pelekis (Greece)

*Spiros Pelekis is from Nafpaktos, Greece. Excited by his love for garage and psych music, he was publisher of the influential Rumble Skunk fanzine, and in 2012 formed the Rumble Skunk record label.*

I've gotta tell you that "top-20" or "top-10" favorite-lists are not my cup of coffee, because I believe that music is kind of like a roller-coaster and things are always changing. But the following stuff came to my mind almost like a flashback. Anyway, time for action now, hope you'll enjoy some personal fave releases from 2000 to now (2014).

## TOP-20 ALBUMS:

**THE GRUESOMES** – "Cave-In!" LP
(Jaguar Club Records) 2000
A 14-track garage punk monster, contains fuzzed'n'fab originals, (just listen to "Hip-No-Tyzed") as well covers of The Sorrows, The Pretty Things and Jury. The vinyl version is getting rare now, but you can find also a CD version. Dig this!

**SHUTDOWN 66** – "Gotta, Gotta Get Me To Out Of It..." LP
(Corduroy Records) 2000
With their second full-length strike, Nick Philips, Bad Micky and their pals go wild and outta time. Ultra killer garage-punk-r'n'b stuff played with teen angst, by one of the greatest bands from the land of OZ (Australia). The true spirit of the underground garage punk is alive & well.

**THE EVIL THINGIES** – "New Shapes In Sound" 10"
(Tear It Up Records) 2002
Cool, loud & fuzzy stuff from King Koen and his pals. The attractive one-of-a-kind sleeve the real thing is pretty hot, including "Enough Of Your Lies," one of my mega-faves ever, plus lots more. A real fuzzed-punk delirium!

**GET LOST!** – "Never Come Back" LP
(Voodoo Rhythm Records) 2002
Yeah! Amazing band, featuring Gerry Mohr & Robert Butler (ex-Miracle Workers & The Untold Fables). Their album is a real masterpiece, including killer fuzzed-punk originals, plus covers of "Spooky," "Leavin' Here," and "One Way Ticket." A cave-true-classic.

**BABY WOODROSE** – "Blows Your Mind" LP
(Animal Records) 2002
An ultra-fab garage-punk-acid-psychedelic masterpiece. The incredible-one-of-a-kind cover artwork this album is really a killer. If you don't have it just do yourself a favor and get it as soon as you can. It will blow your mind, a real blast for your soul.

Essential!

**KEK '66** – "On The Outside Looking In" LP
(Larsen Records) 2002
When The Kliek called it a day, The Kek '66 formed to continue their Dutch-garage-beat trip. Great melodies with catchy songwriting, marvelous original songs, cool covers and a fabulous album not to be missed.

**THE THANES** – "Downbeat And Folked Up" LP
(Screaming Apple Records) 2003
Those Scottish garage-beat kings deliver us a really cool album, which contains 14 top tracks. Amazing originals and well-chosen covers like The Sparklings and Beau Brummels make this full-length a real must have!

**THE CHESTERFIELD KINGS** – "The Mindbending Sounds Of..." LP (Sundazed Records) 2003
Everything you need is here: A flash-blast from the past where the Rolling Stones, The Seeds, The Electric Prunes, The Chocolate Watch Band trippin' out with the kings of Rochester, New York. Don't miss this LP for any reason, OK?

**THE EMBROOKS** – "Yellow Glass Perspections" LP
(Munster Records), 2004
One-of-a-kind full-length by this cool UK band. I'm pretty sure that you'll dig their great mix of garage, freakbeat and popsike to the max. This album features a couple of awesome originals, plus well-chosen covers, including an epic cover of Mike Stuart Span's 60's anthem "Children Of Tomorrow."

**THE UNHEARD OF** – "Revoxination" LP
(Psych Out Records) 2004
One of the coolest USA garage-psych bands around. A fab album with fuzzed guitars, swirling-haunted organ with dark-drugged atmosphere, including superb originals, plus killer covers of The Bad Seeds and The 13th Floor Elevators.

**THE FUZZTONES** – "Salt For Zombies" LP
(Teen Sound Records) 2005
With special guests Sky Saxon of The Seeds and James Lowe of The Electric Prunes, this album's mixing garage punk and psychedelia with incredible results, including killer originals, plus covers of Boss Tweeds and Macabre. Ace stuff!

**THE SATELLITERS** – "Hashish" LP
(Dionysus Records) 2005
This is the real garage-pot party! Germany's garage pride with various releases under their belts. I really dig all their albums so far, but this one has something special. Great originals, plus covers of We The People and The Association. Grab it!

**THE CREATURES OF THE GOLDEN DAWN** – "An Incident At Owl Creek Bridge" LP (Get Hip Records) 2006
Pennsylvania's garage pioneers. After the full-lengths on Dionysus Records, and Collectables, plus a few 7-inchers here and there, the band trapped in the time tunnel. Their brilliant album includes fab originals, plus super-cool covers of Tintern Abbey, The Red Crayola and Thor's Hammer. Just listen to "Sadder Than The Rest" and you'll get the picture.

**THE MAGGOTS** – "Monkey Time!" LP
(Screaming Apple Records) 2006
One of the best garage punk albums I've heard in prehistoric ages, including wild-ass garage originals, plus covers of The Morning Dew and The Cardinals. Get it because it's the call of the Monkey Time!

**THE STAGGERS** – "Teenage Trash Insanity" LP
(Soundflat Records) 2006
If you don't have this LP, gimme a break and buy a copy, or stop reading this book! Organ-fuzzed-trashed-garage-punk stuff at its best, guaranteed for kickin' out some nerds'n'trends. A really great album!

**THE URGES** – "Psych Ward" LP
(Screaming Apple Records) 2007
These cavemen from Dublin, Ireland, will drive you really wild to the caveland. Their first album is simply one the coolest & best garage punk albums ever, and contains 12 ultra-killer originals, where the organ & fuzzboxes are on fire, wild and screaming vocals will crunch your brain, creepy bass-lines, and primitive beats for primitive people. Ultra-highly recommended!

**MARK & THE SPIES** – "S/T" LP
(Screaming Apple Records) 2007
One of the coolest garage-beat-pop albums I've heard in the last few years. Their first album contains 10 fabulous original tracks, plus a José Feliciano cover. Most of their songs are filled with great melodies, groovy-beats, catchy pop-hooks, and surely their songs will stick on your mind for a long time.

**THE OMENS** – "Send Black Flowers" LP
(Hipsville Records) 2009
The real garage punk deal. The only thing I can say is that you gotta get this already classic album of garage punk mayhem. Just originals here, 10 mind-blowing organ-garage-stompers with fuzzed guitars, snotty vocals, pounding beats and great songwriting that surely will shoot you the moon.

**DOLLY ROCKER MOVEMENT** – "Our Days Mind The Tyme" LP (Bad Afro Records) 2010
A splendid album by these Australian maestros. "Our Days Mind The Tyme" is a cool multicolored garage-psychedelic release, including brilliant songs like "The Only One," "Coffin Love," and "Sold For Sinners." Without a doubt this is their finest hour so far.

**LORDS OF GRAVITY** – "The Curse Of Icarus" LP
(Rumble Skunk Records) 2012
Mindblowing fuzzed garage punk stuff from Australia. Actually, this is the very first release on my own Rumble Skunk Records, here in Greece. My girlfriend Elissavet and I wanted to put out this album because simple this band rules! Awesome originals, plus three 1960's covers from the land of OZ. Is out there and still available – just grab it and find out what garage punk is all about.

## TOP-10 7inchers:

**THE INTERCONTINENTAL PLAYBOYS** – "Just Turn On" 7" EP (Larsen Records) 2002
A killer 3-track EP by these Australian garage-punk-trash-sex-a-billy maestros. If you dig The Cramps, The Fuzztones, Tav Falco and Faster Pussycat this piece of wax will come as a pleasant surprise.

**THE CREATURES OF THE GOLDEN DAWN** – "Blood From A Stone" 7" EP (Butterfly Records) 2003
A must have EP from this cool USA garage band, including the incredible and mega-fave "Blood From A Stone" plus three more great songs.

**THE INDIKATION** – "Don't Send Me No Flowers" 7" EP (Larsen Records) 2003
A brilliant release from this cool Norwegian band. You'll find "Three Little Words," their amazing song called "Swedish Girl" (probably their finest hour so far), plus two great covers. A must have for any garage-pop-beater out there.

**ROCKET SCIENCE** – "Burn In Hell" 7" EP
(Voodoo Rhythm Records) 2003
Acid-drenched-fuzzed-garage punk stuff from the land of OZ, and surely one the greatest EPs I've heard in ages. Just play the loud to the max-tremble "Crazy" and things will not be the same for you. This release is not to be missed.

**MAINLINERS** – "Dead Man's Hall" b/w "Daughter Of Dimes" 7" (Crusher Records) 2004
Top stuff. "Dead Man's Hall" is the key, a marvelous song with great guitar work, right on target vocals and swirling organ. The B-side is cool as well. Try to find it without second thoughts.

**THE CRYIN' SHAMES** – "S/T" 7" EP
(Private Release) 2006
Outta sight, outta mind USA combo. Their first release and probably the last one via their own label, comes without labels and track-listing and just with a black and yellow photocopy front sleeve. The back cover missing too, but who cares? Four ultra-fuzzzz to the max garage-punk dynamites with trashy production ala' The Mummies that easily will blow your speakers. "Sick And Tired" – Raw! Fuzz! Punk! Rumble! That's it!

**THE MAHARAJAS** – "Weekend Sparks" 7" EP
(Crusher Records) 2006
A stunner piece of vinyl highly recommended. A superb EP with four cool tracks, highlighted by the organ-moody-upside-down anthem called "(Take A) Look At Yourself." This Swedish band is getting better & better.

**THE SATELLITERS** – "It Came To Me" 7" EP
(Soundflat Records) 2007
An ultra-cool EP by Germany's coolest garage band around.

Three awesome originals, including "Cry, Cry, Cry," an Electric Prunes-ish encounter of acid-garage mayhem, plus an outstanding cover of "It Came To Me" (Q65) will knock you outta your haunted house.

**HARA-KEE-REES** – "The Magic Pill" 7" EP
(Soundflat Records) 2008
The first thing you'll take a look is the trippy Hara-Kee-Ree pill on the cover. A great idea and a cool sleeve. A fab, outstanding EP from these German garage-heads, including three frat-garage-punk originals, plus a top cover of "Every Night." By the way, anyone out there had an experience with "the magic pill"?

**THE MYND GARDENERS** – "I See Through My Own Tyme" 7" EP (Smashed Records) 2009
Amazing garage-psychedelic EP, again from the land of OZ. The Mynd Gardeners is a new band hailing from Australia, influenced by various 60's garage-psychedelic bands, as well as Plasticland and Rain Parade. Their first 7" EP includes "Don't Bother Me Again," a brilliant garage-psych track that will blow your mind, plus three more songs. An ultra-glamorous 7-inch housed in a cool psychedelic cover, comes in a very LTD edition of 100 hand-numbered copies, and available on purple vinyl.

# TOP-10
# NEO-GARAGE PSYCH BANDS

1. THE PHILISTEINS
2. THE MIRACLE WORKERS
3. THE LYRES
4. THE FUZZTONES
5. THE CHESTERFIELD KINGS
6. 1313 MOCKINGBIRD LANE
7. THE MARSHMALLOW OVERCOAT
8. THE UNDERTAKERS
9. THE CYNICS
10. THE BO-WEEVILS

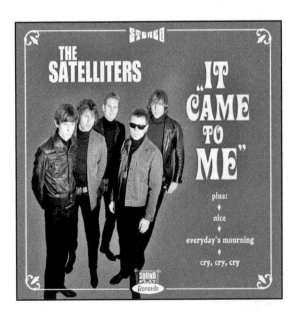

# Fan Submitted Updates

*Music fans and band members share their updates to the original book plus additional information and details.*

# MAINLY CANADA UPDATE

## by Dave O'Halloran

*As noted elsewhere in this book, Dave O'Halloran – known by all as "WhatWave Dave" because of his What Wave fanzine and radio show – is a tireless supporter of honest rock & roll, and en expert especially on the garage scene of his native Canada.*

### BAND UPDATES

### CAPTAIN FUTURE AND THE ZAP GUNS:
Additions to discography: The second 7" is "In Her Klaws" b/w "King Of The Orient," (Rainbow Records) 1986. Punk-rock with garage overtones due to twangy guitar lead on the B side.

### DAS FURLINES:
Also appeared in a short People magazine article. In the 2005 edition of "The Rolling Stone Encyclopedia of Rock & Roll" (Third Edition) 4th printing, there is a long and almost totally bogus entry for Das Furlines. It lists incorrectly that they came from Black Forest, Germany, formed in 1985 and released five LPs including one box set. This is not accurate!

### THE DRAGSTERS:
Also based in NYC, leader Todd Novak and Pete Linzell came from Columbus Ohio (hence the home base listed in the 1995 book). Released a single and LP of 1960s style surf and also appeared on the Brian Wilson tribute, "Smiles, Vibes & Harmony" after befriending "Handsome Dick" Manitoba and playing at his club. Sax player Pete Linzell has appeared on many records for many artists, including The Fleshtones, Raunch Hands, Marky Ramone, and Masterplan.

### THE FIENDS:
Additions to discography: "In Scario" CD (Dionysus) 1995, "Gravedigger" CD (Dionysus) 1998.

### HIJACKERS: (Sweden)
Guitar rock'n'roll combo with some 60s influences (most notably "When I Get Home") from a 7" they released. There's also a Link Wray-styled instrumental on this record.

### THE HYPSTRZ:
Additions to discography: 7" EP on Bogus Records 1979; four covers ("Action Woman" / "Hey Joe" / "Hold On" / "Can't Stand The Pain") recorded live at Jay's Longhorn.

### LOST PATROL:
First EP, (simply titled "5 Song EP" from 1986) is organ driven 60s garage punk with loads of fuzz, there's even a cover of The Seeds' "No Escape." The band continued with only one original member, guitarist Paul Langan, who took the band in a late '60s Janis Joplin-styled direction.

### MERIK TROUT PACT:
They played in a late-60s style, heavily influenced by Jimi Hendrix; released one cassette.

### THE MINSTRELS: (Montreal)
Additions to discography: "Ev'ry Which Way" CD 1992, "St. Laurent des Pins" CD 1993, "West Coast Time Trippers" CD 1997, "Lots Of Rock'n'Rollin'" 7" 1996.

### NOMADS:
Additions to discography: they did release a couple of really cool 10" records in 1996 – "Raw & Rare" on Estrus features tracks from their early cassettes and records as well as an unreleased track, "Lights Out." "The Cold Hard Facts Of Life" is also a 10" from 1996 on Lance Rock Records and contains seven Canadian garage punk tunes from the '60s done in the classic Nomads style. Ugly Ducklings, The Jury, Northwest Company and others are covered. Then there's a cover of Teenage Head's "Picture My Face" (1970s punk) tossed in for fun! *(Editor's note: there are also several more recent Nomads releases to find, including a 2013 album!)*

### ORANGE ALABASTER MUSHROOM:
They also have "The Psychedelic Bedroom" EP 7" 1996, and the "Space And Time" LP, 2001.

### PHILISTEINS:
Were active 1985-1992 in Australia. I have heard one LP, "Lifestyles Of The Wretched And Forgettable" where they do a great version of The Pretty Things' "'Can't Stand The Pain."

### THE PLAYMATES:
Released at least one LP and two singles in 1986 of good jangly pop.

### THE POPPEES:
Also on the "Pop Goes The Anthology" compilation on Bomp (LP and CD), 2010. Also recorded other unreleased and live early '60s beat tunes.

### PSYCHOTIC YOUTH: (Sweden)
Released many LPs and singles with the early releases being the more garage rock oriented. From there they went in a harder rock direction ala The Nomads, veering off into a more Ramones sound with lots of power pop influence.

### PURPLE HELMETS:
Additions to discography: 7" on New Rose, "We Gotta Get Out Of This Place" b/w "I'm A Man."

### THE REMAYNS: (UK)
A four song 7" EP on BamCaruso 1988, on psychedelic vinyl. Four covers of '60s nuggets (Byrds, Paul Revere and The Raiders, etc.) from a side project by Nick Haeffner (of The Tea Set). No liner notes or info of any kind provided.

### THE SHIFTERS: (France)
Early single produced by Dick Taylor (of the Pretty Things). I only have the LP, and it's more Flamin' Groovies-style rock'n'roll than garage.

### SHINDIGGERS:
Also released at least one LP, "Crash Your Party," 1986, on Waterfront Records.

**SONS OF HERCULES:**
More New York Dolls-influenced than straight 60s garage, but they do play with garage bands and fit nicely on the bill. Their 1999 LP, "Get Lost" (Get Hip) has a very cool and snotty version of The Byrds' "I'll Feel A Whole Lot Better."

**THE STAND:**
Changed name to "The Stand GT" because another band had the same name and moved towards a straight pop/rock'n'roll sound, releasing at least three LP's and four singles.

**THE STINGRAYS:**
Noted reissue-record liner-note writer Alec Palao was in this combo.

**3D INVISIBLES: (Detroit, MI)**
Poppy punky monster tunes in a campy/comic book style that are a ton of fun live, as they dress the part. These guys played the O'Halloran wedding party many years ago!

**UNTAMED YOUTH:**
Solo artist Deke Dickerson came out of this combo which had many fine releases.

*BAND ADDITIONS*

**THE ANGRY DRAGONS:**
Formed in early 2007 and hailing from Winnipeg Manitoba. I wrote in Mongrel Zine, "...from the opening chords of "What A Way To Die" they had me up dancing, sweating, and pumping my fists with pure joy. Pure 1966 snot-filled tunes that haven't been heard around these parts for quite sometime! Rip roaring loud guitars from the three gals fronting this awesome combo and a guy way out back, pounding the living daylights out of his drums, just to keep the gals in time." A CD and a 7" are all that remain.

**THE BAKETONES: (Halifax, Canada)**
"Unite" CD, 2010. The cartoon-like drawings of cowboys with guns on the CD cover in no way prepares you for the screaming madness that lurks inside. "I'm A Caveman" leads off the debut CD with a blistering organ/guitar onslaught from which there is no turning back. I only caught these guys live once, when the keyboard players' instrument tipped off the edge of the stage and he instantly dived over top of it, and landed underneath, barely missing a note! Total madness!

**BLUE DEMONS: (Toronto, Canada)**
Self titled CD 2009, Cougar Country/Beatnik Bandit 7" 2012. The Blue Demons are instrumental surf maniacs that wear Mexican wrestling masks on stage and work crowds into a frenzy with their bombastic shows. Barely clothed female dancers writhing to the music on stage sure doesn't hurt the situation.

**THE CHAINS: (Montreal, Canada)**
"On Top Of Things" CD on Get Hip 2002. Early Stones-styled rock'n'roll with some soul sounds interspersed. The drummer formerly played in The Cryptics from Montreal.

**LE CHELSEA BEAT: (Montreal, Canada)**
"Mesdames Et Messieurs" LP 2012. Late-60s influenced guitar/organ based garage/psych with some freakbeat influences that sound very authentic. The songs are sung in a mixture of French and English and sound like a long lost record from that era. Leader/guitarist Pat Meteor is also in Demon's Claws and this is his '60s garage/psych combo.

**THE COUNT BISHOPS: (UK)**
"Speedball" 7" EP, 1975, The Count Bishops LP, 1977, "Good Gear" LP, 1977, Live 10" LP 1978, "Cross Cuts" LP 1979. "Speedball Plus 11" CD 1995. Formed in 1975 these guys took early Rolling Stones R&B sounds and sped them up ferociously, pre-dating the punk movement and helping to fuel it with their wild sounds. Original singer Mike Spenser left before the first LP came out (he appears on the "Speedball" EP as well as the "Speedball Plus" CD) and went on to The Cannibals, featured elsewhere in this book. The band continued on with replacement singer Dave Tice covering garage classics like "Sometimes Good Guys Wear White," "Till The End Of The Day," "I Want Candy," as well as Chuck Berry numbers and some similarly-styled originals. The band came to an end shortly after guitarist Zenon de Fleur died in a car accident in 1979.

**THE FINE PRINT:**
"Standing Out" CD, self titled cassette. London, Ontario combo that sound like a mixture of early Kinks, Who, and Zombies and some of their originals bear eerie resemblance to these bands. Self released a six-song CD in 2010 and What Wave Records released a limited edition cassette in 2011, after which the band packed it in due to school and work commitments.

**FUAD AND THE FEZTONES:**
With The Gruesomes inactive, a couple of them decided to get together with some pals from an indie band (The Stills) and form a '60s styled frat-rock band. They used the name Fuad and The Feztones, and press releases and liner notes claimed they came from Egypt. This fooled a few, but one listen to the vocals and you'll recognize Bobby Beaton's (of The Gruesomes) snotty whine. They played a few live shows, and released an excellent CD, "Beeramid," and a 7" EP.

**THE GERRY ALVAREZ ODYSSEY:**
"Candy Prankster" CD 2006 and "Omega Tea Time" CD 2007. Ex-Gruesome Gerry Alvarez dishes out tasty late '60s U.K. influenced garagepop on his two solo releases. Gerry prefers to remain low key and rarely plays out live, to the chagrin of his record label.

**THE GLADS: (Ottawa)**
"Bad Case Of The Glads" CD 2003, Split 7" with The Midways. Trashy rock'n'rolly garage combo that borrow '60s riffs and add a sense of humor to the lyrics. Singer guitarist Shanks got his start in The 14th Wray, discussed elsewhere in this book.

**THE GREEN HOUR BAND: (Vancouver, Canada)**
Self-titled CD on Kingdom Records 2008, "Coming Of Clockwise" CD, 2010. Heavy psych sounds with some pop and

music hall overtones combine to make some very melodic and catchy tunes. Think mid '60s Kinks colliding with Syd's Pink Floyd, with a slightly updated sound.

### THE HIGH DIALS: (Montreal, Canada)
Evolved from The Datsons (a Mod band that opened for The Gruesomes several times) and started out with a very late-'60s UK pop/psych sound (their "A New Devotion" CD from 2003 captures that sound so well). From there they evolved into a more modern sounding psych band with lots of pop influences.

### LEGEND KILLERS: (London, Ontario, Canada)
"Better Than Hammerin'" EP, 1989, "Legend Killers" CD, 2003, "We're Workin' On It" CD 2006. A bunch of high school buddies got together in 1985 to play their favorite tunes. In the early stages, those favorite tunes were by bands like The Sonics, Fuzztones and Chuck Berry. By the time of their first release they'd moved towards a rough edged power-pop sound and after that went to a much harder rockin' style with some of the earlier songs still in the live repertoire. The Legend Killers are the only band to appear on all the What Wave compilation releases.

### THE MIDWAYS: (Toronto. Canada)
"Pay More and Get a Good Seat" CD, 2004, "Manners Manners" CD, 2007, split 7" with The Glads. Pure '60s garage punk band with cheesy keyboards, snotty vocals, fuzzy guitars and a pounding rhythm section.

### THE PRIMORDIALS:
"Fourteen Prime Numbers" LP, Screaming Apple, 2007. Early 2000's Toronto combo that pound out '60s beat tunes with loads of inspired energy! They were inactive for several years and as of 2013 were just starting to play out again.

### RAISED BY WOLVES: (Vancouver, Canada)
"Hot Blood" CD, 2005. Untitled three song 7" on Kenrock Records, 2005. "Burn It All Down" b/w "Cavestomp" 7" on Zaxxon Records, 2006. They borrowed their name from Canadian sludgeabilly duo Deja Voodoo (see entry in this book) and these cats howl through three chord mayhem liberally dosed in garage, rockabilly and rhythm and blues madness. Rumor has it they've taken time off to raise some cubs.

### RIDE THEORY: (Hamilton, Ontario, Canada)
"Ride Theory" CD, 2002, "In This City" CD, 2005. Four kids that share an interest in early rock'n'roll, beat, and garage music form a band to play the music they love. Lots of catchy guitar pop tunes in the tradition of 60s garage music. Later in the decade, one of the guitarists left and they moved toward a minimalist pop sound under the Young Rival moniker to greater success.

### THE STANCE: (Halifax, Canada)
"Shall Inherit The Earth" CD, 2006, "I Left Love Behind A Long Time Ago" LP 2009. Canadian east coast combo that has taken the 60s garage sound and added elements of soul, early 60s R&B and pop to keep it fresh. Like most Halifax based

bands they are huge fans of The Gruesomes, as the "Live In Hell" cassette (now a CD on Ricochet Sound) was recorded in their hometown of Halifax (nicknamed "Hell" by The Gruesomes).

### THE STOLEN MINKS: (Halifax, Canada)
An EP (on CD and also as a 7") 2005, "Family Boycott" CD, 2006, "High Kicks" CD, 2008. The Stolen Minks started as a four-piece all female band playing an enthusiastic mixture of early '60s girl group sound meets Link Wray in a dark alley. Live, the menacing sounds were rounded out by smiles that could get just about any crowd dancing and having fun. Later their keyboard player left and they moved in a slightly more garage-punk direction with all of the enthusiasm and fun intact.

### SQUARE ROOT OF MARGARET: (Chatham, Ontario, Canada)
Many CDs and cassettes. Psychedelic pop band that has its roots firmly planted in the '60s and have been self-releasing product since the early 1990s. They still play out once in a blue moon.

### THE VON DRATS:
"Dratsylvania" CD 2010, "Goodbye Stinktown" b/w "Instant Soup" 7" on Boppa Do Down Records, 2008. The Von Drat "family" is a gang of identical dressers that wreak havoc live with their energetic mixture of surf, garage and monster mad infected tunes. They always toss in a couple of obscure '60s garage nuggets from deep in their collective record collections.

## *COMPILATION ALBUM ADDITIONS*

### CHRW LONDON UNDERGROUND II DIG DEEPER:
CD 1994. CHRW, London Canada; radio station compilation CD with 14 tracks; Frankenstein 5, It's A Cryin' Shame.

### CRAWLING FROM WITHIN:
This compilation also features Das Furlines, Willie Alexander and The Space Negros amongst others. And also a very early appearance by The Lemonheads, for what that is worth.

### ELECTRIC CARNIVAL:
23-song CD 1992. From the fine folks responsible for Kinetic Vibes fanzine. Willie Loco Alexander, La Secta, Embryonics, Tommyknockers, Pleasure Fuckers, Devil Dogs, Worst, Outta Place, Marble Orchard, Slow Slushy Boys, Cry Babies, Cosmic Dropouts, Dead Moon, Dirteez, Lost Patrol, Scalpers, Sick Rose, Bevis Frond, Breadmakers, Dukes, Juanitos, Mild Mannered Janitors and Cryptones.

### THE ENIGMA VARIATIONS TWO:
Double LP on Enigma Records 1987. A collection of tracks released on LP/CDs by Enigma artists, but there are some unreleased and different versions of songs here. Plan 9, Plasticland, Wednesday Week and many others that aren't in the scope of this book.

### END OF THE WORLD A GO-GO:
Tremor Records 1986. Another Detroit compilation that

has some bands of interest to readers of this book Hysteric Narcotics, 3D Invisibles, Orange Roughies, The Frames, Vertical Pillows and Colors.

## FOLK SONGS FROM THE TWILIGHT ZONE:
Tremor Records, 1988. Yet another Detroit compilation with some bands fans of garage rock will dig: Hysteric Narcotics, 3D Invisibles, Vertical Pillows and Orange Roughies.

## THE GIRLS CAN'T HELP IT:
Rhino Records' modern girl group compilation from 1984 that features mainly poppy 1980s sounding girl groups, but The Pandoras and Wednesday Week are also included.

## GREETINGS FROM THE SUNNY BEACH:
Best Of Closer Records,1984, Closer Records, France. The Barracudas, Dream Syndicate, The Nomads, Eyes Of Mind, and The Pandoras are all on this one.

## IT CAME FROM THE GARAGE VOLUME ONE:
Wanghead Records 1986. Detroit and area compilation in which most of the bands don't take themselves serious, they are just out to have fun. Colors, Venus Envy, Zombie Surfers, Hysteric Narcotics, 3D Invisibles and others of less interest to the readers of this book.

## IT CAME FROM THE GARAGE VOLUME TWO:
Wanghead Records 1987. Like volume one, this contains Detroit and area band that don't take themselves seriously: Zombie Surfers, 3D Invisibles, Lost Patrol, Treblemakers and Natives From Earth.

## I WAS A TEENAGE ZOMBIE:
A soundtrack LP. 1987 Enigma Records. Featuring The Fleshtones doing the title song, along with Smithereens, The Dream Syndicate, Alex Chilton, Ben Vaughn Group and more.

## 90.9 With A Bullet. 20 Years Of Calgary Music on CJSW:
Double CD, 2005. Citrus Park, Color Me Psycho, The Vindicators and Huevos Rancheros.

## REVENGE OF THE KILLER PUSSIES:
(Blood On The Cats Part 2), 1984, Anagram Records, UK. Part one of this series was almost all psychobilly, with volume 2 a few bands that fit into this book, including The Stingrays, Milkshakes, Bananamen, and The Tall Boys.

## SHIT! TOO EARLY:
1991 Oslo, Norway compilation LP on Big Ball Records. Almost all harder-edged bands than what this book is about, but The Lust-O-Rama do have two songs included.

## TODAY'S TOP GIRL GROUPS VOLUME ONE:
Spinout Records 1998. If the title was true, this would be a much better world musically! Here we have a great collection of '60s inspired girl combos from around the world. Just look at the list of bands on this one and you're sure to need it for your next bash, a who's-who of girl garage combos.

The Pebbles
Sit'n'Spin
The Diaboliks
The Godzilla
Poontwang
Holly Golightly
The Neanderdolls
The Meanie Geanies
The Bobbyteens
The 5 6 7 8's
The Prissteens
The Neptunas
The Girl Bombs
The Friggs
The Maybellines

## WHEN MONKEYS WERE GODS:
Tremor Records 1985. Detroit compilation that includes several bands that readers of this book might enjoy: The Frames, 3D Invisibles, Lost Patrol, Treblemakers and Natives From Earth.

## WINNIPEG RIOT!
Dionysus compilation CD, 2006. 18-track CD compilation of all Winnipeg, Canada bands. Compilation, artwork and liner notes all by artist Darren Merinuk, whose artwork has graced the record/CD covers of many of the bands featured in this book. The Horribles, Hot Live Guys, Dead By Dawn, Squareheads, The Fever Breaks, The Surfadelics, The Switchblade Sisters, The Wild Things.

## TIME MACHINE: THE HISTORY OF CANADIAN 60'S GARAGE PUNK AND SURF (1985-95) Stomp Records 1996.
The title is just a bit misleading as this is a 1980s/1990s compilation CD of cool Canuck bands that dig the garage sounds. All the best-known Canadian garage bands from the era are represented here; The Gruesomes, 10 Commandments, The Vindicators, The Fiends and so many more. Lots of lesser-known bands are also included as Canada is a huge country, full of so many regional scenes. Loads of liner notes and cover art by King Merinuk make this the complete 1980s Canadian garage punk compilation.

The Mongols
The Gruesomes
The Worst
The Astronuts
The Cryptics
The Chessmen
The Surfdusters
The 10 Commandments
Shadowy Men on A Shadowy Planet
The Sherlocks
The Vindicators
The Minstrels
Fuzz Aldrin
The Fiends
The Night Stalkers
The 14th Wray
Drums Along The Gardiner
Lost Patrol
The Cheshyres
The Beaumonts

The Treblemakers
The Polyester Explosion
Huevos Rancheros
The Smugglers
Platon Et Les Caves
The Upper Crust
The Frat Kings

## ADDITIONAL WHAT WAVE COMPILATION ALBUMS

### WAVE FROM THE GRAVE:

21 song cassette, 1986 What Wave Magazine, Canada
This is the very first What Wave compilation cassette and came free with issue #10. People were constantly asking what the bands we wrote about in the zine sounded like, so this was our solution. There were lots of Canadian acts on this one as we were just starting to get world wide distribution with the zine. Purple Toads, 3D Invisibles, Monstereos, Boy From Nowhere, 10 Commandments, The Dwarves, Legend Killers, Psychotic Youth.

### THE EIGHTH WONDER:

31 song cassette, 1991 What Wave Magazine, Canada
Yet another cassette compilation from What Wave zine. This one came with issue #20. Falling Spikes, Mr. Haney's Revenge, The Cybermen, The Tommyknockers, 14th Wray, Smokin' Gas Truck, The Cunts, The (Marshmallow) Overcoat, Big Scary Daddies, The Fridge Magnets, The Worst, The Creatures, Planet Of Spiders, 10 Commandments, The Night Stalkers, The Cattle, The Evil Hoodoos.

### LONDON CRAWLING:

22-song cassette 1996 What Wave Magazine, Canada
This was to be the swan song of What Wave zine and was a special all-local (London Canada) issue, including the cassette that came with it, hence this tape has less garage sounds on it. This one came with What Wave 22. Frankenstein 5, Captain Scarlet and the Mysterons, Uranus, Mongrols, Boy From Nowhere and Evil Hoodoos.

### THEE CAVE COMES ALIVE! SONGS FROM THE LOST WHAT WAVE FANZINE TAPES:

Action Records, Greece, compiled by George Rigas. 2004, vinyl only.

This is an authorized compilation of some of the garagiest tunes that were on the What Wave cassettes that came free with W.W. zine. A few of the tracks are slightly different versions (or cleaned-up versions) of songs that originally appeared on What Wave tapes.

The Royal Nonesuch, The Gruesomes, The Chessmen, The Cheshyres, The Mystic Eyes, The Beatpack, The Boy From Nowhere, The Legend Killers, The Projectiles, The Cryptones, The Creatures, The Cybermen, Tyme Eliment and the Ultra 5.

## FANZINES UPDATE

### BANANAS MAGAZINE: (USA)

NYC-based, seven issues so far. Newsprint zine that covers the modern garage sounds from around the world and sometimes delves into the 1980s/1990s garage scene (Midnight Records, Screaming Apple Records, The Hate Bombs, NYC's 1980's garage scene, etc) to get to the roots of the newer bands that claim to be garage. Garage festivals from around the world are given coverage in words and photos and some of the artwork included is just mindblowing!

### THE AVENGERS: (France)

At least one issue was released, and by the articles/interviews it appears to be from the mid-1990's. Written in French, this one covers 1960s bands The Creation, The Sorrows and up to the then current bands like The Marshmallow Overcoat and The Mourning After. Wish I could read this one, as it comes across with tons of enthusiasm!

### BANG!: (Medford, Massachusetts)

1983-1990, at least 21 issues. This one started out covering Boston and area bands and branched out to cover the touring bands of the time. Lyres, Barrence Whitfield and The Savages, Fleshtones, Robyn Hitchcock, Redd Kross all received coverage as well as less interesting (at least to this book) bands of the time.

### CAPSOUL REVIEWS: (NYC)

At least seven issues of this one from the mid 1990s. Small sized, with not a lot of pages, but a fair bit of detailed criticism packed into those pages. The highlight for me was a lengthy interview with Mono Man (of The Lyres) where the interviewer got detailed, opinionated answers from his subject.

### CARBON 14: (Philadelphia)

A thick, slick zine that bills itself as covering art, film, music, smut and wrestling. Certainly a wide range of coverage, but the record reviews alone are worth the price of admission as they cover a ton of cool releases each issue. There have been extensive in-depth interviews over the course of 31 issues, with everyone from The Electric Prunes, The Nomads, The Fleshtones, The Seeds and many other cool bands. There was usually a regional compilation CD, or a 7" record enclosed with each issue, usually featuring some cool garage oriented bands.

### COMME UN BOOMERANG: (Montreal, Canada)

A least for issues with excellent coverage of 1980s garage bands in French 1986-1987. Lots of cool graphics and photos for us French-language-challenged folks.

### THE CONTINENTAL MAGAZINE: (Bellingham, Washington)

Around for a number of years and is still active and at last count, up to number 22. The main focus is modern surf and instrumental combos, but there is definitely some overlap into the garage scene. Well laid out and comes with a CD featuring many of the bands in the particular issue. They are also a CD label and specialize in modern surf combos.

### CRYPT-O-RAMA: (Greece)

At least five issues were released in the early 2000s in this thick, small digest-form zine. Lots of record reviews (divided by label, which is kinda neat) and fairly short interviews with the garage/psych bands of that time period. Well laid out, lots of good quality pictures and tons of info make this a quality zine.

## HOOSIER HYSTERIA: (Indiana)
At least two issues (1984-1985) of mainly Indiana garage bands of the 1960s, but there was an interview with Paula Pierce (of The Pandoras) in the second issue.

## INCOGNITO: (Englishtown, New Jersey)
At least ten issues from 1984 to 1986 and covered the garage bands of the time, Optic Nerve, Lord John, Fuzztones, as well as lots of coverage of the original 1960s combos.

## IN YER EAR: (Canada)
There's at least three issues of this Oshawa, Ontario-based zine that covered the garage and rock'n'roll bands of the era, that being 1987-1989. Lyres, Plasticland, Deja Voodoo, Gruesomes, Fuzztones, and the final issue had a Cynics 7" record with it.

## LIVELY ARTS:
This started as fanzine for the band The Damned, but later issues covered Fuzztones, Iguanas, Nomads and many other garage bands as well as some less interesting bands. At least 12 issues, 1985 to 1989. Kenzo who put this zine out, also put out the Fuzztones zine, "Fuzz Buzz," starting in 1989.

## LOST IN TYME ZINE: (Greece)
This one came out of the cave beginning in 2004, and so far six issues have seen the light of day. The emphasis of this top notch zine is 1980s garage bands and the modern bands with their roots in the 1960s and 1980s. There've been exclusive interviews with many 1980s combos: The Vipers, The Cheepskates, Marshmallow Overcoat, Wylde Mammoths, Chesterfield Kings, Gruesomes, The Fuzztones, Fleshtones and so many more. A compilation CD (of many of the featured bands) and cover artwork by King Merinuk make for a great flashback to the 1980s all in one package!

## MAKING TIME:
There were at least three issues, and it is definitely a mod zine. But there was also coverage of bands such as The Three O'Clock, The Troggs, Fuzztones and others in this small zine.

## MONGREL ZINE: (Vancouver, Canada)
2008-present. One of the few music-related print zines still around, this one covers 1980s garage bands right up to the modern garage sounds of today as well as underground/lowbrow art in a neat package. And it usually comes packaged with a compilation CD containing some of the fave bands of the editors.

## TEEN SCENE:
By Blair Buscareno, I only have seen one issue. This covered the east coast USA scene quite thoroughly.

## UGLY CHILD: (France)
2008. At least one issue of this fine zine (put out by the folks from Frantic City) exist. Coverage of The Gruesomes, Morlocks, Miracle Workers, Gorgons as well as 1960s legends Q65 and The Painted Ship.

# VARIOUS UPDATES
## by Wiebren Rijkeboer

*Wiebbren is a dedicated record collector and has been a contributor to the Dutch magazine "Smiling Ears."*

## THE AARDVARKS:
There is an album, on the U.K. Detour label.

## THE BABY FLIES:
I own "Rain," a 10-song LP on Resonance. They are definitely U.S. east coast; from New York I believe. It's a threesome with a female vocalist. The Baby Flies sound more like The Walkabouts than a garage band.

## THE BARN BALAMS:
Their debut album is titled "Genuine Rock & Roll Medicine Show," from 1988 on the Green Fez label. Though the music isn't that interesting to me, the sleeve is – a nice foldout sleeve with a beautiful picture inside. The picture is dominated by a twelve-string Rickenbacker.

## THE BARRACUDAS:
There is live record on Impossible Records, named "Live In Madrid" (1986). The sound quality is rather good and it consists of 15 songs. Nice sleeve as well.

## THE BEATNIK FLIES:
Although a minor detail, a closer look at the sleeve of "From Parts Unknown" shows that the cover art is by Bobby Belfiore. That must be the Optic Nerve mainman! Also, there is a second LP, "Behind These Walls" (1988), 12 songs on the French New Rose label.

## BIFF BANG POW:
Well worth the mention is the debut 12" of this band. It's named "Pass The Paintbrush, Honey." (Eight songs, 1985, on Creation Records). It's loaded with reverb and drenched in acid, a very nice record – I love it. And again I have to mention the sleeve: a picture of a Vox guitar, backed by Vox amplifiers.

## BLOW UP:
In 1990 they made a CD titled "In Watermelon Sugar" (14 songs on Cherry Red Records). They cover The Feelies' song "Slip Into Something."

## THE BO-WEEVILS:
Their first LP, "Where Particular People Congregate," is a true gem.

## THE BURNING RAIN:
There is also a third record on the Mind And Eye label. And in 1996-1997 they released an 11 song CD, "Ritual Medicine Show," on the same label. Two live songs are included.

## THE CHEMISTRY SET:
On the Romilar-D label there is a CD of this band, titled "Wake Up Sometime!" It's from 1990 and there is also a vinyl version of this ten-song record. They cover The Love song "This House Is Not A Motel."

## CHEROKEES:
In 1987 the Cherokees released an album on Wovoka Records. It consists of ten songs. I don't think it's too interesting. To my ears they sound kind of like The Ramones. It doesn't mean that it's bad, but it isn't psychedelic either.

## THE CLEAN:
The Clean, from New Zealand, released many records on the famous and excellent Flying Nun label, specializing in jangly pop. The singer, David Kilgour, also released a solo album. You should investigate Sneaky Feelings and The Chills. Especially "Send You," the Sneaky Feelings debut, is in my view one of the best records of the 1980s.

## THE COMEDOWN:
The Comedown made an LP in 1991. It's a self-titled 15 song record on Kelt Records. I think it's a great record. They mix different styles, sometimes bluesy, sometimes folky, but the general feel is psychedelic. Strongly recommended.

## THE CRACKED JAFFERS:
The Cracked Jaffers also made an LP. It's in the same vein as the 7" – snotty, crude and loud. It's titled "Hip Pocket Nerve" and consists of eight songs. They are all band originals. The record originates from 1989 and was released by Honk Records. I love it!

## CRYSTALIZED MOVEMENTS:
The "Mind Disaster" LP is a great album. It's drenched in acid and contains lengthy guitar solo's. Crystalized Movements is a one man band – this one man is Wayne Rogers, from Hartford, Connecticut. There's also a second record, "Dog… Tree… Satellite Seers." Now the band consists of four members. The record is on Forced Exposure (1987, 11 songs).

## DM3:
Dom Mariani's first two solo CDs were produced by Mitch Easter. Actually DM3 is more pop than psych. I like the records a lot, but I don't think they are rooted in the garage. The records are both on Citadel. "One Time, Two Times, Three Red Light" (12 songs) is the first one, "Road To Rome" the second. There is also a compilation of B-sides and demos called "Garage Sale."

## THE EYES OF MIND:
The European version of their 12" consists of ten songs. It's on Closer Records. The four supplemented songs are: "She's Got Stars," "The Game," "Train," and "This Place Before." These songs are produced by Bad Religion's Brett Gurewitz.

## FERRYBOAT BILL:
They are from Germany, and released a 7" titled "Cold Rain" b/w "Boogie Man" in 1988 on the Big Store label. They drifted away from the garage in the direction of "big rock." I personally think that they aren't of note for this book.

## FIXED UP:
In 1984 Fixed Up released an LP on Closer Records. It contains 12 songs, mostly originals.

## GREEN HORNETS:
This English combo already have released two LP's.

## HIJACKERS:
I once owned a 7" of these Swedish guys. I remember that in my opinion they were Nomads-rip-offs. I didn't think they were interesting.

## THE HOLLOWMEN:
These Hollowmen made two albums, the one you mention and "Pink Quartz Sun Blasting." This LP is from 1988, it's on Amoeba Records and contains 12 band originals. I like both records very much; the second even better than the first. I think this album can easily be compared with the best work of Eleventh Dream Day. They hail from Des Moines, Iowa. And yes, there is another Hollowmen, but to my knowledge they come from Australia.

## THE IMPOSSIBLE YEARS:
Their debut 12" consists of four songs. The songs are "Attraction Gear," "Her Father Suspects," "Flower Girl" and "9:45." The record is on the English Dreamworld Records, from 1983.

## THE KLIEK:
I would like to mention another live album, "Live At Cafe Mono!" Cafe Mono is a pub in Amsterdam where it's filled to the roof when there are just forty visitors! The guitar player Marcel Kruup also played in The Other Side, and played a guest role on The Landlords' record.

## THE LANDLORDS:
Coincidentally, The Landlords come next to The Kliek. They didn't exist long, and their debut was a flexi with the La Herencia de Los Munster Magazine, named "Gotta Leave." They were famous for their live-appearances, but never made a LP during their existence. After they quit, Kelt Records released in 1988 all of their recorded demos. "For The Record" contains 12 self-written songs (including the flexi). The music isn't very garagey. The Landlords lean strongly on melody. It's jingle-jangle folk-pop with very strong tunes. In all, a great record.

## THE MARGIN OF SANITY:
Two members of The Margins went on to form The Mistreaters. Before they split they left a six-song 12" EP. And what a record it is! Snotty R&B with definite Dutch beat influences. There are five originals and one cover ("Look Out World"). They combine the sound of The Telltale Hearts with the The Chesterfield Kings. In between they remind the listener of the best of Swedish raw beat. The record is an absolute killer. A crying shame they quit, although they rose from the grave as The Mistreaters (which didn't live long either). The 12" was released on Chainsaw Records.

## THE MARYLAND COOKIES:
There is another LP from The Cookies; in 1986 they recorded seven songs. It's called "Flesh, Trash & Heat" and was released on Rainbow Music. They play a cover of "I Can Only Give You Everything."

**THE MELTED AMERICANS:**
The self-titled LP on Mad Hatter Records was released in 1988. It contains eleven band originals. The music is firmly rooted in the garage. Nice songs filled with lightweight distortion and loaded with Farfisa. In short, the record is great. Psych at its best. And there is more! In 1989 they released a second LP on the Dutch Resonance label. It's titled "Evil Monkey Bowl" and also contains eleven self-written songs. The production is better than on their first album, and the songs are at least as good. Two killer albums! Viva Melted Americans!

**THE MYSTREATED:**
They are the best British R&B band from the 1990s. "Ever Questioning Why" is from 1995. It contains fourteen fuzzed-out originals and is packed in a gatefold sleeve! "Lovely Sunday Dreaming" is later, with twelve originals. Both records are on Twist Records. I also know that there is a 10" record, also on Twist Records.

**NO MAN'S LAND:**
The No Man's Land I am writing about is from Greece. They released an LP in 1988 titled "Zaiion." It's on Pegasus Records and was distributed by the famous Hitch-Hyke Records. The music is kind of acid-blues with a female vocalist. A nice effort. I would also like to note the great sleeve art.

**THE NUTHINS:**
The Nuthins released an LP on Mark Le Gallez' Twist Records, 1995. "One Step Forward" is in mono and contains 14 songs. Nice, very nice.

**THE 1-2-5:**
The debut LP by The 1-2-5 contains eight band originals and eight covers and it was released on the Italian Misty Lane Records. Good record.

**THE OTHERS:**
"Dreams - The Woody Pad Recordings" I think is one of the best 60s records of the 1990s. Stuffed with great cover versions, superb, honest playing, gritty production and on top of it all great art on a thick cardboard sleeve. This is super stuff. To make it even more special, there only have been 1,000 copies pressed. Released in 1997 on Psych-Out Records. What a gem!

**PLASTICLAND:**
The first LPs are also out on CD. Unfortunately there are no extra tracks included. A brilliant pop-psych band; "Color Appreciation" is a masterpiece to my ears.

**THE PLAYMATES:**
"Long Sweet Dreams" was released by What Goes On Records (UK) in 1986 and contains eight songs. They remind me a lot of The Watermelon Men.

**THE PLAYN JAYN:**
"Friday The 13th" is a live record, it's the bands' debut, released on A&M in 1984. I think the second record, "Five Good Evils," is a nice effort, released on ABC Records in 1985.

I like this record a lot, nice harmonies, jangling guitars and good songs. The band is fronted by two lead singers. Eleven songs written by the band and a nice picture-sleeve.

**THE PLIMSOULS:**
We should mention their debut LP, "The Plimsouls," was released in 1981 on Planet Records. "Zero Hour" is also a classic song.

**THE PRIME MOVERS:**
"Sins Of The Fourfathers" (1989), released on Cyanide Records, was the first LP of the (UK) Prime Movers. Graham Day and Allan Crockford were members of The Prisoners – when The Prisoners quit, Crockford formed The James Taylor Quartet with another ex-Prisoner, Jamie Taylor. After some instrumental LP's Crockford again teamed up with Day and formed The Prime Movers. Their debut inhabits all the elements which The Prisoners were famous for; pounding beat, strong vocals and a perfect mix of U.S.-garage and U.K.-beat (although it doesn't beat "Thewisermiserdemelza" LP.)

**THE SAPPHIRES:**
There is some Sapphires vinyl: in 1987 "The Sapphires" was released on Swingin' Door Records. It contains twelve songs. Their record has some fine moments, but not enough to my ears. The sound is pure garage, but the most songs fail to get any grip on the listener. Missed opportunity, I think.

**SOUL HUNTERS:**
I think this is special. The "Nick And Nick And The Psychotic Drivers" record is from 1988 and it is superb! The band consists of members of Soul Hunter accompanied by the godlike Nick Saloman (the great Bevis Frond). According to the text on the sleeve: "This is not the first album by Soul Hunters, this is the last one by Bevis Frond neither. This is a manual for particular phases of mental excitement, you have to listen to this album (play loud) in a dark room with a small green light." It's a great record with lengthy very psychedelic songs. Italian garage (a la Sick Rose) combined with Bevis' fluid, lysergic guitar solos. It consists of six crazed-out songs, which vary in length from five minutes to nine minutes. An Italian/UK collaboration of the finest sorts! "Extasy Game In My Brain" contains one of the best solos I've ever heard. It was released on Contempo Records.

**SS-20:**
Actually, SS-20 was a side-project of Skooshny. The drummer and guitar-player added a female-singer and made two LPs. "The Son Of Fantasy" LP contains nine songs, among them the noted "Trouble," "Arnold Layne" and "You're Gonna Miss Me." In 1996 Skooshny released their first record on Minus Zero Records, titled "Even My Eyes." It's great!

**STEEPLE JACK:**
The track listing of the "Serena Maboose EP: "Hot Summer Again," "Fallin' Leaves And Autumn's Thrills," "I Was Born In A Jungle," "If I Had Possession Over Judgement Day" (the Robert Johnson original), "Nobody Around You," and "The Sky Is Full Of Shadows." The second LP, "Pow Wow," contains eight songs.

### THE STEPPES:
The Steppes were a great band. Not a garage band but more a psychedelic folk band, I still enjoy their records, especially "Drop Of The Creature." Their 'U.K.-psych' influence is very strong.

### SUN DIAL:
In 1990 the released their debut LP (only on vinyl), "Other Way Out," on the Tangerine label. Six long songs, very psychedelic in the Hendrix way; the guitar plays the main role. I don't think it has anything to do with "garage" (no matter how you define the genre), although the record has its fine moments. A year later the record was released on CD on U.F.O. Records, and two songs were added. Sun Dial drifted later on towards indie-pop and electronic music (some songs reminded me of Joy Division; doom-laden synth parts and pounding drums). After some CDs they returned to a kind of blues-influenced, acid, prog-rock. "Acid Yantra" (1995, on Beggars Banquet) is a good example of the absorbed influences (including their interpretation of the U.K. "shoegazer" sound, i.e. My Bloody Valentine or Spacemen 3).

### THE SUNSET STRIP:
This Australian band also released an LP 1986 on Au-Go-Go Records. The self-titled record contains seven lengthy songs. Their music reminds me of their fellow countrymen The Scientists and The Beasts Of Bourbon. It also makes me think of Alex Chilton circa "Like Flies On Sherbert" (which, by the way, is a masterpiece itself). Typically down-under blues-type: dark, slow music. I think in the context of this book they are of minor interest.

### PUSHTWANGERS:
They are Swedish, from Stockholm. Beside singles, they at least released two LPs. In 1984 a 12" mini-LP (self titled) on Blackboard & Chalk Records, contained seven band originals. In 1986 "Here We Go Again" was released on the Amigo label: twelve songs, all written by the band. Their music is in the Nomads-vein: rather straightforward, dirty garage-punk.

### TANGLE EDGE:
The record houses in a beautifully drawn sleeve. Psychedelic alright!

### THE TELL-TALE HEARTS:
Also have two live records released on the Australia's Corduroy Records (both in a limited edition of 500). The recordings are both from the same show in Springfield, Missouri, and contain different songs. "A Bitchin' Rave-Up With..." contains fifteen songs and "Live Volume 2 - Later That Same Night In Springfield..." contains ten songs. Poor sound quality but a great performance!

### THE THOUGHT:
The predecessors of The Thought were The Rousers. They released one great LP of snotty, teenage beat songs. It's called "A Treat Of New Beat," released in 1980 on the Torso label. Melodic, punky power-pop songs, great! I think The Thought is less interesting than The Rousers. The self-titled

Polydor 12" sounds ok to me, but I have never understood the fuss when their MCA LP was released. I think it's a self-indulgent effort; glossy, bombastic production.

### VICE BARONS:
I know that there at least three 12" records from this Belgian band.

### ADDITIONAL BANDS:

### MYSTICS:
A foursome from Geneva, Switzerland. They released in 1983 an album on Lolita. It's called "Dandies Are Back." It contains eleven songs and is produced by The Barracudas' Robin Wills. Jeremy Gluck and Chris Wilson also contribute to this LP.

### THE REACTION:
This quintet is also from Switzerland. They released an LP in 1986 on the domestic Blow Records. It includes twelve self-written songs. The sound is crude, yet polished (lots of Farfisa), the songs are upbeat and rather light-weight. It's OK, but to me not more than that.

### THE SPORTING BACHELORS:
The Bachelors are from the New York state. They released a ten-song LP on Dionysus Records in 1990. Nine Originals and one cover, the Dutch Q65's "Cry In The Night." "Love Letters To Joanna" is a great album to my ears.

### CARNIVAL SEASON:
This band from the Birmingham, Alabama were label mates of The Watermelon Men in Europe. Their sound also has a lot in common with the Swedes – melodic, edgy, light-psychedelic music. They released some records: a three song 7" ("Won't Get Heard") on the U.S. Rat Bone Records in 1985; a three song 12" ("Please Don't Send Me To Heaven") in 1986 on What Goes On Records; and an eleven-song LP also on WGO Records in 1987, titled "Waiting For No One."

### ACTION NOW:
This Californian band released a twelve-song LP on the European Lolita label in 1984. It's early garage, like The Three O'Clock or The Last. I think it's a nice record. The record contains songs written by Paula Pierce, like the great "Stop Pretending" (apparently before The Pandoras recorded it themselves).

## MAINLY GERMAN UPDATE
## by Axel Gieseking

*Axel published the garage-oriented "Something Wild" fanzine in Germany in the 1990s.*

### BALLROOM STOMPERS (Bremen, Germany):
This Beat-band later released a four-song EP on String Records with unreleased tracks, but they had already split up at that time. Members of them can now be found in AGENTENMUSIK.

## THE BONGO BEATIN' BABIES (Kassel, Germany):
Not really a Garage band, but their seven-song demo-tape from circa 1993 includes versions of "Jungle Hop," "Walk Don't Run" and "Swinging Creeper." They released one song on the "Songs The Cramps Taught Us" compilation CD.

## CAVE 4 (Solingen, Germany):
They also have a 10" LP out on Plastic Bomp, a punk label, and two more LPs, one of them for the U.S., were also planned. They are also featured on some compilations. They were a very busy German surf act.

## CHOCOLATE FACTORY (Hamburg, Germany):
They also have released their "45 Minutes Out Of 3 Years" LP. Their bass player went on to LOONEY TUNES, a well-known surf & instrumental band from Hamburg with a third album planned for 1997.

## DAYTONAS (Sweden):
These cats also have an LP out on Corduroy called "Don't Look Now But It's..." (The Daytonas).

## DEPARTAMENTO B (Pamplona, Spain):
A garage-a-billy band formed in the mid 1980s. They released a song on the "Munster Dancehall Favourites" compilation album series, a self released four-song EP including a cover version of the Tall Boys' "Island Of Lost Souls" and had a song on a Rockbilly Christmas compilation CD. In the mid 1990s they self-released a cassette called "Memories Of A Psychotic Band." The tape included a total of 10 songs with mostly covers of "Mad Daddy" (Cramps), "Have Love Will Travel," "California Sun" and "The Crusher." The EP is included as well.

## ELECTRIC FAMILY (Frankfurt, Germany):
They started as a '60s garage-band doing on their debut EP on Trash City Records titled "Ain't No Friend Of Mine" in 1990, but soon got infected by that grunge virus and their second 45 is more Mudhoney-styled than anything else.

## THE EVIL SEED (Zurich, Switzerland):
Garage-influenced Rock'n'Roll. I only know about some live-recordings from 1989. Singer and guitar player Laurent also played with a "psychobilly" bands such as AXEMAN'S JAZZ and also the LIZARD KIDS, a "trash-a-billy" trio.

## GRAMPA'S TOMBSTONE (Quedlingburg, Germany):
A Cramps-styled band that has put out two or three demo-tapes and later changed their name into the YUCCA SPIDERS in 1996.

## LIPSTICK KILLERS (USA):
I own a Voxx 45 from 1980 by this U.S.-outfit. Side a "Hindu Gods (of Love) is great 1960s punk, the flip "Shakedown" is Stooges/MC 5-influenced.

## THE ORBIT KINGS (Winterthur, Switzerland):
To me they are the "Swiss Fuzztones." The guitar and organ player has a great collection of rare Vox guitars and amps and looks way cool with his deep-black bowl-cut, Beatles boots and necklace made of chicken bones. I have an eight-song

demo-tape from1993/1994. Cover versions of "Human Fly," "Searchin'" and "Ain't No Friend Of Mine" are included but my fave is the probably their own composition, "Cage Sisters." No vinyl was released. In 1996 they disbanded. Two members went on to the band TAB HUNTER.

## PRUNCLE & THE PERLIPSES (Eriangen, Germany):
Not really a 1960s band, but they have a huge folk influence. One song on their six song tape from the early 1990s reminded me very much on the late U.K. Stingrays.

## THE SHOO-CHAIN BROTHERS (Toulouse, France):
A garage-punk band from the south of France with a massive '77 influence. Fronted by Gildas Cosperec, a busy person of the trench garage-scene. The band released a split-EP with local fellows SPACE BEATNIKS on the own Zombie Dance label and songs on many compilations, mostly tapes and EPs with fanzines, also for my own fanzine, *Something Wild*, in 1994. A new split-EP was slated for the mid-1990s, plus another song on my own Jungle Noise label.

## SLINGBACKS (London, England):
They have two 45s out on Vinyl Japan, a song on the soundtrack LP of the "Hot Carumba" movie by Josh Collins, and on an EP available with Submerge Fanzine (England). The band included Babs, later in the DIABOLIKS.

## SWINGING LONDON (Munich, Germany):
The A-side of their 45 "Space Cowboy" isn't wimpy Mod-Pop to me. I think it's great 60s garage. They reformed in 1995 for a performance at the Beat-o-Mania festival. A live-LP and video of this event exist. At least one member of the band also played in the HEARTBEATS and HAMBERDEACONS.

## TAB HUNTER (Winterthur, Switzerland):
Primitive Garage-Punk with two ultra-fuzz guitars (including a Vox Phantom) and stomping drums. No bass included or needed. They got a great five-song EP out on their own. In their live-shows show they are a garage-band with humor.

---

# MAINLY ITALIAN UPDATE

## by Pierpaolo Rizzo

*Pierpaolo is the creative force behind the excellent Italian psych-pop band The Backwards.*

## AARDVARKS:
The 1994 LP/CD "Bargain" on Delerium Records (originally recorded in 1991 and slated for release on UFO Records) features new versions of some of the tracks on previous singles, plus more of Small Faces "Ogden" era sounding songs.

## ACID FLOWERS:
A nice folky garage band from Milan, Italy; they disbanded in 1989 after various tracks on compilations, an unreleased single ("Sidelong Smiles") and a low budget video of the song, "A Pity."

## ACT:
They might have been mod-ish in the early 1980s, but soon they became ordinary R'n'B fare.

## AFTERHOURS:
After their more Velvet Underground-oriented debut, later efforts draw more on the late 1980s grungy U.S. sounds. They started to gain some critical success when they started singing in Italian.

## ALLISON RUN:
A great band. They split after a major label contract was signed, and a second LP was recorded but left unreleased. Amerigo Verardi (their leader) went on for a solo career first under the name "Morgan" (one LP) then "Lula" (one disappointing CD sung in Italian); a new solo limited edition LP slated for Destination X Records.

## BACHELOR PAD:
They also released an LP on Imaginary Records called "Tales Of Hoffman," apparently very psych-pop art.

## BAG ONE:
After the release of a new demo tape circa 1995 in Prisoner/ Yardbirds mould, their leader Jimmy Girardi announced a 7" release.

## CHEMISTRY SET:
They were to release an LP called "Sounds Like Painting" in 1989 on Voxx Records; the master tapes reportedly still in the label's vaults. They later managed to put out a few EPs on Imaginary Records but their sparkle had gone, and by the time they got a major label contract their music was standard pop (and they changed their name to simply "The Set").

## CLIQUE:
After two EPs ("Introducing The Clique" on Guild Records, and "Early Days" on Detour Records, the latter with James Taylor on keyboards) they released two 7" ("Reggie" & "Bareback Donkey Riding") and a CD/LP ("Self Preservation Society") with nice originals and a few, competent cover versions such as "1-2-5" and "I'm Gonna Make You Mine."

## CROAKERS:
From Geneva, later they switched their name to Boogaboos, but disbanded without any recording; they reformed, with me on bass, with a more psych folk-rock sound, in New England style.

## GOODCHILDE:
A Medway band featuring members of Prisoners, Daggermen and Kravin A's, previously known as Johnny & The Bandits; they released a nice (power pop- Prisoners) LP ("Elizabeth Talking Through My Head") in 1994, a 7" "Sarapeutic" (1995) and another CD.

## LODOVICO ELLENA:
He is a founder member of the Effervescent Elephants, Mirrors, and Folli Di Dio – and not the name of a band.

## FLOR DE MAL (later known as FLOR):
Not really psych-pop, they originally had an R.E.M. flavor (they apparently were friends with them), with a Mediterranean sensibility too.

## FLYTE REACTION:
Mick Crossley *is* the Flyte Reaction.

## HITCHCOCK'S SCREAM:
An interesting cross between psych and new wave, they released a great mini- LP on Vox Pop in 1990, "Badkarmababakool!" Members were from Italy, Belgium and Ireland.

## IMPULSIVE YOUTH:
A mod-pop band fromi Milano, whose members later played in The Pow, Backwards, Bag One; one demo tape was released in 1987.

## JACKIE STEWART SAID:
I wouldn't consider them psych-pop, but guitar-pop (in the early Creation Records production style).

## KRYPTASTHESIE:
A CD ("Inner Whirl") is out on Delerium Records, with their mixture of Ozric-meets-Krautrock kind-of sound.

## L.A. CHOIX:
Born out of the minds of Concobeach & Valeria (former Impulsive Youth members), theirs was a mixture of psych, garage, folk, jazz, punk, progressive sounds which was fascinating. They had a 1989 EP "Awake! It's 1989" and the 1991 LP "Wild Oats," both on Jon Point Zero Records. Another mini-CD, again on Point Zero Records. ("Party Goes On") was released in 1996, although far from the inspiration they brought to the earlier releases.

## MARGIN OF SANITY:
A 12" EP was released in 1985.

## MR. JONES:
A mini-LP was released on Crazy Mannequin Records; it's folk, not psych.

## NICK RIFF:
A Delerium Records artist; his first LP was not a reissue of his tape. His later release was recorded with a full band.

## NICOTINE SPYRAL SURFERS:
Started with a garagey-psych 7" EP ("I Had A Dream"). Their sound later evolved into an acid-dense mix which was not fully appreciated. After a 7" for Dionysus Records, they split up, leaving unfinished tapes for an LP they never completed.

## OUT OF TIME:
Their sole LP sounded a bit like later-era Long Ryders.

## PALE DAWN:
No other releases except the High Rise 7".

**PETER SELLERS & THE HOLLYWOOD PARTY:**
A 1990 LP ("Making a Romance Out Of Swiftness," on Apples & Oranges Records) ended their career, their sound had by then become much more 1970s Rolling Stones oriented. Other side projects with more or less the same members:

**PIKES IN PANIC:**
Good garage punk, after the split some of the members formed the Italian beat band I BARBIERI.

**POLVERE DI PINGUINO:**
A more Stooges-like sound here.

**POW:**
Definitely mod, but a nice tendency to broaden their views (check their last LP), they split in 1993. Discography: "Net Wt. 4 Oz." (mini-LP on Crazy Mannequin, 1989), "The Sidescenes EP" (Vox Pop 1990, co-produced & played piano), "Craziest Hits" (1991 LP on Vox Pop, I played various instruments.), "Maximum Punk'n'Beat" (7" on Face Records, 1992). They also helped on the Backwards LP.

**PRESCRIPTION:**
From the U.K. an LP was released on Target Records ("Psychedelicatessen," 1993) on which sitars, guitars and organs merge to form a nicely intoxicating brew.

**PRIME MOVERS:**
Following the Prisoners' split, Graham Day formed this band with his wife Fay (who played organ with Makin' Time) and put out several LPs, on which a more prominent influence of very early Deep Purple emerges; nevertheless a good band, which split in 1994. Graham later came back with a new (reportedly funkier sounding) band, Planet, and an EP was released. The Prisoners then reformed for a while.

**QUARTERED SHADOWS:**
Definitely no psych-pop in sight here, more Nick Cave-meets-Sicily.

**RED ROSES IN THE SAND** (a 7" "Love Song" with Nikki Sudden). Incidentally their first cassette single was a split with a cover of the Pink Floyd outtake "Scream Thy Last Scream," credited as "Syd's Last Painting."

**SCIACALLI:**
After a 12" ("It's A Love In!" on Destination X, 1994), they showed their ambitions to make more money, shifting towards a more Oasis-oriented sound (as their later EP, "Mi Sento Portare Via," released on Irma Records, a Sony subsidiary, proves), although still partially retaining their 60s roots. A full CD ("Ora Zero") was apparently shelved.

**SETTORE OUT:**
I never thought they had anything to do with the contents of this book; Italian rock, I suppose, very tame.

**SIR CHIME AND THE LOVERS:**
Sort of rough sounding Nick Cave lovers, not psych at all.

**SLEEVES:**
A band from Genova, which wasn't really 60s sounding (their cover of "I Had Too Much To Dream" was not credible), they actually copied Dream Syndicate, and while better to hear live, studio recordings were much tamer. Their CD release is also not recommended.

**STEEPLEJACK:**
Their leader, Maurizio Curadi, was Birdmen Of Alkatraz's guitarist on their first EP. His last demo recordings (very eerie and Syd Barrett-sounding) deserve an official release, but since 1992 he hasn't produced new material.

**SUBTERRANEANS:**
From Firenze, Italy. A spacey Watchband/Elevators combo with a self-produced 10" on SHADO Records.

**SUBTERRANEAN DINING ROOMS** (two LP's on Crazy Mannequin, "There's No Rock'n'Roll Without A Spanish Knife" and "Ghosts In The Sun"; they were previously known as Pinky Silence & Mad Horses)

**TIMES:**
A whole bunch of releases from them. They started as a pop-art mod band, later LP's sounded much different (acid house or something like that).

**VIEWS:**
Their second LP "Mummycat - The World Number 2" on Crazy Mannequin was excellent.

**WOBBLE JAGGLE JIGGLE:**
The "Overflow" cassette was released on a limited edition LP on Magic Gnome in 1995.

**COMPILATION ALBUM ADDITIONS:**

**ANDY WARHOL:**
Unfortunately, in this case, covering the whole first Velvet LP (plus Hitchcock's Scream doing David Bowie's "Andy Warhol") turns out to be boring. This LP was re-released on CD by Vox Pop in the late 1980s.

**AREZZO WAVE:**
This is actually a music festival which takes place every year in Arezzo, Italy. After the event a double-LP (and later a double-CD) set came out, featuring all bands (newcomers and guests artists). In 1993 even the Backwards appeared, our last ever gig.

**BRIAN JONES DIED FOR YOUR SINS:**
One of the first (pre-Crazy Mannequin) compilations featuring bands from Milano. Not really interesting, apart from a couple of songs from Acid Flowers and Peter Sellers & The Hollywood Party.

**A NIGHT WITH A CRAZY MANNEQUIN:**
A promo-only sampler cassette, featuring previously released material from Crazy Mannequin artists (it is also the last Crazy Mannequin release).

**PEOPLE ARE STRANGE:**
Their release "Funhouse" has a whole side recorded live at Backdoors, a club in Firenze.

**SOMETHING ABOUT JOY:**
This LP was also available on CD with some bonus cuts (among them by The Pow).

**THE DREAM AND THE JOKE:**
This 1987 package consisted of a 7" split featuring Peter Sellers and Pinky Silence ("What Exactly Is A Dream"), a cassette compilation featuring various bands ("What Exactly Is A Joke"), plus a booklet with various poems.

**THE INVASION OF THE TAMBOURINE MEN:**
A mini-LP on clear vinyl (some copies had splattered color), released in 1987.

**LUCIFER'S FRIENDS:**
Another Crazy Mannequinn compilation, released in 1988.

**WORONZOID:**
A low budget two-LP sampler from Woronzow featuring released and unreleased material from the label's roster.

---

# MAINLY U.S.A. EAST COAST UPDATES

## by Blair Buscareno

*Blair published the Teen Scene fanzine and is an expert especially on the New York-area garage sound.*

**BELMONDOS:**
Boston/Worcester confabulation with a ? & the Mysterians meets-the-Fleshtones sound. They did one tape in the early 1990s, then disappeared. The returned in the early 2000s and were slated to play with The Cynics & Pretty Things on August 25, 2001 as part of the Cavestomp series in NYC.

**THE CELLAR DWELLARS:**
Two members of The Cellar Dwellars (Mark Ebeling & Susan Mackey) ended up in The Omega Men, who did a CD for MuSick in the mid-late 1990s and have various compilation cuts.

**THE MANEATERS:**
They were a NYC all-girl garage outfit in the mid-1980s.

**THE MOSQUITOS:**
The Mosquitos recordings were the band that got me into everything (garage) in the first place (since I'd gone to junior high and high school with band songwriter/vocalist Vance Brescia). The EP disappointed most of the fans. Luckily, a bunch of us have our live tapes to remember what the band was really like – Damn, they were amazing!

They even did an all-acoustic show once in honor of the 1960s NYC Folk City venue. They performed complete rearrangements and a bunch of new covers. Mindblowing with killer vocal work, too.

"Hang" is my favorite song of theirs – That one used to get us going crazy. That descending riff and then "You were only seven-TE-EE-EE-EN." That downbeat would see us jumping in the air using each other's shoulders as a launching point. Pure bliss. (*Editor's note: "Hang" is one of my fave songs of all time!*)

A Mosquitos show was amazing at the home stomping grounds of Sparks (a club) in Huntington, Long Island (New York), where their manager, Scotto, ran the show for an Italian guy named Angelo. There was pre-show tailgating. The bar's parking lot was jammed, as was the closed-for-the-night gas station below, and even a good portion of the school parking lot a block or two away. Heady times for those of us in our late teens.

**THE SHAMBLES:**
Believe it or not, there were two other bands named The Shambles with garage ties (other than the San Diego entry). One was a short-lived Long Island/New York City project put together by Gena Brower (briefly in the Phase One Psychotics, but replaced by Jill Brown, also known as co-writer of The Headless Horsemen's "Can't Help But Shake," also a member of The Cheetah Beats) and Laura Scheer (sister of Secret Service mainman Wayne Manor). They had garage influences, but also a good sense of melody.  This band never released anything to the general public.

The other Shambles was a Philadelphia bunch featuring a pre-Mondo Topless Sam Steinig. More 1960s pop than garage, but still solid. Not sure if they released any records, but they had a bunch of cassettes.

At one time in NY in the mid-late 1980s, there were two bands named **THE FUGITIVES**. One was mostly straight-up rock and based in NYC. The other was a Long Island group with strong musicianship and vocals, good songwriting, and a penchant for the pop side of things, though they could rock when they felt like it.

There was also an additional band named **THE VINDICATORS** based in Long Island, NY (mainly Smithtown, but also Huntington). This group did one EP on Fuzzola II Records. The first pressing ended up with the hole off-center. And I think the sleeve listed more songs than were on the vinyl. Beautifully fuzzed-out trash. The band included Secret Service guitarist Rob Normandin as well as then-Plastic Device keyboardist Chris Xefos (who'd go on to be a member of King Missile some years later.)

**THE SENDERS:**
The same Senders band that electrified The Max's Kansas City scene in the late 1970s got back together in 1988 and recorded a live LP (for Midnight) at CBGB's that May. That October they began what would eventually reinvigorate the NYC Rock'n'roll scene, playing free Monday night shows at the Continental Divide. They'd do two months in a row, without a guest band opening, take a month off and let someone else headline, then do it again.  Mixing garage, R&B, blues, and rockabilly, they also had a definite

link to the old 1970s punk scene (since they'd played it). The band has always had incredible players and put on great shows.

## RAT BASTARDS: (NYC 1987-1988)
Original lineup was Eric Tretbar (drums), Pete Ciccone, Andy Gortler, Joey "Psycho" DiCurzio (all three on guitar), and Steve Baise (drums). They never put anything out, but these guys were a wild garage, punk, & surf combo. (Stuff was recorded, but never released.) Later, Tretbar would head home to Minneapolis and get back together with the Funseekers there. Joey left to go roadie for Savatage and the summer was spent as the Surfinks. When he came back, the band had brought Paul Corio in on drums and had decided to be a four-man group.

Their last gig ended up being the Bad Music Seminar in early November 1988 (the show that featured the first-ever Billy Childish show in the U.S., with Thee Mighty Caesars). They went into the studio and cut a record, but the band broke up. Some of that recording ended up being the debut disc by The Devil Dogs (which initially featured Gortler, Baise, and Corio in the lineup). Corio would end up leaving the Devil Dogs to join up with Ciccone in The Vacant Lot.

## PRIME MOVERS: (Boston, MA)
Also reunited in 1995-1996, playing the Garage Rage show at NYC's Coney Island High. In addition, they did a single at the time for Clamarama Records.

## BEN VAUGHN:
He's become known as the producer of bands like Los Straitjackets, not to mention his film and TV work, especially the ultra-cool sounds on he TV shows "3rd Rock From The Sun" and "That '70s Show."

# OHIO USA UPDATES

## by William Grapes

*William was very active in the Cincinnati, Ohio garage scene, playing in and with many of the bands below.*

### AUBURNAIRES:
Their sound on their first release was more of an early sixties R&B sound. Their subsequent releases had more of a contemporary guitar sound and would render them irrelevant to this book.

### BUZZ:
The bass player and drummer went onto the Cybermen while the guitarist went onto, among other projects, the Chrome Cranks, and G.G. Allen and the Murder Junkies. Not much of a leap.

### CYBERMEN:
We released a comp of their work in 1996 on Estrus. We also played a show with the Cynics in Cincinnati and at Garage

Shock in Austin. Regarding our release "Insideoutsideupsidedown," if one were to place a bet that the title came from a Yardbirds tune, one would be disappointed. The title came from a Salvation Army song "Upside Down." I liked the way the font looked and, combining the words with the Mod/Pop Art "directional" idea, I came up with the lengthy title.

I always viewed our sound as the direction the original American garage bands were going. They were heavily British influenced so that influence made more sense to pursue then trying to sound like the American garage bands. In other words, I preferred to go to the originating source rather than be influenced by a secondary source.

## DOC AND THE PODS:
They were an incredibly fun live band.

## EL KABONG:
Two members of this group (Bass-Mike Huegen/Guitarist-Steve Ostrov) formed the Cybermen. You have a demo listed but none was ever produced. A public access video does exist from 1987 but that is the extent of their recording. *(Editor's note: I was, indeed, sent a cassette of El Kabong titled "Demo" – perhaps this is the audio from the video.)* A purely subjective note on my part: Steve Ostrov is possibly the best guitarist involved with the 1980s garage scene.

## KEEPERS:
Cincinnati band from the early to mid 1980's. They moved to Boston and were never heard from again. They did leave behind one incredible EP with very Beatlish/Byrdsish harmonies and structure.

## THANGS:
Trashy frat rock combo with two singles. They morphed into the Buzzcock-styled Tigerlilies which recorded for Atatvistic Records out of Chicago.

# THE CANNIBALS BAND BIO

## by Mike Spenser (band member)

The Cannibals was one of the first '60s garage bands in the U.K. to explore this genre of music in its rawest state. We literally used all the original equipment, much of it brought over by me, a native New Yorker, who was around the first time this music roared into life. In 1976 the Cannibals were formed and as the band got known for exemplifying this music, more bands sprang up including the Stingrays, Milkshakes, and countless other groups around the country.

I then opened the first Garage Club in south London, in Brixton, in 1979 and then the more famous club in the Clarendon Hotel (Hammersmith, West London) which ran for six years. Various "Nights of Trash" were staged at different locations around the country and as a result I developed and promoted these groups tremendously.

Groups which made their first starts in his clubs and festivals were My Bloody Valentine, Thee Hipnotics, Mega City 4, Senseless Things, Purple Things, Vibes, Stingrays, Milkshakes, Prisoners, the Commuters and countless other groups.

I believe The Cannibals paved the way for this movement in the UK and though we have not gained as much recognition as we deserve, we are the flag-bearers without whom much of the garage scene in Britain might never have been so productive.

**Albums:**
Bone To Pick,1979
Trash For Cash, 1983
Hot Stuff,1984
The Rest of... 1985 (France)
Please Don't Feed...The Cannibals, 1986
(Play It Again Sam - Belgium)
Cannibals/Surfadelics (split album),1986
And The Lord Said......Let There Be Trash! 1990
The Brest of...The Cannibals
(compilation of the "Rest of and the Best of") CD only, 1997

**Singles:**
Good Guys/ Nothing Takes The Place Of You, 1977
Nadine/Baby You Can't , 1978
Pick and choose/I could SeeRight Through You, 1978
Send me a letter/All shook up (original)
300 copies given away free at Dingwall gig, 1979
Submarine Song/Paralytic Confusion, 1980
Christmas Rock'n'Roll/New Years Eve Song, 1984
You Drive Me Mental/Paralytic Confusion(different version)
        as "The Five Young Cannibals" 1986
The Kings Of Trash/Blow me over 1986
        as "The Five Young Cannibals"
Magical Carpet Ride (original)/Dave Goodman's "Save Stonehenge" 1988
Axe the Tax (Anti - Poll Tax Protest song)/We the People, 1990

**TV appearances:**
FR3 (France): City of People, Action Woman, Paralytic Confusion, Lipstick on your collar, Submarine Song 1984,1986, 1987
BSB (UK) Axe the Tax, 1990

## BAND BIO FOR THE CAPTIVES

## by David Pauwels (band member)

The Captives first came together in 1986, in a small Canadian town where three 15-year-old kids with no athletic talent decided they would start a band as soon as they learned to play their instruments. Darren Richards and André Lapointe learned guitar, while I (Dave Pauwels) picked up the bass. By word of mouth around the local high schools they found their first drummer, Mike White, and started rehearsing in the Pauwels' suburban basement, learning Beatles, Stones and Yardbirds songs and falling in with the local scene of mods, skinheads, punks, and other small-town teenage delinquents.

We played their first show at the local hockey arena on Halloween of 1987, wrecking through their set with all the nervous energy of a first prom date. Soon after that show

Mike left and later joined the Chessmen of nearby Hamilton. Bob McVicar took over on the skins and the Captives started gigging in the Southern Ontario area, wherever a bar owner would overlook their underage status.

Oursound changed as they absorbed more garage influences, grew their hair longer, and started to smoke cigarettes. We played with the Chessmen, Cynics, Frankenstein V and Gruesomes, though their best shows were the teen dances they held in rented union halls in their hometown of Brantford (where A. Graham Bell made his first crank call), or local house parties thrown by kids whose parents didn't know better.

Bob left after two years, and Jamie "Bam Bam" Walters became their third drummer. They continued to play shows, but by then there was less and less of a scene for garage music. The band eventually split in 1989-1990.

## THE FRANKENSTEIN 5
London, Ontario, Canada

**James Bond: (organ, vocals, harmonica)**
**Jason Kipfer: (bass)**
**Mark Ordas: (guitar, vocals)**
**Rob Munro: (guitar, vocals)**
**Mark Wood" (drums)**

**Discography:**
"Kill & Go Hide," What Wave tape compilation 1989
"Can You Dig It," cassette release 1993
"It's a Cryin Shame," on the 'Dig Deeper 2' CD compilation
"Kill & Go Hide," 1989-1994 CD released 08/2000

## THE SATISFACTION
Toronto, Ontario, Canada

**Carson Binks (bass)**
**James Bond (organ, vocals)**
**Gaven Dianda (guitar, vocals)**
**Chad Jagoe (drums)**

– *by James Bond, 2000*

## BAND BIO FOR THE GIRL BOMBS

## by Erin Truscott (band member)

The Girl Bombs started out in Hamilton, Ontario in 1996. We were three girls wanting to play the '60s garage punk they loved in a city that had been the site of such bands as The Chessmen and The Swingin Gurus. A move to Toronto for school brought The Girl Bombs closer to other area bands like The Polyester Explosion and The Kingmixers.

Live shows are where we were at our best, always ready to blast out songs and laughs with great spirit. The live cassette catches that spirit though recorded within the first few months of The Girl Bombs existence. Having mostly stuck to playing within a 10 hour driving radius, we had the chance to travel to some great festivals like Fuzz Fest '97 in Atlanta and the second Las Vegas Grind.

Erin Truscott: bass, lead vocals and screams
Suzanne Richter: guitar, back up vocals and screams
Michele Taffs: drums and back up screams

Discography:
Play it Live 8 song live cassette, 1996
Blow Up with...4 song 7" EP, 1997
        Misty Lane Records, Italy
Options 3 song 7" EP, 1998
        Wee Wanna Records, Canada
Some comps we're on...
Today's Top Girl Groups vol 1 1998
        Spinout Records, USA
Syrup & Gasoline vol 1 1999
        Grenadine Records, Canada
Kittenblood Compilation vol 2 1999
        Thunderwoman Records, Germany
Time to Time 1999
        Teen Sound Records, Italy
Themes for Bathing Beauties and Woodies 1999
        Teen Sound Records, Italy
Video:
live and interview 1997
        F*UTV garage compilation

---

# THE DUPONT CIRCLES

## by Michael Bennet (band member)

The Dupont Circles were formed in 1988 in Washington, D.C. Previously known as The Spills, the band played sporadically throughout the late 1980s and early 1990s until venturing into the studio for the first time in 1995. Ditching its repertoire of garage covers (Standells, Byrds, Squires, Flaming Groovies, Velvets), the band attempted to blend its love of Nuggets-style garage, 1970s punk, Beatlesque pop, and 1980s post-punk indie-pop into a 1960s influenced, but contemporary garage pop stew. Far from prolific, the band followed up the limited edition (300 copies) pressing of its garage-oriented debut 7" "Sarah The Weather Girl," with a four song EP covering more varied musical terrain, displaying influences ranging from Joe Meek to Syd Barrett to the Monkees.

Michael Bennet – guitars, organ
Bob Primosch – vocals, drums
Kelly Ross – bass, organ

Discography:

Sarah the Weather Girl b/w Everywhere Girl (Cara 001) (1995)
53 Bicycles EP (Cara 002) (1999)

Compilations:

Pop American Style (March Records) (1995)
Starring Nao (Rover Records) (2001)
Will There Be Time For Tea? (Morgan Leah Records) (2001)

# UNTAMED YOUTH
(Columbia, MO, USA)

Deke Dickerson – guitar and vocals
Steve Mace – bass/vocals
Steve Rager, Doug Walker – organ/vocals
Joel Trueblood and many others – drums

Beginning in 1987, as teenagers, Untamed Youth were taken in by Billy Miller and Miriam Linna of Norton Records and Kicks Magazine (and now Kicks Books), playing local parties, bars and all over New York City where they became a hit. Although the band "officially" called it a day in 1993, as of this 2014 writing the Untamed Youth still play very special shows (such as music festivals), and still illicit the same frenzied audience response.

In 1988 the band recorded their first LP "Some Kind Of Fun" for Norton Records, and returned to Norton for a second LP "More Gone Gassers" just a year later, touring and playing shows almost constantly. Amazingly, both of these LPs (as a matter of fact all Untamed Youth recordings) hold the same high intensity craziness as do their live shows and stand up to years of listening enjoyment.

The Untamed Youth were never really a "garage band" in that screaming, fuzztone, marble mouthed vocals, modern garage-band-style sense of the word. Instead they turned the scene back to its original roots – with true '66 styled garage twangy guitar mixed with totally "frat-tastic" antics, making them the ultimate party band.

Taking cover songs like "Beer Bust Blues" by the Scottsmen, and mixing them with originals like the surfy instrumental "Pabst Blue Ribbon" which (when played live) featured members of the band both chugging said beer and creating a "Beer-Cano" (a volcano of beer) over the audience was always a treat. No matter how many times you witnessed their live show, with the same silly antics, it was always just plain entertaining and fun!

By the early 1990s Deke and Mace decided to try moving to California. They gathered together a few more like minded souls and released some records for Estrus, but found that they just couldn't get the steam rolling behind the band. Mace eventually moved back to Missouri, but Deke stayed in California, essentially putting Untamed Youth to rest...for a bit.

But fans couldn't let the band rest, and luckily neither could the band. Since "breaking up," Untamed Youth has released several records for Estrus, Norton and Double Crown Records, and played sold out shows whenever they get the right opportunity.

– by Glynis Ward, 2014

# THE BOTTLECAPS
(Holland)

They label themselves "premium garage rock"' and although they seem to be searching for their own exact sound there is some solid songwriting and plenty of passion in their presentation. Their demo CD "Meet The BottleCaps" (on Pure Coincidence Records in the Netherlands, 2013) has a bonus video featuring a Puch brand moped (scooter), the Dutch answer to the Lambrettas and Vespas in the U.K.

# THE DEAF
(Holland)

It could be easy to dismiss The Deaf as a hi-fi powerpop band presenting themselves as a rebellious garage act. It doesn't help that singer-guitarist Frank "Spike" van Zoest first rose to fame with punky pop chartbusters Di-Rect (and still plays with them), nor that Spike claimed he founded The Deaf after seeing Dead Moon once, "because a chick on bass is cool." That quote, however, may very well be written by a biased journalist, since The Deaf flaunt a genuine love of sixties garage rock & roll, with Phantom guitars, Farfisa organ and Vox equipment all in place, songs to match, and plenty of energy on stage. Spike is also known to be very supportive of fellow Dutch garage bands, bringing the whole idea of garage music to a whole new audience. Any band that rocks out regardless of what some critics may say is worth checking out – so hey, they may have that in common with Dead Moon after all.

# DR. REVERB
(Holland)

Mostly in the vein of Man or Astro-man?, this trio played surf with some pretty out-there twists. Playing in white fall-out suits and what looked like hockey masks, with plenty of virtuoso guitar madness and a drummer who plays what they called "No Mercy Beat." They unraveled when two band members got too busy with other bands. Their anonymous presentation was taken to the limits when they started using their logo symbol instead of the band name.

"Dr Reverb metalizes Dr Varlot," CD, Dr Reverb Records, 1998
Untitled CD, Dr Reverb Records, 2000
Split 7" EP with The Napoleons, Tombstone Records (USA) 2002

# THE KIK
(Holland)

The Kik are a Beatles-obsessed Dutch pop band, with huge mainstream success (here). They use many garage "props," including Vox amps, Vox guitars and a Vox Continental. They band began as The Madd, a band that stayed close to the sixties-garage sound (but also chose to record in Holland's top-notch state-of-the-art Wisseloord studio).

The Kik also have a true love for sixties pop, sometimes with a psychedelic edge. Their Beatles-pastiches almost enter Rutles-parody territory, but for all the mainstream exposure they rightfully get they are still capable of writing more than a handful of original sixties-pop gems. The fact that they sing in Dutch (more specifically, in a Rotterdam accent) makes them stand out in their home country.

Albums: "Springlevend" (2012) and "2" (2014).

*Bottlecaps, The Deaf, Dr. Reverb, and The Kik - by L.T. Selmer*

---

# PIERCED ARROWS
(OREGON, U.S.A.)

## by Eric Geevers

When Dead Moon folded in 2006 it was clear that this would not be the end of the road for Fred and Toody. Within months a whole news set of songs emerged with drummer Kelly Halliburton; the band now named Pierced Arrows (named after the Pierce Arrow automobiles Fred loved as a kid). Kelly, originally a bass-playing veteran of the hardcore scene, was elected to pick up the drums again after years of neglecting the drum sticks.

Fully prepared to start at the bottom and play support slots, and nervous like any new band, Pierced Arrows soon found themselves billed as a main act – something they hadn't dared to suggest – and they were back on track making albums and touring again in no time. The last Dead Moon release, a 2-CD compilation on SubPop, may have helped getting Pierced Arrows off the ground, and their second album was released on Vice Records.

So, are they Dead Moon under a different name with another drummer? Not really. Yes, they have the same set-up with the drums all the way up front. Yes, they play the same no-frills, patented Fred Cole songs, but there are some new influences and they now even record in a real studio.

With two full albums under their belt that are just as good as any Dead Moon album, a third on its way, and a growing legion of dedicated fans, we can safely say that Pierced Arrows are further proof of the stubborn course followed by Fred and Toody ever since The Weeds a.k.a. The Lollipop Shoppe way back in 1967.

"Straight To The Heart," LP/CD, Tombstone Records, 2008
"Descending Shadows," Vice Records 2010

# THE GORIES
(Detroit, MI, U.S.A.)

## by Fernando Jiménez
(of the band The Smoggers)

When I was just a teenager, with pimples all over my face, I started to love The Ramones, The Cramps and other bands whose retro-sound was funny, energetic and trashy. Those bands are rock and roll and garage-punk for me. And, of course, The Gories carry on this tradition.

The band was formed in Detroit in 1986, featuring Mick Collins and Dan Kroha on guitars and vocals, and the drummer-girl Peggy O'Neill. Their sound is a mix of garage-punk stomp and trash blues. After three albums and a few singles they taught the rock and roll world of the possibility to change the sound of music itself.

After they recorded songs such as "You Little Nothing" and "Charm Bag" at the Garageland Studio, their first album, "Houserockin'," was made quickly. In 1989 this stuff wasn't a hit but the band recorded the follow-up LP, "I Know You Fine, but How You Doin'," in 1990, and then they signed to Tim Warren's German underground label Crypt Records for the release of "Outta Here," the last release of the band in studio.

Although they never sold many records, today they are considered one of the most interesting underground bands of their era. Interestingly, they were not what most people would consider "good" musicians, and they made a lot of noise.

When they broke up in 1992, after "Outta Here" album, The Gories were considered part of the new wave of old-school R&R bands such as New Bomb Turks, Raunch Hands, The Makers, The Mummies, Oblivians and Billy Childish's bands.

In September 2008 a reunion of The Gories and a tour in U.S.A. and Europe was announced: the Gories and the Oblivians would play together! After this the Detroit band has played occasionally. The last great show they played was at the Funtastic Festival in Spain. The "Detroit sound" is still alive!

I always believed they were an awesome band with crude musicians, which is an important part of their story. Maybe The Gories' rock and roll attitude isn't your cup of tea, but I'm sure that many people would want to drink "Thunderbird SQ" (wine) with The Gories! I have always loved them.

## ALBUMS:

"Houserockin'"- Wanghead Records, 1989
"I Know You Fine, But How You Doin'"
    New Rose Records, 1990
"Outta Here" - Crypt Records, 1992
"The Shaw Tapes: Live In Detroit 5/27/88"
    Third Man Records, 2013

## SINGLES, EPS AND SPLIT RELEASES:

"Nitroglycerine/Makin' Love" - New Rose Records, 1990
"Give Me Some Money/You Don't Love Me" - Sub Pop, 1991
"Here Be The Gories" - In The Red Recordings, 1991
"Baby Say Unh!" - Estrus Records, 1992
"To Find Out" - Giant Claw, 1992
"Bug House Waterbug and Roach Traps" -
    Get Hip Recordings, 1995
"Lord High Fixers & Gories" - Hate'Zine Records, 2000
"Dirtbombs & Gories" - Fortune Teller Records, 2004

## COMPILATIONS:

"I Know You Be Houserockin" - Crypt Records, 1994

---

# SAN FRANCISCO AND THE CHARMKIN REBELLION

## by John Kennedy

I was a radio DJ and club promoter in the San Francisco area in the 1980s and was primarily concerned with the '60s garage punk scene. There wasn't much of a scene for that stuff in S.F., but there was a little one.

I used to book a lot of the '60s-styled punk shows around town that featured out-of-town acts like The Chesterfield Kings, The Lyres, The Pandoras, and all that stuff, but the audience for it was all just S.F "freaks," nobody was really dressing that way or taking any particular inspiration from that movement.

The band The Trip (on the Battle of the Garages Volume 2 compilation) moved here, but as soon as they got here they sort of broke up. They were a little older and not so dedicated.

The Morlocks moved here in the spring of 1985, and they became a complete sensation here. Nobody had ever seen anything like it, and they hit a chord somehow. In L.A. or San Diego, where there were lots of these sorts of bands playing, they would play pretty small places, but in S.F. this one band was headlining all the biggest clubs for some reason. They were actually making a living *being* the Morlocks.

At this time (mid-1980s) more and more local kids who were really into the '60s started showing up. There was even a short-lived local band called the Way-Outz, who played Pebbles covers but dressed like metalers, who opened a few Morlocks shows but never caught on. I would call them the first local '60s punk band but they were so lame I suppose they dont count.

In San Francisco the Mods did not hate the "psychs" like they did in southern California. Everyone got along, and Mods were actually coming to Morlocks shows. Weird as hell. But some of the Mods started growing their hair and "moving up" from '64 to '66. I remember the Berkeley Mod scene starting to embrace the garage thing around this time, and by about 1986 there were a few who were too groovy to be called Mods any more.

Bart Davenport was sort of their leader. He must have been about 16 in 1986, when he started playing with what was definitely S.F.'s very first and most important locally-grown garage band, The Horseless Headmen. *(Editor's Note: don't confuse this band with the Headless Horsemen from New York City.)* This band also featured a huge long-haired "freak" and 1960s music expert named Christof Certik on Vox guitar, and a wild Chinese "ape-man" named Russell Quan singing.

These guys started playing in S.F. and Berkeley around the summer of '86 (I remember because I saved all my show fliers). They opened for the Tell-Tale Hearts' only-ever S.F. show, and started to get kind of well-known around town. They were really entertaining to watch. Real weirdos, like a real 1960s band in many ways.

I remember the Horseless Headman made a recording for some label in Australia but the record never came out. They had a song called "SS Nightmare" that I played on the radio a lot, and which I have heard several people refer to as one of the best '60s/'80s song of all.

The Horseless Headmen broke up, and Bart started a new group called The Birminghams. He sort of returned to his Mod roots with this band, which featured his long-time partner on guitar, Xan McCurdy, who later when on to the internationally famous band Cake.

The Birminghams were a great band. Xan was such an amazing guitar player it was hard not to love them. They were all kids. All teenagers. And so incredibly talented and perfect. They were taking the Mod thing to places that other Mods were not willing to go. They were doing a sort of early Who / Small Faces kind of thing, rather than just standard R&B or Ska like all the other lame Mod bands.

They got to be friends with another new band from San Diego called The Event, which was a complete revelation to us all. They were the first Mod band any of us ever were aware of that played what we non-Mods thought of as "real" Mod music, which was stuff like The Creation and The Action, and John's Children and The Move and all that '66 - 67 era stuff.

They had bouffant hairdos and ruffled shirts and belled trousers. They were incredible. The LP they later made on the Voxx label was not at all a good representation of how amazing they were. Anyway, they really had a deep effect on Bart, who started to embrace all that stuff, too (he always loved it to begin with), and The Birminghams took on more and more of that pop-art mid-60s Mod thing. They really ruled the scene here for about a year or so, but stuck too much to the Mod scene, in my opinion.

They could have been huge if they had branched out a little, which is what they did when they became The Loved Ones

a little later. Bart, Xan, and Mike Therieau from The Event started The Loved Ones, which became a pretty well-known blues-R&B band that toured the world in the early 1990s.

They were not strictly a '60s garage band any more, so it doesn't really have relevance here. But they all went on to be quite successful (in a small way).

But the other guys in the Horseless Headmen, Russell and Christof, went on to form another '60s punk-garage band called The Creeple Peeple. This time Russell Quan was on drums, and another guy named Matt Brown from Richmond, Virginia was the singer. There was also a Farfisa organ player named Trent Ruane. The bass player's name was Jules, but I don't recall his last name.

The Creeple Peeple were just as great as the Horseless Headmen, and were kind of the main local '60s punk band at that time, about '87 - '88. That was a time when it seemed like that whole scene was over. There were no more bands like that in L.A. or San Diego, it seemed.

The Tell-Tale Hearts were broken up, the Morlocks were broken up, the Unclaimed were broken up, the Miracle Workers had gone Stooges, the Chesterfield Kings were going New York Dolls.. Anyway it almost seemed as if The Creeple Peeple were the last band standing. In a way it was sort of too late, and they were doomed from the beginning. But they played some incredible shows and made a cassette that was sold here and there. I recently saw one for sale on a list of '60s/'80s records for $100, and someone bought it!

It was a great little recording, and I still like to listen to it. Very primitive, but not at all too punk or too heavy the way most of those (supposed) '60s bands were at that time.

I remember a conversation I had with Christof at one of their shows, where he was saying he thought they had missed the boat, and was feeling discouraged. He was like the very first "Charmkin" in the S.F. area, so he felt a little let down that it had never fully caught on there. *(See the end of this feature for more about the term "Charmkin.")*

He was also complaining that the other guys in the band were getting more into what we called "Frat Rock" at the time, which was the earlier '60s punk stuff, like The Sonics and Wailers and whatnot, stuff that was less British sounding, and rawer, often with sax and frantic surf rhythms. He didn't like that stuff.

He was telling me they were looking for a gimmick, the way real '60s bands sometimes did, that would be their look and their theme. We joked about possible ideas, and he was telling me they were seriously considering pirates, vampires, and maybe mummies.

Well, what ended up happening was they chose mummies. And they also kind of went a little further into that frat-trash rock thing. So Christof quit. And Russell and Trent joined with Larry and Maz from a San Mateo band called The Batmen to form the now-famous Mummies. So The Mummies ended up being the last standing relic from that '60s scene in the 1980s. They were the only band of its kind that I was aware of for many years.

But gone were the 1960s clothes or hairdos, and the music was different. It was punk-ish, and deliberately low-fi and trashy. It was great fun, but it wasn't strictly 1960s any more. And it more reflected an earlier time, less interesting to me. I agreed with Christof.

But Russell went on to be the sort of torch-bearer of the '60s punk thing and still is. He played with all sorts of groups over the years. The Phantom Surfers and the Dukes of Hamburg are about all I can think of right now. But in S.F., if there was any sort of band playing that kind of music, Russell was always in it.

But none of them were really the full-blown thing ever again after the 1980s. No one put any effort into the look, which was a big part of it. I know that seems superficial and unimportant to some people, but it really was not at all trivial. The look was a huge part of that whole music scene, and the music just became standard and unexceptional when played by a bunch of guys in T-shirts and sneakers. That is my opinion.

Christof went on to be in a bunch of interesting bands, none of which were really that 1960s thing any more, except one called Benjamin Kitestring, which was one of the best local bands I ever saw. They had that sort of '67 - '68 British sound, a little like the Move or the Pretty Things or something. Hard to put your finger on it. I know they were all into those Rubble compilations that came out in the late 1980s and '90s, and were emulating that stuff.

The whole '60s scene here was really swept up by those compilations. Bart and his Mod cohorts were all raving about those records, and Christof too. Russell and Trent hated it. Funny how those lines were drawn.

Anyway Christof even had a stint in the Brian Jonestown Massacre for a minute in the late 1990s. That is another story...

**About the term "Charmkin" :** This is a term that for a while was the catch-all term for 1960s punk people. There was never a word for it that didn't sound embarrassingly corny. "'60s punk" or "garage" or even just "'60s" sounded so stupid to us. So we needed a word. Naturally we all remember how the Gravedigger V says it between songs on their Voxx album.

Here is the story as I remember it: The guys in San Diego, which was the epicenter of that scene in the U.S. (for a while), used the term Charmkin to refer to the girls in L.A. who were dressing '60s to be trendy, and kind of overdoing it with too much jewelry (like Madonna or the Bangles or something). That is what I have heard.

But what I do know is that Christof went to L.A. to hang out with The Primates (they were good friends) around '87, and the Primates had a friend who used the word Charmkin to just refer to all of them, all the '60s people. He had taken the San Diego usage and expanded it. But it was just him at that time using it, and Christof thought it was hilarious, so he brought it back to S.F. and started using it all the time here. The scene here was so small that it easily caught on, and stayed in the common vernacular to this day.

In the 1990s, Tom Guido, the fellow who re-opened the Purple Onion in S.F., and who was '60s-obsessed, used the term ad infinitum, and even started a fanzine called The Charmkin Rebellion. I understand that today there is a band that has this name! I have been all over the world and run into people everywhere who use the word Charmkin to describe '60s people. It is not universal, but it is amazing how widespread it is.

# New Photo Pages

*More favorite neo-garage-psych record and fanzine covers.*

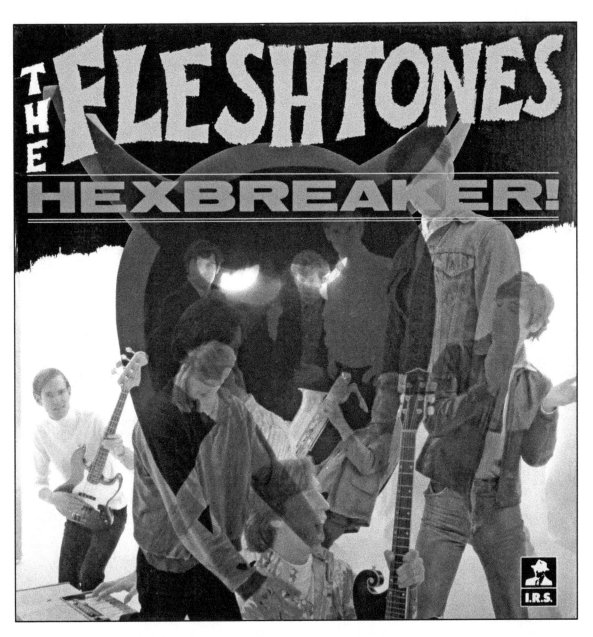

The Astronauts    Rocket To Mars    Astromono

THE GARAGE DAYS VOL 2
**ROOTS OF SWEDISH POP**
531 487-2

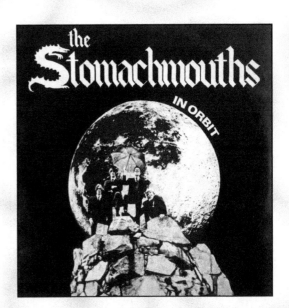

453

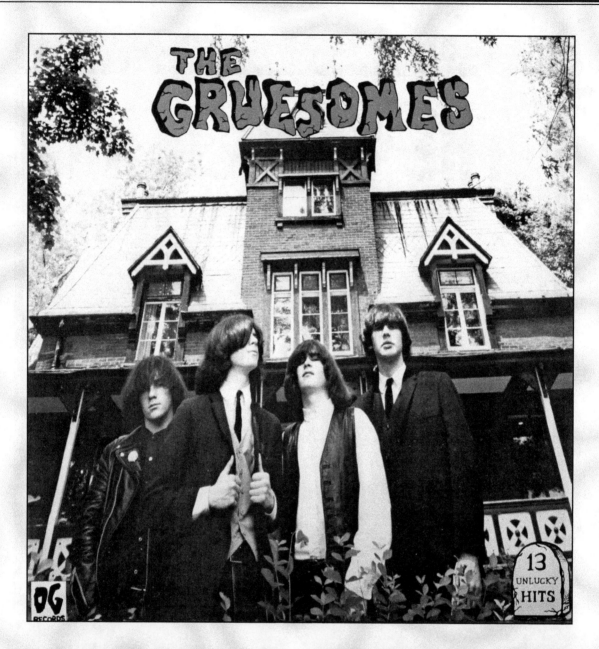

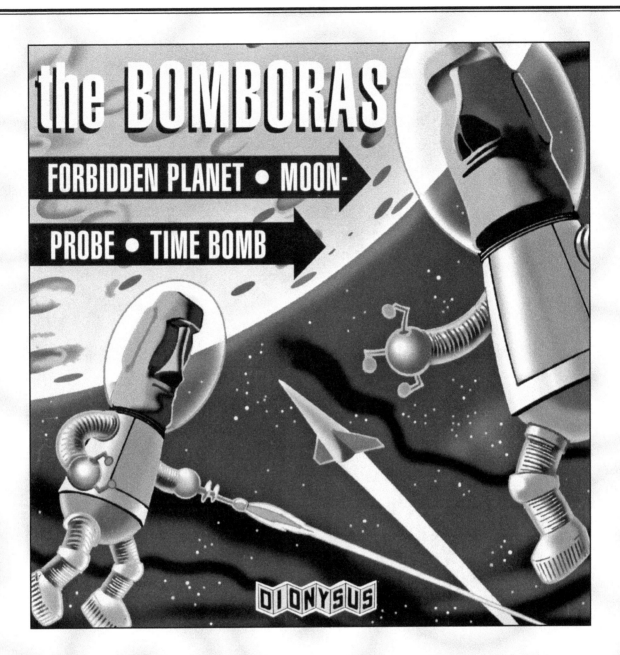

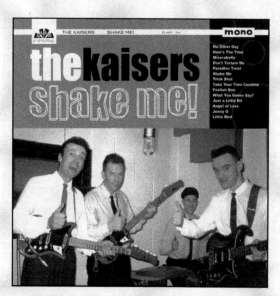

# HERE COME
## THE HIGH LEARYS

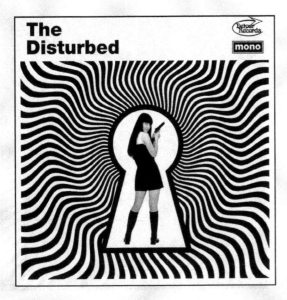

The Disturbed

mono

Meet **The Paranoiacs**

TWIST 26
LOST TREASURES 2

DO YOUR THING <==STEREO==> 360 SOUND
(i) RAIN ON ME
(ii) CREEPIN' OUT TONIGHT

THE RESONARS

BRIGHT AND DARK

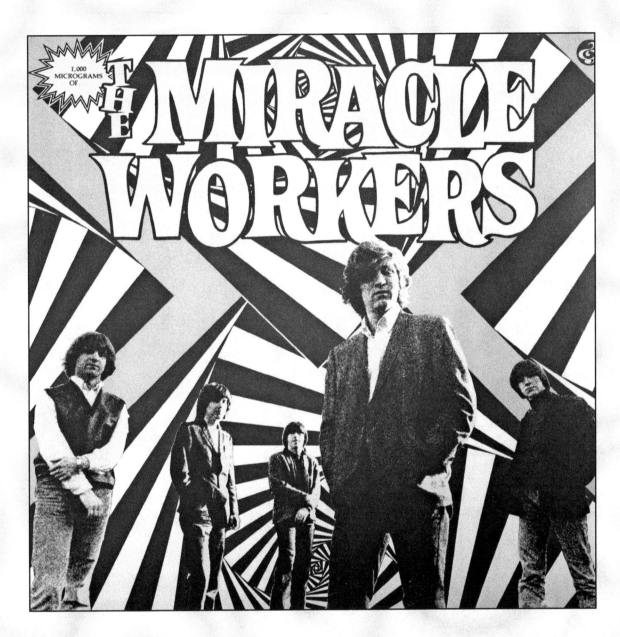

1,000 MICROGRAMS OF... THE MIRACLE WORKERS

Stereo

TRUE WEST

The Rain Parade

YESTERDAY'S THOUGHTS-JOHN FRANKOVIC-THEE HANDS OF TYME
CACTUS COOPER-NICK BENSEN-ACTION RECORDS
INCLUDING CD WITH
cosmic gardeners-fantasyy factoryy-yesterday's thoughts-cactus cooper
into the abyss-in the labyrinth-mandra gora lightshow society
desperate friends-john frankovic-quarkspace-thee hands of tyme
psychedelic avengers-teddy boys from the crypt

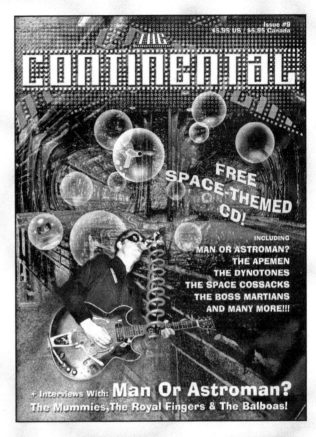

Issue #9
$5.95 US / $6.95 Canada

# THE CONTINENTAL

FREE SPACE-THEMED CD!

INCLUDING
MAN OR ASTROMAN?
THE APEMEN
THE DYNOTONES
THE SPACE COSSACKS
THE BOSS MARTIANS
AND MANY MORE!!!

+ Interviews With: **Man Or Astroman?**
The Mummies, The Royal Fingers & The Balboas!

SKUNK #1 FANZINE

THE BAROQUES-"BEAT IM SOZIALISMUS!"-THE
UGLY DUCKLINGS-FUN THINGS-THE UNHEARD OF-
BABY WOODROSE-MANDRA GORA LIGHTSHOW
SOCIETY-NULL CITY RECORDS-THE MEANIE
MEANIES-YESTERDAY'S THOUGHTS-THE
PHILISTEINS-DEAD MOON-THE HYDES

LOST in TYME

issue #1
June 2004

CONTAINS A
21 TRACK CD
COMPILATION
with exclusive
previously unreleased
and demo material

exclusive interviews

MARSHMALLOW OVERCOAT
STEPFORD HUSBANDS
JENS LINDBERG
BOB URH
UNHEARD OF

SOUND EXPLOSION
THE GRAVES
LES SYNAPSES
MOD FACTOR
MOCKER MONKEYS

News
Reviews
Fanzines
Records

# 1980s Fanzine Reproductions

*Author Timothy Gassen published "The Psychedelicatessen" fanzine from 1986-1991. At first an offshoot of his "Randy Love's Flower Hours" radio show (later also named "The Psychedelicatessen"), this zine is a representative example of the paper publications of the 1980s garage era. Fanzines like this one started crudely but evolved and helped to nurture the garage community before the instant information access of the Internet era.*

# THE PSYCHEDELICATESSEN

A NEWSLETTER OF THE <u>RANDY LOVE'S FLOWER HOURS</u> RADIO PROGRAM

INSIDE:

THE FUZZTONES

HEAVY MENTAL

SOUNDS FROM LSD

OVERSEAS PSYCH
AND GARAGE

RADIO NEWS

RECORD REVIEWS

CONTACT ADDRESSES!!

<u>THE CREEPS</u>: SWEDEN'S
LATEST VINYL KINGS
HAVE THE LP OF THE YEAR!

volume 1, Dec. 1986

LISTEN EACH FRIDAY NIGHT FROM 9 to 11 PM on KXCI, 91.7 FM

# the FUZZTONES

Rudi Protrudi, who played in his first band when he was only a "tyke" in 1967, provides DJ Randy Love with a little insight on what it takes to be a Fuzztone.

From the leg biting to the brow beating, the Fuzztones slammed out their psychedelic rock on a European tour and Protrudi looks back at the irony of it.

interview by
Randy Love

Randy Love: What's happening with you?

Rudi Protrudi: As it stands right now we have a new drummer, Mike Checkize(? jg). We're still looking for a guitar player. Each person in the band is doing something on the side until we can get the Fuzztones back together. I'm doing an instrumental band, with the other two guys from the Fuzztones, and that's called Link Protrudi and the J-Men. That's real rockin' Link Ray kind of stuff. We (Fuzztones) have a live album that should be coming out pretty soon - some stuff that we did in Europe.

RL: Can you tell us about that European tour?

RP: It was wild

What do you want to know?

RL: What was the reception of English fans to the Fuzztones?

RP: For the most part the English kids loved us. I think they haven't ever heard any bands like us because we really play American rock 'n' roll. We came over there and just pretty much peeled off the most American hard rockin' stuff that we could.

There were a couple places we didn't go over all that great. Places where we were opening for The Damned. The kids just didn't want to hear anything but The Damned. And sometimes at places like that they'd throw beer bottles at us or lit cigarettes -- sometimes they'd jump up on stage and try and beat us up. But we had some big roadies.

RL: It seems like a lot of the American groups, like Yard Trauma, are getting more attention over seas than they are here (USA).

RP: That was pretty much the case with us too. I think the main reason is because American teenagers seem to be really jaded. We always go over well here (US) but in comparison to Europe there was no comparison.

Places like Germany, France, and Italy are really repressed and when they get a chance to see a band that really rocks, the kids go crazy. In Italy we had people jumping up on stage and biting our legs. . . . Just really crazed things that would never happen here.

RL: From the video I've seen and different magazine articles I've read about the group -- you seem to have a reputation for being mystical or a voodoo quality. Is this coming from a some publicity monger or is there a mystical force behind the Fuzztones?

RP: I guess all could say is the rumors aren't totally unsubstantiated. I could say that not all our energy level comes from pure adrenalin.

As far as this music goes - it just gets repressed and rears its ugly head again. Bo Diddley and Jerry Lee Lewis were the punks of their generation. They said 'I don't want my kids listening to this.' And the next thing you know - they put Elvis in the army, and Chuck Berry in jail and they black-balled Jerry Lee for marrying his cousin. The next thing you know you had stuff like Frankie Avalon.

Then the Rolling Stones came out and brought it all back. When the Stones came out your parents went 'oh these guys are dirty, they have long hair, they're pigs. . .

The next thing you know they were repressed and you had things like disco.

Rock 'n' roll - the whole idea of it is to rebel - to have something to say as youth instead of having everybody put their morals down your throat. The thing that I think is so sad now is all kids here sit in front of the tv and watch all this stuff their parents can watch with them.

There's no seperation between the kids and the adults. Here I am, older than kids now-a-days and I'm saying 'I don't know what's wrong with this generation, they're lame.' They're listening to lame music. . . and I'm ten years older than them.

## OVERSEAS REVIEWS: SWEDEN AND GERMANY EXPLODE, AND ENJOY THE CREEPS IS THE PSYCH/GARAGE LP OF 1986!!!

Man, oh man, Europe has gone bonkos over that shakin' 60s sound, and are pumping out their very own garage grunge. The best example of the year, the best example from ANY place in the world this year is the debut LP from Sweden's THE CREEPS, "Enjoy The Creeps." (Tracks On Wax, Box 2175, 53102, Lidkoping, SWEDEN). They take the cake with an incredibly well produced yet raw platter full of originals soaked in mid 60s punk, soul, garage, and love, baby, love! There are only 3 cover tunes here, and the Sonics covers are blended PERFECTLY into one swirling tribute. Vocals are also a highlight on the LP, with soaring souled-up

Ismail Samie (L) of The Backdoor Men and Hans Ingemansson of both the B-Men and The Creeps are overjoyed with my reviews. We call Ismail "The Thing."

screams drenching the listener like a downpour of cool. They even have their own theme song! You can also catch THE CREEPS on the Swedish compilation LP "A Real Cool Time," but that track is a pale attempt compared with this LP. Tracks On Wax also has many other cool bands in their camp. Could I please get a catalog? Please?

And down there in good ole' Germany, things are scorching too. Robert Jelinek and Hans Ingemansson of The Creeps also double their time in THE BACKDOOR MEN, who have 2 singles out. I can't find their 1st single, but the 2nd one on FAB Records is a killer! (FAB, Koldewwystr. 12, 2000 Hamburg 61, West Germany.) A great Stones-ish A side, backed by an instrumental barrage of psycho noise. Give me more! Reinhard Holstein's Glitterhouse label isn't sitting still either. They have a number of 7"s out already, the foremost being the EP by THE BROKEN JUG. The Jug has a more prominent keyboard sound, and it helps to paint a subdued yet manic world. The production is lean and mean, and done on a home 4-track! Man, this is a record to be proud of.

Back to Sweden, THE STOMACHMOUTHS continue their aural assault. Their 7" on Got To Hurry Records (Yxsmedsgrand 4, 111 27 Stockholm, Sweden) never lets up, with some of the tightest drumming I've ever heard. There's garage, rockabilly, distortion and fun waiting for you on blue vinyl, no less. Theire new LP on GTH is GREAT, but I only have a test press, with no titles! Yet it is one of the best of the year. Look for a domestic release of it on VOXX RECORDS.

*MORE* ⟶

Back on Glitterhouse, let's not forget the incredible worldwide compilation LP "DECLARATION OF FUZZ" (Glitterhouse Records, Lange Strasse 41, 3471 Lauenforde, West Germany). 18 entire tracks from the finest new psychedelic/garage monsters from the farthest corners of the US and Europe. Sweden's CORNFLAKE ZOO shines, please tell me where I can get some more of their stuff. GREEN TELESCOPE are also great, and they have a 7" out on Glitterhouse also. Italy's SICK ROSE is cool as well, but let's face it, there are NO weak songs on the entire LP. I hate to admit it, but it's better than my Beasts From The East LP, but then we were shooting for a different sound. Anyway, this is a great introduction into the world of psycho junk rock & roll, baby!

My god, there's a band from Kent, England that's put out a 7", an LP, and 2 12" EPs all in a little more than a year. And they're all FABULOUS records. The name of the group is THE DENTISTS, and I don't know why they haven't been snatched up by a big label. The guitar sound is there; somewhere between sweet melody and distortion, with Beatle-esque vocals and melodies thrown in as well. Surely not revivalist nor power-popish, THE DENTISTS have discovered a world that is only their own. I don't have the debut 7" (does anyone have one?), but the 12"s are available through Tambourine Records, 6 The Willows, Rainham, Kent, ME8 7DW. Some People Are On The Pitch They Think It's All Over It Is Now is the LP, and it's probably their best. Start with it. Then comes the You And Your Bloody Oranges EP, with 6 great songs, and the Down and Out In Paris and Chatham EP with 5 sizzlers. Boy, oh boy, a day with a Dentists song is a good day!

*END*

DEMENTIA 13 LP, Midnight Records, PO Box 390, Old Chelsea Station, NY, NY 10011.

In case you don't know, Midnight is a record store, label, and mail order service from NYC. They've been spitting out a good number of interesting LPs and 7"s for the past 2 years or so, and the cryptic debut LP from Dementia 13 is no exception. Bare bones production doesn't detract from the manic psychedelic guitar and quavering vocals. The touches of Handrix, Syd Barret, etc. all swirl around into a distinctive, wierd, and wonderful result. This is real psych music, not posing.

Also check out Midnight for great LPs and 7"s by The Tryfles, Plan 9, Outta Place, Vipers, Mod Fun, Suburban Nightmare (now The Dwarves), Morlocks, Plasticland...The variety is amazing. I've done 2 special shows on Midnight releases, and there's a lot to discover. Also, there's an early Fuzztone track on the Midnight compilation LP "Hangin' Out At Midnight." Give it a try. It has some surprises, too. (I almost forgot again. The 2 LPs of pop/garage by The Cheepskates are cool!!!!)

The
# PSYCHEDELICATESSEN
Magazine

ISSUE #2  WINTER, 1988          "A Smorgasbord of Rock 'N Roll"

Los Negativos:
Spain goes garage!

**THE CYNICS/THE MARSHMALLOW OVERCOAT/
MOJO NIXON/GREG SHAW/SOUNDS FROM L.S.D./
THE CORNFLAKE ZOO/SCENE REPORTS/
REVIEWS AND MORE GROOVYNESS!**

# A Cynical look at vinyl

While the 1960s sported several CYNICS from Texas, these guys and a gal hail from Pittsburg, PA. They've been knocking around for more than 3 years now, and have accumulated 5 singles, 3 different compilation appearances, an LP, and another soon-to-be released 12".

The first 2 singles came out on the groovy LA label Dionysus; the debut featured an original backed with a cool cover of the Chocolate Watch Band's version of "Sweet Young Thing." The sound is a bit tentative compared to their later efforts, but the spirit of the tracks win out.

The 2nd 7" is a classic; the blistering original "No Place To Hide" b/w a right-on version of the Century's "Hard Times." Line-up changes seem to occur with each new release, and new vocalist Michael Kastelic really belts it out here!

Unpredictably, the 3rd single is a soaringly melodic folk-punk outing that would make any Byrds fan happy. The guitars chime away in all their glory; truly great stuff! And "Lying All The Time" is supposed to be included in a horror film entitled "The Cellar," but no word on when that is to be/has been released.

The 4th 45 is meant to be a fan club only release, but you can find a few through some mail-order stores. It's the first basement recordings by the initial line-up, many musicians ago. Each 45 is numbered, and there is no picture sleeve. (I should have mentioned that all of the other 45s have very attractive picture sleeves.)

The latest single has the A side from the LP, and a fuzzed out non-LP B side entitled "Dancing On The Wall." This brings us to the "Blue Train Station" LP, a collection of 13 mind-bending, fuzz hammering tunes, complete with cool

cover, liner notes, photos, etc. If you like your garage fast, hard and sincere, this is the place to start. As I said, a follow-up LP should be out early in 1988.

Of course by now you're begging for more tracks, so start digging for those compilation LPs. Firstly, on the Voxx "Beasts From The East" collection there's the melodic "Let Me Know." On the German Glitterhouse release "Declaration Of Fuzz" we have "No Place To Hide." (That's also on their 2nd 7".) And lastly, so far, on the Dionysus sampler "Sounds Of Now" they have "Get Away Girl."

I've heard live tapes of the band, and they can certainly replicate their fuzz sound on stage. They've been touring up and down the Eastern seaboard, but haven't been able to make it out west yet. When they do, don't miss out on one of our generation's best pure rock bands.

But until you can experience them in the flesh, search those record bins and get CYNICAL before it's too late!!! (EDITOR)

# ¿Rock 'n Roll en Español?  ! Si!

reported by Angel Maetzu Coso

Writing a short report on the new Spanish scene isn't easy. What's happening here can hardly be summed up in a few words ...anyway, I'll try to do it!

In my modest opinion, there are some of the world's most promising rock bands here in Spain. You don't believe me? I know most of you haven't heard their records or demo tapes, but I'd like to play down the difficulty of getting them. (Why don't you write to us?) (I think what Angel is trying to say, is that the Spanish bands are world-class, even if it's difficult to find their product in the US. Editor)

These groups are recuperating and bringing up to date the best elements of the 60s sounds (imaginiation, intensity, passion, rebelliousness), which you can hear in their records and live shows. Here's a list of some fine releases by Spanish 60s styled bands:

---

LOS NEGATIVOS: "Piknik Caleidoscopico" LP (Victoria Records)
Los Negativos (from Barcelona) were our revelation in 1986. This hip psychedelic pop quartet has a fabulous album and 2 singles out.(They're featured on the cover and elsewhere in this issue!)

BRIGHTON 64: "La Casa De La Bomba" 12" (EMI Records)
The latest record from our most important mod combo is a fantastic Rhythm 'n Soul mini-LP. Exciting tunes and inspired production make it one of the coolest 80s Spanish records.

LA GRANJA: "La Granja" LP (Tres Cipreses-Dro Records)
Another good psycho pop group. Enjoy their debut LP! It's real groovy!

LA FRONTERA: "Si El Whiskey No Te Arruina...Las Mujeres Lo Haran" LP (Polydor)
Wild and nasty second studio-record by this powerful garage 'n western quintet from Madrid.

LOS ELEGANTES: "Paso A Paso" LP (Zafiro Records)
Los Elegantes (from Madrid) are one of our veteran bands. Their second album is full of pop/soul songs and great melodies. These latest months they've been working in the studio with Elliot Murphy. Stay tuned.

BATTLE OF THE GARAGES #4, Compilation LP (Voxx Records)
Los Negativo's "Viaje al Norte" and Sex Museum's "Drugged Personality" are included!!!

SEX MUSEUM (from Madrid), the Spanish garage-teen kings, have no records of their own yet. But if you want to get their live tapes or demos, write to: Servicio Informativo de Sex Museum/Aptdo Correos 17.193/28080 Madrid/Spain.

(I honestly have no idea how to obtain the above-mentioned records in the U.S., except for the Battle Of The Garages #4, which is a domestic release. I personally have never seen or heard of them in any mail-order catalog, but maybe a call to Midnite records in NYC might help...Editor.)

We also have a bunch of good fanzines, written in Spanish by real fans, devoted to 60s bands and their 80s children. I recommend to you the following ones:

REACCIONES
(the best Spanish modzine)
Apartat de Correus 360098
08080 Barcelona
SPAIN

"54321":
The Los Negativos Fan Club
Newsletter
c/ Massens 15, Ent 3a
08024 Barcelons
SPAIN

ROMILAR-D
(a must for garage-punk
fanatics!)
Juan Hermida
c/Guadalajara 7, 3o F
28042 Madrid
SPAIN

GARAGELAND
(the most important R 'n R zine
in the capital city)
c/J.A. Mendizabal no 19, sexto
C.iz.
28008 Madrid
SPAIN

LA HERENCIA DE LOS MUNSTER
(which covers all good 80s
stuff)
Apartado 38
Santurce, Vizcay
SPAIN

There are some clubs where
the bands can play in each
important town (but we need
more!) and some indy labels put
out the records by our groups.
But unfortunately the European
tours of U.S. Garage/Psychedelic
combos never includes Spain, and
their records are hard to get,
or are very expensive! Hey pals,
why not give us a chance? It
would be great if bands like The
Chesterfield Kings, Tell-Tale
Hearts or Yard Trauma (just to
name a few) could play in
Spanish cities, and have their
records released here!!

*A groovy Spanish concert poster*

CONTACT:
Angel Maeztu Coso
c/Fontflorida 64 3er 4a
08004 Barcelona
SPAIN
(Please include 2 IRCs with your
letters for a reply!)

(Angel hosts a radio show in
Barcelona that features the
world-wide new garage movement.
It's amazing that scenes like
Spain's can happen with limited
exposure to the wealth of
releases available here in the
U.S., so help out our Spanish
friends and write them a few
letters!!! Editor.)

# A BREAKFAST BOWL OF COOL:
# THE CORNFLAKE ZOO

*"We know. Yes we
know. That it all
ends...........
on Hippie Hill."*

In the first issue
of this magazine, I
covered the German
and Swedish garage
scenes, but I didn't
discuss one of my
favorite new bands:
THE CORNFLAKE ZOO.

They were probably
tripping while eating
some Frosted Flakes,
and Tony the Tiger
suggested their name.
I don't know. But they
certainly deliver the
"trippy" side of the
current Swedish psych-
garage explosion.

They burst upon the
scene with a 1985 45
on the essential
Tracks On Wax label.
The now long-out-of-
print debut contained
a super-charged
version of the 60s
punk classic "Hey
Conductor," with an
original tune stuck
on the B side!

**SWEDEN'S NEWEST HITMAKERS: THE CORNFLAKE ZOO**

An original called "13 Stations"
brought them more attention via the
"Declaration of Fuzz" comp; as I've
mentioned before, this is perhaps
the finest sampling of world-wide
garage mánia. (on Glitterhouse
Records, available through Midnight
or Metro Music mail order.)

The CORNFLAKE ZOO sound is one
of balance; the raw edge of 60s
punk is tempered against a more
melodic and precise style. The
excellent musicianship also helps,
with stand-out keyboards in
particular!

Their first 12" is a 4 song EP
entitled "The End Of The
Beginning," and it is one of the
best new psych discs yet released.
There are two different versions of
the original "Hippie Hill," another
original trip number called "Rainy
Day," and a cover, unexpectantly,
of the Arlo Guthrie tune "Los
Angeles."

All are real gems, with the
honky-tonk piano on "LA" bringing a
new dimension to the band. The
originals are all tightly produced
and performed, with something new
jumping out of the mix with each

listen! The EP is on Eternal Love Records in Sweden, and I don't think it has been imported to the U.S.

Also out is a new 45, which I can't find, and a full-length LP, I think, but I'm woefully behind in collecting the European product. Hopefully some U.S. indy label will license this stuff for domestic release, so it's more readily available. (Voxx recently collected some tracks from Sweden's Stomachmouths for domestic release; I'd welcome a similar deal...)

To find out the latest on the CORNFLAKE ZOO, drop them a line, and get hip to the Swedish trip!

CORNFLAKE ZOO
c/o Joe Wegner
Sommarv. 14
182 74 Stocksund
Sweden

# East Coast reports

CONNECTICUT:
THE LEADER IN ROCK? Not Quite...

I talked to Joe Guidone of THE NOT QUITE on the phone recently, and we shared many ideas on the state of the garage/psych scene. Here he gives a taste of what the New England band scene is like at the moment...

"The New England scene is wierd: aside from NYC which is a totally different animal, Connecticut is mainly a wasteland for places to play, but with 1001 bands.

NEW JOHNNY FIVE, PAISLEY JUNGLE (since moved to Boston), MOTIVE 8 are bands which have wide appeal to the D.O.R. set (Dance Oriented Rubbish). Very popular, and Motive 8 will put out vinyl soon. MIRACLE LEGION (despite denials to the contrary) are illegitimate sons of REM. They're also very popular with the college set. (I remember being in a record store, and hearing the first Miracle Legion record. I thought it WAS REM! Editor.)

Remember, Connecticut hosts Trinity College in Hartford, U Of Hartford, and New Haven has the dreaded Yale, U of NH and Southern Ct. College...

DA WILLOWS aren't bad, have a self-released EP, and are searching for an identity - slightly left of REM and a bit right of new pop like The Cure or something.

Some of these bands have had members kicking around since time eternal (circa 1976 or so). One band, THE BELL SYSTEM, is re-grouping and hopefully will bring a Velvet Underground, Cleveland roots sound back soon. VALLEY OF KINGS has disbanded and re-grouped under the name CAMERAFACE.

Very young bands with potential from the central area of the state include 12TH SEPTEMBER and GREEN PANIC. These are musicians kicking it out after high school or a college class.

Oh yeah, everybody has to have a perennial bar-band, and THE REDUCERS are just that; good, but have mellowed a bit over the past few years. To their credit, they have 3 self-released LPs under their belt.

On the garage side (finally) (FINALLY! Editor) are THE MALARIANS, from Northampton MA, a band whose LP doesn't quite reflect their live punch; a Count Five prep-rock look and sound. A band from New Haven, THE DOUBLE KNOT SPYS, contains some people your mother warned you about. They prove to be a lethal sewer level grunge outfit!

THE GOREHOUNDS from Portland ME. are a crazed five-piece, with Bob Martel from THE DARK CELLARS on guitar/jug. They have a swamp sound; very grungey and unpolished. Check out their 45.

THE BROOD are still kicking it out, but I'm not certain as to whether they'll be releasing more on vinyl soon............"

All for now -
Joe

THE NOT QUITE have been around in various forms for more than 3 years now, with individual members having been active in the Connecticut "scene" since the late 70s. The current lineup includes Rob MacKenzie on bass/vocals, Joe Guidone on rhythm guitar/vocals, Tom Donnelly on drums, and Morrison McCarthy on lead guitars. Recently joining has been Gry Kaspersen on keyboards (from Norway.)

I first came across them on the excellent ROIR cassette compilation "Garage Sale", where they contributed an original song, "Paint Me In A Corner." It's a great example of garage punkadella, with plenty of heart and guts! More recently, THE NOT QUITE had a track included on the Glitterhouse compilation LP "Declaration Of Fuzz." Once again they showed their stuff; great playing and a sense of urgency.

So it was with eager anticipation that I waited for their long-overdue debut LP. It has been in the can for more than a year, and it has now finally been licensed to Resonance Records of the Netherlands. It is an import-only here in the US, with VERY limited quantities, so act now!

I haven't even found a copy, but the band was kind enough to send an advance casette, and it's definitely been worth the wait! The majority of material here are originals, along with a few well-selected covers. "Wars Or Hands Of Time" is a great song, and THE NOT QUITE make it all their own. On a limited edition bonus 45, included with the LP, you'll also find incredible covers of the Who's "Circles" b/w "Green Slime," the

1967 movie song that The Fuzztones also have covered. While The Fuzztones version is a classic, this version is the most psychedelic that could ever be produced.

On the original side, THE NOT QUITE show a great dexterity in their songwriting. The folkish ballad "I' Don't Know How To Tell You" displays great melodies and a soft touch, while "Mushroom People" exhibits a darkly ominous tone of nuclear angst. For pure garage, there's "Get Lost Girl," "Get Away," (with an instantly hummable chorus), etc. Absolutely no duds among this bunch; and a lot of chances taken. This is definitely not a safe attempt at revivalism; this is a fresh band with their own voice. Garage/pop/psychedella, it's all here, and with enough guts to pull it all off.

Now if I can just find a copy of the LP for myself!

—EDITOR

write to   THE NOT QUITE
c/o Joe Guidone
PO Box 2363
Enfield, CT. 06082

# THE NEW YORK SCENE

*NEW YORK, NEW YORK, A WONDERFUL TOWN, THE SLUMS ARE UP, THE SLUMS ARE DOWN...*

*JOHN R.REINERT*

*(John is a good guy who sends me cassettes of cool stuff that I'm not familiar with. He digs all kinds of rock, and gives us an overview of live shows in NY. While these reviews are dated, they still give us an idea of the vibrant NYC scene. Huh? Editor.)*

*The "underground" scene here in the NY/NJ area has really been*

*intense lately. Some of the most incredible shows have been at NY's THE RITZ. A real classy club, a bit over-priced, generally $13 to $15 for 2 or 3 bands, but the shows have been well worth it!*

*Recently, The Ritz has presented shows by NY's own rap/pranksters THE BEASTIE BOYS, along with NY's premiere hardcore outfit MURPHY'S LAW. Look for The Boys, Murphy's and that crazed ska/funk outfit FISHBONE to be doin' the arena scene real soon, so catch them at a club if you can. Also recently at the Ritz, NY's best and foremost* hardcore/reggae band THE BAD BRAINS. The Brains played 2 different nights, and both were totally sold out. The first night had Canada`s S.N.F.U opening, as well as 3 other harcore bands. The second night featured Boston`s own "funcore" band GANG GREEN, as well as a re-union of San Francisco's FLIPPER.

I don`t remember too much of Flipper`s set; I got clobbered by a big dude who decided to stage dive during one of the slower songs, and I wasn't paying too much attention. I regained my senses by the time the Bad Brains hit the stage, and although all the opening bands were outrageous, The Bad Brains proved they could still rock the house like no other band in the world!

Playing sold out shows recently at a great club in Hoboken, NJ called MAXWELL`S have been SOUL ASYLUM on 2 different occasions, SACCHARINE TRUST, and CAMPER VAN BEETHOVEN, those LA wierdos. Although the Club's a bit small, its price stays put at $6 for 2 or 3 bands, and you generally have a great time!

But the stage has that been hottest is at the club that started it all: CBGB's. The stage that in the past featured such bands as THE RAMONES, BLONDIE, TALKING HEADS, RICHARD HELL, and a host of others, is now presenting some of the finest bands in the new "underground" scene.

Recent shows have included SOUL ASYLUM, BIG BLACK, HAPPY FLOWERS, KILLDOSER, and PUSSY GALORE. Also appearing lately have been THE LEAVING TRAINS along with Grateful Dead sound-alikes ALWAYS AUGUST, and one of the best new NY bands DAS DAMEN. Watch for their new LP available from SST RECORDS.

Also, another great club unfortunately closed, but luckily re-opened for 2 outstanding shows. (John, you forgot to tell us what the name of the club is! Editor.)

The first show featured SONIC YOUTH, FRIGHTWIG and FIREHOSE. Firehose are Mike Watt and George Hurley from THE MINUTEMEN and new member Ed from Ohio. All the bands were well recieved, but the crowd was totally into the sounds of Firehose. The show ended with members of Sonic Youth, Firehose and former BLACK FLAG bassist Kira doing an all-star jam!

The other show featured those grand-daddies of punk rock THE DICTATORS as well as MURPHY'S LAW (boy, they sure get around). A great time was had by all until the Great White Castle Burger Fiasco. (What the hell was that? Editor.) It wound up with the bouncers beating on the audience; not a real happening experience for sure!

On the garage side of things, there have been great shows by: LINK PROTRUDI AND THE RAY MEN, playing a sold out show at the FUNK CAFE to a very enthusiatic audience. "Link" of course is RUDI PROTRUDI of THE FUZZTONES doin' some surf instrumental kinda stuff. Speaking of THE FUZZTONES, look for a cross-country tour in the near future, as well as a new live LP. (THE FUZZTONES live LP is just out, and the band is now in Europe playing big concerts!!! Hi Rudi, and fuzz rules! Editor).

Also playing S.O. shows lately: THE FLESHTONES and DAS FURLINES (featuring Deb O'Nair formerly of The Fuzztones) at Maxwells. The BEN VAUGHN COMBO had CBGB`s rockin with their garage sounds, and MIDNIGHT RECORDS artists THE MIGHTY MOFOS also had a great show there.

With shows like these, the New York scene can only get stronger. LONG LIVE ROCK!!!!! (Thanks John, and watch out for those slow songs! Editor)

# THE U.K. GARAGE DISEASE!!!

Yabba Dabba Doo, what's shakin' in ye good olde UK? Being something of a strange nation, most cool things music-wise are stolen from the USA and a coupla other places, diluted down to almost nothing and sold to the masses as new and exciting. The once exciting London trash scene has lately become a sad parody of itself and only bands like THE STINGRAYS, THE JAMES TAYLOR QUARTET (ex-Prisoners) and THE PURPLE THINGS are worth catchin'.

What's happenin' now has been brewing up for a coupla years but has only begun to ignite fairly recently. Most importantly it's going on outside of London, a definite advantage if it doesn't want to be smothered by hype and bullshit. Guys'n'gals of 16, 17 or even younger are beginning to get off on the garage sounds of Pebbles, Nuggets and anything else they can get their hands on, and, more importantly they're starting to form bands to play the kinda stuff they wanna hear. I guess it's a total reaction against the absolutely insipid brainwashing crap touted thro' the media.

## Scottish Fuzz: THE THANES !!!

The coolest combo we've got are THE THANES, who may be better known to some of ya as The Green Telescope. They've moved on to a more beat pop sound and are the real gear these days. Their debut EP "Hey Girl" and LP "The Thanes Of Candor" are out now on DDT and you really should hassle your local beat emporium to get both. (I WANT THEM NOW! Ed.)

THE THANES are based in Edinburgh and there's quite a scene building up there. Trouble is that most of the guys are in more than one group. Lenny Helsing, Thanes vocals and guitar, drums with THE STAYRCASE and THE OFFHOOKS and until recently did the same for the now deceased BEEVILLE HIVE V. 24 hours a day just ain't enough!!!

Obviously this situation limits activity and in particular gigs. Very rarely do any of these boss combos step outside Edinburgh let alone Scotland, so us poor southerners have

practically no chance of ever seeing their crazzee live shows. There's always tapes tho cus apart from THE THANES, no garageniks have made it onto vinyl...yet! THE STAYRCASE are totally wild teen punk tho' their last recording session did cool it down a bit, from a hurricane to a storm. Something like having a trashcan tipped over your head with some primitive being battering it.

One of the best and youngest (Louie the guitarist is 15!!!) prospects are THEE WYLDE THINGS from Hastings on the South coast. Attempting to create some primitive teenage action in this sleepy area is no mean achievement but these guys are doing their utmost. Now that they're writing their own mean originals, there will be no stoppin em.

Before signing off there's a few more cool cats you should know about. THE BEAT POETS from Glasgow ain't comin' straight from the garage but their instrumental-mutant-surf stomps with guitar and sax duels are damn near perfect. Also, they have some vinyl out in the shape of a 4 track 12" on 53rd and 3rd Records. Also of note are THE AARDVARKS from Ealing and THE TYME ELEMENT from Huddersfield.

Of course there's a load more who have only just begun crawling from the wreckage themselves. All are 100% ignored by the UK press, who would probably only tag em revivalist anyway. Vinyl-wise "Garage Goodies #2" is set to feature THE THANES and a couple more, while Satellite plans to feature nearly all of em on a UK volume in their "Raw Cuts" LP series in early '88.

The enthusiasm and energy of these guys'n'gals is awesome and in a year or so we're gonna be hearing a lot more about them. STAY TUNED TO THIS INFECTION!!!!!!!!!!!!!!!!!!!!

Written By BOSS HOSS

HASTINGS CRYPT JULY 22ND

The "Seeds" of a new UK sound!

# ATTACK OF THE LIMEYS!!!!!

## THE BEAT INTERNATIONAL/SATELLITE RECORDS SCENE, DADDY-O...

### Written by Chris Green

In early 1987, Beat International rose from the ashes of Criminal Damage Records, a punk oriented label (in attitude at least) which over 4 years had reactivated THE LEATHER NUN and THE MEMBRANES and introduced THE JACK RUBIES, THEM HOWLIN' HORRORS, ANGEL CORPUS CHRISTI, the Raw Cuts series and countless other projects to the world.

Beat International blasted off recently with the release of the first full length LP by THE SURFIN' LUNGS entitled "The Biggest Wave." A recent defect from the Big Beat label (confusing, huh!), they're without question Europe's top surfin' crew. The LP will thaw those chilled bones thru' the long winter months, unless you're somewhere hot in which case you'll sweat a bit more! The guys have been bangin' on the door of International stardom for some 8 years now and finally there's a chink of light.

The related Satellite Record label has concentrated on the RAW CUTS LP series and 2 were released this past summer: Volume 3/German Underground is a psych pop beat trip with the instigators and leading lights of the cool German scene featuring THE LEGENDARY GOLDEN VAMPIRES, THE CHUD, THE BEATITUDES, SHINY GNOMES, DIZZY SATELLITES, NIRVANA DEVILS, BROKEN JUG, LES BLACK CARNATIONS. Volume 4/Australian Nitro is a crushing chemical encounter of vicious Rock and Psychedelic Punk Sleaze from Adelaide featuring MAD TURKS FROM ISTANBUL, LIZ DEALY & THE 20 SECOND SET, THE CONEHEADS, KING SNAKE ROOST, THE ASSASSINS, THE SPIKES, BLOODLOSS, FEAR & LOATHING, PRIMEVILS.

In case you're not familiar with this series, each LP concentrates on current garage, psych, beat, rock (call it what you like) activity in one country and picks 8 or 10 of the very hottest groups to contribute 2 cuts each. They have been described as "kinda like modern Pebbles" which is close. 7 more volumes are being worked on and the next 3 are ready to go late '87/early'88.

But Satellite ain't just a vehicle for Raw Cuts. Early 1988 will see the release of the debut LP by BLOODLOSS and also an LP by Texas' crazeee T.TEX EDWARDS. In addition there will be a "best of" LP by THE BROKEN JUG and hopefully an LP by Los Angeles' MARASUPIALS.

Beat International/Satellite are distributed in the USA by Rough Trade, Midnight and numerous importers. All releases are available direct at 5 pounds (UK) each plus 2 pounds postage surface, or plus 5 pounds airmail. Make International Money Orders payable to BEAT INTERNATIONAL, 91 SWANSEA RD., READING, RG1 8HA, ENGLAND.

## THE MODERNIST SOUND OF THE UNICORN...

Another prolific label in the UK is UNICORN RECORDS, located in London. They feature the "modernist" sound of the English underground, or in other words, the Mod scene. I've heard that the Mods have a strong contingent there, and the Unicorn product backs this up. They have 2 excellent compilation LPs out of international modernist music called "Unicorn One" and "Unicorn Two." The variety of sounds is incredible, with a high rate of first class tracks. Highlights include THE LEOPARDS (U.S.), SEX MUSEUM (Spain), THE PICTURES (U.K.) and HIGH STYLE (Japan!). Fun indeed.

They also have a 4 song, 4 band 7" EP out, (I just love 7" EPs), called "The Phase III Mod Bands" that also hits the spot. On the LP front, THE RISK have a 12" entitled "An Invitation To The Blues" that sports bright pop-style production and some great vocals. The only miss is a "funky" number called "Work" that, uh, should have been an outtake. From the Washington D.C. area comes MODEST PROPOSAL, but it took Unicorn's good taste to finally release a British LP of their sounds! The production is in more of a "rock" context here, with hard-driving mod stylings spicing things up. Some catchy melodies and a good sense of humor as well. Way to go Yanks! I think that Unicorn has several other releases available, but this is all that I have right now. For more info write them at UNICORN RECORDS, 11a PRATT STREET, CAMDEN TOWN, LONDON NW1 OAE, ENGLAND. (Editor.)

# The
# PSYCHEDELICATESSEN
## Magazine

## The Untold Story Behind Tucson's 1960s Legends:

# THE DEARLY BELOVED

"a smorgasbord of underground rock"

**THE BLACKLIGHT CHAMELEONS' guide to NYC, THE BROOD,
LEE JOSEPH, THE MARSHMALLOW OVERCOAT, 60's and 80's
RECORD REVIEWS, A GUIDE TO WHO BOOTLEGS,
and another Tucson legend exposed:
THE SOT WEED FACTOR!!!!**

ISSUE #3, 1988

# A Journey Through Tyme With...
# THE BLACKLIGHT CHAMELEONS

Once upon a time there was a magical group called The Mad Violets, with a sound distinctive, addictive and hypnotic. From the ashes of the Violet's fire sprang The Blacklight Chameleons, and the distinctive magic endured in the guitar of Dino Sorbello. An EP appeared on Voxx Records, and now a full LP on their own National Brain Child Records. Struck with "lineup" disease, the Chameleons took on many shapes, and even now they twist and turn to find a stable form. But Dino need not worry; the LP is a brilliant document of a psychedelic map, with many roads to travel and many destinations to find. Ah, and that guitar, that whirling, sprinkling, reeling guitar. Travel now with Dino as he takes us through the Blacklight corridors of New York City...

"In the earlier daze of the 'scene' here in NYC (early 1980s) we suddenly had a ton of local talent. There was The Fuzztones, Vipers, Outta Place, Cheepskates, Mad Violets, etc. and at that time the emphasis seemed to be on who was gonna beat the other bands first to cover that week's favorite song off one of the Pebbles albums. It was garage cover city, man (with the exception of the Violets who played originals, I'm proud to brag), and everyone also became very diggative on the clothes and the bowl haircuts and Beatle boots and wyld op-art looks, sounds and smells. All this revolving around The Dive ( NYC club.) As tyme passed and brought us through the changes, bands broke up and reformed, spin-offs and one-nighters, something interesting started to happen. Newer groups started to play originals and, lo, began to pursue more individual style and sounds but still keeping with the spirit of the neo 60s. One major element missing however was that essence of the 1960s; the philosophy of a united front and an alternative to the crass bullshit of the status quo, the revolution of the spirit. No, nothing deeper than the clothes, haircuts and fuzzboxes going on here. (This sounds like my editorial on page one! EDITOR)

But the bands at least got better. Now we have THE OPTIC NERVE who are turning out great originals in a folk/early R&B kinda combination. THE SECRET SERVICE have perfected the mod look formula and have a brain crushing attack, very strong and likeable live show. THE HEADLESS HORSEMEN have developed an excellent sound sorta based on things like the early Who, Elevators, etc, but the sound is theirs. Check out their LP. I should mention that all of these bands are right now putting out new records so look for them.

We (THE BLACKLIGHT CHAMELEONS) also have an album out, and we've gone in a directly psychedelic direction, sort of poppy at times, but the idea is to be modern with all the influences of the more timeless aspects incorporated. Heavy. THE CELLAR DWELLARS, from Harrisburg, Pa. show up to play a lot, and they have an 45 out; also from that town are the members of the COOL ITALIANS now calling themselves THE MISANTHROPES, hard R&B like Pretty Things, etc. THE VIPERS are still around upholding the sacred Pebbles tradition. They're gonna open for the Iron Butterfly reunion gig at The Saint. (formerly the Fillmore East) There is a killer hippie psych band out on Long Island who recently played a Minds Eye show, called THE MELTED AMERICANS, excellent.

And THE CREEPING PUMPKINS continue to blossom with the absolute best fuzz sound this guit man has ever heard anywhere. I think it's just a Big Muff (distortion box) with a Phantom Vox, but MAN. We also got THE BLACK ORCHIDS on the fringe, being a bit more yer basic rock 'n roll; 2 guys and 2 luvly girls, and THEY got a record coming out too! If I forgot anybody, it's due to brain damage.

The club scene here is just too inadequate to support all these great bands, there's the real tragedy, but the groups are here and records are appearing, so get vicarious. Hoping to get a club opened on planet Erra in the star system Pleiades. People there are gonna be fascinated..."

Ahhh, I guess the good news in NYC are the bands. Now for the sad part; where can those bands play? Dino looks deep in his crystal ball and continues...

"Well ever since sometime in July way back in '86 when nearly all of the

reliably cool clubs got 86'd in favor of urban yuppie desecration, it's been tight. Right now if you got a band, or like to see them, there are only a handful worth considering. Rising rents, bribing the right fire inspectors, the right mobster for a liquor license etc...well maybe it's not quite like that but the real name of the game around here is to have that huge profit margin instead of just enough to cover expenses. Never mind about having a local scene identity, something that might attract creative people, we only want SUCCESSFUL people, remember, nothing sucks seeds like sick sex. Here's what's left:

AVENUE A, in the warm months all you gotta do is hang out beer in a bag in your hand and sooner or later everyone walks by and you say what's happening and if you get a good answer you go there too. Or you stay out and meet them girls or watch the local skins create yet another senseless act of violence as they are always the last to know we are all on the same side. (This STILL sounds like one of my editorials! EDITOR).

On that street THE PYRAMID is still having good shows that don't cost much. Lots of weeknight shows that get good bands in, besides the local underground heros there's plenty of out-of-town bands stopping in while on tour. Sleepy audience though. Not far away on 1st Ave is the LISMAR LOUNGE that caters a bit more to the hard rock kinda glam junkie heavy metal scene, but it's been good for a rare garage or even, dare I say it, psych show, and it's cheap too. CAT CLUB has the same orientation, but with too much attitude and no love for music, plus loads of bridge and tunnel types to make every night "amateur night." And there is NIRVANA, high above Times Square where you can look all the way down to the sidewalks from the stage as you play and it's a really beautiful room, richly appointed in an Eastern Indian motif (itsa restaurant by day.) They always give out tons of free passes for their shows but watch it, a beer costs 5 bucks. A new club has opened on the upper east side called DRUMS, nice room and sound, all the college favorites play there, some industry showcasing, but it costs loads to get in and a hip flask would also save you a year's salary there too. Starting to get the picture? The clubs are generally filled with apathetic types who can't be bothered to react to a band unless someone is disrobing or meeting violent death onstage, 2 tricks we may try at our next show...

The goodest thing happening right now is still the MINDS EYE series happening at TRAMPS. The irrepressible Ivy and Ann work to bring you the purest strains of psych and textbook garage bands. There is the amazing Capt. Whizzo Light Show; the Cap'n being a veteran light man from the actual 60s, go-go dancers and always a good crowd and good vibes, if you know what I mean. It's probably the closest thing to the good scene we had going at the Dive back in the mid 80s. That was the past and this is the present; the future is not going to be in this town."

Dino speaks only the truth, so heed his advice. While you're at it, run, as quickly as your mind can carry you, to a store near you and grab THE BLACKLIGHT CHAMELEON's LP "Inner Mission."

# THE BROOD

Interview By Richard Ward

In the wyldes of Portland, Maine resides the seminal all-girl garage group, The Brood. I was fortunate enough to catch up with the band at the Big Cahuna Club in NYC where they played with the Cynics and The Optic Nerve. Needless to say, they put on a killer show. We were dancing on tables, chairs and even the floor to the wailing sounds of the bands and Mr. Wizard's psychedelic light show. The Brood are one of the wyldest live acts around and this comes across on their recordings. They have singles out on Get Hip, Primitive, an upcoming LP on Get Hip and various flexis and trax on comps and the such. All rule. But enough of me. Let's hear from The Brood ...

**Q:** Even if you've done it a zillion times: Tell me about the formation of the band.

**A:** In 1983 Chris got her Baldwin guitar in a pawn shop in Lewiston. Betsy was playing her boyfriend's Mosrite bass, & Richard got material for us to play. One of the first songs we learned was "Writing on the Wall" & "Crying Shame."

**Q:** How and where were your first gig?

**A:** Our very first show was an outdoors benefit (July 16, 1983) at Green Hills Farms in North Parsonsfield, an isolated yet scenic place for retarded people. It was Sunday afternoon & later we picked blueberries. A couple weeks after that we played our 1st advertised show in Portland opening for the Chesterfield Kings, and the place was packed! We got an encore & did "Let's Talk About Boys" which completely blew everyone's minds.

**Q:** Who is in the band now and how did Allyson's (impending) marriage with Peter Maniette (of The Wylde Mammoths) come about? Do you have plans to replace her? Hope so; love that Farfisa.

**A:** In July of '87 we did a show with The Wylde Mammoths where she first met Peter. By the time you read this we should have the spot filled.

**Q:** The Brood have long been a fave of the Flower Hours (radio show) & the Psychedeli. How is it that it has taken this long to get an album out?

**A:** Over the years we recorded a few songs here & a few songs there. Then we gave a few out here & a few out there, leaving behind 16 songs (12 originals) that really work well together, almost like a "concept" album. The cover has a nifty photo that portrays what the songs are about & the liner notes tie it together. We're pleased, although it has taken so long. If we were on the ball this could of come out about a year ago, but it will be worth the wait, "In Spite Of It All."

**Q:** What kind of instruments do you play?

**A:** CHRIS: Baldwin or Silvertone guitar.
BETSY: Burns or Vox bass
CRYSTAL: Trixon or Rogers drum kit
ALLYSON: Vox & Farfisa organ

**Q:** Who (what) are your fave acts (each) of today - live and/or on record?

**A:** CRYSTAL: A veritable plethora...
BETSY: Right now I listen to the Cynics' "12 Flights Up" LP alot. Recent antique store find was an Animals album. I listen to alot of stuff from the time I get up til I go to bed.
CHRIS: I dig alot of those Australian groups that Glen Baker writes about. For new stuff, my fave record is "Sgt. Puppet" by Kenne Highland.

**Q:** Tell us about your best live show - or even your fave live show.

**A:** CHRIS: My favorite show happens to be the biggest fiasco ever. It was at a small red-neck tavern in Portland with a bad reputation, but they wanted to have bands at their place and guaranteed us enough money to cover rent. We were psyched to play there because of a light-up dance floor, but when we got there they made us set up to the side of it in a tiny space where they moved a couple of tables out. Then we went in the girls room to brood over a bottle of "Janis Juice" (So. Comfort), just before we got to that last drop, the bar-maid came in & caught us and nearly threw us out right then! The clientele, as we should have known, was not into 60s fuzz-punk AT ALL, and the dykes were yellin' for us to play songs off the juke box. The manager kept flicking the power on & off, until the bass amp finally blew a fuse. I kept breaking guitar strings & had to stop each time to change 'em cuz I didn't have a backup guitar. At the end of the night the owner literally threw the check at us.
BETSY: Any show we stole beer at, especially the ones where we didn't get caught. Like the time at "Folk City" with The Dead Milkmen, there were cases of beer in the band room (not for us), & we opened & took as many as we could and left!
CRYSTAL: I quit school & ran away from home when I was 16, to play at CBGBs. The Headless Horsemen got us the show.

**Q:** Would each of you describe a perfect day for you? Be realistic if you must.

**A:** CRYSTAL: Wake up from a good dream (around 11am). Then have someone make me breakfast, which included among other things: beer. Then go out and do something like have lunch & drink more beer. Then take a nap & wake up & have a couple more beers & go out to see a band. Finally, after a few more beers, fall asleep with my sneakers on.
BETSY: Staying in bed all day, kind of like Elvis. Lotsa food, beverages, TV, magazines - entertainment galore.
CHRIS: My perfect day begins at 4:30 in the morning with a call from Capt. P.J. Then I head for a pot of fresh brewed coffee at The Miss Portland Diner. Next we hit the road for hours of crazy lawn sales and flea markets. In the afternoon, drive down to Old Orchard Beach to relax & read the latest issue of Neat Stuff before heading out to the twilight run of the Powder-Puff derby at Oxford Speedway. Then it's off to the twin drive-in where the creature double-feature is showing "Horror Of Party Beach" and "I Married A Monster From Outer Space."

# The
# PSYCHEDELICATESSEN
ISSUE #4, 1989 IN REVIEW

Magazine

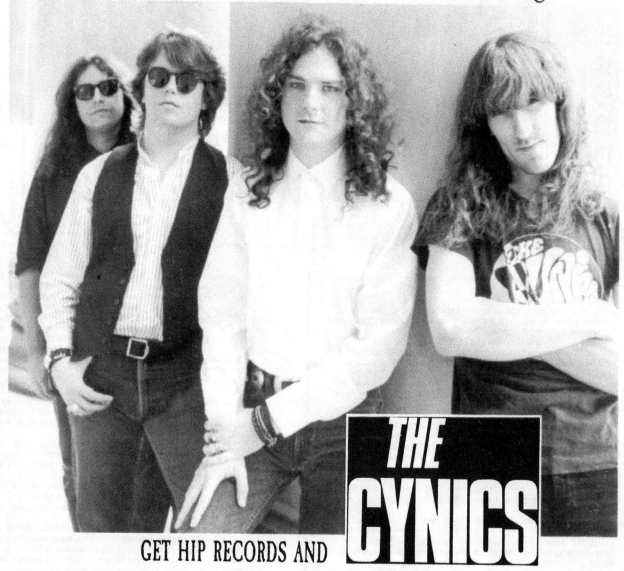

GET HIP RECORDS AND **THE CYNICS**

JIGSAW SEEN * THEE FOURGIVEN * THE WHO

MARSHMALLOW OVERCOAT * SIDEWINDERS

PLUS MILLIONS OF UNDERGROUND RECORD REVIEWS!

# THEE FOURGIVEN - R.I.P.

Yup, it's true. I'm still in shock. Thee Fourgiven has split! AAARRGGHH!!! One o' the best bands in L.A. - no, one o' the best bands in th' WORLD has broken up! No more shall we hear that howlin', guitar-crunchin' manical noize that Thee Fourgiven cranked out so well! Man, it makes this psychotic hillbilly wanna cry.

At the time o' their break-up, Thee Fourgiven consisted of Rich Coffee on vocals an' guitar, Ray Flores on Mosrite bass, Bela Horvath on drums, and new T4Ger Mojo Jones on guitar, also. Whutta band, whutta band! Power in every chord, energy in every beat; shit, man! This wuz hi-octane rock-n-roll! Psycha-fuzz Grungeadelia at it's best!

Thee Fourgiven first started in early 1984, but that ain't th' beginnin' of our story, true believer. Our cryptic tale begins in Indiana in the 1970's. A young Rich Coffee, after foolin' 'round in a coupla bands, joins the Gizmos. Yes, he WAS in 'em wif Kenne Highland and Eddie Flowers! They played some gigs, cut some wax, but, for some reason, Rich knew he had a higher purpose, so's he an' Eddie moved out to L.A. to form a band, a band which never came to fruition. In 1979, Rich found a ticket to a gig by those neolithic ravers, the Unclaimed. He got to be mates wif 'em, and, in 1981, he joined 'em! An', yeah, he wuz in 'em wif those Long Ryders Sid'n'Barry. They quit in th' winter of '81, so, in late 1981, Ray Flores joined the band. Eventually, Matt Roberts, T4G's original drummer, joined, and, in 1983, The Unclaimed recorded their 12" EP as a four-piece (T4g an' Shelly Ganz). Rich, Ray, an' Matt started T4G while they were in the Unclaimed. However, in early 1984, Rich an' company got sick of Shelly an' quit. Thus, Thee Fourgiven wuz official! Yeah!

Their first recording, "Spiders In My Sink", was included on the Garage Sale cassettes compilation on ROIR. Then, in May 1984, they recorded "Yeah" for the Battle of the Garages Volume 3 compilation (Voxx Records).

In the fall of '84, they recorded their first LP, It Ain't Pretty Down Here. They had offers from both Dionysus Records and Midnight Records, but, seein' as how Lee Joseph (Dionysus Mastermind and Yard trauma bassist) was a good buddy ol' pal, they went wif Dionysus, and, in spring 1985, the unsuspecting world was exposed to th' 60's Punk vs. 70's Noise sound of Thee Fourgiven!

Shortly after, France's Lolita Records approached T4G and wanted to release an alternate version of It Ain't Pretty..., so they slapped on 3 diff'rent tracks, and the LP wuz releases in France under the title of Viola!. They then began work on their second LP. However, they had a slight... problem. Y'see, Matt wuz haven' some personal problems, and, in late '85, he went on a vacation to England and mysteriously (!) didn't return (Gasp!)! What to do, what to do. Well, it turns out that Ray had a good friend, Bela Horvath, who pounded th' skins in th' skatecore band, The Skoundrelz, Ray'n'Bela were longtime skating partners, an' Bela wuz a killer drummer, so's he joined Thee Fourgiven, an' now their second LP could finally be started on!

During this tyme, T4G also recorded "Wrong Side of Your Mind" for The Deadly Spoon compilation (Bona Fide Records), an' they even recorded a single for West Germany's Mystery Scene Records called "She Shines", backed with a psycho cover of Alice Copper's "Be My Lover". Better yet, they released a mini-LP on LSD Records in Germany, Songs of Ordinary Madness, which collected alla their compilation cuts an' other junk. Yowza!

Things REALLY started swingin' in 1987, tho'. T4G released their second ultra-killer LP, Testify!, on Dionysus, and whut a Psycho-Blowout that waxwork was (and still is)! Git it! Now! At the same time, they went on their first tour of Europe, along wif the Miracle Workers(Yeah!) and New Jersey's late Mod Fun. It wuz a hectic scene, an' LSD Records STILL owes T4G, Lee Joseph, an' others LOTSA MOOLA for that tour! Boycott LSD Records 'till they fork over dat cold hard green! Rock'n'Roll Revolution in the streets!

Anyways, shortly after the first European tour, they went on ANOTHER tour of the Olde Worlde, this time wif The Unclaimed an' Lee Joseph (who found out he was supposed to open th' gigs when he got there!). During this frantic tour, Shelly Ganz wimped out an' split The Unclaimed. Whutta Sad Sack! Fortunately, Lee filled his spot. Groovy! As a result o' this tour, the compilation (Rock and Hard Rolls) Live in Europe 1987 wuz released on Dionysus, consisting of cuts by Lee Joseph (kool acoustic stuff), The Unclaimed (with Lee! Boss, man!), and, o' course, 5 manic tracks by Thee Fourgiven. Also, a song, "Love is Fading", was recorded for The Dimensions of Sound compilation (Mystery Scene Records), and a cut offa Testify!, "I Want My Own Highway", was included in Rad Rash, Volume 6 of Thrasher's Skate Rock cassette compilation series.

After their second tour, they released their 3rd LP in 1988 called Salvation Guaranteed, and it's their best! Heavy Fuckin' Killer! It wuz 'posed ta be on LSD Records, but since LSD flaked on 'em, they stuck with good ol' reliable Lee and released it on Dionysus. Kill for this LP!

Right after recording Salvation Guaranteed, they added Mojo Jones on 2nd geetar. Things were goin' good, too! They were giggin' a lot, they were workin' wif Australia's Au-Go-Go Records on a 7", Italy's Lost Trails 'zine wanted to release a single, What Wave Records in Canada wanted some live stuff fer a compilation, an' they were also workin' on a cut for a Next Big Thing compilation! Whoo-eee!

However, as Rich said, "...it was just time to do it". So Thee Fourgiven parted ways (amicably, I might add). Mojo has retired from music (at least for now), Ray an' Bela are gonna form a new band, and Rich...Hell, cats, Rich already HAS a new band! Him, Lee Joseph, and Jomar Guccio (ex-drummer for NJ's The Mad Daddies) have formed The Tommyknockers, an' they're a-gonna rock yer socks off! Be on the lookout! Do the Crusher!

Any future T4G junk, you ask? Well, could be. They have an interview in the latest issue of Flipside (#59 an' there's talk of a posthumous like LP, but, as Rich said, "...it'll take AGES!" However, I'm puttin' out a 'zine, Garage Punk U.S.A., which has an interview wif 'em. Also, it comes with a cassette compilation which includes 5 live T4G ditties. Yeah, buddy! Write if'n yer interested.

Thee Fourgiven are gone, but not forgotten. Their musical legacy will be felt by all! Damn, I'm gonna miss those cats.

- Hardy Gilbert
1515 Woodland St. S.E
Decatur, AL 35601
USA

## TOMMYKNOCKERS
7" EP

I've just received the Tommyknockers 7" EP, on cool multi-colored vinyl. The 3 song platter has very close stylistic ties to the Thee Fourgiven sound; Rich Coffee writes all 3 songs and sings as well, so that's not a surprise. The guitars are perhaps a bit more "heavy", but Rich's identifiable playing is intact. Reminds me a bit of some early Steppenwolf. Am I off the mark, Rich? My fave tune is "You'll Find Out", with a biting riff and fine backup vocals by Lee Joseph. The EP is on the Sympathy For The Record Industry label... reason enough to help out Rich's new band by picking up The Tommyknockers' first disc!

- EDITOR

# PSYCHEDELICATESSEN

ISSUE #5, 1990: SPECIAL FREE EDITION

Magazine

NORTHWEST
GRUNGE LORDS : **GIRL TROUBLE**

Plus **MONO MEN**

**MARSHMALLOW OVERCOAT**

PLUS BILLIONS OF UNDERGROUND RECORD REVIEWS

# There's Nothing like Having
# GIRL TROUBLE

Girl Trouble is one of those bands determined to keep rock and roll alive. Since 1984 they've done their best to spread the word about loud, raunchy, sweaty, human music, and their best is good enough for me. In concert these folks go berserk, with front man Kurt Kendall stripping down and getting dirty; Kahuna pumping out the git grunge, Dale Phillips cool and lean on the bass, and the ever-steady Bon Von Wheelie thumping the skins. The sounds range from the sleaziest instrumentals known, to classic garage fuzz, to just plain R & B goodness. They've been dismissed by some as Cramps copy-cats, but this comparison is shallow and wholly unfair. Listen to the music, feel the energy, watch them in action; then you'll know they have their own bag, and it's full of original rock lunacy!

I conducted a mail interview with Bon, and she was patient enough to supply me with the following information:

1) Your first LP is incredibly cool. What kind of response has it garnered, and is it still available?

Bon: We're glad you liked our 1st LP, and we're glad some other people liked it too. We have gotten some great reviews which is nice, and many people write to us that own it. Sub Pop sold out the first pressing and told us they didn't think it was popular enough to re-press. Someone (or lots of someones) must have convinced them otherwise, because they have reprinted it and it's again available in stores and through the K mailorder newsletter. (See address on next page.) It's hard to know how well the album has done but it seemed to pave the way for other projects we are doing on our own Wig Out label.

2) The LP was put out by Sub Pop, but you don't have the stereotypical "Sup Pop sound." Where do you see yourself fitting in with the Northwest "sound"?

Bon: I think it is unfortunate that the so-called Sub Pop sound has also been dubbed the Northwest Sound by lots of magazines around the U.S. and overseas, since there is actually such a variety of bands in the Northwest. It's true that many bands are hopping on the Sub Pop "grunge" bandwagon, hoping to get put through their star-making machine to become the next big thing, but not every band is interested in this hype. We are a Northwest band, born and raised in Tacoma, Washington. So we fit in there somewhere but I'm not sure how. Our influence is the 60's Northwest Sound, which to us IS the Northwest Sound, and I think our style reflects some of that, especially the fact that we consider ourselves a dance band. We have a great audience in the Northwest who will dance and participate. They are enthusiastic and pretty open-minded about different type of bands. We seem to get good crowds to our shows, which is great.

3) You have a new 12" upcoming with the super-cool Lee Joseph. Could you describe what the new record is like?

Bon: Yes, Lee Joseph is a super cool guy. We are thrilled to have a new EP coming out on his fabulous Dionysus label. It's called "Stomp and Shout and Work It On Out!" and is a collection of our favorite 60's Northwest covers. The style is basically the Northwest rhythm and blues made popular by 60's dance bands. The songs include: "Take A Look At Me" (originally done by Mr. Lucky and the Gamblers), "Hey Mrs. Jones" (Tiny Torry and the Statics), "Out Of Our Tree" (The Wailers), "Little Sally Tease" (Don and The Goodtimes), "Leaving Here" (Jimmy Hanna and The Dynamics), and Louie Louie (Sonics version). This EP sort of developed by accident. We always end up doing some Northwest covers in our set because they are such cool, danceable tunes. When we recorded our

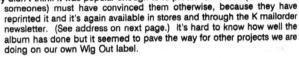

material last year at Velvetone (studios) we discovered that we had 3 Northwest tunes included. Tim Olsen, our co-producer, suggested that we put out an EP of our favorites. We told Lee Joseph about our idea and he thought it was a good one and offered to release it on Dionysus. We jumped at the chance to be on his label.

4) Why should anyone listen to underground rock music anymore? Is it relevant in the 1990's?

Bon: We like rock 'n roll that's raw, basic and uninhibited. Right now that's considered underground. Interesting things are happening by bands that play underground music. Hopefully someone will be out there to listen to all types of music, so these bands will have an audience. All music made is relevant.

5) How do you respond to people who try to put your music down by dating it in a specific period or style? (Example: "60's garage"; "50's instrumental"...)

Bon: When people mention "60's garage" or "50's instrumental" to describe our music they are usually being positive rather than negative. It can be a drag to be classified in certain styles or time periods because I think our sound is made up of all the influences of the four members of our band. I love Frank Sinatra, Dale listens to early Pink Floyd, Kahuna likes Sig Sig Sputnik and Brazil 66, and Kurt is a big Janet Jackson fan. It seems that those interests can be just as influential as The Cramps (who we've been compared to way too much), Link Wray or The Sonics. Once in a while, though, someone will try to put us down with the "stuck in the 60's" line. I vividly recall an incident on a tour where this little 19 year old creep got a ride with us after a show. He told us what he thought of our band and called us "60's throwbacks." Kahuna, who was driving the Girl Trouble van at that time, took him on the G.T. Auto Thrill Ride. It was kind of scary for the rest of the band, so I'm sure this kid was petrified. You should never call us "60's throwbacks" while Kahuna is driving.

6) Do you have any immediate future plans?

Bon: Our plans include putting out another single on our own Wig Out label and getting serious about mixing the songs for our next LP. We've got it recorded but not mixed. We'll be attempting to publish another Wig Out magazine in the next couple of months. We've also been playing lots of local shows lately; the last one we opened up for Thee Headcoats, which was a big thrill for us. We'll also soon play with the Shadowy Men From a Shadowy Planet and Yard Trauma. The tentative plan is for us to back Zebra Stripes up on a couple of tunes and that will be a blast we are looking forward to. When we can get around to it we'd like to do another small tour of the West Coast.

7)   How do you keep your spirits up in the competitive world of rock and (hard) roll?

Bon: We try not to pay much attention to what all the other bands are doing or how fast they are climbing the ladder of success. We move slow and steady at our own pace. Playing gigs, making records and publishing Wig Out has always been fun for us and still is. We are always cooking up some new idea for our stage show or new weird angle for Wig Out that we get a laugh from. Band projects can be hard work but they are also fun. When we played with Thee Headcoats we talked 2 friends, Margaret and Stella, into performing a dance routine with Kurt on a couple of songs. We had a hilarious time working out the moves and it looked amazing on stage. Things like that keep us interested.

8)   Who is the most popular band member? Are you all friends, or just "band-mates."?

Bon: There doesn't seem to be any one popular member of Girl Trouble. In fact we feel like the un-popular guys most of the time. We've never been part of the in-crowd. If we weren't in a band we'd still be hanging out together. We go to parties and shows together or to Kahuna"s for cable TV and videos. Other bands think it's weird that we are always together, but I can't imagine how it could work any other way.

**DISCOGRAPHY:**
Riverbed/She No Rattle My Cage 45
Old Time Religion/Tarantula 45
Hit It Or Quit It LP
Batman/The Truth 45 (with Steve Fisk)
Sub Pop 200 compilation LP
Here Aint The Sonics compilation LP
When Opposites Attract/Gospel Zone/Homework 45
Christmas compilation 45
Stomp And Shout And Work It On Out 12" EP
Estrus Records compilation 45

**Available from:**

**K Mailorder**, PO Box 7154, Olympia WA, 98507
**Estrus Records**, PO Box 2125, Bellingham, WA 98227
**Dionysus Records**, PO Box 1975, Burbank, CA 91507

**the Chesterfield Kings**

ESSENTIAL RECORD DEPARTMENT!

You MUST have these records to really understand this music. Of course the 2 LPs by the teen grunge royalty, <u>THE CHESTERFIELD KINGS</u> ("Here Are" and "Stop") can be ordered from Mirror Records, 645 Titus Ave, Rochester, NY, 14617. OG Music sent me some incredible stuff from Montreal. <u>THE GRUESOMES'</u> LP "Tyrants of Teen Trash" came too late for review, but let's just say that it's staying on my turntable for a few months! Also get the <u>JERRY JERRY</u> LP "Road Gore", as well as the OG samplers!!!(OG Music, Box 182, Station F, Montreal, Quebec, H3J 2L1.)Get the <u>OPAL</u> EP and the <u>"CLAY ALLISON"</u> EP, both CLASSICS, from Serpent Records, PO Box 25371, Los Angeles, CA., 90025. <u>GREAT PLAINS'</u> first 2 LPs can be found through Homestead Records, PO Box 570, Rockville Centre, NY 11571-0570. You'll get a big surprise in the variety of folkish/rockish/eclectic sounds from the Plains. And they're from Ohio!! Go Bucks! <u>BUY INDY RECORDS</u>

# About The Author & The Knights Of Fuzz

## ABOUT THE KNIGHTS OF FUZZ

"The Knights of Fuzz" has evolved from the first printed paper edition in 1991 (under the title "Echoes In Time") to the expanded paper edition in 1995, to a CD-ROM version in 2001, and then as an electronic book as part of the 2006 "Knights of Fuzz" video DVD.

In October 2001 Jon Weiss of Cavestomp Records, Little Steven Van Vandt, and author Timothy Gassen staged a release party in New York City for the "Knights of Fuzz" CD-ROM. It was just six weeks after the 9/11 terrorist attacks on New York, and it was a great celebration of life through rock and roll. Timothy Gassen emceed the show with garage-great Dino Sorbello as the between-sets DJ.

Gassen was able to hand-pick some of his favorite bands to play that night, with The Cheepskates, The Gruesomes, psych-pop kings Plasticland, The Fuzztones (with Deb O'Nair back on keys), and Sean Bonniwell and Ron Edgar of The Music Machine on the bill. A truly magical night was had by all!

Gassen also christened two volumes of "Knights of Fuzz" CD releases for Inbetweens Records in Holland, for reissues of The Other Side and The Crimson Shadows. The U.S. band Thee Knyghts of Fuzz even named their combo in honor of the garage spirit we have attempted to capture in this book.

The 2006 video "Knights of Fuzz" DVD featured a new documentary and music videos for The Chesterfield Kings, Fortune & Maltese, Cynics, Untamed Youth, Girl Trouble, The Woggles, Les Breastfeeders, Marshmallow Overcoat, Vipers, Yard Trauma and more. Gassen restored a classic clip for The Fuzztones, and created new videos for Plasticland and The Miracle Workers.

The DVD also contained a full-length audio compilation album and a 2006 electronic version of the book. In 2014 a video-only version of the DVD became available.

And now the "Knights of Fuzz" is available again as a paper book. We hope it continues to find its way into the hands of true garage fans – as it has already for decades.

*Author Timothy Gassen, "The Guru Of Garage."*

## ABOUT THE AUTHOR (2014)

Timothy Gassen has remained involved in every phase of the underground music scene since 1980. He created and performed with several garage and psychedelic rock groups, among them Reptile House, The Marshmallow Overcoat, and The Purple Merkins. In 2014 The Marshmallow Overcoat, one of the longest-running garage-psych bands of all time, celebrated its 25 year history with the "Very Best Of" two-LP vinyl set.

An acknowledged and passionate expert on the garage and psychedelic music revival, Gassen was nicknamed "The Guru of Garage" by legendary Bomp! and Voxx records label honcho Greg Shaw.

Gassen works as a record producer, independent record label publicist, record sleeve annotator, music composer and publisher, record company A&R person, and album licensing coordinator. He's managed an alternative music nightclub, edited and published fanzines – and for five years created, produced and hosted a weekly garage-psych radio show.

The multi-media artist holds a Bachelor Of Fine Arts degree in Motion Picture Production from The Ohio State University. Specializing in writing and directing, Gassen produces films, DVDs and music videos (including a DVD version of "The Knights of Fuzz" in 2006 & 2014), and has worked on the sets of Hollywood films. He owns and operates his own film, video, audio and publishing company, PCMP LLC (Purple Cactus Media Productions), and Garage Nation Records.

Gassen has continued as a professional music, film and media magazine and newspaper feature writer since 1979, and is published globally. In 1995 Gassen won an Arizona Press Club award for feature writing. This is his fourth book.

# YOU'VE READ THE KNIGHTS OF FUZZ
## ... NOW SEE & HEAR IT!

**THE KNIGHTS OF FUZZ DVD**

## MARSHMALLOW OVERCOAT
2-LPs, gatefold sleeve, 28-songs, colored vinyl
**"The Very Best Of"**

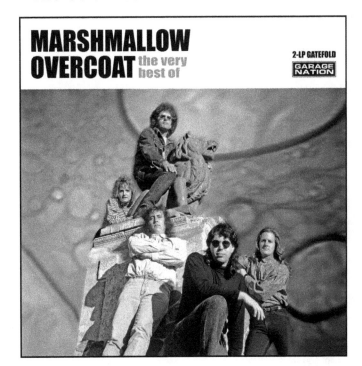

and announcing ...

the debut of
## THE NOBLE KRELL